Robert Hoadley

Robert Hoadley

DESIGN GRAPHICS

SECOND EDITION

C. Leslie Martin

PROFESSOR OF ARCHITECTURE
COLLEGE OF DESIGN, ARCHITECTURE, AND ART
UNIVERSITY OF CINCINNATI

THE MACMILLAN COMPANY
COLLIER-MACMILLAN LIMITED, LONDON

Dedicated to
Mildred Martin
whose cooperation and help
made this book possible

PRINTING 91011 YEAR 456789

Earlier edition © 1962 by C. *LESLIE MARTIN*

Library of Congress catalog card number: 68–10247

THE MACMILLAN COMPANY
866 THIRD AVENUE, NEW YORK, NEW YORK 10022

COLLIER-MACMILLAN CANADA, LTD., TORONTO, ONTARIO

PRINTED IN THE UNITED STATES OF AMERICA

PREFACE TO THE SECOND EDITION

After *Design Graphics* had been used for several years the opportunity to improve it was most welcome. Minor changes have been made in numerous pages of the text and in many illustrations in order that the second edition may provide additional information and be clearer and easier to understand. Several pages of material have been reorganized and improved. Additions of one to six pages have been made in a number of areas in order to provide more complete treatments of those subjects. These include lettering, several phases of perspective, shadows, and rendering techniques.

C. L. M.

PREFACE TO THE FIRST EDITION

The principal methods by which thoughts of one person can be conveyed to another are, first, by means of oral or written speech, second, by means of drawings or pictures, and third, by means of three-dimensional models. It is a well-known saying that "one picture is better than a thousand words." Speech has its limitations as well as its advantages. It introduces the elements of imagination with differences of visual interpretations of word descriptions. These interpretations vary with the training, environment, and temperament of the individual. Two persons who have listened to the same speech may interpret the information in entirely different ways. There may be wide variations in their visual conceptions of an object which has been described to them by words alone. Drawings and models supplement speech in describing objects. They give more precise descriptions which permit little variation in interpretation.

Graphics is here considered to be the process of drafting and representation through which designs are developed, explained to others, and finally translated into information from which the finished objects are produced. In most design work the graphical representations are the drawings and renderings of some object which is to be made. The drawings may be larger, the same size, or smaller than the object represented. A drawing is usually made smaller than a large object in order to keep it at a reasonable size. Tiny objects are frequently shown with enlarged drawings in order to make the designs clear.

Drawings are used to develop, present, and explain in detail the designer's creations. First, they are used in the creative process in developing the design from the ideas of the designer. Second, drawings are used to present the design in terms that the client can understand, criticize, and approve. Third, working drawings and specifications are made to explain all details of shapes, sizes, materials, and workmanship to the persons who supervise and perform the work of making the finished object. Drafting is the principal medium of expression which is used to convey the ideas of the designer to others. These ideas should be expressed as simply, correctly, clearly, and attractively as it is possible to present them. This requires that the designer and the draftsman must be able to (1) choose the type of drawing best suited to the purpose, (2) do effective layout work, (3) make correct, neat, clean-cut, expressive drawings, (4) add tones, textures, colors, and shadows when these are appropriate to the use of the drawings. In order to do these things expertly it is necessary for the designer and draftsman to acquire knowledge and skills in graphical representation. They must learn to coordinate mind, hands, and eyes to produce the best results of which they are capable.

Graphical representation is important to many persons of greatly varied interests. Some are interested in architecture, city planning, engineering, commercial designing, interior decorating, or industrial designing. Many others are interested in less formidable and often very modest projects. Many of these persons who use graphics, whether as professionals or amateurs, need to be able to draw well in order to explain their designs clearly. They also need a general knowledge of all methods of representing objects by drawings in order to be able to select the best type of drawing for each purpose. It is hoped that this general graphics text will be helpful to many persons in different types of design work.

C. L. M.

ACKNOWLEDGMENTS FOR THE SECOND EDITION

I wish to express my very sincere thanks for their cooperation and help in obtaining and preparing manuscript material for the second edition of *Design Graphics* to several persons.

To Dr. Harold R. Rice, Dean of the College of Design, Architecture, and Art of the University of Cincinnati, and Professor Richard H. Wheeler, Head of the Department of Architecture, for their consideration and encouragement during very busy periods of writing.

To Mildred Martin for advice, for the unselfish use of much of her time in typing and assembling typed and printed manuscript, and for helping with corrections on drawings.

To Professor Karl H. Merkel for help with perspective drawing, and to Associate Professor John M. Peterson for help with photography.

To Roland T. Docter, graduate student in city planning, for his very skillful aid and cheerful cooperation in preparing many drawings, and for doing many other helpful things.

To four students in the Department of Architecture—Richard E. Dierkes, Isaac W. Gilliam, John E. Chapman, and Michael F. Conly—for providing skillful and willing help with drawings at a time when help was badly needed.

To the architects, professional designers, delineators, and students who provided very valuable materials for illustrations of different techniques of rendering.

C. L. M.

ACKNOWLEDGMENTS FOR THE FIRST EDITION

One of the greatest experiences that comes from writing is the feeling of gratitude and appreciation for the many persons who have either directly or indirectly helped to make the publication possible. The author wishes to express his special appreciation to the following persons for their highly valued aid in this project.

To Dr. Ernest Pickering, Dean of the College of Design, Architecture, and Art of the University of Cincinnati, for very valuable practical advice and help.

To Mildred C. Martin for listening to innumerable explanations without ever seeming to be bored, for cheerfully and conscientiously typing and retyping the text, and for always being a willing party to discussions of problems in the contents and composition of the manuscript.

To Professor Robert A. Deshon for his initiative and skillful aid in the preparation and standardization of drawings and for his cooperation and assistance in providing examples of student renderings.

To Assistant Professor Robert Gebhart for his reading and criticism of the typed manuscript and suggestions concerning the relations of text and drawings.

To Assistant Professors John M. Peterson and Bruce E. Goetzman for illustration material from their classes.

To four students of the College of Design, Architecture, and Art—Roland T. Docter, Brocky C. Eustice, Byong Hee Jon, and Dennis S. Malone—who inked and finished a large proportion of the drawings. Their skill, interest, and intelligent cooperation were a great help in completing this work.

To the professional designers and delineators who furnished illustrations providing the valuable link with professional practice.

To the students whose work is reproduced here, to David E. Thomas and Philip J. Joehnk, who helped with photography, and to many other students of the College of Design, Architecture, and Art whose problems and needs suggested much of the information presented here.

To the preceding writers on the subjects treated here for their creations, which provided a foundation of knowledge for compiling and developing this manuscript.

C. L. M.

CONTENTS

PART ONE / ELEMENTS OF DRAFTING

PART TWO / MULTI-VIEW DRAWING

PART THREE / PARALINE DRAWING

PART FOUR / PERSPECTIVE DRAWING

PART FIVE / SHADOWS ON DRAWINGS

PART SIX / RENDERING TECHNIQUES

PART ONE

Elements of Drafting

CHAPTER 1

AN APPROACH TO GRAPHICS

Drafting requires the coordinated efforts of mind, hands, and eyes. Acute vision and skillful hands help to produce excellence of drafting technique. However the resulting drawing may be of little value unless a great deal of thought and study have gone into producing a correct, truthful, and clear representation of the design. Intelligent and accurate thinking is just as necessary for fine and useful drafting as for satisfactory performance in mathematics, science, and other subjects.

Eventually the procedure in drafting becomes automatic for a large proportion of the work. However, the really good draftsman never stops thinking out solutions that will make his work speedier and more accurate. The amateur automobile mechanic who takes a motor apart for the first time does a lot of worrying, scheming, and planning. The experienced mechanic does most of the work automatically. The same things are true of the beginner and the trained draftsman. The experienced draftsman often proceeds confidently and automatically without conscious mental effort for a large proportion of his work. The beginner must do a great deal more thinking and planning in deciding on the order of work and in solving in the most efficient, easy, and accurate manner the problems that arise as his work progresses. A beginner with no graphics training should not be discouraged by inferior performance on his first drafting projects. If he works conscientiously he will discover as time goes on that he has become as proficient as those who have had previous training. He should also remember that he probably has advantages in other subjects that were not studied by people who took drawing.

In drafting, the easiest method is the best if it is accurate. An intelligent system of procedure, which provides planned progress step by step, is essential to good drafting results. This requires constructive thinking. No book, however large, can provide detailed solutions for every problem the draftsman will encounter. It is essential that the reader understand not only the illustrations and accompanying text of this book, but also the principles used. Then he can apply the information to other objects and other problems. This requires effort on the part of the reader, insight into the theory used, and vision to see its possible applications. Drafting is essential to the development and manufacturing of a design. To the creative designer a thorough knowledge of the mechanics of drafting; the mastery of a precise, clean-cut, interesting technique; and a working knowledge of all systems of representing objects by drawings are of great importance. This knowledge and skill will enable him to correctly present his ideas in a manner that can be understood and appreciated by others. A careless, dirty, fuzzy drawing is not attractive and an inaccurate one is not satisfactory to any client.

Few clients have the patience and tolerance to continue with a designer who is not producing correct, interesting, and understandable sketches and polished presentation drawings. Designers in many fields are proud of a knowledge of drafting methods and a mastery of drafting technique. It is a great source of personal satisfaction to be able to draw easily, systematically, and expressively; to see the drawing develop to serve efficiently the purpose for which it is being made.

CHAPTER 2

INSTRUMENTS FOR DRAFTING

The beginning draftsman may be bewildered by the variety of equipment he sees in the display cases and on the shelves of the dealer. It is the purpose of this chapter to describe the commonly used items of drafting equipment and explain the type of work done with each. After reading this material the beginner should be able to make a better selection of instruments for his use.

The quality of the equipment used determines to a great extent the quality of the student's work. It is possible to do good work in spite of the handicap of poor equipment. It is possible to do better work and do it more easily with good tools. High quality instruments will last longer, require less sharpening and adjusting, and operate more smoothly and accurately than cheap instruments. The person who expects to do drafting over a period of years should buy fine instruments.

A list of instruments and materials for drafting work is given here. Suggested sizes are given in parentheses for some items. However, the sizes should be varied to suit the work to be done. Smaller boards and T-squares may be adequate in some cases.

ESSENTIAL EQUIPMENT FOR DRAFTING

Illustrated in Fig. 1 I

1. Set of drawing instruments.
2. Drawing board (23 in. x 31 in.).
3. T-square (30 in.).
4. 30° x 60° triangle (10 in.).
5. 45° triangle (6 in.).
6. 12 inch triangular scale of type needed.
7. Refill pencil and 4H, 3H, 2H, H, F leads or drawing pencils with same leads.
8. Sandpaper pad.
9. Erasers for cleaning, pencil, ink.
10. Pens for lettering and freehand.
11. Penholder and penwipers.
12. Erasing shield.
13. Drafting tape or thumb tacks.
14. Bottle of black drawing ink.
15. Paper as required.

USEFUL ADDITIONS TO THE PRECEDING LIST

Illustrated in Fig. 1 II

A. Adjustable triangle.
B. Pencil pointer.
C. Sharp knife.
D. Irregular curves.
E. Dusting brush.
F. Rule.

THE SET OF DRAWING INSTRUMENTS. The most important and expensive item of drafting equipment is the set of instruments, Figs. 1 III and IV. The various pieces are contained in a case made especially to fit them. There is a great deal of variation in the quality of case instruments and also in the number of pieces in a set. There may be as few as two major items with a few attachments, or as many as twenty major pieces. The essential operations performed by any set whether large or small are: (1) the inking of straight lines with a ruling pen, (2) drawing of pencil and ink circles with compass, (3) dividing and transferring spaces with the dividers. Any set, however small, that will perform these three operations in a satisfactory manner is adequate. It is not always possible to judge performance by appearance of equipment. Some compasses and ruling pens that lack polish and refinement in appearance do very precise work. Others may be made to sell on sleek appearance but do not have the precision of manufacture and high quality materials to do good work. It is a pleasure to have instruments that are graceful in design and have a good feel when handled. This is especially true if they are accurate and durable also.

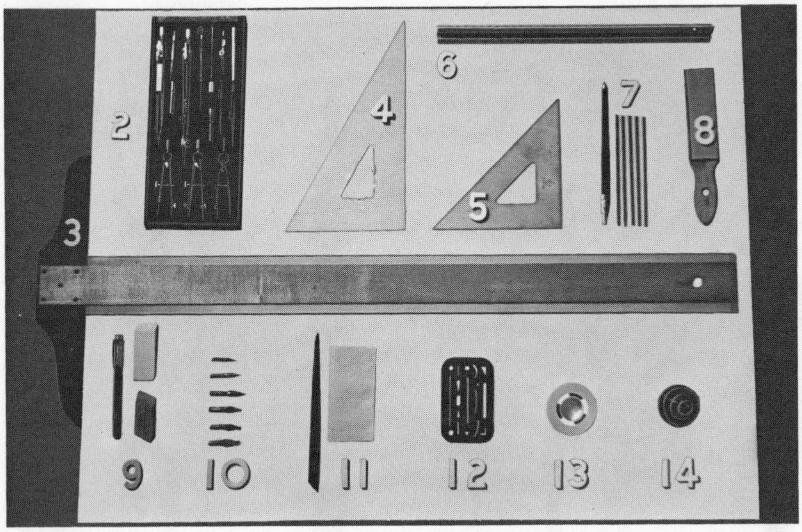

(I) ESSENTIAL DRAFTING EQUIPMENT

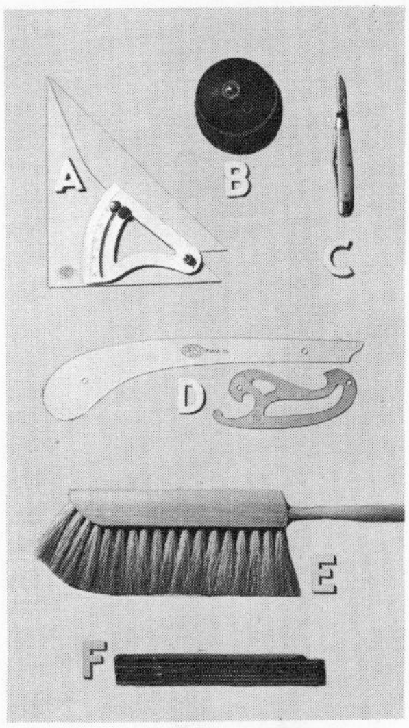

(II) ADDITIONS

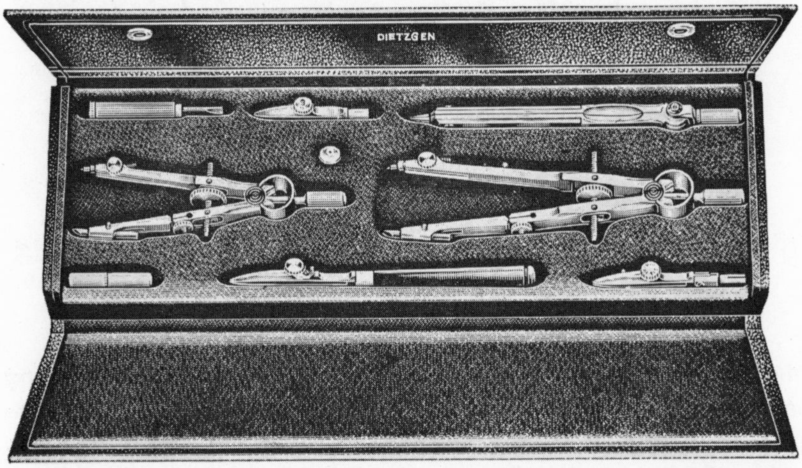

(III) A SMALL SET OF DRAWING INSTRUMENTS

ILLUSTRATION BY COURTESY OF THE EUGENE DIETZGEN CO.

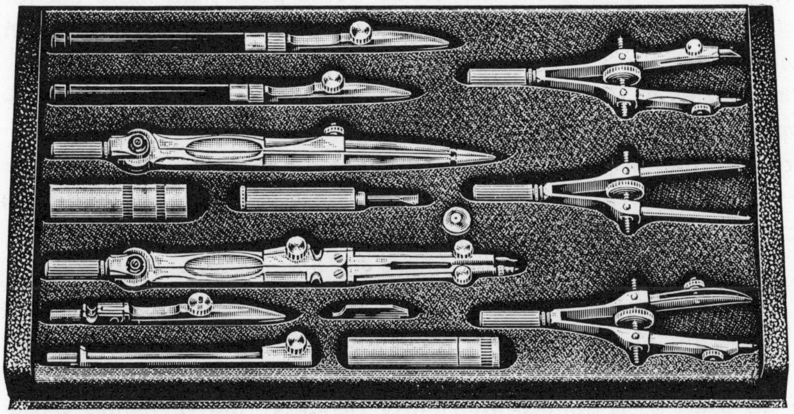

(IV) AVERAGE SET OF DRAWING INSTRUMENTS

ILLUSTRATION BY COURTESY OF THE EUGENE DIETZGEN CO.

FIG. I INSTRUMENTS AND MATERIALS FOR DRAFTING

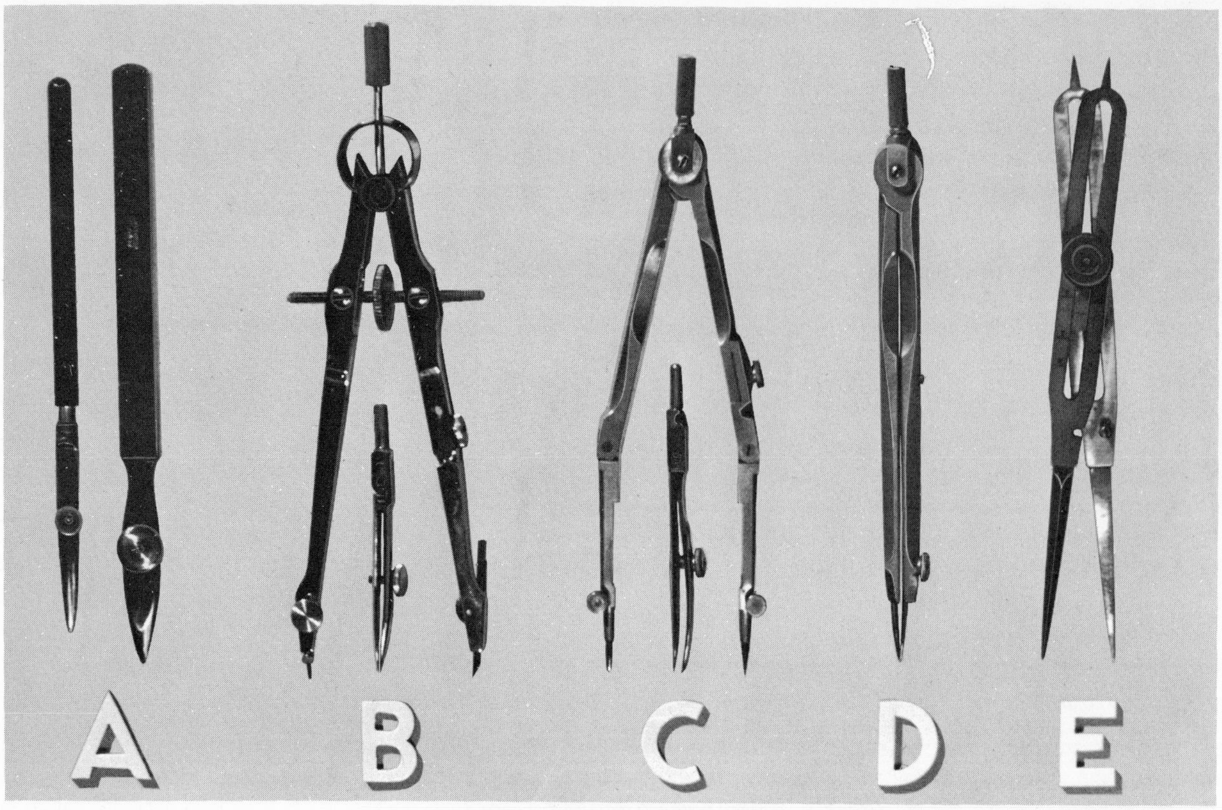

FIG. 2 LARGE DRAFTING INSTRUMENTS

A. The ruling pen is an essential part of a set of instruments. The smallest set has one ruling pen, medium sized sets have two pens, and large sets may have several. Although it may be convenient at times, it is not necessary to have more than one ruling pen. The ruling pen is made to draw ink lines along the ruling edge of a T-square, triangle, or irregular curve. The points on some ruling pens are narrow in the direction of the line drawn, others are quite broad. The narrow ones are easier to use for exact beginning and ending of lines. The broad detail pens hold more ink for long lines. Both are satisfactory for general use. Quick-opening devices for easier cleaning between the blades are provided on many ruling pens.

The compass is used for drawing circles in pencil and ink. There may be either a single compass for general use or several compasses for specific purposes.

The large bow compass and large friction join compass are made for general use. They are satisfactory for a rather wide range of circle sizes. They will make circles from $\frac{1}{4}$-inch or less minimum up to 10-inch or greater maximum diameter and with extension bar up to 15- or 20-inch diameter. There are some compasses that are made for very small, and others for very large circles.

B. A large bow compass that can be used for circles of a wide range of sizes is sufficient for some draftsmen. Such a compass is usually made with a center adjusting screw and is provided with attachments for either pencil or ink. Some have an extension for larger circles and some include two needle points so the instrument can be used as a somewhat clumsy dividers. The adjusting screw holds the instrument from either opening or closing. The instrument is usually sufficiently rigid for drawing dark pencil lines. The adjusting screw operates rather slowly for extreme changes of radius.

C. The large compass with friction joints can be adjusted to radius quickly. A hairspring is sometimes provided on one side for tiny adjustments. This style of compass has knee joints that can be adjusted to keep the points perpendicular to the paper. These joints are easier to adjust when they are both at the same distance from the handle. When one is nearer the end of a side than the other, adjusting seems more awkward. This type of compass is likely to change radius when pressure is exerted for dark pencil lines. For light pencil lines and ink work it is usually quite satisfactory.

D. Dividers are not always included in the smallest sets of case intruments. They are useful in transferring sizes from one drawing to another, enlarging and reducing sizes of drawings, measuring a repeating distance accurately, and dividing a straight or curved line into equal segments. Dividers are of two types, the bow dividers (F) and the large friction joint dividers (D). The latter may have a hairspring for more accurate final setting.

E. Proportional dividers are made for reducing or enlarging measurements to a chosen ratio. The person who has to make many large drawings from small ones or vice versa will find this instrument a useful addition to the set. However, there are also drafting methods of accomplishing the same results and they sometimes require less effort. The length of the points of a proportional dividers must not be changed. Any change of length of one or more of the four points makes the proportional scale on the instrument inaccurate because it is based on a definite length for each point.

F. Small bow compasses are made for the specific purpose of drawing very small circles. There are usually separate bows for pencil and ink. However, some small bow compasses are made with interchangeable pencil and ink points. The bow pen or pencil will draw circles from $\frac{1}{8}$-inch or less diameter up to about a 3 or 4-inch maximum. They are more delicate than the large compasses and are more accurate and easier to use for the small work for which they are intended.

G. Drop compasses are made for very small circles. They are so designed as to be most efficient for this specialized work. A drop compass is so constructed that it is easy to keep uniform pressure on the drawing surface with both the needle and marking points and also easy to rotate the marking point.

H. The beam compass is used for drawing large circles in pencil or ink. It consists of a metal or wood beam to which the needle point and the marking point are clamped with a screw device. The radius is changed by moving the units containing the points closer together or farther apart on the beam. There is usually a screw adjustment in the mechanism of one point for small changes of radius. There may be complete separate devices for pen and ink, or a single element with interchangeable sets of points. The beam compass may include either beams of different lengths or extensions that add on to the length of the original beam.

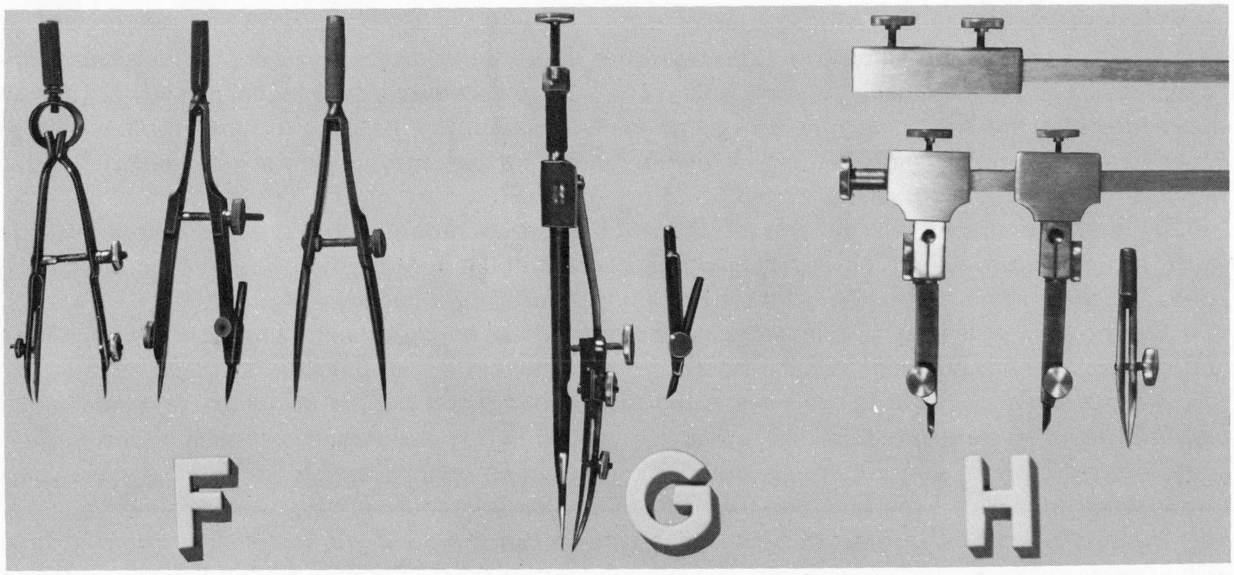

FIG. 3 SMALLER AND LESS USED INSTRUMENTS

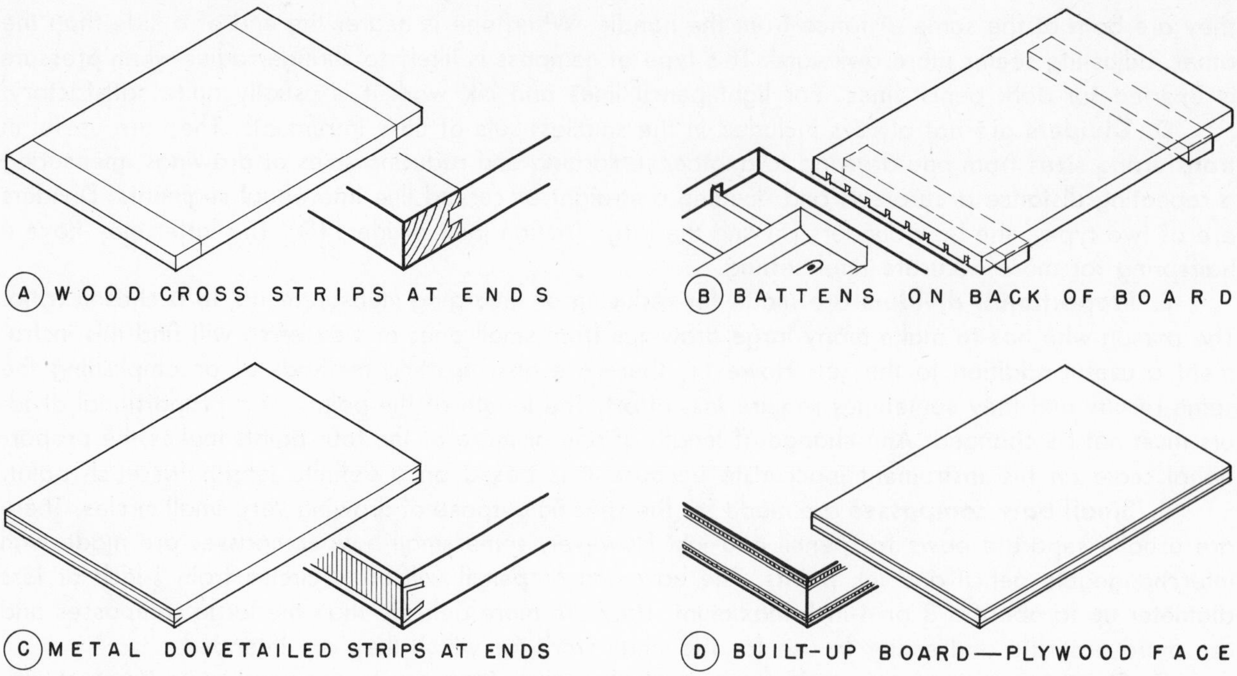

FIG. 4 VARIATIONS IN DRAWING BOARDS

OTHER DRAFTING MATERIALS. Drawing boards, T-squares, triangles, and other drafting materials vary in design and quality. Brief information about these essential items of drafting equipment will be given in the following paragraphs.

The drawing board should be made of some firm wood having a uniform close grain. White pine and basswood are two good materials for boards. A drawing board should have straight edges and perfectly smooth, plane working surfaces. It should not become warped or crooked from changes in humidity or from normal use.

Solid wood boards are made in three styles as shown in Fig. 4: (A) with cross strips at the ends forming a continuation of the board surfaces, (B) with battens applied on the back of the board, (C) with dovetailed metal end strips.

A. The first style has the advantage that both sides can be used. However, it has several disadvantages. (1) It is more likely to warp, split, or to have crooked edges on the long sides. (2) Expansion and contraction may cause the cross strip joints to open. (3) It may also leave the cross strips either longer or shorter than the center of the board so that they interfere with the use of the T-square on the long sides of the board.

B. The second style with battens on the back makes a stronger board, which is less likely to warp. It has uniform expansion and contraction over its entire surface, and has four good working edges. It takes up more room in a locker and may be used on one side only.

C. The third style has the advantages of both the other two. The metal braces allow expansion and contraction. All four edges of the board are straight and both sides can be used.

Anyone making a board should know that good solid wood boards are made of a number of pieces of wood so turned as to minimize warping caused by expansion and contraction; and furthermore that cross pieces and battens are not fastened rigidly throughout their lengths, but have some arrangement that allows the board to expand and contract without splitting.

D. Built-up wood boards of light weight are manufactured in various styles. Some have a hollow center braced with heavy paper honeycomb pattern filler. On one of this type the working surface is made of a single layer of veneering; on another each flat surface is made of about $\frac{1}{8}$-inch plywood composed of three layers of veneering, Fig. 4 D. These boards are much lighter than solid

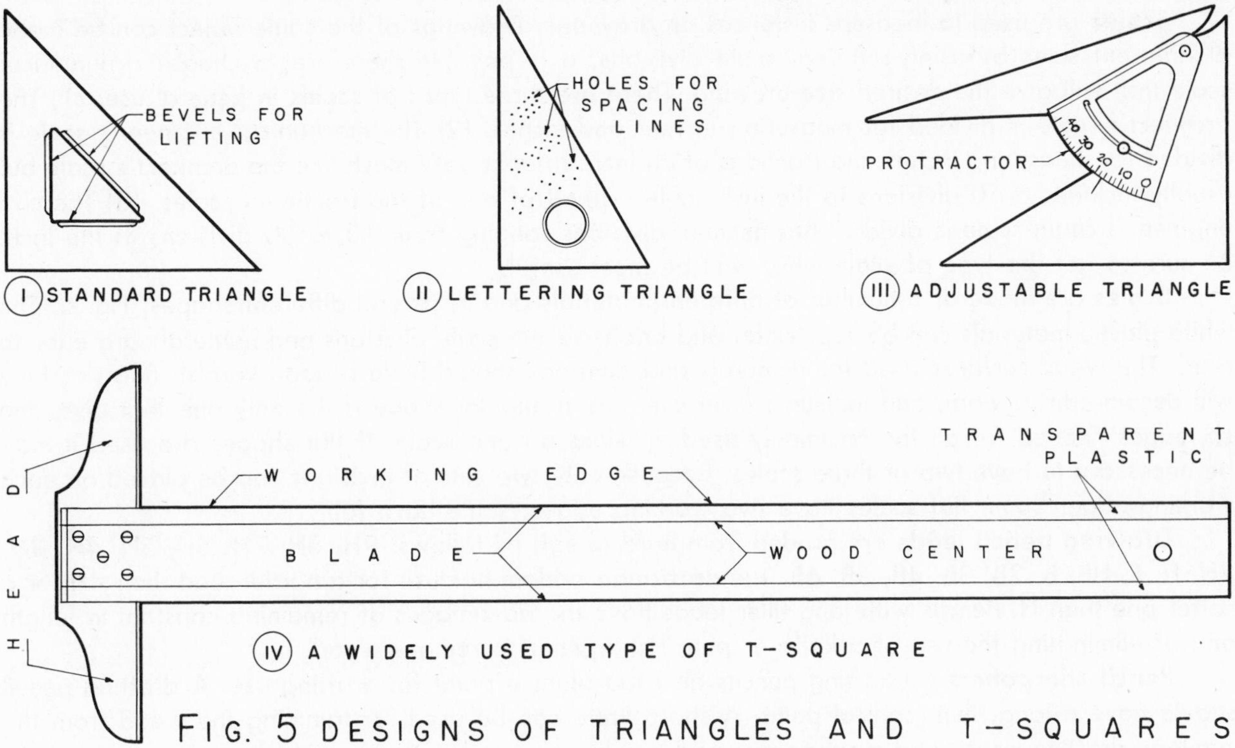

FIG. 5 DESIGNS OF TRIANGLES AND T-SQUARES

boards. The one with the three-ply veneering seems to be quite stable in dimensions so that all four edges remain straight.

Triangles of tough transparent plastic are the most satisfactory ones. High grade triangles are usually thicker than the inexpensive ones and they are made with bevels on the inside edges, Fig. 5 I. The fingernails can get under the beveled edges to take hold of the triangle. When the triangle has a square edge all around the open inside it is very difficult to lift. But it can be beveled with a file, a piece of sandpaper over a strip of wood, or more crudely with a knife. The edges of the inside of the triangle should be beveled equally from both sides. This does no damage because the inside edge is not intended for drafting use. Some triangles are made with a series of regularly spaced small holes to be used for spacing guide lines for lettering, Fig. 5 II. This device is useful for standardizing the various heights of lettering for a drawing.

Adjustable triangles, which can be set to a scale of degrees on the triangle or set to match a given angle on a drawing, are very useful in some drafting work, Fig. 5 III. The draftsman will find such a triangle a decided convenience in making dimetric, oblique, and perspective drawings and in casting shadows at angles not given on the fixed triangles.

Special drafting devices are often used in professional drafting rooms. The parallel rule is frequently used instead of a horizontal T-square. It is a straightedge that is controlled with cords and pulleys so that all of its positions are parallel as it is moved up and down the board. It is not removed from the board in ordinary use and cannot be turned at other angles. The drafting machine is a combination of scale, adjustable straightedge, and protractor.

The T-square should have straight edges on the blade and a straight working edge on the head. The head should be fastened rigidly to the blade so there is no movement between the two parts. T-squares are made of wood entirely, of wood having transparent plastic edges to the blade, of metal with plastic edges to the blade, and of solid stainless steel, plastic, or other materials. Wood is not entirely satisfactory for the drawing edges. It is likely to have slight imperfections, irregularities in grain, or other defects that cause uneven lines. The edges are easily damaged so that the T-square is ruined or must be repaired. Good plastic edges have the advantage of being tough, close grained, and transparent. Wood T-squares with plastic edges are most generally used, Fig. 5 IV.

Scales are used to measure distances on drawings. Drawings of the same object can be made at different sizes by using different scale divisions. It is possible therefore to choose a numerical scale that will give the desired size drawing. There are three types of scales in general use: (1) The *architect's scale* is divided for measuring in feet and inches. (2) The *mechanical engineer's scale* is divided for measuring inches and fractions of an inch. It looks very much like the architect's scale but usually includes a 50 divisions to the inch scale instead of one of the fractional scales. (3) The *civil engineer's chain scale* is divided into decimal divisions ranging from 10 to 60 divisions to the inch. Be sure to get the type of scale which will be most useful.

Scales are made of a number of different materials and in several different shapes, Fig. 6. The white plastic materials can be kept clean and bright so the scale divisions and numerals are easy to read. The wood surfaces used for numerals and divisions should have a good varnish finish or they will become dirty, worn, and indistinct from use. The triangular shape is the only one that gives the six edges needed for all the commonly used divisions on one scale. If flat shapes are used it may be necessary to have two or three scales, because only two sets of divisions can be placed on each working edge. Some flat scales have two working edges, some have four.

Drawing pencil leads are graded from hard to soft as follows: 9H, 8H, 7H, 6H, 5H, ***4H***, ***3H***, ***2H***, ***H***, F, HB, B, 2B, 3B, 4B, 5B, 6B. The draftsman seldom has use for a harder lead than 4H, or a softer one than H. Pencils with long filler leads have the advantages of remaining constant in length and of eliminating the use of a knife or pencil sharpener to remove wood.

Pencil sharpeners for writing pencils give too blunt a point for drafting use. A drafting pencil should have a long, thin, conical point. A sharp knife can be used for trimming the wood from the common drafting pencil and a sandpaper pad can be used to grind the lead to a point on any type pencil. There are special pencil lead pointers made for use on either refill or common drafting pencils. One widely used type is shown in Fig. 7. There are also special pencil sharpeners made for wood pencils which remove the wood and point the lead for drafting use.

Erasers are of three general types: (1) cleaning erasers, (2) pencil erasers, (3) ink erasers. An eraser should not discolor or make a smudge on the paper. Ink erasers should not be so coarse as to roughen and scratch the paper. Old erasers are often hard and smear instead of erasing.

Penholder and pens are used for lettering and freehand forms. Pens are needed to provide a good variety of line widths. There are many pens made for fine line work. Ball point pens are used for medium lines and "Speedball pens" for medium to very wide lines.

The erasing shield is a thin rectangular sheet of metal or plastic having a number of perforations of various shapes and sizes. It is used to protect the drawing and paper near the place being

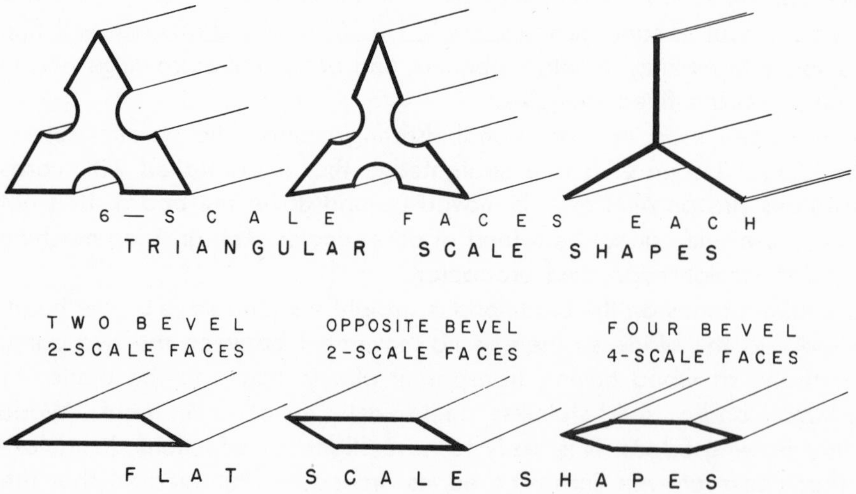

FIG. 6 SHAPES OF DRAFTING SCALES

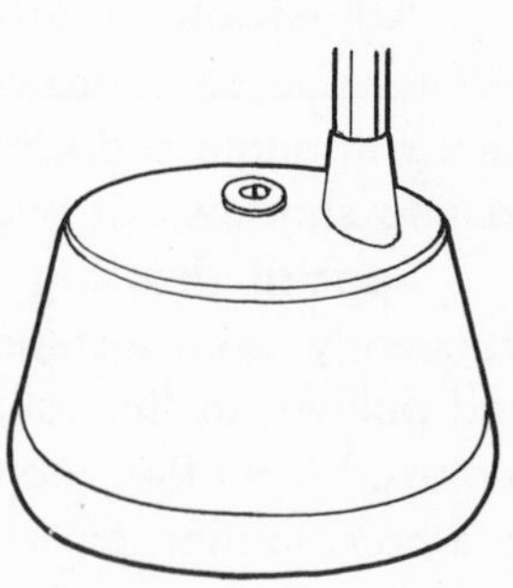

DRAFTSMAN'S MECHANICAL POINTER GIVES A LONG POINT

FIG. 7 PENCIL POINTER

erased. The erasing is done through one of the openings. An old erasing shield worn thin around openings is better than a new one.

Paper fasteners are a necessary nuisance. They are used to hold the paper securely in place on the board. They are a nuisance because all types form an obstruction to movement of T-squares and triangles.

The paper can be fastened to the board with thumb tacks, drafting tape or staples. Glue is sometimes used for mounting paper for rendering but very seldom used for drafting problems. Thumb tacks should have points that are small enough so they can be pushed into the board and removed from it easily. The head of the thumb tack should be shaped so the T-square and triangle will slide over and not bump against it.

Drawing paper, which may be detail paper or other opaque drawing paper, is used for drawings that are to be drawn and inked on the same paper and for drawings that are to be traced onto tracing paper or cloth. It should have a white or light colored surface that is tough and thick enough to stand erasing and then take ink without having the lines blur.

Tracing paper should be tough enough to stand some wrinkling and folding without breaking. It should withstand pencil erasing. Some thick tracing paper will take ink erasing. Tracing paper may be too transparent. The kind that is clear as glass looks attractive but it is difficult to work on it. Unless there is some particular reason for using them, avoid oily, glassy, brittle, or grainy surfaced tracing papers. It is convenient to have two rolls of tracing paper, a narrow roll for sketches and small drawings and a wide roll of correct width to make the largest sheets required.

Irregular curves are used as guides in drawing curved lines other than circles or arcs of circles. There are three general types of irregular curves: (1) The rigid type, which is made in a great number of variations of shapes and sizes of a transparent material such as that used for triangles, Fig. 8 I. (2) The adjustable type, which can be bent to the shape of the curve to be drawn, Fig. 8 II. This type is made of a combination of steel, rubber, and lead or other materials that will retain the shapes into which they are bent. (3) The flexible spline type, which is held in position by weights, Fig. 8 III.

The rigid type is the most useful for sharp curves. The ships curves and adjustable curves are best for medium shape and length curvature of lines. The flexible spline is especially useful for very long gradual curves.

The dusting brush is useful for removing eraser particles, dust, and lint from the drawing.

Marking instruments with one's name or initials for identification is a precaution that should be taken as soon as the student is sure that his instruments and equipment are to be kept.

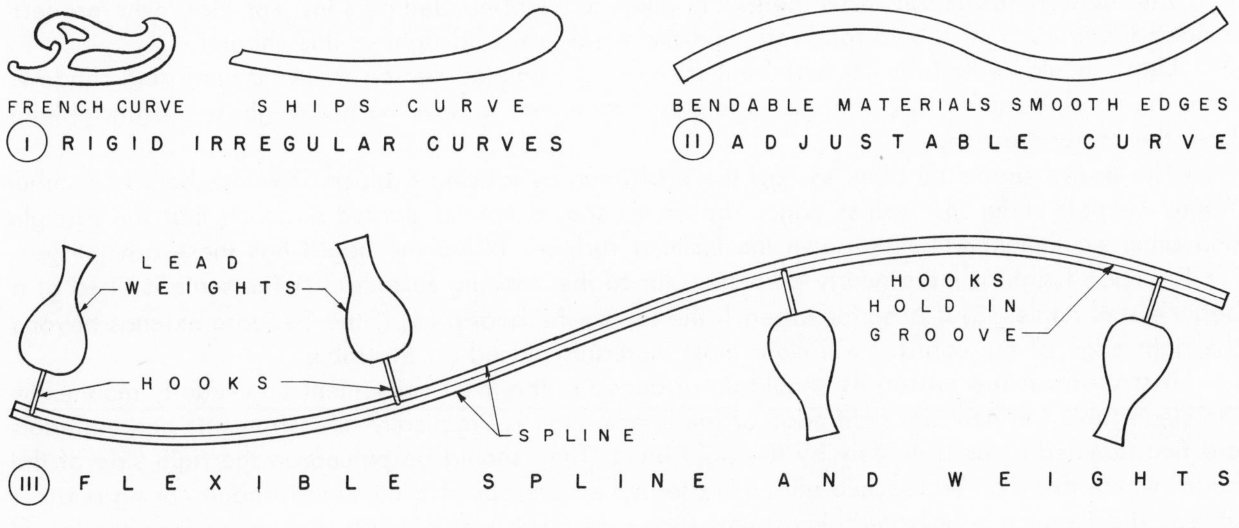

FIG. 8 TYPES OF IRREGULAR CURVES

CHAPTER 3

EFFICIENT USE OF DRAFTING EQUIPMENT

Some of the advantages of the correct use of drafting equipment are listed in the seven numbered paragraphs below.

1. The hand doing the drawing is kept over the triangle or T-square along which the line is drawn and not rubbed over the drawing. As lines are drawn, the T-square, triangle, and hand are moved away from the new lines, not smeared over them.

2. The hand that holds the pencil or pen is turned so the line is visible as it is drawn. The hand is not between the line being made and the eye of the draftsman.

3. The pencil is held so that it will not extend under raised places on T-square or triangle and make crooked lines.

4. The pencil is so sharpened and used that it will make many uniform fine lines before it needs re-sharpening.

5. The top edge only of the T-square blade is used for drawing purposes because, (A) the hand is in a better position to draw there, (B) the two edges may not be exactly parallel, (C) the operation of drawing along the two edges may throw the lines out of parallel.

6. The T-square is used on one edge of the drafting board only because triangles are more accurate and more dependable than drawing boards in giving perfect right angles.

7. The triangle is turned one direction only for vertical lines, (A) so that lines will be parallel even though the triangle may not have an exact right angle, (B) so that the hand is over the triangle, not rubbing over the paper and newly drawn lines.

CORRECT DRAFTING METHODS. The best methods of using drafting equipment should be learned and used by the draftsman. The methods described here have been developed to provide good working conditions, to give accurate results, and to avoid mechanical errors.

The drawing table should be large enough to provide space for the board, for spreading out the instruments, and for any necessary books or papers. The drawing table and stool should be of correct heights so that the draftsman can work either standing up or sitting down. Most draftsmen prefer to sit down part of the time and stand up part of the time while working.

Instructions for use of instruments are given for right-handed persons. For those who are left-handed the word right should read left, and the word left read right in this chapter.

Light should come from the left front for the right-handed person to avoid confusing shadows from the hand, T-square, and triangle. It is most convenient to have both daylight and artificial light from the same direction.

The board should be tilted toward the draftsman by placing a block of wood, books, or other steady support under the farther edge. The board should not be slanted so much that the triangle and other equipment will slide down the inclined surface. Tilting the board has these advantages: (1) The line of sight is more nearly perpendicular to the drawing surface. (2) The scale is tilted at a better visual angle. (3) It is easier to reach the top of the board. (4) If the T-square extends beyond the right edge of the board it will clear most materials placed on the table.

Instruments and materials should be arranged in the most convenient and orderly manner on the clean table top near the right edge of the board, Fig. 9. Practically all instruments and materials are first handled or used entirely by the right hand. They should be placed on the right side of the board where they can be reached easily. Try to make each object accessible without moving another object. The T-square is operated almost entirely by the left hand. When it is removed from the board it may be placed to the left or above the board. Keep the board as free as possible of instruments

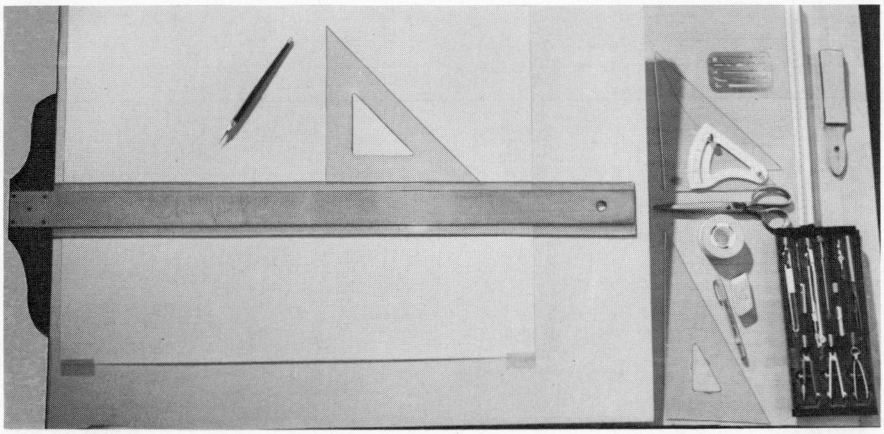

DRAFTING EQUIPMENT ARRANGED FOR RIGHT HANDED PERSON

FIG. 9 ARRANGING THE DRAFTING EQUIPMENT

EQUIPMENT ARRANGED FOR LEFT HANDED PERSON

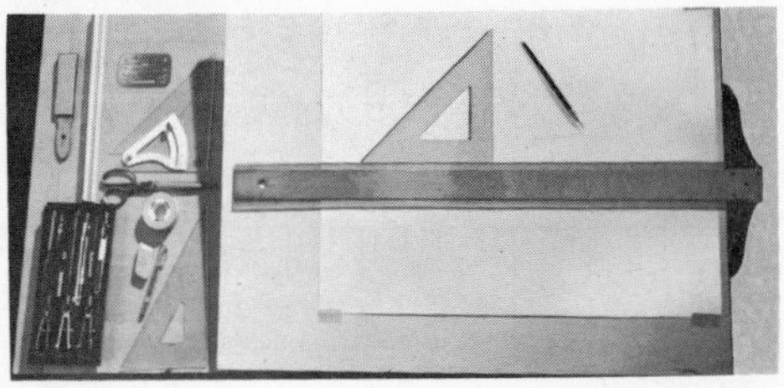

and materials. Although the draftsman normally works from the bottom edge of the drawing, which is the low edge of the board, he may when drawing on some areas find it convenient to take his position on the left side of the drawing.

PENCILS. Sharpen all pencils before beginning to draw. The blank ends of the wood pencils should be sharpened so that the letters and numbers indicating the grades of the pencils remain on the opposite ends. In sharpening a pencil the wood should be removed in a neat cone shape, with either a sharp knife or a special pencil sharpener until about one half inch of the lead is exposed. Take very small shavings when using a knife. Do not take big gouges of wood. The lead should be ground to a needle point on the sandpaper pad or file. Hold the length of the lead almost parallel to the grinding surface so the point will be long and thin. If the angle between the axis of the lead and the surface of the sandpaper is too great the point will be blunt and will dull rapidly when used. Rotate the pencil when grinding the lead so the point will be perfectly round. After the point is shaped remove the black dust by wiping it with a piece of cloth or by polishing it on a scrap of paper. Keep the pencils sharp. A sharp pencil makes neat, accurate lines.

When sharpening the lead on a refill drafting pencil with a sandpaper pad be careful not to grind the metal end of the pencil that holds the lead. If necessary extend the lead farther than the position where it will be clamped for use, then return it to the use position after pointing.

The grade of pencil used has considerable influence on the neatness of the work. When a pencil is too hard it requires heavy pressure to make a line. This pressure makes a groove in the paper with the line at the bottom of the groove. It is difficult to erase the lines made with a hard pencil that presses grooves in the paper. After erasing, the grooves may still remain to disfigure the paper. When a pencil is too soft it soon becomes dull from use. The lines smear when the instruments are moved over them and the paper becomes dirty in a short time.

The best rule is to use the softest pencil that will give a neat, fine line. The paper and the weather have some influence on the grade of pencil used. Slick paper requires a softer pencil than soft, grainy, or rough paper. In damp weather it is necessary to use a softer pencil than when the atmosphere is dry. The grades on the list of materials provide a sufficient range for most work.

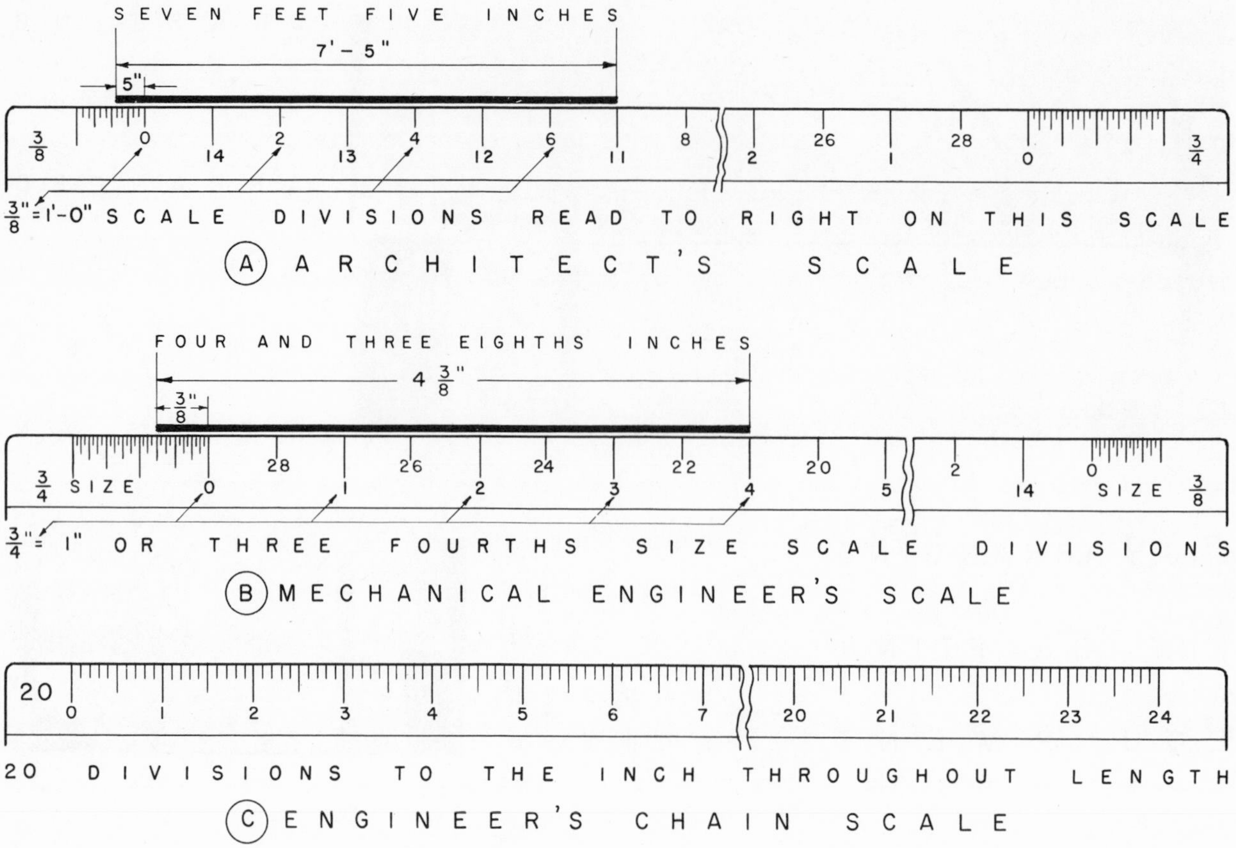

FIG. 10 THREE COMMONLY USED DRAFTING SCALES

THE SCALE. The word scale is applied to the entire instrument and also to any series of divisions on the instrument. The scale is used primarily to measure distances in making drawings.

The architect's scale is designed for measuring in feet and inches. By using the $\frac{3}{8}'' = 1'\text{–}0''$ scale, $\frac{3}{8}''$ on the drawing represents a distance of one foot on the object. For convenience in the use of the scale the first space is divided to give parts of a foot on the architect's scale, Fig. 10 A. Where possible these small divisions give inches and in the larger scales, where space permits, various fractions of an inch. In the smaller scales the smallest subdivision may represent two inches. In all cases the total distance divided into small divisions represents one foot on that scale. It is then simple arithmetic to determine what each division represents.

In using the architect's scale to measure a distance in feet, the measurement starts not at the end of the scale but at the 0 point, which is in the position shown in Fig. 10 A between the divided space and the next adjoining undivided space. To measure 7 feet 5 inches the feet are measured in one direction from the 0 point and the inches in the opposite direction as shown in Fig. 10 A. Both the architect's and mechanical engineer's scales have two scales on one edge. One begins at the 0 on the left end and the other at the 0 on the right end. Each of the two scales has a sequence of numbers beginning at the 0 point. These numbers overlap. Care must be taken to use the correct set of numbers for a given scale.

The mechanical engineer's scale is designed for measuring in inches and fractions of an inch. The basis for the small divisions is the common fractions of an inch such as $\frac{1}{8}$, $\frac{1}{16}$, etc. The divided space usually represents one inch. This scale is useful to the designer of furniture and other small objects where the common fractions of an inch are used.

The mechanical engineer's scale is used to measure inches and fractions of an inch in the same way that the architect's scale is used to measure feet and inches. The scale in Fig. 10 B shows the dark line to be $4\frac{3}{8}$ inches long.

The engineer's chain scale is a simple decimal scale. The divisions vary from 60 to the inch to 10 to the inch. There are no smaller divisions of a unit such as those on the architect's and mechanical engineer's scales. The scale along one edge has equal divisions throughout its length, Fig. 10 C.

When drawing to scale a great variety of numerical scales is desirable so that a drawing may be made as large or as small as required. If $\frac{1}{2}''$ scale is used in making a drawing, the drawing is a certain size. By using $\frac{1}{4}''$ scale the drawing can be made only half as large, and by using 1″ scale it can be made twice the size of the $\frac{1}{2}''$ scale drawings, Figs. 11 I, II, III.

In laying out measurements with the scale the points of measurement can be marked by dots, V-shaped marks, or by short straight lines perpendicular to the length of the scale. The latter method is the best, but sometimes different markings are used to help distinguish between lines. Keep the marks light enough so they do not disfigure the drawing.

Most people have a tendency to make measurements either too large or too small. If this slight error is repeated a number of times, the total distance may be appreciably in error. The effects of this tendency can be minimized either by keeping the scale in one position for a number of measurements or by measuring from a base point.

Measurements should be laid out vertically at the left ends of horizontal lines and horizontally at the bottom ends of vertical lines, with the scale held perpendicular to the lines to be drawn. It is then quite convenient to draw the lines in the correct directions for T-square and triangles.

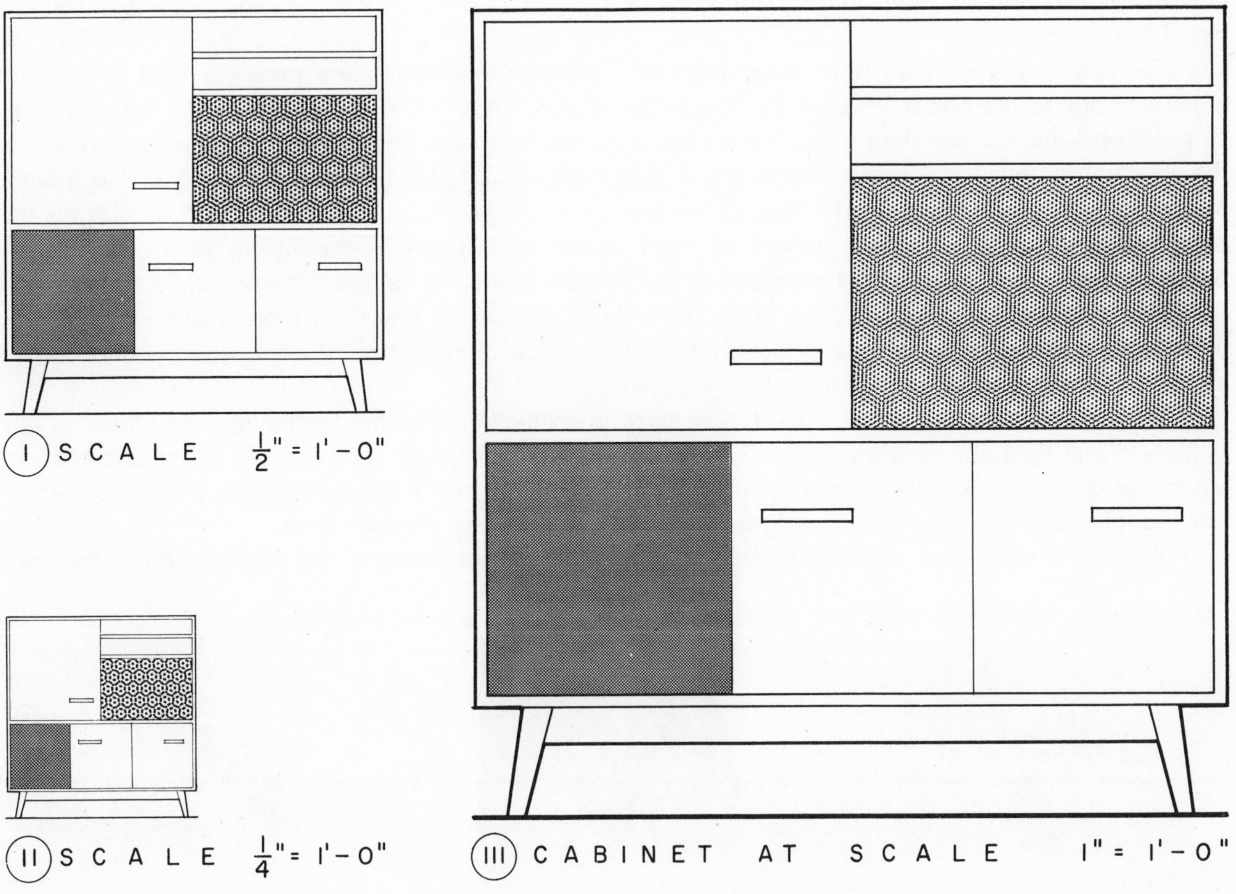

FIG. 11 MAKING SCALE DRAWINGS OF AN OBJECT

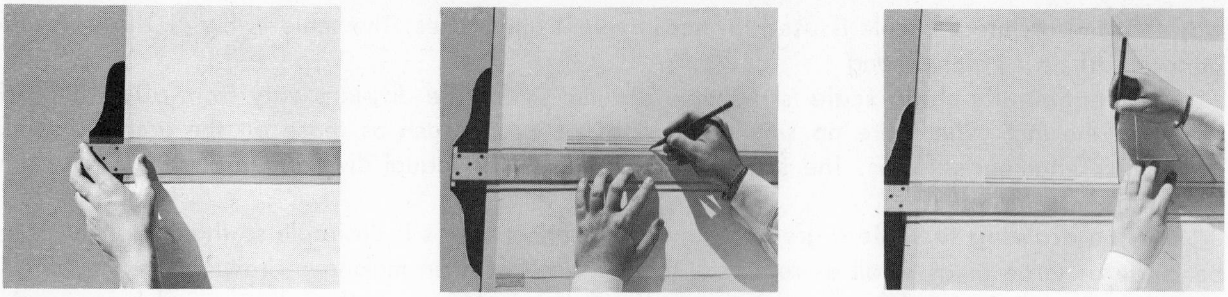

(A) MOVING T—SQUARE (B) HORIZONTAL LINE (C) VERTICAL LINE

FIG. 12 RIGHT HANDED DRAFTING ABOVE—LEFT H. BELOW

THE T-SQUARE. The T-square is used for drawing parallel lines across the paper from left to right, and as a rest for the triangles in drawing vertical and slanting lines. The top edge of the T-square is called the working edge. It is used for drawing lines and supporting the triangles. Lines drawn across the board with the T-square will be called horizontal lines. Lines perpendicular to the horizontal lines will be called vertical lines.

To draw a line with the T-square, use the left hand first to move and then to hold the T-square, leaving the right hand free to draw the line from left to right, Figs. 12 A, B. Place the head of the T-square in contact with the left edge of the board. Then slide it up or down until the working edge of the blade is in proper position for drawing the line. Grip the T-square by the head when moving it, then slide the hand along the blade to the holding position. Hold the T-square in position with the left hand placed partly on the paper and partly on the blade of the T-square, Fig. 12 B.

For drawing lines along the ruling edge of T-square or triangle, the pencil is held in a plane perpendicular to the paper through the line to be drawn, Figs. 12 B, C. The tip of the tapered pencil point and the line are then a small distance from the T-square. The top of the pencil is inclined in the direction in which the line is drawn. Hold the pencil about $\frac{3}{4}$ inch from the point with the thumb, forefinger, and middle finger. The tips of the other two fingers can steady the hand in placing the pencil and then slide along the surface of the T-square or triangle as the line is drawn. Rotate the pencil slowly in one direction when drawing so that the point will remain symmetrically shaped and will give a thin even line for a long time. The side of the pencil point must be brought against the ruling edge without touching the paper or the top surface of the straight edge, then pushed down along the ruling edge into contact with the paper.

The experienced draftsman uses a little more pressure to make the beginning and end of a line definite. Form the habit of drawing the line once and leaving it alone. If necessary, erase and redraw, but never go back and forth over lines. The working edge of the T-square and the outside edges of the triangles are the only guiding edges to be used in drawing straight lines.

When several lines are to be drawn with the T-square, start at the top and draw the lines

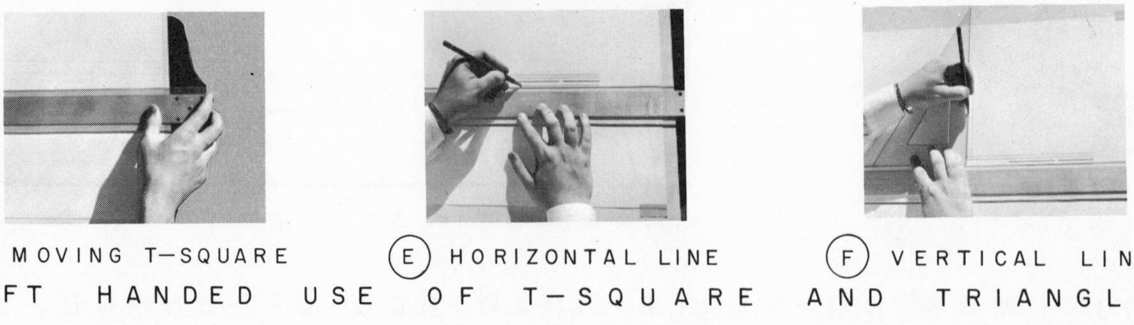

(D) MOVING T—SQUARE (E) HORIZONTAL LINE (F) VERTICAL LINE

LEFT HANDED USE OF T—SQUARE AND TRIANGLE

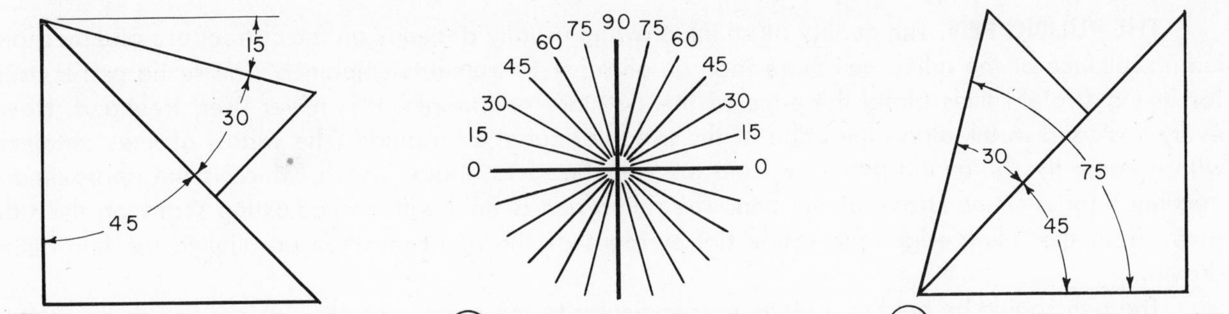

(I) A 15° POSITION (II) POSSIBLE ANGLES (III) A 75° POSITION

FIG. 13 ANGLES GIVEN BY TRIANGLES ON T-SQUARE

in order from top to bottom of the drawing. Thus the lines drawn remain visible and each new line, as it is drawn, can be seen in its relation to the completed lines. Furthermore, working back and forth over lines is reduced to a minimum and the drawing is kept cleaner. Always start at the left and draw toward the right along the top edge of the T-square. Two T-squares do not ordinarily make identical lines. Use only one T-square on a drawing. The T-square is used in one direction, across the board, and against only one edge of the board, the left edge.

TRIANGLES. All lines perpendicular to those drawn with the T-square are drawn along the triangle resting on the top edge of the T-square. The triangle is turned with the vertical edge to the left, Fig. 12 c. The line is drawn from bottom to top, that is, away from the draftsman. The pencil is inclined with the top farther away from the T-square. Do not start to draw at the corner of the triangle that is against the T-square. Leave room so the line begins a short distance above the T-square.

In drawing lines with the triangle the left hand holds the T-square and triangle together and keeps them from slipping along the board. This can be done by dividing the holding surface of the left hand between the triangle, T-square, and board so that part of the surface of the hand rests on each.

When drawing a long vertical line with the triangle it is best to start near the T-square at the bottom end of the line and draw up nearly to the tip of the triangle. Then move the triangle and T-square up higher to start at the end of the line just drawn and continue it. Repeat as many times as necessary. The triangle will probably have to be shifted to the left or right so do not attempt to hold it in the same relation to the T-square when moving up to continue a line.

When drawing a series of vertical lines, draw the left line first then draw each line in order toward the right. Thus the triangle does not rub over the lines drawn and all lines remain visible. When the lines are longer than the triangle draw the bottom parts of all lines before moving the T-square up to continue the height of the lines.

The draftsman will find that it is sometimes better to make exceptions to the preceding rules for sequence of lines. For example, when several horizontal lines extend between two verticals it is better to draw the verticals first.

The various angles obtained with the triangles on the horizontal T-square used singly and in combinations are shown in Fig. 13 II. It should be noted that all lines that slant up and to the right are drawn up, that all lines that slant down to the right are drawn down except in the one case of the 75° combination when the line is drawn up and to the left to keep the hand over the triangle as the line is drawn. When all possible lines are drawn through a point with the single and combined triangles resting on the horizontal T-square the lines will be spaced 15° apart. The draftsman should shift his position whenever it will help him to draw lines in different directions easily and naturally. It is usually sufficient to move a little to the right or left and twist around to a more comfortable relation to the drawing. The position below the drawing should be maintained when possible. Drawing the object upside down should be avoided.

THE RULING PEN. The quality of an ink drawing usually depends on the correct use and mechanical excellence of the ruling pen more than on all other instruments combined. The ruling pen is used for inking straight lines along the edge of the T-square or triangle. It is never used freehand. However, it is used to ink along the edge of the irregular curve as a guide. The widths of lines obtained with a correctly sharpened pen vary from the very finest to about $\frac{1}{16}$ inch, which is the approximate maximum for a single stroke of the pen. The ruling pen is held with the adjusting screw on the side away from the ruling edge. The inside flat surfaces of the point must be parallel to the line being drawn.

The pen should be held in a plane perpendicular to the paper and through the line to be drawn. It can be inclined slightly in the direction of the motion or be held perpendicular to the paper. If it is inclined too much the edges of the points will not be parallel where they touch the paper. The line will then vary in width and its edges may be uneven.

Before starting to ink a drawing be sure that the pen is clean and that the paper, T-square, and triangles are free from lint, dust, and particles of eraser. Use the dusting brush on the paper and a clean cloth for rubbing dust from the T-square and triangles. Any tiny bit of lint or eraser may catch on the point of the pen as it is used and cause the lines to blur. It will continue to cause trouble until the pen is cleaned. When cleaning the pen be sure not to leave any lint on it.

The ruling pen is filled with ink by touching the tip of the filler, which is in the stopper of the ink bottle between the blades of the upright pen and allowing the ink to run down into the point between the blades, Fig. 14 A. Care should be taken to see that there is no ink on the outside surfaces of the pen. If there is too much ink in the pen it will run out rapidly causing the lines to spread and making a blot. The pen can usually be safely filled about $\frac{1}{4}$ inch or $\frac{3}{8}$ inch from the point.

Do not fill the pen until it is to be used, because the ink dries rapidly. Form a habit of cleaning the pen with a penwiper before laying it down and before refilling it when it is used continuously. If the penwiper is moistened slightly it will work more efficiently. If the ink should dry in the pen, do not scratch it out with a knife, but open the pen and clean it by rubbing with a moist cloth.

The ruling pen should make neat, fine lines of uniform width having perfectly straight true edges on good inking paper. Draw the lines once and in the same directions that pencil lines are drawn, Figs. 14 B, C. It is impossible to make good lines by going back and forth over them. If the pen does not make good lines, there is something wrong with it or with the way in which it is used. Find out what is wrong and correct it.

Faulty lines, other than those due to conditions of the ruling pen, may be caused by one of the following technical mistakes:

1. Too much pressure against the ruling edge will bend the spring blade of the pen and cause the space between the points to vary or will hold them together. This may cause a line of varying width, or a thin wiry line, or the ink may stop flowing from too much pressure.

2. The points of the pen may be held tightly together by the adjusting screw so that the ink cannot flow between them easily and reach the paper. This may cause a line of uneven width that is thin and wiry or no line at all.

3. Touching the top surface of the ruling edge with the tip of the pen may cause the ink to run down between the pen and ruling edge and make a blot.

4. Ink left on the outside surfaces of the pen may run down the ruling edge to make a blot.

5. When the pen is tilted out of the plane perpendicular to the paper through the line drawn, one point may not touch the paper. This will cause a ragged edge on that side of the line. When the pen is tilted so the point is in the angle between the paper and ruling edge, blots result from the ink getting onto the ruling edge.

6. Blots are sometimes caused by sliding the T-square or triangle into the wet line. However, the lines should be allowed to dry without the use of a blotter.

7. When the blades of the pen are not held parallel to the line being drawn, the pen will make a scratchy line when turned at a slight angle in one direction. It will either run away from the ruling edge when turned in the other direction or make an uneven line. With practice the hand automatically turns the ruling pen to the right position and brings it down to touch the paper correctly.

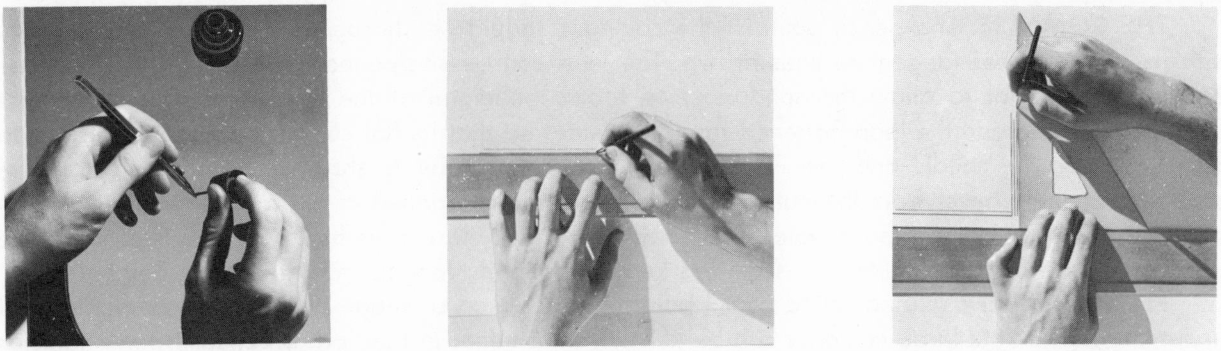

(A) FILLING THE RULING PEN

(B) DRAWING LINES HORIZONTALLY

(C) DRAWING LINES VERTICALLY

FIG. 14 INKING WITH THE RULING PEN

8. Too much ink in the pen causes bulbs at the ends of lines and sometimes causes the ink to spread and make uneven lines or blots. These defects are more likely to appear when ruling thick lines. Learn the limits of thickness within which your ruling pen gives good results.

DIVIDERS. The right hand alone is usually sufficient to hold, open, adjust, and use the dividers. The friction joint instrument is opened by pressure of the thumb and middle finger on the bevel or against the inside edges of the sides of the instrument as shown in Fig. 15 D. In adjusting the instrument it is pressed together by the thumb and forefinger and opened by the outward pressure of the middle (second) and third fingers. The pressure on the friction joint should be so adjusted that the dividers can be opened and closed easily, but with sufficient resistance to movement so the setting will not change while the instrument is being used.

Dividers are used for dividing spaces, for transferring measurements, and for enlarging and reducing drawings. Dividers are useful in transferring distances from one drawing to another, and for repeating equal spaces through the same drawing. They are more accurate than the scale for this work. Furthermore, since the procedure is mechanical, there is less chance of error.

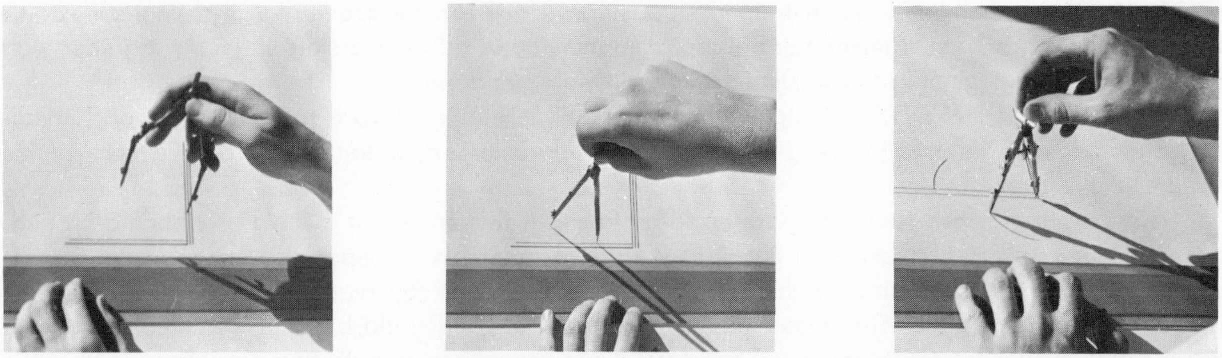

(D) ADJUSTING A FRICTION JOINT INSTRUMENT

(E) STEPPING OFF DISTANCES WITH THE DIVIDERS

(F) DRAWING CIRCLE WITH THE LARGE BOW COMPASS

FIG-15 OPERATING THE DIVIDERS AND COMPASS

THE COMPASS. The pencil point of the compass should be sharpened to a flat wedge shape with the flat surfaces tangent to lines drawn. The lead can be sharpened while it is in the compass if care is taken not to allow the sandpaper to touch the metal of the instrument. The instrument should be opened and the lead flattened from both sides so that its flat surfaces are perpendicular to a line between the needle and pencil points. Some persons prefer to sharpen the pencil for a compass with a single bevel from the outside. The lead can be sharpened in this manner without changing the radius even when the needle and pencil points are close together. The length of a needle point should be adjusted so that it is always kept just slightly longer than the pencil point.

For very small circles a round pencil point is better than a wedge point. When drawing small circles the legs of the large compass can be kept straight because they are practically perpendicular to the paper. When larger circles are drawn the joints of the compass should be adjusted so that the points are perpendicular to the paper. There are two reasons for this: first, so that the needle point rotates on its axis when circles are drawn; second, so that the radius is unchanged as the lead wears. If the compass were used with the points at an angle to the paper the needle point would gouge a hole in the paper, and the radius would become shorter as the circles were drawn. In using the compass with the pen point, the pen, when properly sharpened, makes a neat line when held perpendicular to the paper but is likely to make an uneven line if the pen is tilted toward or away from the needle point. This is most noticeable when wide lines are drawn.

The friction joint compass is held and adjusted in the same manner as the dividers except that both hands are used in adjusting the knee joints to keep the points perpendicular to the paper.

The lengthening bar is used in drawing circles too large to be drawn without its use. It is placed in the compass at the joint where the pen and pencil points are inserted. One end of the lengthening bar holds the pen or pencil point and the other is attached to the compass.

When drawing lines with a compass the right hand only is used, Fig. 15 F. However it will be found necessary to use both hands when the lengthening bar is used. In order to get a neat line the instrument should be revolved slowly and leaned slightly in the direction of motion to keep a uniform pressure on the paper.

BOW INSTRUMENTS. The bow pencil and bow pen are used to draw small circles in pencil and ink. The bow dividers is used for spacing, transferring measurements, and enlarging and reducing sizes when the spaces are small. The pencil lead on a bow pencil can be sharpened to a wedge point for most circles as is done on large compasses. However a round tapered point such as is used on drafting pencils will give better results for very small circles. The bow pen or pencil should have the needle point adjusted so that it is just slightly longer than the pen or pencil point. The bow dividers should have the points of equal length. Small adjustments of radius of the bow instrument are made with one hand with the instrument in position. However, for speedy large changes in radius the side adjusting bow instrument can be approximately adjusted by pressing the sides together with the left hand, then spinning the adjusting nut with the right hand.

CARE OF EQUIPMENT. Drafting equipment requires intelligent care to keep it in good condition. The following information is given to help the beginner understand how to take care of his equipment.

The drawing board should be supported by laying it flat on top of a table or standing on end. If the board is left in a strain, it is likely to warp. Do not leave it supported on opposite corners with two corners up in the air or leaning against the wall on one corner. Never drag a board across the floor or slam it around. The edges may be splintered or roughened by such treatment. Keep the board clean. Never leave it near a hot radiator. Keep the edges smooth and straight.

The T-square should be left flat on the board or suspended by the end of the blade to avoid warping. If the T-square is dropped it may be knocked out of alignment with the drawing on which it is being used. If the head of the T-square becomes loose it should be tightened securely. In extreme cases it is sometimes necessary to remove the head from the blade, clean the contact surfaces of the wood by scraping with a knife or sandpaper, give them a coating of glue or model cement, then replace the head.

The triangles should not be left in warped positions as they are easily deformed by continuous pressure. They become soft when subjected to heat. When a triangle does become warped it can sometimes be straightened by pouring hot water on it and, if necessary, bending it several times in the direction opposite to the warp. In some cases the hot water straightens the triangle without any bending.

The sandpaper on the sand pad should be used as long as it will point the pencil. It is usually too coarse at first and works better after it has been used a while.

Drawing ink dries rapidly. Keep the stopper in the bottle except when filling the pen. Shaking the ink produces bubbles which take the ink from the quill making it difficult to get any ink.

Paper should be kept clean and free from wrinkles, folds and scratches. It is discouraging to start a drawing on a dirty, mutilated piece of paper. It is stimulating to start out on a perfect sheet.

The case instruments are usually made of corrosion-resisting metals. However, the points of the dividers, compasses, and pen blades are sometimes made of steel which may rust if they are not kept clean and dry. The case instruments should be kept in perfect working order. Avoid bending or dulling the needle points. Keep the points adjusted to correct length. Keep the pencil points sharp and the pen points sharp and clean. Adjust the friction joints on compasses and dividers so they will work just right. Leads for the instruments can be obtained by splitting the short lengths of old pencils and removing the lead or using refill leads.

It is much more pleasant to work with equipment which is ready for use than to use equipment which is in poor condition or has to be put in condition while it is being used.

ERASING. A good rule for erasing is to use the softest eraser which will do the work.

The art gum or other soft cleaning eraser is used to keep the paper clean while drawing, for erasing light pencil lines, and for cleaning the entire drawing and removing pencil lines after the drawing has been inked. The cleaning eraser is very good for removing pencil lines that have been drawn with a soft pencil using a very light pressure. The paper should be dusted with a clean, soft cloth or dusting brush after using an eraser. When the art gum is used for cleaning a large area, precautions should be taken to avoid getting eraser crumbs scattered over the drawing equipment.

The pencil eraser is used for erasing smudges and pencil lines that cannot be removed easily with the cleaning eraser. It is also used for erasing ink lines when it is desired to avoid scratching or roughening the paper. If the eraser is brightly colored watch carefully to see that it does not discolor the paper. Hard pressure and rapid movement causing the eraser and paper to become heated are likely to cause discoloration when colored erasers are used. The eraser will work more efficiently if the direction of movement is changed frequently.

The ink eraser is made of rubber containing sand, ground glass, or other abrasive grit. It is used for erasing ink lines and blots. It is quite likely to scratch or roughen the paper. Therefore it may be necessary to smooth the paper down in some way before inking over the erased area. The paper can be smoothed by rubbing with the thumb nail or other hard, smooth rounded object that will not discolor the paper. Finishing the erasing with a pencil eraser helps to smooth the paper in some cases. When inking over an erasure have only enough ink in the pen to make the line.

An ideal eraser should remove the lines quickly, leaving the paper in good condition. The eraser should not polish, roughen, or stain the paper. Roughened places in the paper become dirty more quickly than the surrounding surfaces. They will not take the ink well.

The erasing shield is used to confine the erasing to the desired area and protect lines near the erased area. An erasing shield wears down to a thin edge around the openings after it has been used a long time. A worn erasing shield with its sharp edges allows the eraser to work right to the edge of the shield while the new shield will leave a space that the eraser does not reach.

The erasing shield serves another useful purpose by wearing the eraser down and removing its dirty surfaces, thus keeping the surface clean where it comes in contact with the paper and avoiding discolorations of the paper.

A sharp knife, knife eraser, or razor blade is sometimes used to trim the edges or ends of lines when other lines or washes do not have to run over the erased areas. The knife eraser cannot be recommended for erasing lines or areas because it roughens the paper.

CHAPTER 4

TECHNIQUE OF DRAFTING

The objectives in drafting are (1) to produce a drawing that is made to appear as simple as possible so that it can be easily understood, and (2) to make the drawing attractive and expressive.

In looking through a number of drawings of the same object even the inexperienced person may be impressed with the varied effects produced by different persons. The character of a drawing may be anemic, érratic, delicate, refined, forceful, heavy handed, or brutal. Three of these characteristics are illustrated in Fig. 17. A good drawing is something more than a monotonous repetition of lines. It is a means of emphasizing the forms and divisions of an object, of suggesting materials and textures, of giving an impression suitable to the object depicted. In the example of Fig. 17 I, the lines are thin and weak. There are no variations in weight of lines to form accents and divisions or to subordinate less important lines. In Fig. 17 II the lines are all very heavy. There is no feeling of refinement in lines. In Fig. 17 III a very heavy line is used to silhouette the entire drawing. Emphasis is given to important divisions and areas by use of heavy outlines. Unimportant lines are subordinated. There is both refinement and forcefulness in the drawing.

Drafting has been employed as a tool for artistic expression in the fine arts as well as in the applied arts. Paintings by Mondrian and the drafted art of Josef Albers are two examples of drafting techniques in fine art. Commercial art works in packaging and in advertisements often employ crisp ruled lines and drafted patterns. Drafting is then very often a medium of expression for art work other than the commonly accepted uses such as interior design and architecture.

A person in design work can do better, more expressive, creative designs if he has a good working knowledge of all methods of drawing and is skillful in the techniques of drafting.

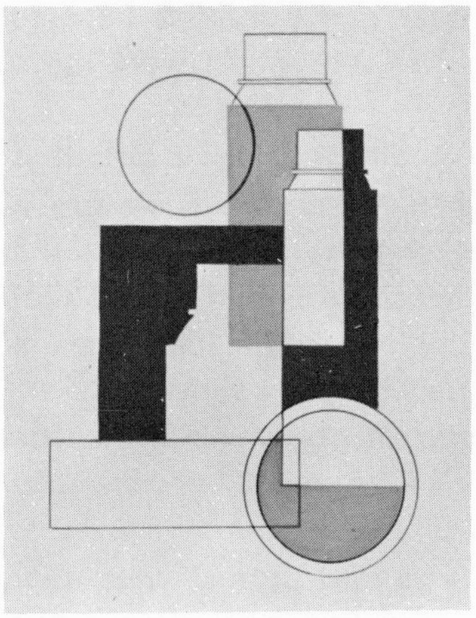

STUDENT WORK—S. SCHMIDT

(A) DESIGN LINES

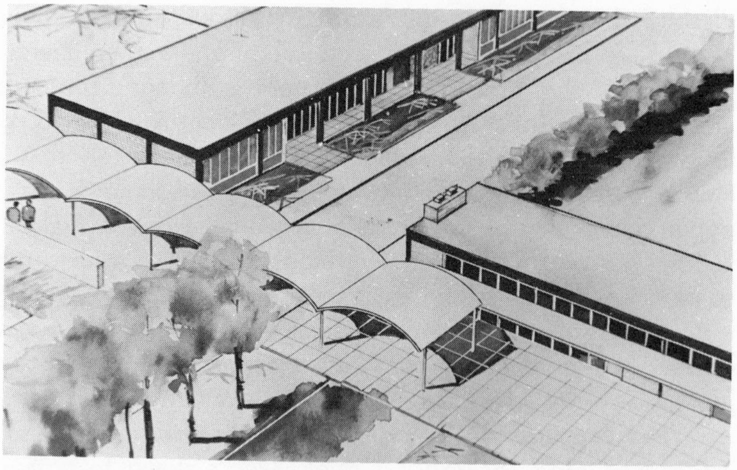

STUDENT WORK BY ROBERT MARTIN

(B) LINES A PART OF RENDERING

FIG. 16 DRAFTING IS USED IN PRESENTATION

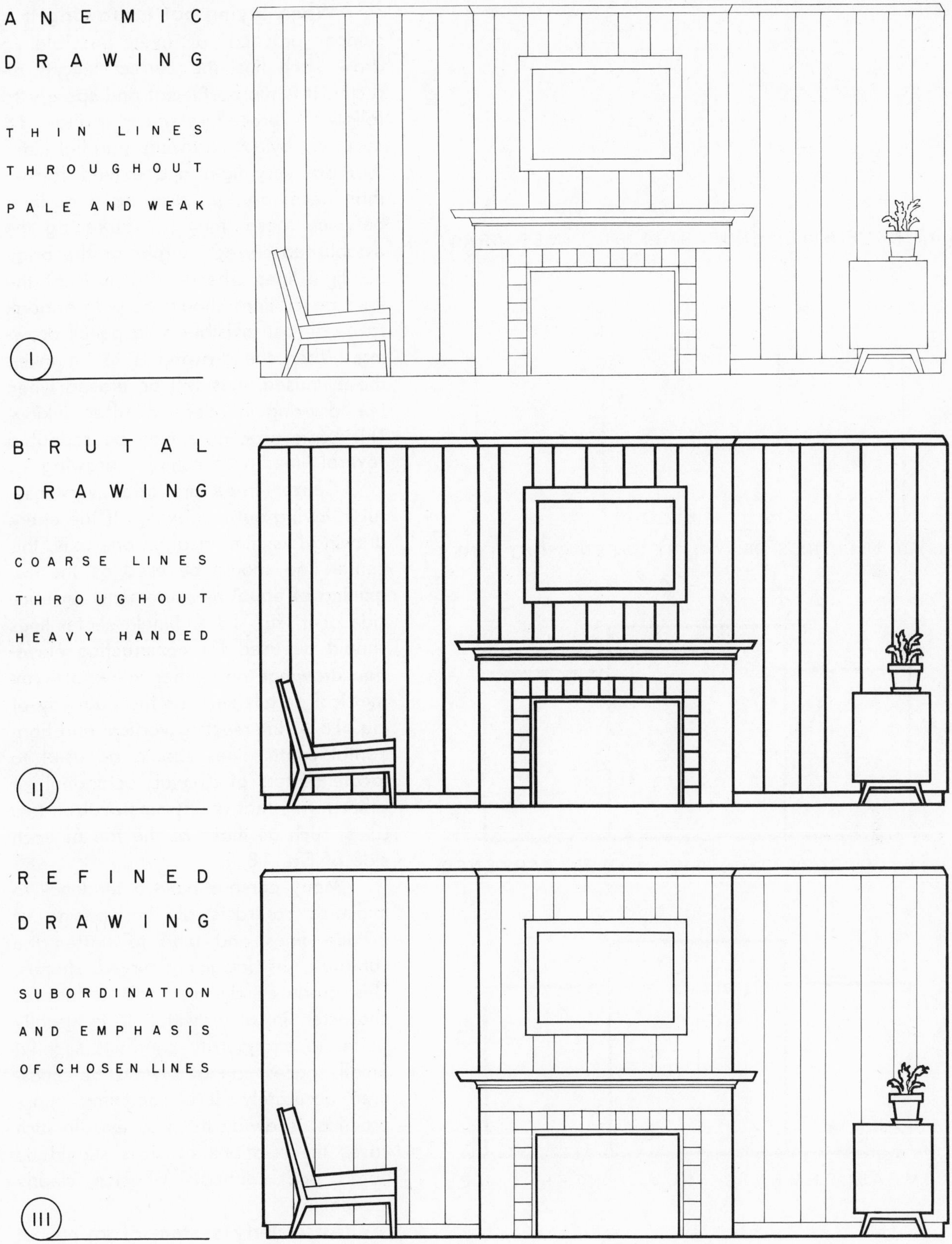

FIG. 17 EXPRESSION IN DRAFTING

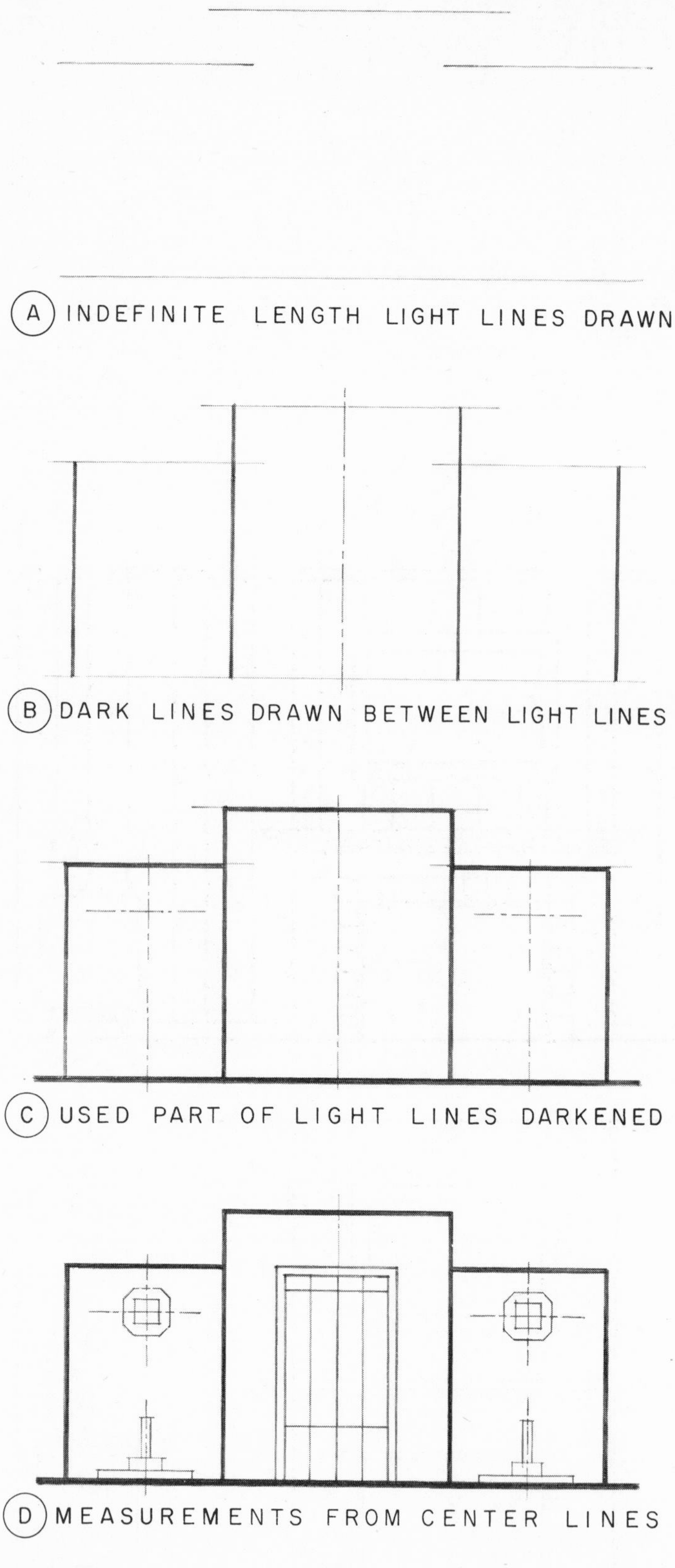

FIG. 18 ESTABLISHING LENGTHS OF LINES OF A DRAWING

When laying out a drawing it is seldom practical or even possible to draw each line the correct length directly. It is more efficient and speedy to follow the procedure shown in Figs. 18 A, B, C, by (A) drawing parallel lines that are very light and extend farther than necessary, (B) drawing dark lines between these, then (C) darkening the established correct lengths of the original light lines. The unused parts of the light pencil lines should be pale enough to be almost invisible on a pencil drawing. When the drawing is to be inked these unused lines will be erased when the drawing is cleaned after inking. This basic procedure may be repeated several times on a complex drawing.

Center lines are often very useful in laying out a drawing. If the entire drawing is symmetrical on one axis, this center line should be used as the beginning of equal measurements on each side of it, Fig. 18 B. Single center lines should be used for constructing elevation drawings and other views of symmetrical details such as the doorway of Fig. 18 D. Intersecting vertical and horizontal center lines should be used to locate centers of circular, octagonal, or other forms that are symmetrical on two axes, such as those at the top of each side of Fig. 18 D.

Many persons have a tendency to minimize contrasts of the spacing of parallel lines and tend to flatten the curvature of irregular curved shapes. This produces dullness and a lack of character in a drawing. It is usually better to exaggerate contrasts slightly. Small spaces cannot always be measured accurately. It is sometimes more practical to divide them by eye. In such cases the relations of sizes should be noted and contrasts of size clearly maintained.

An orderly system of laying out a drawing as shown in Figs. 19 I, II, III, IV is one phase of technique in drafting. In layout work the whole drawing is more important than any of its parts.

Major divisions of the drawing are more important than minor ones. Better, more accurate, and more speedy results are obtained by laying out (I) the limits of the entire drawing, (II) the major divisions, (III) minor divisions, (IV) small details and surface treatments.

This procedure provides an automatic means of checking accuracy and will prevent cumulative errors. It first assures that the drawing is located in the best position on the paper, then that successively smaller divisions fit correctly in the larger spaces. The reverse of this procedure is to start at one edge, perhaps the bottom, and add one small area at a time. Because practically everyone makes individual measurements either too small or too large, the final resulting size may be appreciably in error. Unless some system of checking at intervals is used, an error in measurements may not be discovered by the draftsman until the entire drawing is completed. Furthermore, the drawing may not be well placed on the sheet of paper when it is completed.

Speed in drafting is related to some phases of technique. Speed in obtaining results does not depend so much on actual hurrying as on the system used in drafting and on the correct, accurate, and efficient use of equipment. The person who works from large areas to small detail in a progressive order, who thinks as he works, who checks each step carefully once and then proceeds, will get results in a short time. The person who works frantically, uses incorrect procedure, or fails to check by appearance and mechanical means will make errors and have to erase and start over so often that he accomplishes little. Confidence in the accuracy of equipment and in the correctness of the developing drawing are essential to rapid progress with the drawing. An alert and attentive mind in searching out and using the best means of constructing the drawing is an essential part of speed in drafting.

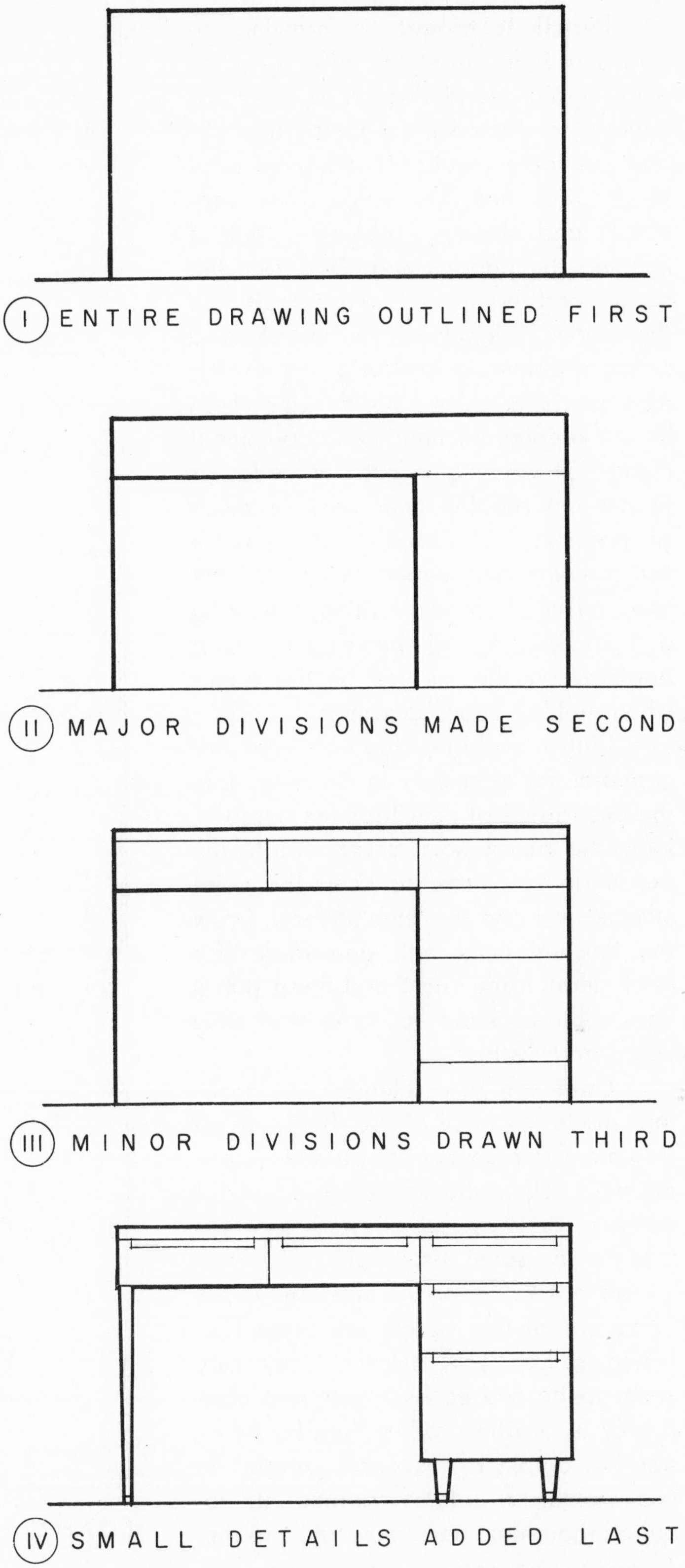
I ENTIRE DRAWING OUTLINED FIRST
II MAJOR DIVISIONS MADE SECOND
III MINOR DIVISIONS DRAWN THIRD
IV SMALL DETAILS ADDED LAST

FIG. 19 SYSTEM USED IN LAYING OUT A DRAWING

Pencil technique in drawing includes a wide variety of effects in line work and in rendering. It is easy for anyone to draw with a pencil and obtain mediocre results. It is not so easy to produce first-rate work. One very simple and obvious problem is that of keeping the paper clean. Dirt from the hands and equipment will transfer to the paper. Cleanliness is therefore a major problem in drafting. The draftsman can help to keep his drawing clean by (1) keeping his hands and equipment clean, (2) working in such an order as to prevent rubbing over lines as much as possible, (3) covering all parts of the drawing and paper except for the area on which he is working, (4) using a light coating of powdered eraser particles on the surface of the paper when making pencil drawings.

Sharp, uniform, clean-cut lines are essential for precision in drafting. Use the best grade of pencil for the purpose, keep the pencil point sharp, rotate the pencil as you draw to keep the point symmetrical and the lines uniform. Draw the finished lines with one stroke for neat clean work. Start and finish pencil lines with pressure to make the ends sharp and distinct.

Lines are basic elements of drawings made in pencil or ink. Their correct treatment is essential for polished drafting work. Lines should meet precisely at corners, or may be allowed to cross slightly for some types of work. They should not fall short of meeting. Minor variations of line weight are often confusing rather than helpful. They may seem to be caused by errors and inaccuracy in drafting rather than by intention. To obtain a noticeable contrast in line weight a greater variation is required than most persons would assume. A one-to-two ratio is about the minimum and a one-to-three ratio is better for effective contrast of line weight.

Broken lines, which are made with dots, dashes, or combinations of the

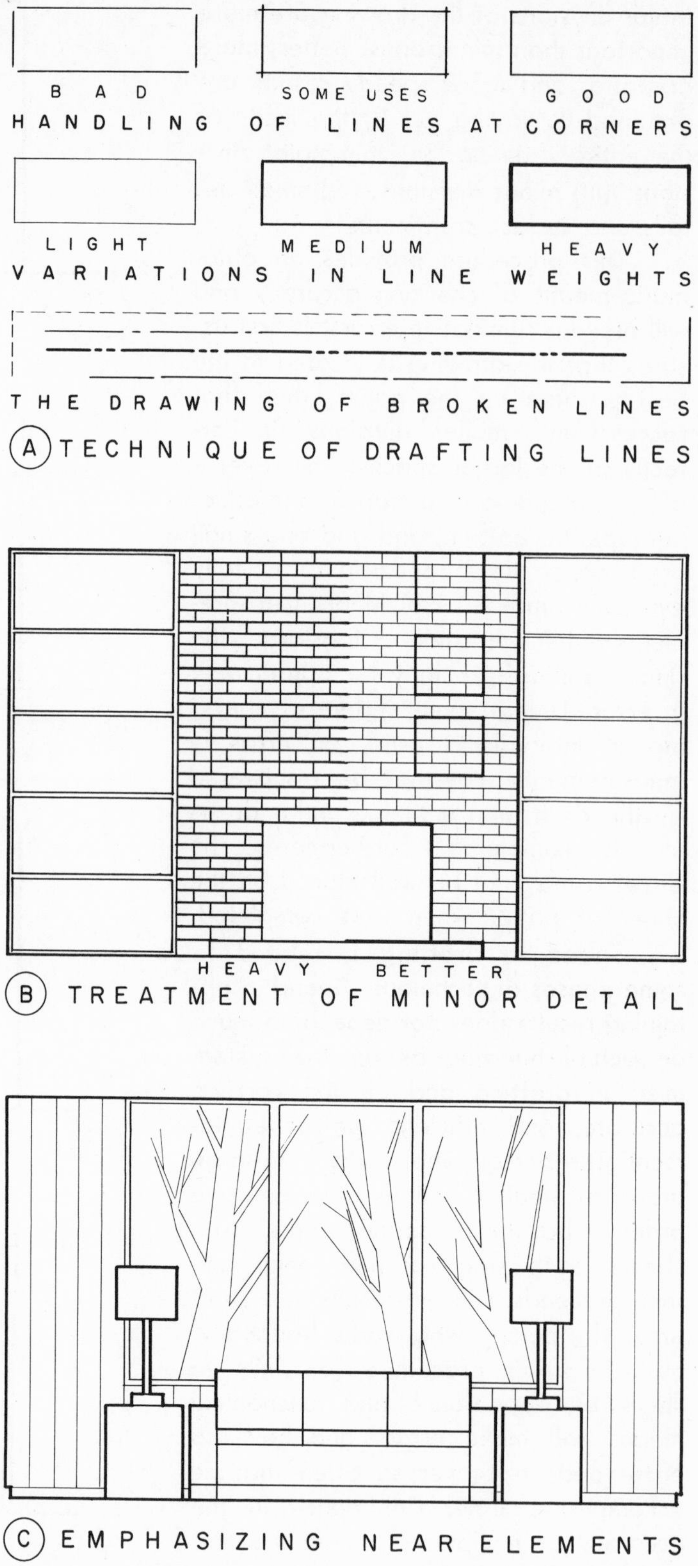

FIG. 20 CHARACTER IN LINE TECHNIQUE

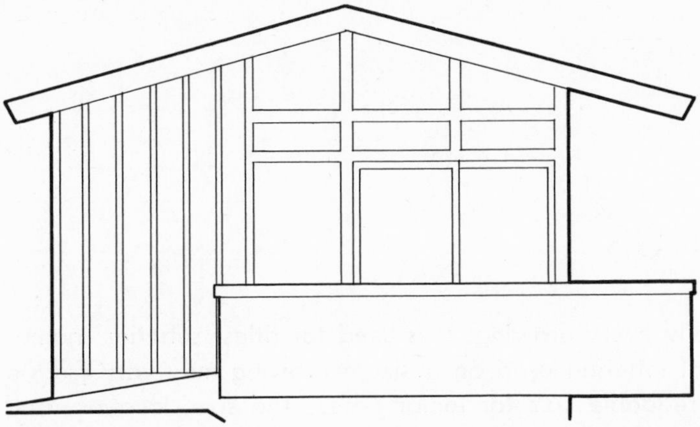

(I) SILHOUETTE EMPHASIZED

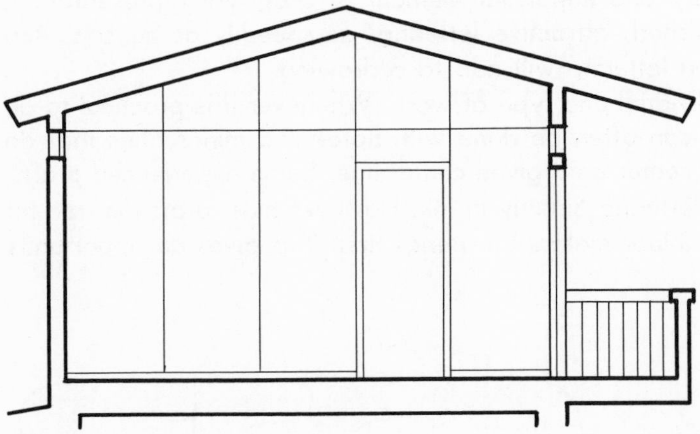

(II) OUTLINING OF CUT AREAS

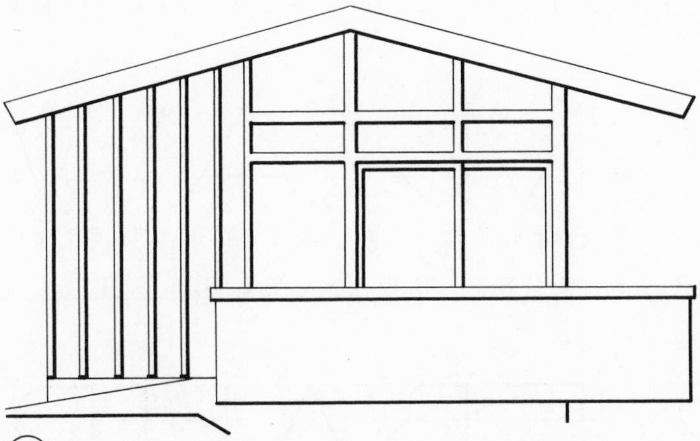

(III) SHADE LINE DRAFTING

FIG. 21 SOME USES OF HEAVY LINES IN DRAFTING

two, should be as mechanically precise as it is possible to make them, Fig. 20 A. Choose a good relation of space and lines and stick to it with a dotted line or a dash line. When dots and dashes are both used in the same line use a very definite contrast of length of dot and dash.

Overemphasis of repeating minor details is a common mistake in drafting. Divisions of materials such as stone, brick, or tile may appear harsh and offensive when made prominent. Such elements can be treated in a conventionalized manner or, when drawn completely, be subordinated by using thinner or lighter lines, Fig. 20 B.

Darker lines are sometimes used throughout nearer elements to emphasize them and make them appear closer to the observer, Fig. 20 C.

Good judgment of weight of lines for different parts of a drawing is very important. Do not be afraid to use some heavy lines. They add life to the drawing and when correctly used make it more easily understood. Heavy lines can be used as a silhouette around the entire drawing, Fig. 21 I; to separate the visible areas of the object from the hidden structure when the drawing cuts through the object, Fig. 21 II; for shade lining to emphasize the shadow casting edges of the object and make projecting areas more obvious, Fig. 21 III. Usually the lower projecting edges and those at the right are used for this purpose. However, some other system may be employed if it is more effective on a given object.

Heavy lines are almost always used at the base or ground line of an object. They can frequently be used effectively to emphasize the edges of overhangs and to separate different materials and major elements.

The draftsman should decide what he wishes to accomplish with different line weights and then use those that are most effective for each drawing.

CHAPTER 5

LETTERING ON DRAWINGS

Lettering is a necessary part of practically every drawing. It is used for titles, subtitles, names of areas or elements, and notes. The sizes of lettering used on a single drawing may vary from a very large size for the title to the smallest readable size for minor notes. The size, location, and quality of the lettering used have a great influence on the appearance and usefulness of the finished drawing. Well-placed lettering can make a drawing seem simple and easy to understand. Bad design in layout and details of lettering text will cause even a good drawing to be confusing and difficult to comprehend. Since lettering is a necessary and important element of graphical representation, the draftsman should learn to do clear, polished, attractive lettering, as speedily as he can. Bad lettering will spoil any drawing whereas good lettering will add to a drawing.

Lettering procedure varies with the individual and type of work. Whenever it is practical to do so, ink lettering is done directly in ink. This can often be done with notes and minor titles that do not have to begin and end at fixed points or center on a given center line. Some experienced draftsmen may also do titles and other important lettering directly in ink. However most draftsmen prefer to do all lettering other than very small and minor material in pencil first. This gives an opportunity

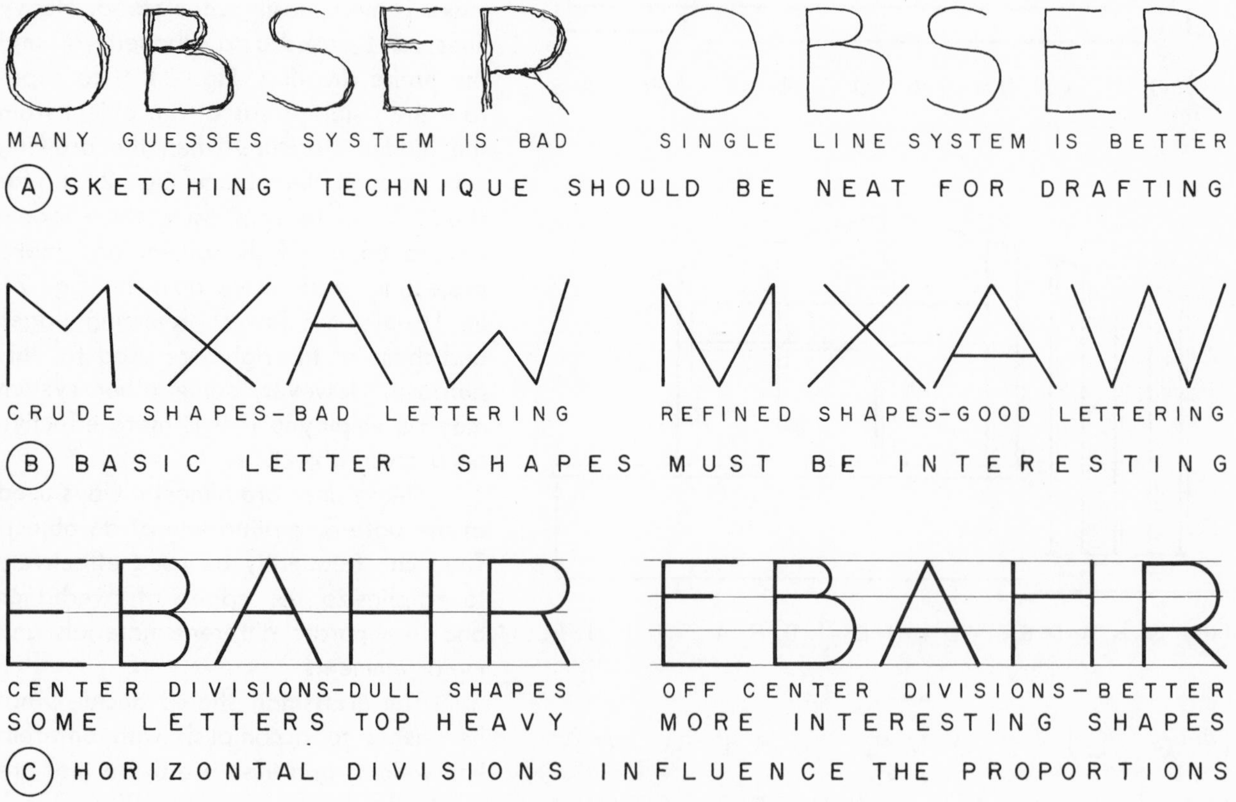

FIG. 22 BASIC PRINCIPLES OF FINE LETTERING

ABCDEFGHIJKLMNOPQRSTUV
I THE THIN OR COMPRESSED ALPHABET
GIVES MANY TALL LETTERS IN A SMALL SPACE
ABCDEFGHIJKMI
II NORMAL OR AVERAGE WIDTH ALPHABET
GIVES PLEASING PROPORTIONS FOR MOST USES
ABCDEFG
III THE WIDE OR EXPANDED ALPHABET
COVERS WIDE SPACE WITH FEW LETTERS

FIG. 23 WIDTH VARIATIONS IN LETTERS

to work out spacing. Sizes and locations of the lettering can also be checked before inking. Whenever lettering is done in pencil, the same grades of pencils should be used as those for other drafting purposes. It is more difficult to letter with ink than with pencil, so do not plan to improve crude pencil lettering when it is inked. Make the pencil lettering as perfect as possible before inking. Whether pencil or ink is used, form the habit of going over a line once only. Good lines can seldom be made by scratching back and forth over them. A number of guesses at the form of a letter will not produce precise and polished letter shapes, Fig. 22 A.

Guide lines should be drawn in pencil at the top, bottom, and at helpful intermediate levels for each line of lettering, Fig. 22 C. These lines help to secure uniform heights and consistent divisions of letters. The guide lines are usually so light that they can remain on pencil lettering and can be erased after ink lettering is completed.

Attractive lettering is not made by using individual letters that are ordinary, crude, or uninteresting in shape, Figs. 22 B, C. It is essential that each letter be beautiful. The person who hopes to do fine lettering must study his A B C's in detail and learn the characteristics of each letter from the example which he is following. When he designs an alphabet of his own, he must take infinite care to polish each letter to as near perfection as possible. Each letter must be coordinated with all the other letters of the alphabet.

Proportions of letters vary in different alphabets. In most alphabets one group of letters including B, H, and E have the horizontal divisions above center. Another group that includes A, P, and Y have the divisions below center. This helps to produce good proportions and gives a feeling of unity in the alphabet, Fig. 22 C. Horizontal divisions on center are usually considered unattractive. For style effect the horizontal division is sometimes made either above or below center on all letters. The widths of letters can be made to vary greatly and still be perfectly legible. Fig. 23 II shows letters of normal or average width. Figs. 23 I and III show thin and wide letter shapes.

FIG. 24 THE CORRECT SPACING OF LETTERS

THE CORRECT SPACING OF LETTERING. After selecting an interesting alphabet for use, the next problem is spacing the letters to produce the most pleasing optical effect. The first idea of most beginners is to make an equal distance between the closest edges of all letters, Fig. 24 A. Unfortunately the shapes of letters vary. If all had identical edge forms, equal distances between all edges would give good spacing. However some edges of letters are vertical, some are inclined, some curved, and others have projecting horizontal members. The problem is to space the letters so as to make them appear to be the same average distance apart. The apparent background area between each two letters in a word must be equal in order to give a smooth and pleasing pattern Fig. 24 B.

The background area between letters is obvious with some letter shapes. With others it is not so readily apparent. The simplest background shape between letter edges is a rectangle such as that between an ND combination. Slightly more complex is the truncated triangular area between a slanting edge and a vertical edge as with AN, Fig. 24 C. The mechanically correct spacing of the word AND is then simple. The average width of the horizontal space between the AN must equal the width of the ND space to give equal background areas.

More complex letter edges complicate the problems of the background areas. Some letter shapes partially enclose an area. Only a part of this area seems to be background and the remainder belongs to the letter form. The letter C is one of the most extreme ones of this type. A curving area extending into the open edge of the C is considered as background. The amount of this area varies with the distance across the ends of the curved line of the C. With a large opening the background extending into the letter includes a large proportion of the entire space within the C, Fig. 24 C. A small opening will reduce the amount of the area inside of the C that is included in the background space between the open side of the C and the next letter. The system of mechanical analysis of areas between letters now becomes less precise because it depends on the judgment of the individual making the lettering. It will be found that the same procedure as that used for the C will apply to the E, F, L, and other irregular letters. An allowance must be made because only a part of the area at the irregular edge of a letter seems to be background. This amount varies with the thickness and length of the horizontal members of a letter such as E. In the case of an L, most of the area will be background, because the form does not make much of an enclosure of area to the right of the letter.

Good spacing of letters in words depends on the sensitivity of the draftsman to good composition and on his judgment in working out a feeling of continuity and balance within and between words.

Extremely irregular spacing of letters in words will make the text difficult to read. It may even suggest word divisions that do not exist, as shown in the word UNLAWFUL, Fig. 24 E. These irregularities of spacing destroy the even pattern of lettering and may produce a feeling of confusion and lack of order which make reading the lettering an unpleasant experience.

The closest spacing of letters in a word is limited by the minimum amount of area necessary between the two adjacent letter edges which require the largest space. The LA combination requires the most space in the word UNLAWFUL. The horizontal part of the L can be shortened and the edges of the L and A pushed close together, Fig. 24 D. However, this reduction of space is limited by a clear separation of letters and the necessity of maintaining a distinct form for the L that will not be out of character with other letters used. In some work it is satisfactory to have the L and A overlap. However this is rarely done. The minimum area between each two letters in the word UNLAWFUL is set by the amount required between L and A, Fig. 24 F. Furthermore other words used in the same title or continuity of words should conform to this spacing. It is impossible to space letters satisfactorily when straight line edges such as those of MIL in MILKY and UNL in UNLAWFUL are close together. The large spaces of such combinations as LK, TT, LA, and TY determine the minimum working space between each two letters of words where they occur.

Words should be spaced far enough apart to make word divisions clear but not so far as to give a spotty disconnected effect, Fig. 25 I. A commonly used rule is that the space between two words should be the amount obtained by omitting an average width letter from a word. Even this amount may in some cases seem excessive for the clear separation of words, Fig. 25 II.

LEND IS A TERM OF

(I) WORDS TOO FAR APART — SPOTTY

LEND IS A TERM OF TWO

(II) GOOD SPACING OF WORDS

FIG. 25 SPACING OF WORDS IN LETTERING

FIG. 26 THREE TYPES OF LETTERS

MECHANICALLY CONSTRUCTED LETTERS. Titles and other large lettering used on drawings are often made with instruments. The straight lines of these letters are made with T-square, triangles, and ruling pen. The curves are made with the compasses. All of the lines should be made mechanically. Mixing of freehand and mechanical lines in the same lettering is not satisfactory. The freehand lines waver and are not as precise in their width as the lines that are drawn with instruments. They give a ragged, uneven effect that ruins the precision of mechanical lettering.

The slanting lines of letters can rarely be made with the triangle resting on the horizontal T-square. The triangle must be turned to secure the best slant for each letter. Care should be taken to assure that the same letter is made the same shape throughout a given plate with the exception of minor variations for more satisfactory spacing. The vertical balance or symmetry should be carefully maintained in letters that use V shapes. These include A, V, Y, M, W, and X.

Construction lines such as those shown in Fig. 26 A are used to block out letter shapes, to locate centers of circles and semicircles, and to mark the ends of semicircles for drawing mechanically constructed letters. These pencil construction lines are almost exclusively horizontal, vertical, and 45° lines. The diameters of all semicircles should be drawn to locate the ends of the semicircles and beginnings of the connecting straight lines. Their correct use will prevent bumpy transitions, which are caused by making the arcs extend too far or stop short of their correct lengths. When a semicircle connects to two tangent straight lines as in letters B and U always draw the semicircle first. It is much easier to draw the straight lines one at a time to meet the semicircle than to make the ends of the semicircle connect perfectly to the ends of the two straight lines.

The thickness of line made with a single stroke of the ruling pen and compass is often satisfactory for mechanical lettering. The same thickness is used for every letter and every line in most cases. When the lettering is not extremely large a combination of heavy and light straight lines can be worked out within the line thickness limitations of the ruling pen, Fig. 26 B. Curves are built up by first drawing the outside and inside with thin lines, then filling in.

Shaded letters should have a standard set size for all thin lines, and another size for all the thick strokes, Fig. 26 B. When these two sizes are used throughout all letters, there is a feeling of unity. When the size of a wide or thin stroke is allowed to vary, confusion may result. It is important to locate the thin and thick strokes according to some system and not just by chance. The shaded Roman lettering was developed from pen lettering with a flexible freehand pen. The pen

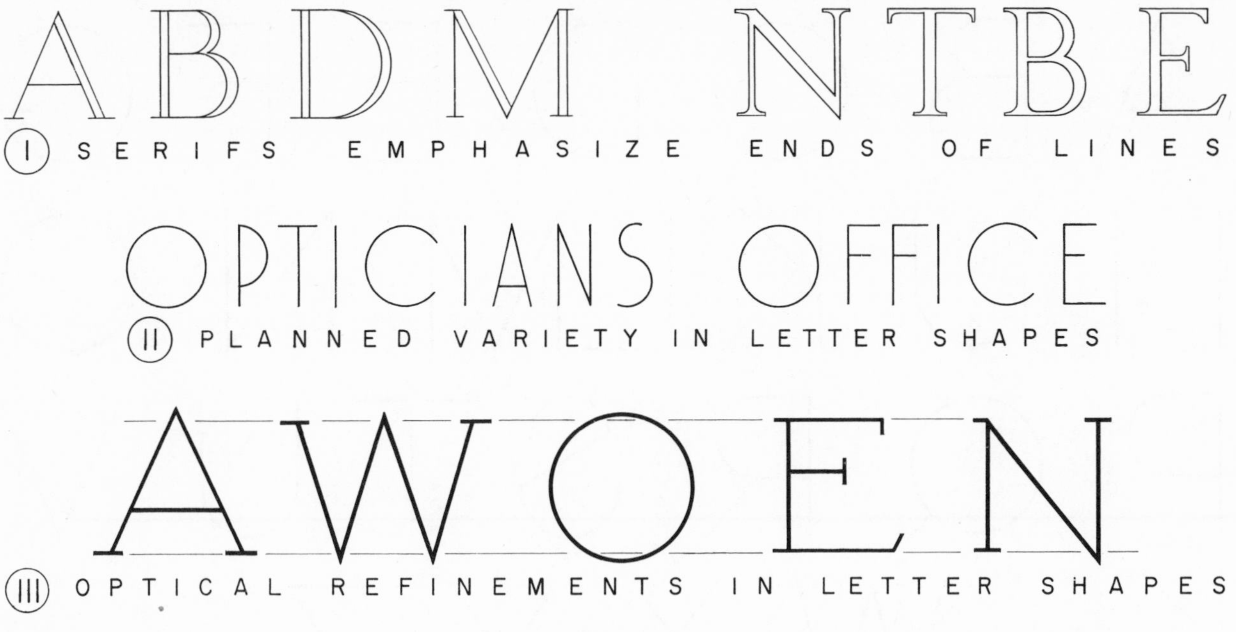

FIG. 27 DETAILS OF LETTER SHAPES

made thin upward and horizontal strokes, and spread on the down strokes to make heavy lines. Most shaded lettering follows this system.

Built-up letters are used when a single stroke of the pen will not give the required width of lines. This is usually done by outlining each black area and then filling in with a small brush or speedball pen. Built-up letters are made either with a uniform width of all the elements or with a combination of wide and narrow elements, Fig. 26 C.

Serifs are the small cross strokes made at the ends of lines and used as extensions at corners, Fig. 27 I. It is a common error to use these on the I and J when the other letters of the alphabet do not have them. When serifs are used, they should be used throughout the alphabet on all letters wherever they can be used appropriately. They are not used at the angles of A, V, W, the center of the M, or on the bottom angle of the N. Serifs look better when they are kept rather small. It is a mistake to allow the curves of the serifs to extend so far that they destroy the straight lines that they terminate.

The shapes of letters are usually made similar throughout a title or plate. Thus all letters used appear to be narrow, or all appear to be wide. Furthermore it is usually considered best to keep the same general characteristics of letters in so far as possible throughout the entire alphabet. If a circular O is used then other curves are made circular. When an oval or angular form is used in the O then other letters keep the same characteristic. This system gives harmony of form and proportions throughout all the lettering. It is most widely used and is satisfactory for many lettering uses.

Planned dissimilarity of form of letters is sometimes used to create contrast and attract attention. The contrasting shapes should produce an interesting and satisfactorily balanced pattern. This device is most frequently used in trademarks and advertising matter, Fig. 27 II.

Optical corrections are made in some lettering. They are more common on large than on small lettering. The purpose of these corrections is to make letters of various shapes at the top and bottom seem to be exactly the same height, Fig. 27 III. A letter such as an E, which is horizontal at the top and bottom, seems higher than the point of an A at the top and lower than a W at the bottom. Points of letters are extended slightly beyond the horizontal guide lines to correct the illusion of their being too short. Circular shapes at top and bottom usually require a smaller correction than the pointed forms. It is better for most beginners to ignore these refinements and bring all letters exactly to the horizontal guide lines at the top and bottom.

ABCDEFG
HIJKLMNO
PQRSTUV
WXYZ

(A) CAPITALS MADE WITH COMPASS AND RULED LINES

abcdefghijklmn
opqrstuuwxyz

(B) LOWER CASE LETTERS USING A SINGLE RADIUS

ABCDEFGHIJKLMNOPQ
RSTUVWXYZ

(C) COMPRESSED LETTERS WITH RULED AND COMPASS LINES

FIG. 28 SINGLE STROKE MECHANICAL ALPHABETS

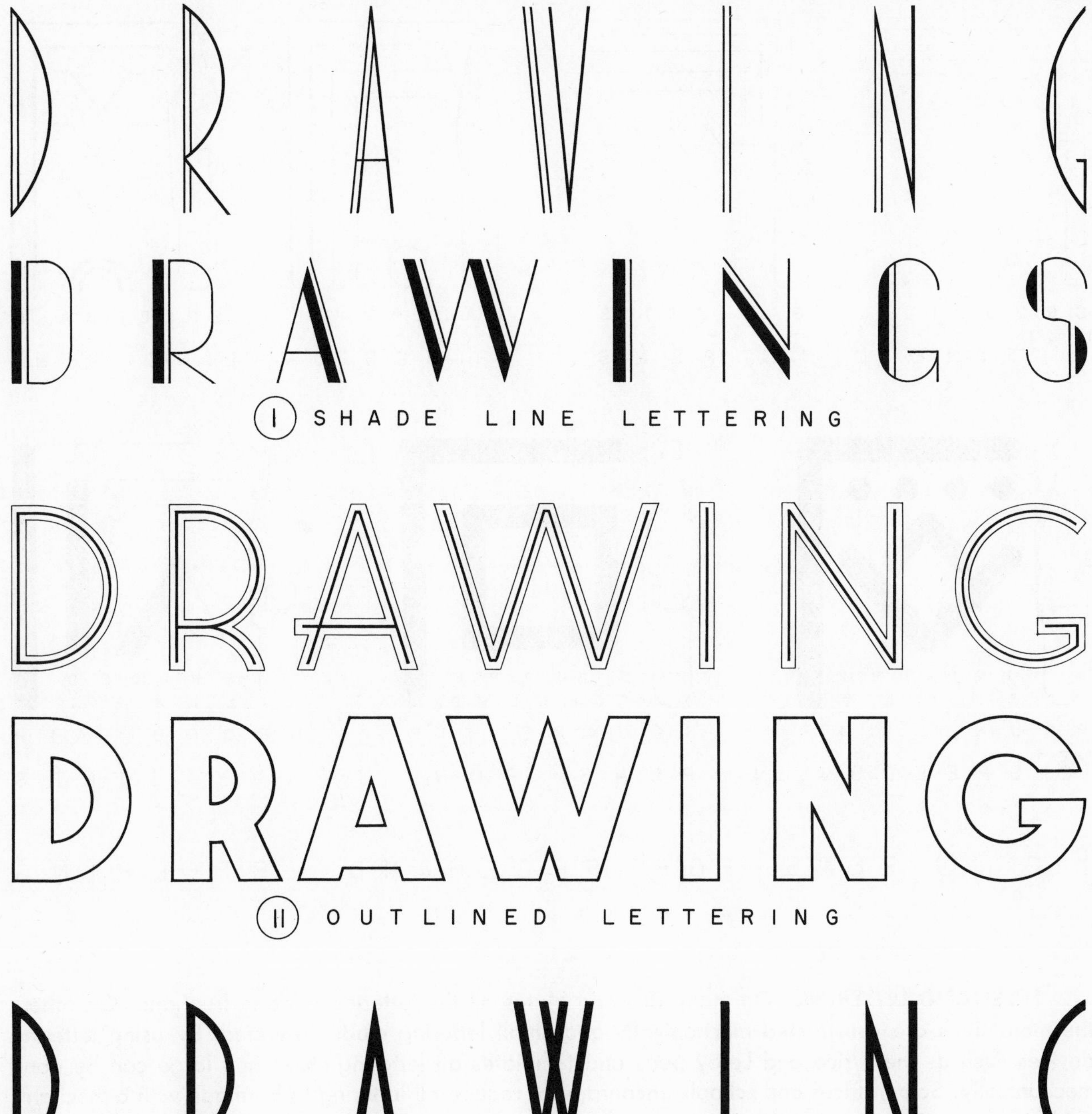

FIG. 29 SOME VARIATIONS IN LETTER FORMS

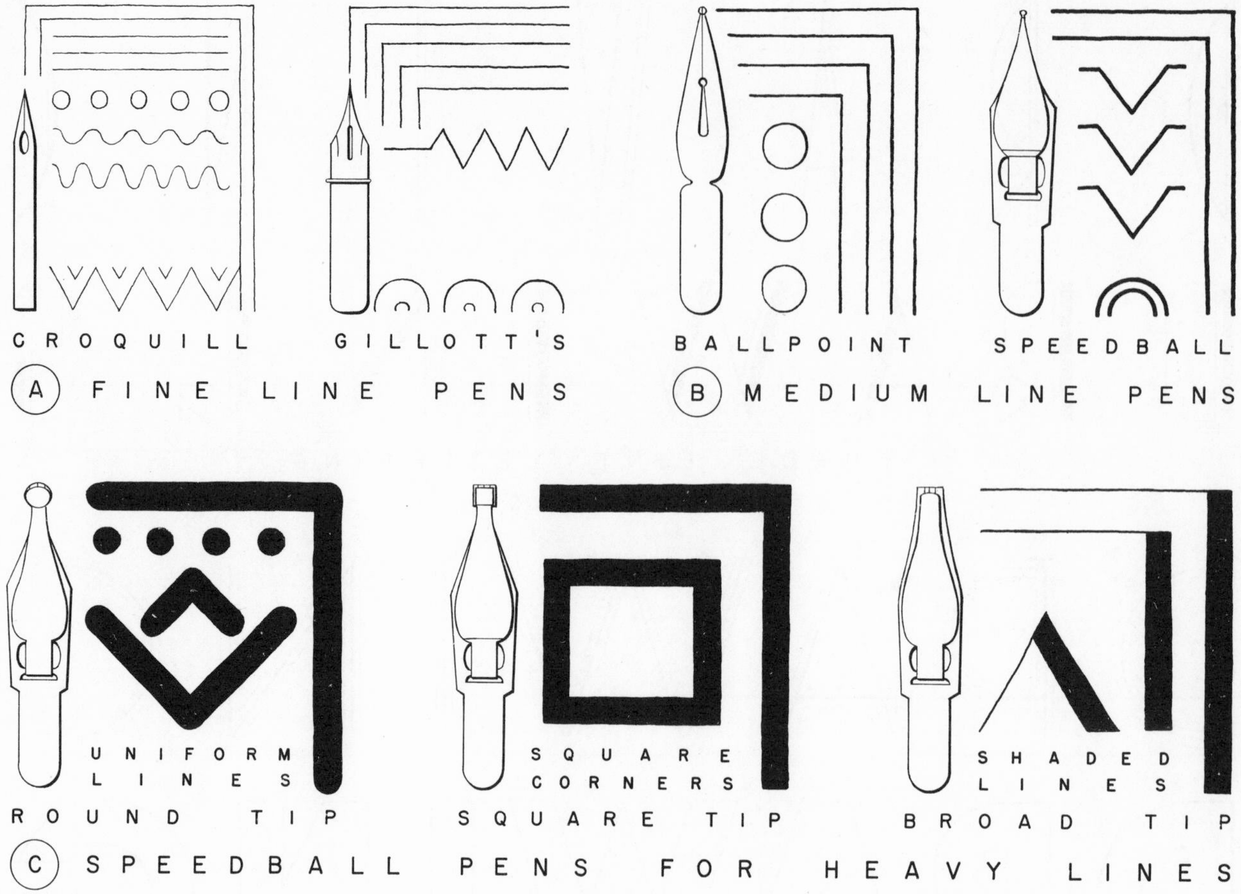

FIG. 30 PENS FOR FREEHAND LETTERING

FREEHAND LETTERING. On many drawing plates all the lettering is done freehand. On others the main titles are constructed mechanically and small lettering made freehand. By using lettering devices such as the Wrico and Leroy pens and templates all lettering small and large can be done mechanically. Some offices and schools encourage or require all lettering to be made with a mechanical lettering device, or require the use of applied or transfer lettering, on some projects. However the ability to do good freehand lettering is often expected of students, draftsmen, and designers. Style of lettering is limited when using mechanical lettering guides or manufactured letters.

A wide variety of lettering pens is available at stationery and drafting supply stores. The draftsman should select a number of these that will give line widths ranging from the finest available to the largest he expects to use. The first step in using the pens should be to try all of them in order to become familiar with the type of line obtained from each one. Most new pens are protected from corrosion by an oily film. This film should be removed by use of soap and hot water, by rubbing with a damp cloth, by filling with ink and wiping vigorously, or in some other manner. After the oil is removed the ink will flow to the point of the pen and it can be used.

Fine line pens are most difficult to use, Fig. 30 A. The point must be sharp and if the pen is pushed toward the point it will stick in the paper. Therefore only strokes away from the point and to the side are possible. Too much ink in the pen will cause wider lines, and when the pen is almost dry the lines will be thin. It is necessary to refill the pen frequently and keep a moderate amount of ink in it. Because the point is small, the nibs of the pen are flexible. The least pressure spreads them apart making a wider line. A very delicate sense of touch and good coordination are neces-

FIG. 31 FREEHAND LETTERING ALPHABETS

sary to get uniform thin lines from a lettering pen. A good rest for the arm all the way from the fingers to the elbow gives better control of the pen. Better results are obtained by allowing the fingers and muscles of the arm to relax than by being tense and taking a "death grip" on the pen. Some persons can letter with an arm movement and get very good results. There is a great deal of variation of ability between individuals to do good small lettering. It is encouraging for the person who is having difficulty to see the work done by someone who does very perfect lettering. It is astonishing to find how many draftsmen have such perfect control of a pen that they can make letters that are easily read at $\frac{1}{32}$ inch high and can put style and polish into lettering $\frac{1}{16}$ inch high. Lettering is rarely used less than $\frac{1}{16}$ inch to $\frac{3}{32}$ inch high on drawings.

Pens for medium to heavy lines are comparatively stiff, Figs. 30 B, C. Their points do not spread sufficiently under normal use to widen appreciably lines made with them. Some pens for heavy lines require pressure to produce good lines. Most pens other than the finest line ones have reservoirs that hold the ink and keep it from feeding to the point too rapidly. Some of these open for cleaning. Pens should always be cleaned before the ink has an opportunity to solidify in them.

Practice is necessary in order to become skillful in freehand lettering. Effort with the hands and eyes alone may produce skill in handling pens. However, mental effort is essential to any real progress in producing polished and artistic lettering. The mind must know just what each shape will be, precisely where each stroke goes, in order to provide the confidence necessary for excellent lettering. The mind must analyze each letter, almost each stroke, to see if it is exactly right. To the word practice we must add intelligent and painstaking if real progress is to be made in lettering.

(A) SHAPE AND DETAIL VARIATIONS

(B) THREE DIMENSIONAL LETTERING

(C) OUTLINED LETTERS ARE LIGHT

FIG. 32 MEDIUM LINE FREEHAND LETTERING

FIG. 33 HEAVY LINE FREEHAND LETTERING

TITLES. The design and composition of titles and subtitles is a major division of lettering on drawings. The size, weight, style, and location of this lettering are important design elements. The draftsman designer should choose lettering that he thinks will not detract from but will help his drawing. Heavy black lettering may overpower and distract attention from delicate and refined drawings. Heavy lettering may be in character with a drawing that has heavy lines and black areas. Ornate and elaborate titles are not often suitable for simple drawings. Lettering may intentionally be made to contrast with a drawing for design purposes. However, it is usually more satisfactory to have a similar character in the lettering and drawing. Vertical lettering is in better harmony with the predominately horizontal and vertical lines found in most drawings than inclined lettering with its emphasis on oblique lines in one direction. Choose a type, size, and weight of lettering for the title that will add to the attractiveness of the drawing.

In laying out a title there are two common conditions: (1) wherein the exact length of the title is not important, and (2) wherein the title should be a definite established length.

When the exact length is not important the center line of the title may be located and the horizontal guide lines drawn to establish its height on the final paper. The center letter or space is located by counting the letters and spaces between words in the title. The title is then lettered from the center out. The last half may be completed first and then the first letter of the title located at the same distance from center as the last letter. This method works rather easily and accurately for most titles, although some minor adjustments may be required, Fig. 34. Another method is to work out completely the lettering of the title at the required size on scrap paper and then transfer it to the final paper of the drawing. This method requires a repetition of the lettering.

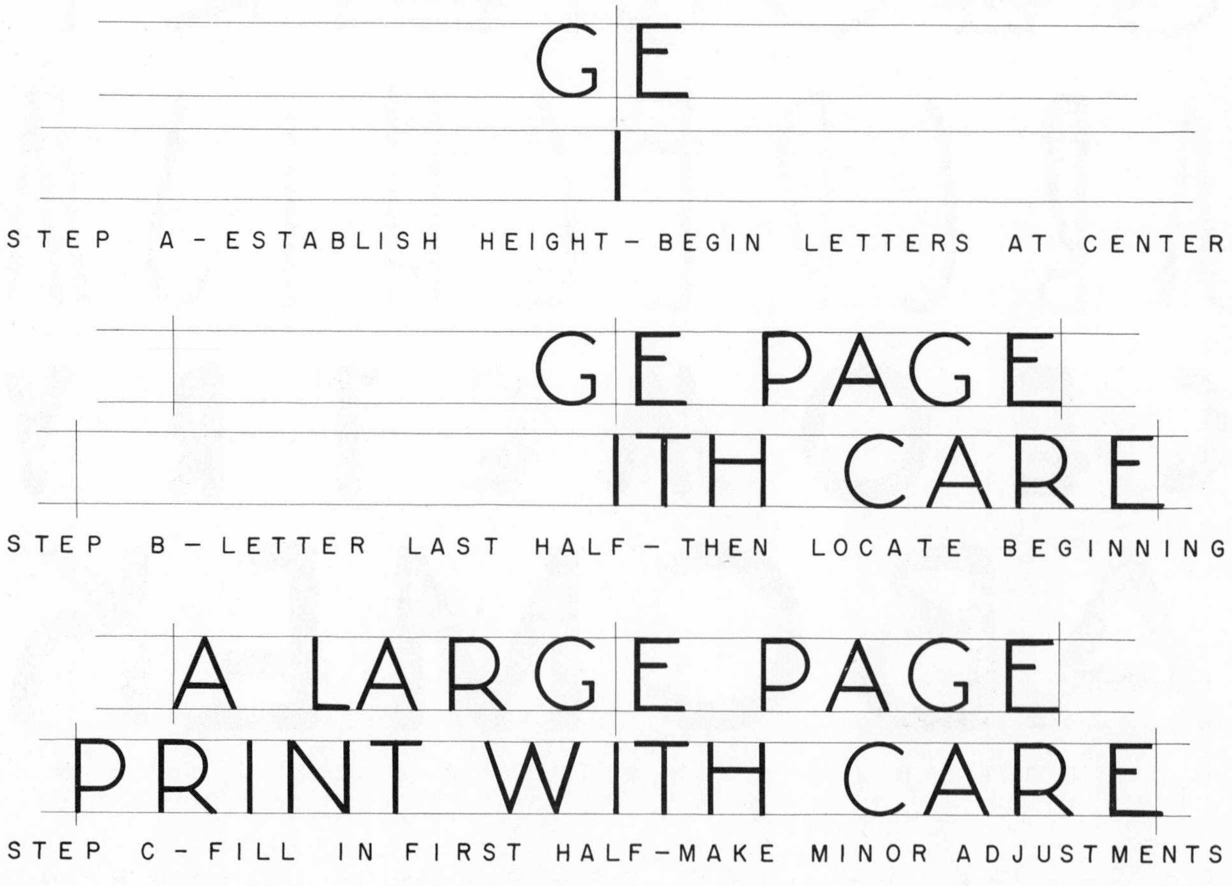

FIG. 34 TITLE WHICH CAN VARY IN LENGTH

When the lettering is made to fit a given space the height and length of each line of lettering should first be outlined precisely. There are two general methods that can be followed to fit the line of lettering into its space. (1) The lettering can be drawn directly in place by a system of dividing the distances. (2) The lettering can be laid out on scrap paper and then transferred to position on the plate with any necessary adjustments so it fits the given space.

In using the first method the number of letters in the title is counted and each space between words counted as a letter. In the title A MODERN ROOM of Fig. 35 there are 13 letters and spaces combined. In lettering this title, first letter the A on the left and the M on the right. Letter R, which is number 7, will be in the exact center of the title and O and R, which are numbers 4 and 10 respectively, will be the center letters of each half of the title. After breaking up the space in this manner, the remaining small spaces are filled in as shown in step III to complete the title. When the number of elements is more difficult to divide some ingenuity is necessary in developing a workable method of spacing letters. The title at the bottom of Fig. 35 A WALNUT CABINET has 16 letters and spaces. It does not have a letter or space between words on center. Furthermore, it is slightly unbalanced with an I on the right side of center. Different methods could be used to space this title; some persons may prefer to use one system, some another. The important thing is to think out a logical procedure that will get good results. A suggested procedure which locates center lines of letters is: place A at the beginning of the title, then add an A beyond the end of the title estimating spacing for the location of this letter. There are now 17 elements instead of 16. Number 9, a space, is in the center and a light X may be used to suggest the space. Now the spacing will divide to single letters by using the order 1 to 5 given on the lines above the lettering.

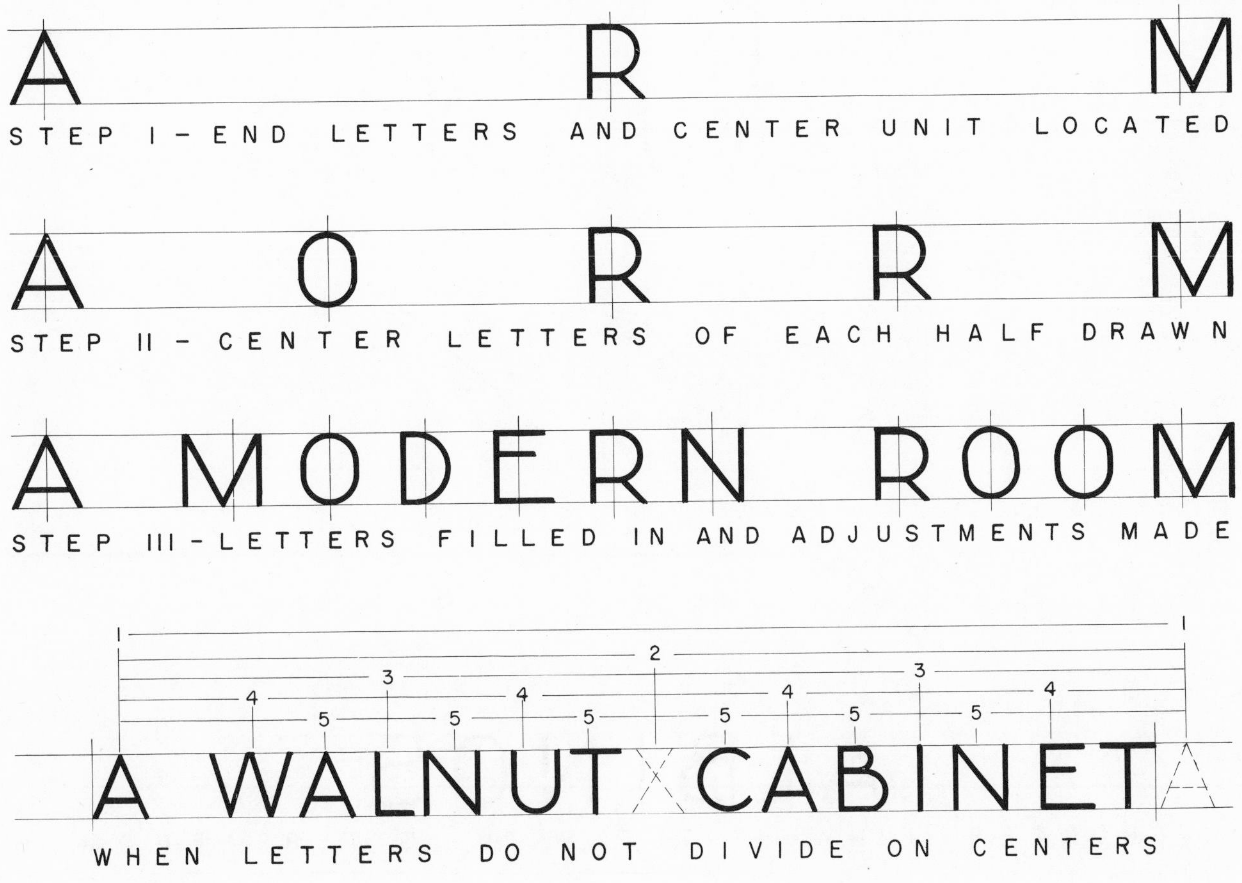

FIG. 35 TITLE TO FIT IN A DEFINITE LENGTH

The second method of fitting a title into a given space requires that the lettering be executed on practice paper at the size to be used, Fig. 36 B. It is then transferred to the final drawing with any necessary adjustments. The preliminary lettering should be spaced correctly but the letters need not include all refinements of the final title. The preliminary will probably occupy too much or too little space and this error should be divided proportionately by counting one unit for each space between letters, and two units for each space between words. In the title MOLDED PLASTIC WARE there are 14 spaces between letters and 2 spaces $\times$ 2 = 4 unit spaces between words—a total of 18. One eighteenth of the error should be added to each space between letters, and two eighteenths to each space between words to increase the distance for the title. These amounts should be subtracted if the preliminary was too long. The total distance of the correction to be made can be divided into the required number of parts by one of the methods shown in Figs. 68 A, D, or E.

A second procedure for obtaining an approximately correct spacing of the finished title from a trial title will seem simple to an experienced draftsman. Draw the vertical center line of each letter

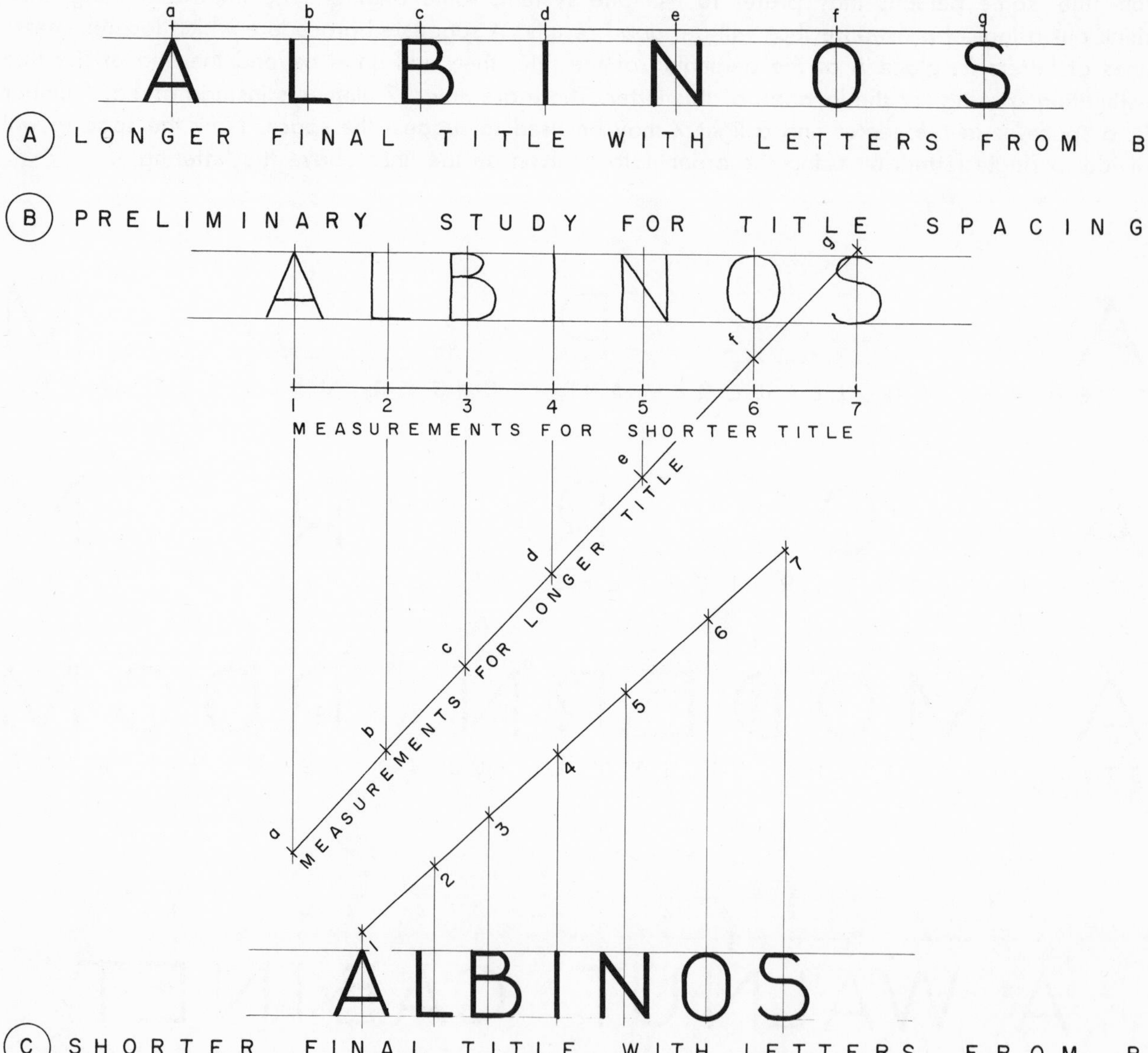

FIG. 36 TITLE SPACING FROM A TRIAL TITLE

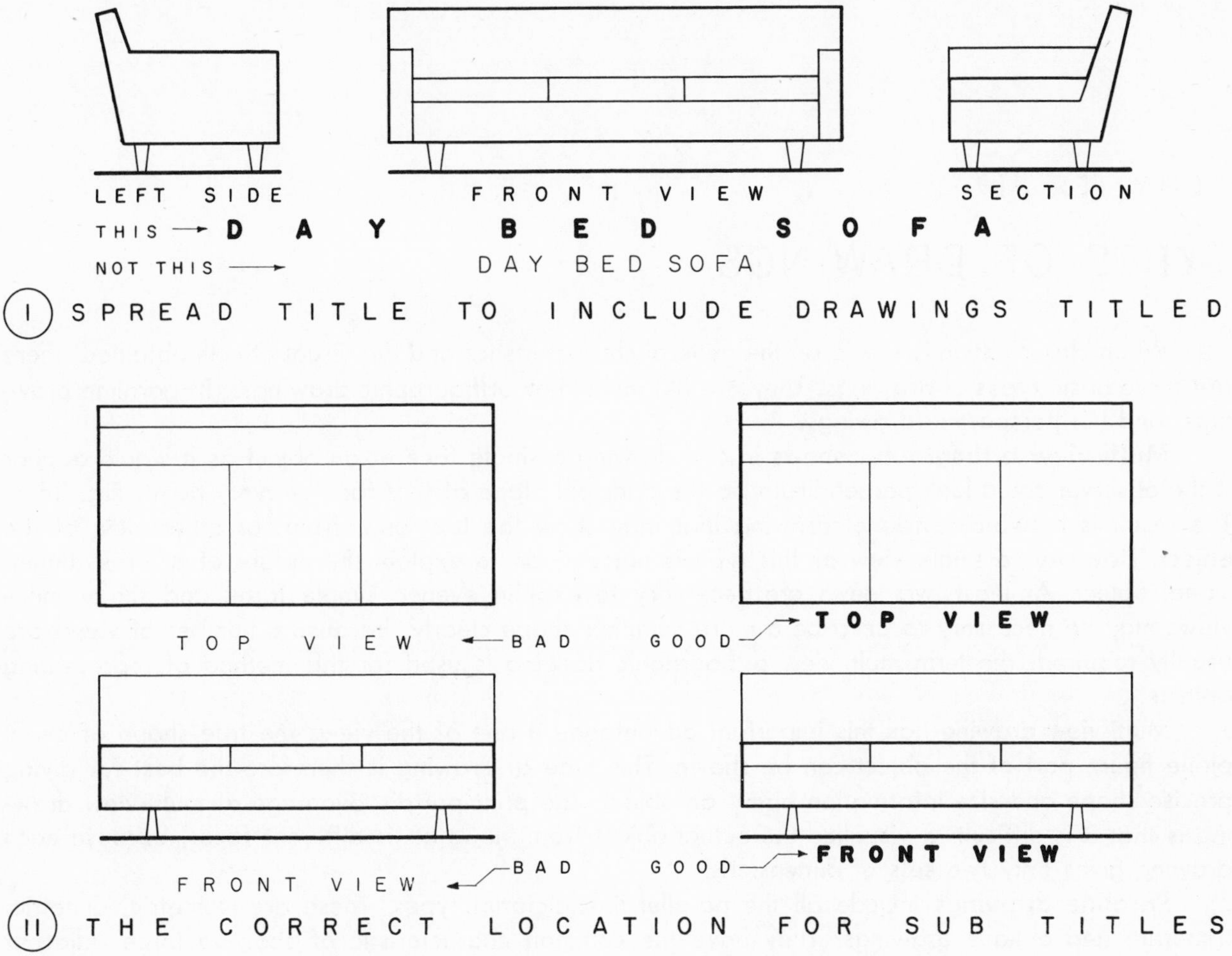

FIG. 37 COMPOSITION OF TITLES FOR DRAWINGS

in the preliminary, Fig. 36 B. Lay out the vertical center lines of the first and last letters of the finished title, Fig. 36 A for longer final title and Fig. 36 C for shorter final. Use a straight-edged strip of paper. If the final is to be longer than the preliminary, mark off the distance a–g between the centers of the first and last letter of final on the edge of the paper strip. Slant the paper strip across the lines through centers of preliminary lettering and adjust until the marks at a and g fit the first and last center lines. Transfer spacing of center lines of letters to strip and thence to final where strip is used horizontally to locate the center line of each letter as shown in Fig. 36 A. When the final is shorter than the preliminary, take measurements off the preliminary with horizontal strip, then slant strip between verticals through centers of the end letters of final. Dot off centers and draw vertical center lines of letters from dots to letter positions. The letters of the preliminary study are now drawn or traced in position on their center lines on the final title, Fig. 36 C.

Large distances between letters make the work of spacing much easier than when a minimum space is maintained. Widely spaced letters are easy to read and give an attractive appearance. The wide spacing spreads a title out so that it may refer more clearly to a long object or a series of drawings without overemphasizing the lettering with excessive height, Fig. 37 I.

The correct relation of a number of subtitles to the drawings to which they refer is essential to easy and correct reading of a plate. The titles should be so placed that there is no slightest possibility of an error as to which drawing is referred to by each title. This is one of the most important phases of composition of lettering, Fig. 37 II.

CHAPTER 6

TYPES OF DRAWINGS

When classification is based on the general characteristics and the visual effects obtained, there are three basic types of drawings. They are (A) multi-view orthographic drawings, (B) paraline drawings, and (C) perspective drawings.

Multi-view orthographic shows in one drawing a single face of an object as it would appear if the observer could look perpendicular to the principal plane of that face at every point, Fig. 38 A. The result is a two-dimensional drawing that may show the top, end, front, or other view of the object. However, a single view of this type is not enough to explain the nature of a three dimensional object. At least two views are necessary to explain even a simple form, and six or more views may be necessary to describe a more complex shape clearly. Because a number of views are usually required, the term multi-view orthographic drawing is used for this method of representing objects.

Multi-view drawing has this important advantage: in one of the views the true shape of every plane figure part of the object can be shown. This type of drawing is therefore the best for giving precise shape and size information about an object. The principal disadvantage of multi-view drawing is that it is difficult to visualize the actual object from views of its different faces, because each drawing gives only two sets of dimensions.

Paraline drawings include all the parallel line pictorial types. These are isometric, dimetric, trimetric, and oblique drawings. They have the common characteristic of showing three adjacent faces of an object in a single drawing. For example the top, front, and one end of a desk may be shown in one drawing. This gives the effect of a view toward one corner of the object. It produces a drawing which represents all of the three dimensions and is therefore easily understood, Fig. 38 B.

Because all lines that are actually parallel on the object are made parallel, the drawings of this type are easily constructed. Because the lines are drawn parallel, an artificial effect is obtained. Lines on the near parts of the object are made the same length as similar more distant lines. This makes measuring on the drawing easy but makes the more distant parts appear too large.

Perspective drawing gives the truest picture of the object but is the most difficult type of drawing to construct, Fig. 38 C. Because the more distant parts of the object are smaller, few measurements can be made directly to scale on the drawing. A perspective drawing, correctly made, is just as true a picture of the object as is a photograph.

Drawing classification according to the relation of the projectors to the picture plane is commonly used. This system also gives three types: (1) orthographic drawing with projectors perpendicular to the plane of projection includes multi-view, isometric, dimetric, and trimetric; (2) oblique drawing having parallel projectors oblique to the picture plane; and (3) perspective drawing with projectors converging to the eye or station point position. This system does not group the resulting drawings logically according to appearance and use, important factors to the designer.

Projectors are the imaginary lines of sight of the observer that would enable him to see the object as it is represented in a drawing. They are an element of the basis of the theoretical background of each method of representing objects by drawings. In some methods of perspective drawing they are actually traced to locate points on the drawings. They have no practical use in constructing other drawings. The theoretical bases of each drawing type explain why drawings appear as they do. This theory is not necessary for the construction of most drawings. In fact it is often confusing to the beginner rather than being helpful. It is not emphasized in this text.

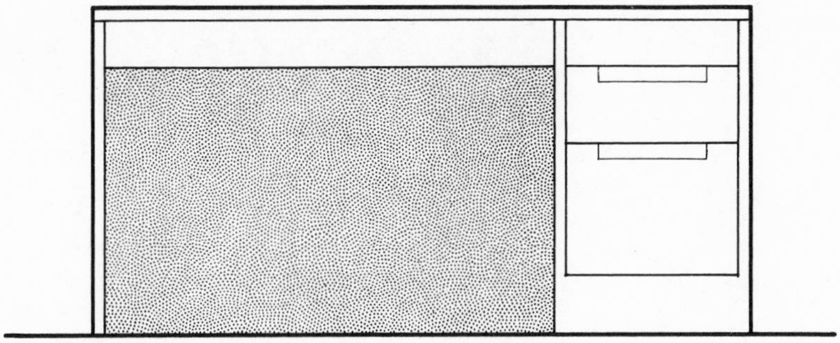

(A) MULTI—VIEW DRAWING

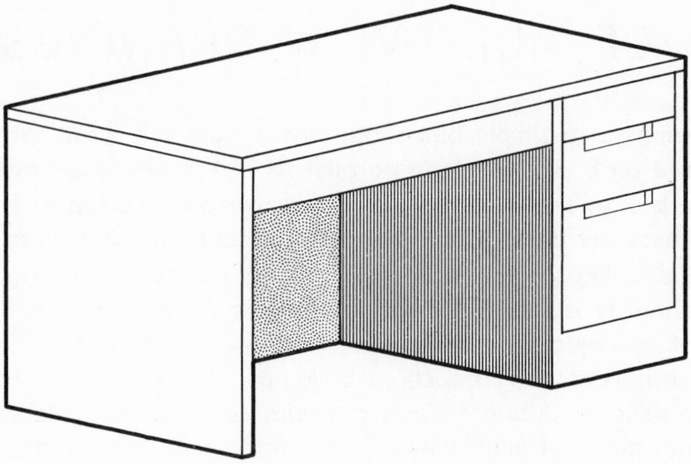

(B) PARALINE DRAWING

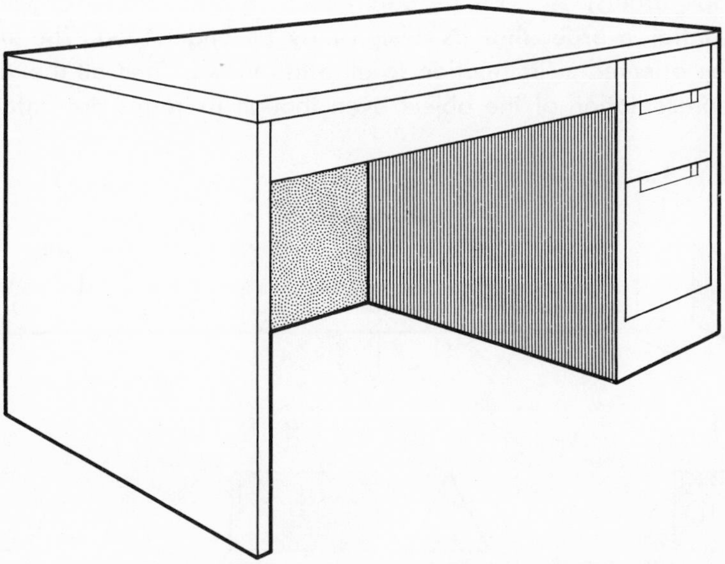

(C) PERSPECTIVE DRAWING

FIG. 38 THREE MAJOR TYPES OF DRAWINGS

PART TWO

Multi-View Drawing

CHAPTER 7

PRINCIPLES OF MULTI-VIEW DRAWINGS

In multi-view drawings of a simple box shape, each view will show only one face of the box. When the front is drawn on a picture plane parallel to it, the projectors are parallel to the sides, top, and bottom of the box as shown in the pictorial drawing at the top of Fig. 39 A. The observer is looking parallel to these surfaces, which are perpendicular to the picture plane and appear as lines in the multi-view drawings of the side and front at the bottom of Fig. 39 A. Because each view gives only two of the three sets of dimensions, two or more multi-view drawings are necessary to explain the shape of an object as shown in comparing Figs. 39 A, B, C.

The multi-view drawings of objects such as buildings, chairs, or radio cabinets that have definitely different characteristics in different views are relatively easy to understand. They have different shapes in side, front, top, and other views. It is usually easy to tell whether these drawings are turned correctly for the normal positions of the objects. The drawings of such objects can be easily understood even when they are not arranged according to an accepted standard arrangement.

Other objects such as parts of mechanical devices often have no familiar forms or single positions by which the tops, fronts, etc. can be determined. A standard arrangement of the views of such an object is essential in order that its design may be understood. The standard arrangement allows each view to be oriented in its relation to all other views. Then all the views combine to give an understandable representation of the object even though its forms are unfamiliar.

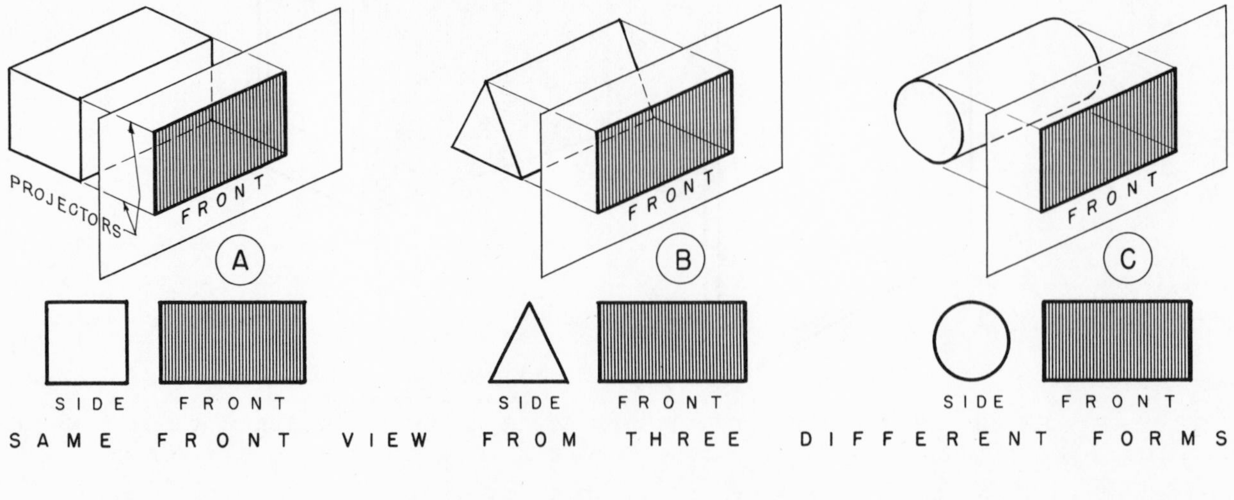

FIG. 39 TWO OR MORE VIEWS NEEDED TO EXPLAIN SHAPES

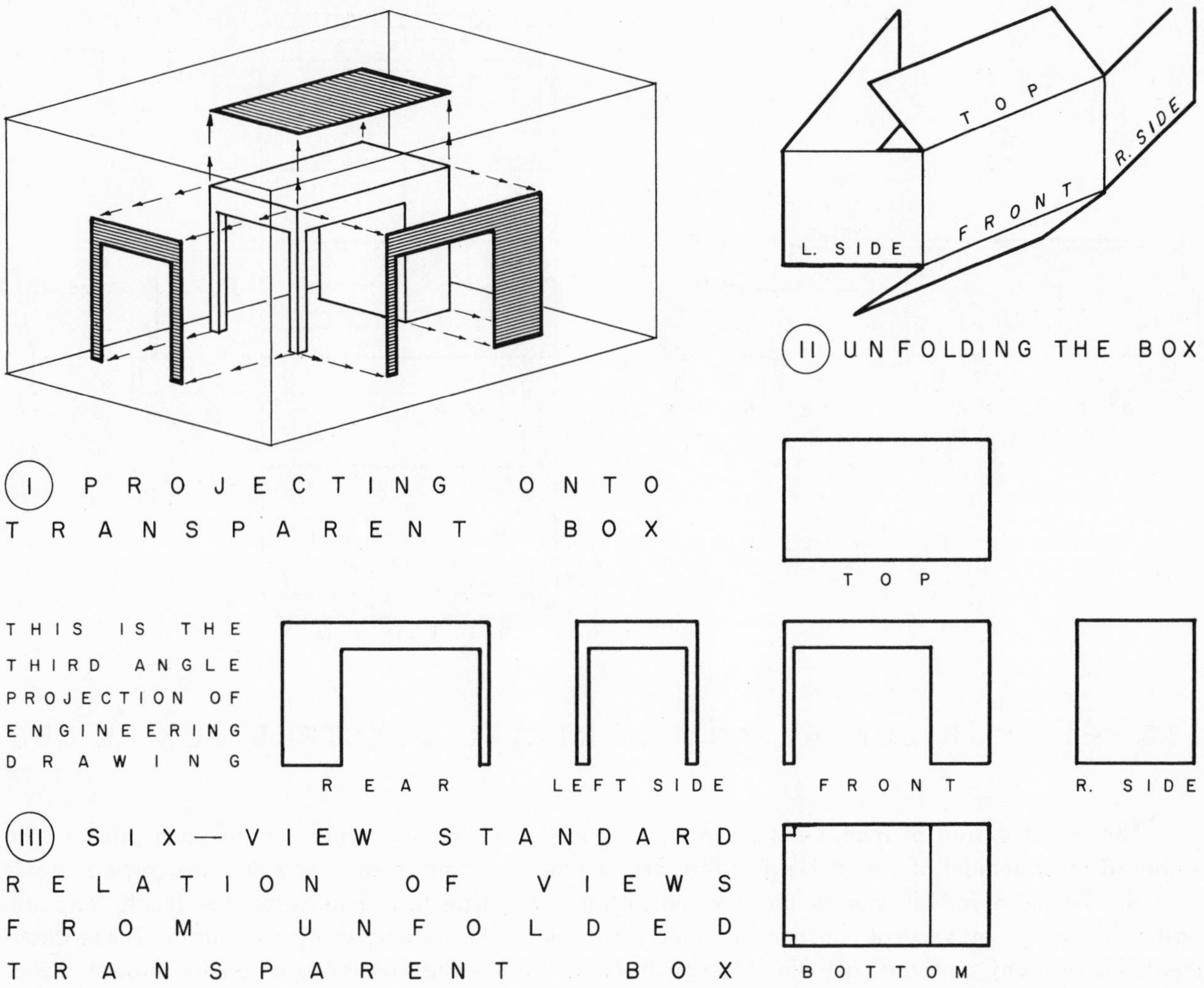

FIG. 40 SIX—VIEW STANDARD DRAWING ARRANGEMENT

THE SIX-VIEW STANDARD ARRANGEMENT OF MULTI-VIEW DRAWINGS. When a transparent picture plane is used parallel to each side of a box-like object, these six planes meet to form a box enclosing the object, Fig. 40 I. By projecting onto each side of a picture plane box, a drawing of each face of the object is obtained. If the top, bottom, and two sides of the picture plane box are hinged to the front and if the rear is hinged to the left side, all the views can be unfolded into the plane of the front, Figs. 40 II, III. This is the American standard arrangement of views.

Variations from the standard arrangement of views are often made in some fields of drawing. The following are some of the reasons for such variations: (1) The views may be so large that they cannot all be presented on one sheet. (2) Different scales may be used on the views of the same object. Usually one important view is drawn at a larger scale. (3) Composition in presenting a design may be improved by variations from standard. (4) Custom may require variation from the American standard arrangement. It is customary in architectural drawing to have all views on horizontal planes (called plans) turned with the principal entrance to the bottom of the drawing.

When drawing an interior the views are hinged to the rear of the transparent box and rotated into its plane. It may be preferable to turn the ceiling the same way as the floor plan. The ceiling is then either seen from above and represented by hidden lines, or assumed to be seen in a mirror on the floor, drawn with visible lines, and called a reflected plan.

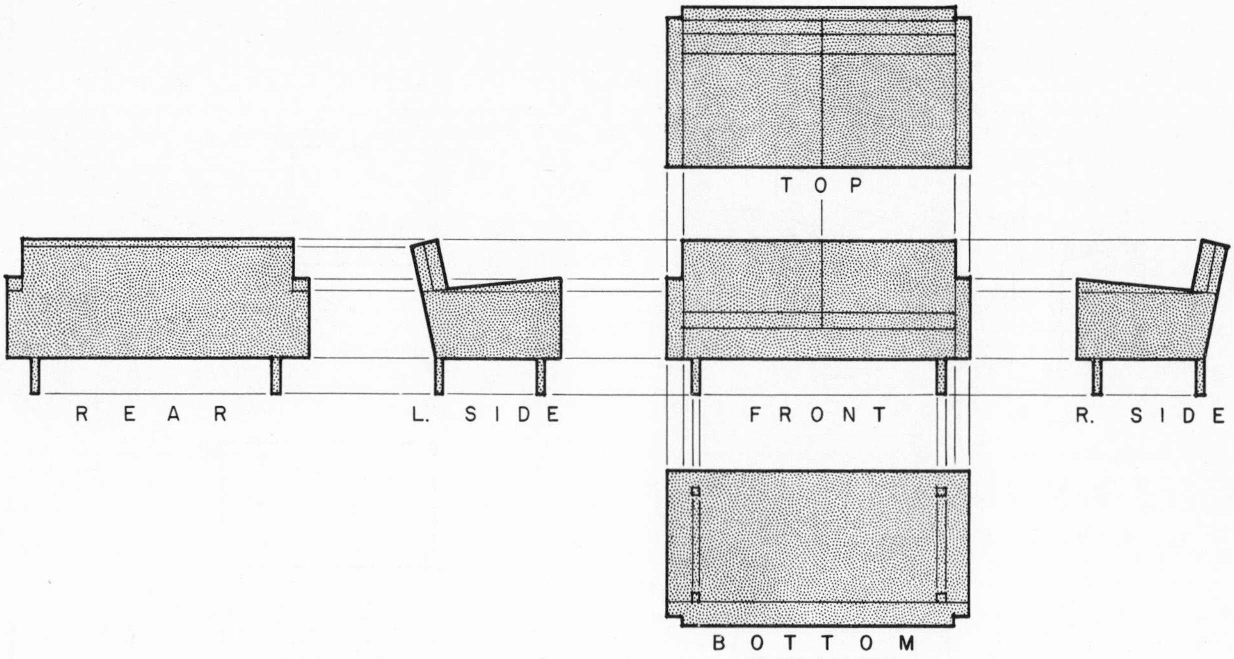

FIG. 41 HORIZONTAL AND VERTICAL CONSTRUCTION LINES

The construction of multi-view drawings is made easier by their relations to each other in the standard arrangement of views. Heights that are common to front, rear, and sides are carried across with the T-square for all four of these views. Widths are transferred between the front, top, and bottom drawings by vertical construction lines drawn with the triangle on the T-square. These alignments horizontally and vertically simplify construction, reduce the possibility of errors through variation of heights and widths, and make the interpretation of drawings easier, Fig. 41. Measurements can be transferred from top or bottom views to side or rear views in different ways. A scale, dividers, or a straight edged strip of paper can be used for this purpose.

Geometric construction methods can also be used to transfer dimensions from top and bottom to the side views. These constructions require the tracing of the sizes around a right angle. This can be done either with 45° intersections as shown in Fig. 42 A, or with quarter circles as shown in Fig. 42 B. In using either of these methods of transferring sizes around a right angle the draftsman must be alert to see that the final spacing is correct and accurate. The arcs should be tangent to the horizontal and vertical projectors. The points of tangency are located accurately by drawing the horizontal and vertical lines through the center of each arc. These lines are the perpendiculars to the tangents. The 45° turning lines continue the spacing correctly around the corners on this example because they are the bisectors of 90° angles. By turning the 45° lines in the opposite direction the sequence of spaces is reversed, and the drawing is incorrect, Fig. 42 C. To transfer widths with construction lines from top, front, or bottom view to the rear view it is necessary to turn the measurements through 180°. This is usually done by turning two right angles with two 45° lines, Fig. 42 A, or two quarter circles, Fig. 42 B. However semicircles can be used for this purpose when the drawing space is available.

The procedure in laying out multi-view drawings may vary with the object drawn and the draftsman. The usual procedure is to construct the front and top together, then construct the sides, rear, and bottom from these first two drawings. To locate the position for the side view, measure any desired distance A–B to the side of the front view and draw a vertical line through B. Draw a horizontal line from the lowest edge of the top view to meet the vertical line at C. Point C is then used as the center of arcs or the beginning of the 45° turning line, Fig. 42 B.

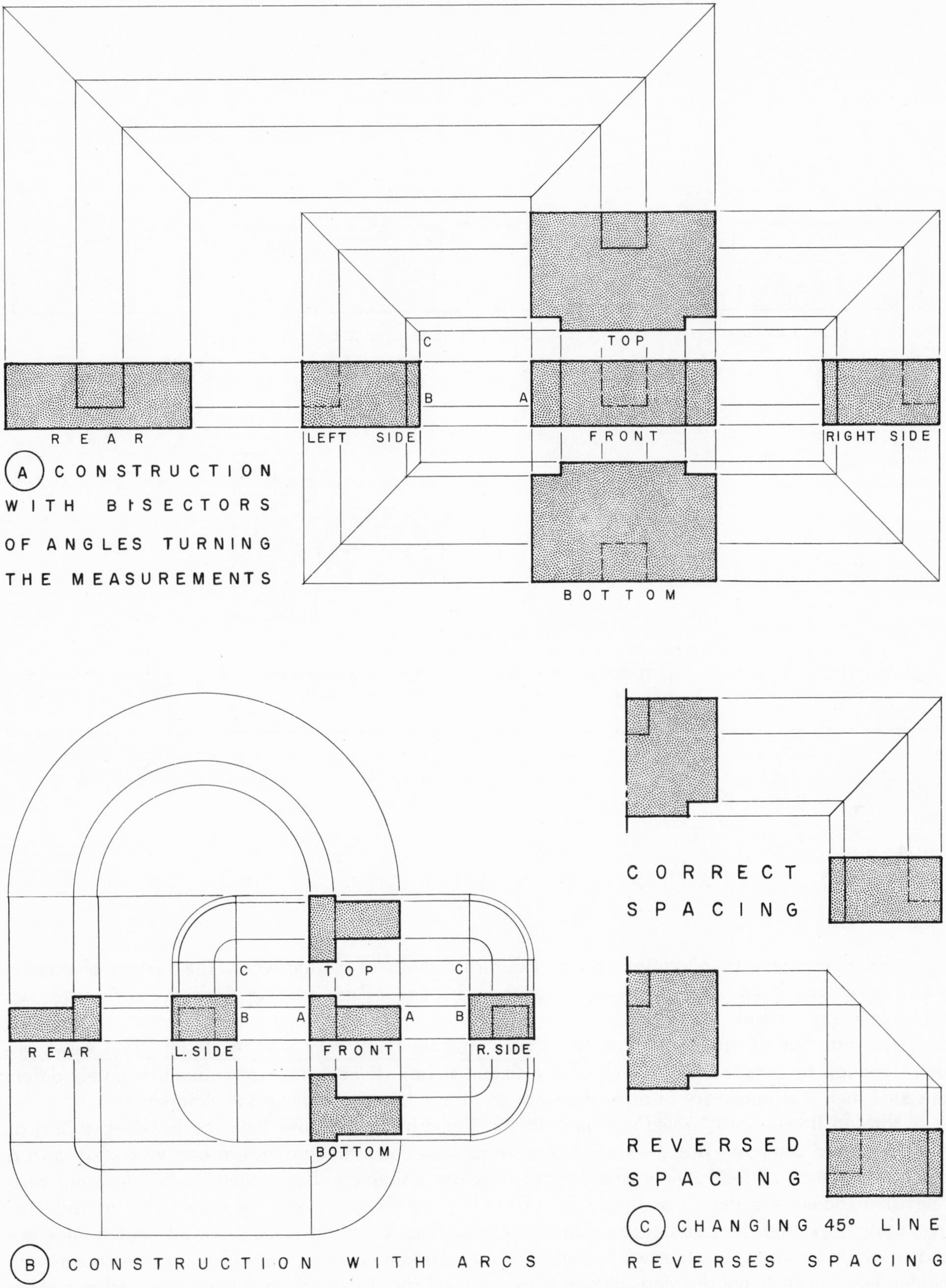

(A) CONSTRUCTION WITH BISECTORS OF ANGLES TURNING THE MEASUREMENTS

(B) CONSTRUCTION WITH ARCS

(C) CHANGING 45° LINE REVERSES SPACING

FIG. 42 CARRYING SPACING AROUND CORNERS

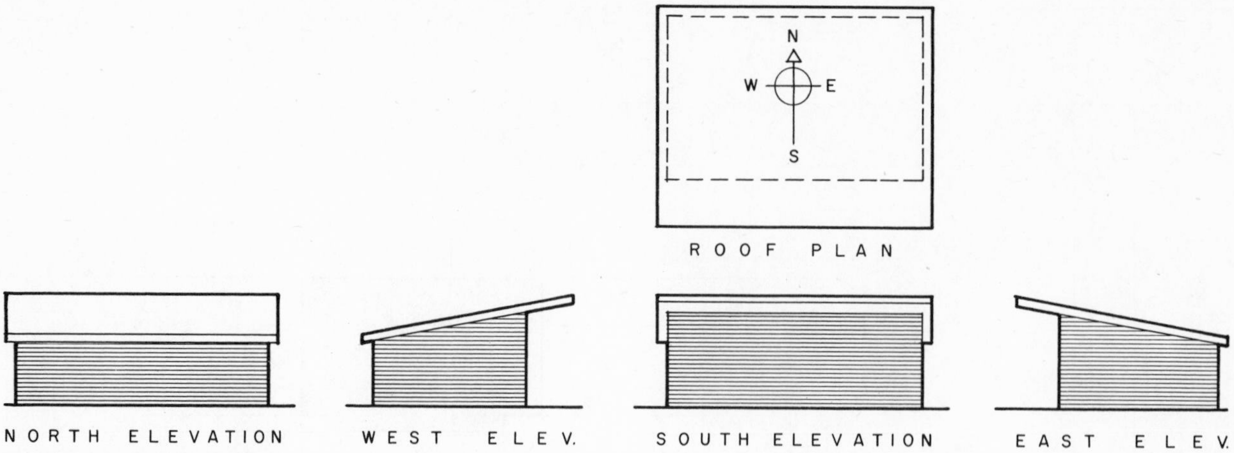

(A) COMPASS DIRECTION NAMES OF VIEWS

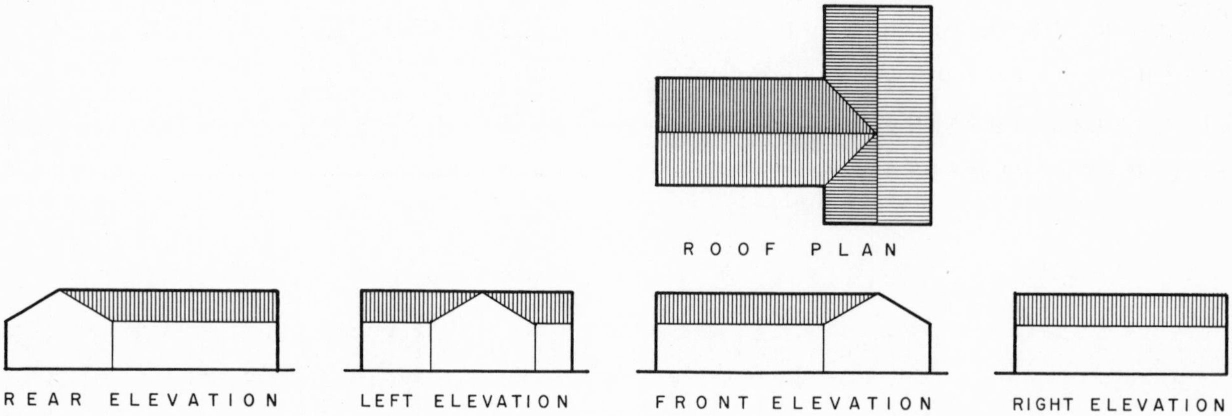

(B) STANDARD ARCHITECTURAL NAMES OF VIEWS

FIG. 43 VARIATIONS IN NOMENCLATURE OF VIEWS

The nomenclature of views varies in different types of design work. The system of naming views which has been used on previous pages is the one of engineering drawing. In Fig. 43 two other common systems are shown.

The number of views required to explain an object will vary with its design. Two views are often enough for simple objects such as a cylinder or box. If each face of a box-like object differs in detail then it is necessary to have drawings of all six faces to explain the differences.

Hidden lines, which would not be visible in the drawing because they are between a part of the object and observer, are shown with evenly spaced dots. Hidden lines in one view may give a clear explanation so that a view where these lines are visible can be omitted. In the drawings of a television cabinet the shapes and positions of the legs of the object can be shown with dotted lines in the top view and the bottom view can be omitted, Fig. 44 III. In some work all hidden lines are shown in all drawings. In other work, parts that are explained with visible lines are not shown with hidden lines. In sectional drawings hidden lines are used for parts that have been removed in making the drawings as well as for lines that are hidden by a visible part of the object.

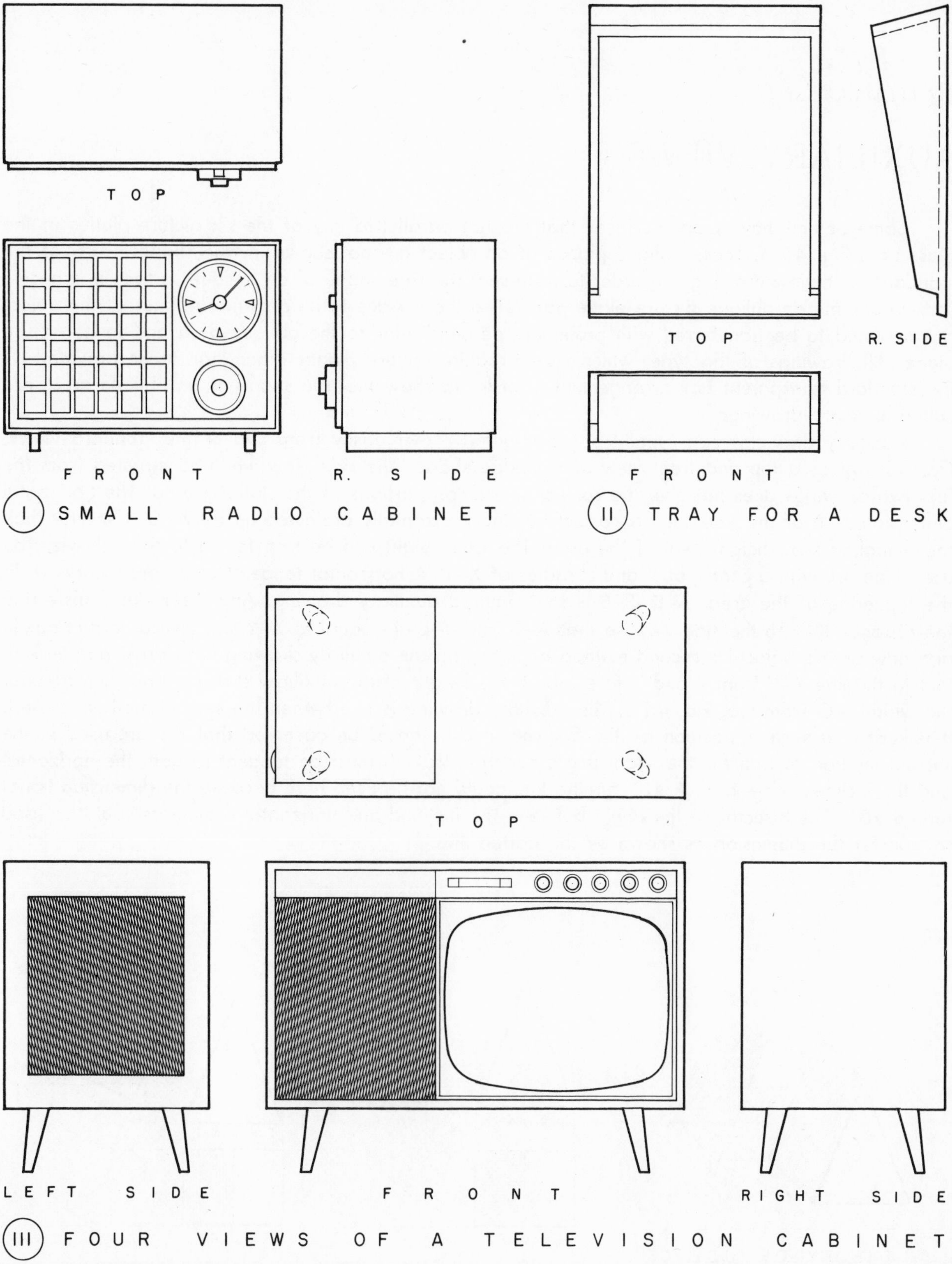

FIG. 44 EXAMPLES OF MULTI-VIEW DRAWINGS

CHAPTER 8

AUXILIARY VIEWS

Some objects have plane surfaces that are not parallel to any of the six picture planes of the glass box, Fig. 45 A. These oblique planes of an object are not shown in true shape in any of the standard multi-view drawings. In order to represent the true shape of an oblique surface it is necessary to assume an oblique picture plane parallel to the surface to be drawn. The lines of the object are assumed to be transferred with projectors perpendicular to the oblique area and to its picture plane. All drawings of this type, which would require picture planes other than those provided by the standard transparent box arrangement in order to show the true shape of an oblique area, are called auxiliary drawings.

Auxiliary drawings can usually be constructed rather easily from two of the standard views. Fig. 45 B gives a top and front view of a wedge shape. The side view when constructed from the first two drawings does not give the correct size or proportions of the slanting area. The horizontal dimension A–B of the side view is correct but the horizontally projected height A–C is shorter than the actual or slant height X–Y of the area. The true height can be transferred to the side view by use of an arc with a center at X and a radius of X–Y. A horizontal tangent to the arc locates D–E, the top edge of the area. A–D–E–B is the required auxiliary drawing. Any means of transferring the distance X–Y to the side view so that A–D and B–E are equal to X–Y will give a correct auxiliary view of this object. A second method of obtaining the auxiliary drawing is to draw perpendiculars to the line X–Y from X and Y to establish the height of the auxiliary drawing and then transfer the width F–G from top, Fig. 45 C. The auxiliary drawing is tilted when the second method is used. It is kept in a vertical position by the first method. It should be observed that the arc used in the second method to transfer the width is greater than 90°. It must be tangent to both the horizontal and the inclined projectors. A 45° turning line could not be used here because the dimension is not turned 90°. The bisector of the angle between the inclined and horizontal projectors could be used to transfer the dimension as shown by the dotted line.

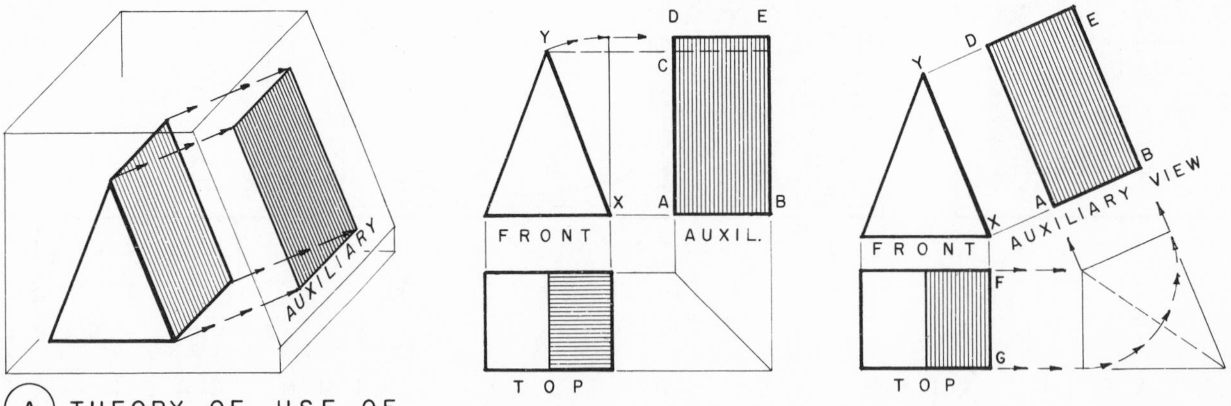

(A) THEORY OF USE OF AUXILIARY PLANES (B) FIRST METHOD (C) SECOND METHOD

FIG. 45 THEORY AND CONSTRUCTION OF AUXILIARY VIEW

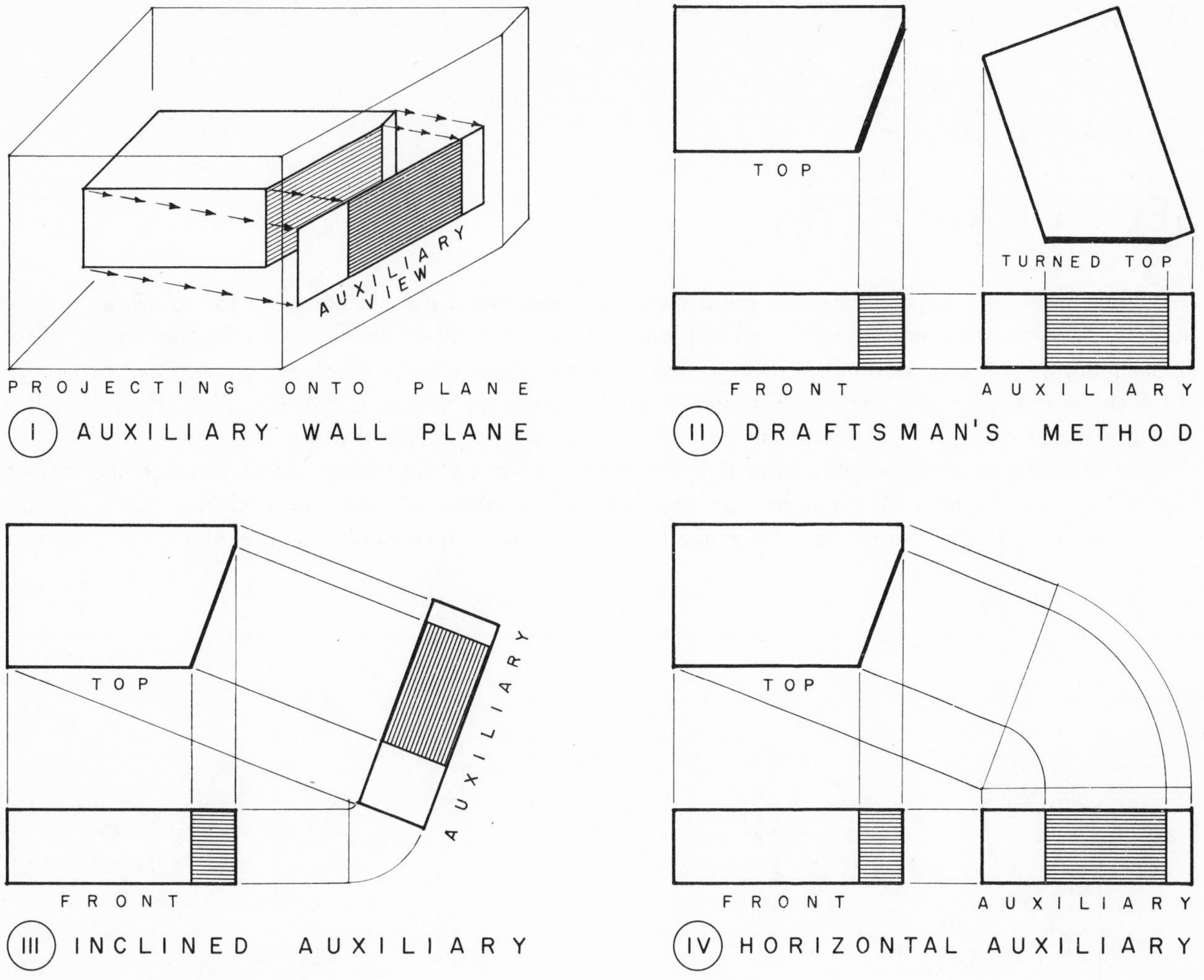

FIG. 46 VERTICAL PLANE AUXILIARY DRAWINGS

VERTICAL PLANE AUXILIARY DRAWINGS. Fig 46 illustrates construction of vertical plane auxiliary drawings. The pictorial drawing I shows the relation of the object, transparent box, and auxiliary plane while the remaining drawings explain three methods of working out the auxiliary view.

The draftsman's simple method is to turn the top with the oblique wall planes in a horizontal position as shown in II. The vertical projectors from the turned top view and horizontal projectors from front view locate the lines and points for construction of the auxiliary elevation. When the top is available on a separate piece of paper it can be turned to correct position and attached to the board for this use instead of making a new drawing of the top view.

Methods of descriptive geometry and engineering drawing for constructing auxiliary views are shown in Figs. III and IV. In III the projectors are drawn perpendicular to the line representing the auxiliary surface in top view. The heights are then transferred to these projectors and the auxiliary drawing constructed in the inclined position. In IV the projectors from top have been turned into a vertical position with arcs. The heights are carried over from the front view with the T-square. This second method brings the auxiliary view into horizontal alignment with the front view. This may seem logical because this auxiliary is a wall auxiliary or oblique side view and is normally in a horizontal position. In the examples the slant areas to the right and left of the true shape areas have been included in the auxiliary drawing. However, these oblique areas may be either shown attached to the true shape area but unfinished, or omitted entirely.

CHAPTER 9

SECTIONAL VIEWS

The preceding illustrations for multi-view drawing are views looking at the outsides of the objects. Any drawing that is made on a plane through an object to show the interior and hidden construction is called a sectional drawing. There are two general classifications of sectional drawings: (1) A drawing made on a horizontal plane cutting through the object is called a *plan,* Fig. 47. (2) A drawing made on a vertical plane cutting through the object is called a *section,* Fig. 48.

In making a sectional drawing it is assumed that a cutting plane passes through the object, Fig. 47 A, that the part of the object on one side of the plane is removed, and that the remaining part is projected onto the plane with projectors which are perpendicular to the plane, as shown in

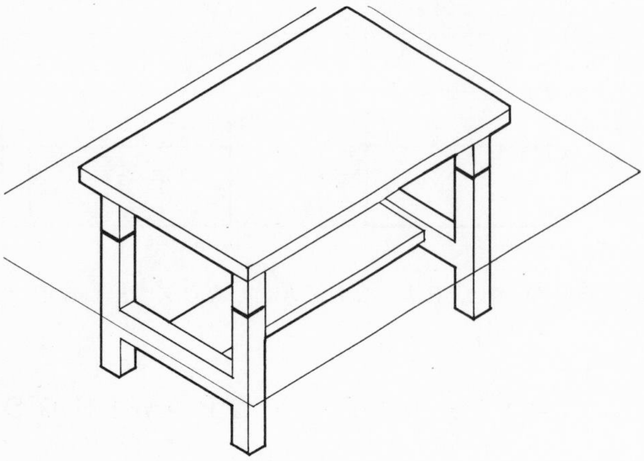

(A) SELECTED POSITION FOR HORIZONTAL CUTTING PLANE

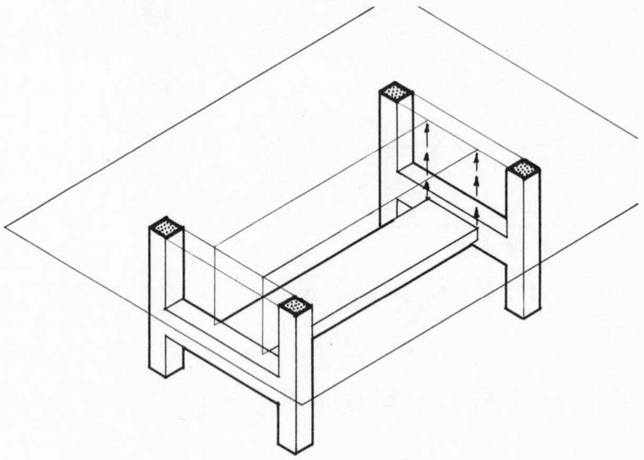

(B) OBJECT REMOVED FROM ABOVE THE CUTTING PLANE

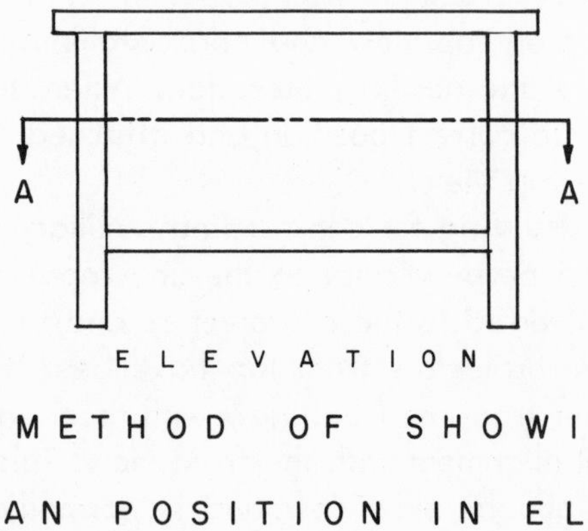

(D) METHOD OF SHOWING PLAN POSITION IN ELEV.

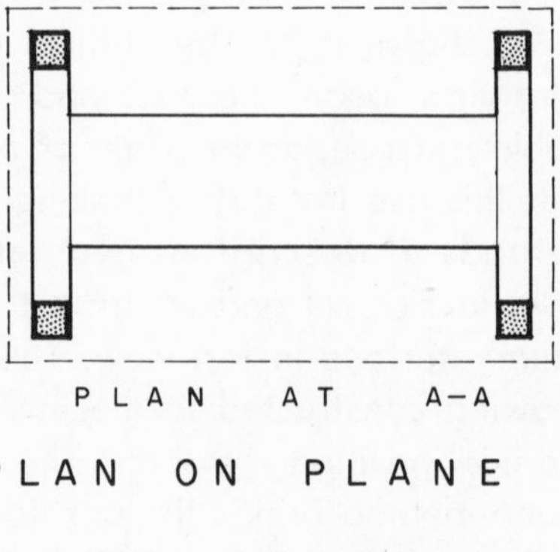

(C) PLAN ON PLANE A—A OF PART BELOW PLANE

FIG. 47 DRAWING A PLAN THROUGH AN OBJECT

the pictorial view of Fig. 47 B. The multi-view drawing obtained according to this theory then appears as shown in Fig. 47 C. The legs of the table were cut by the plane. They are drawn in heavy outline and are also shaded to classify them as cut areas. The visible parts beyond the cutting plane are drawn with light solid lines. Parts that are considered as being removed or that are concealed can be shown with dotted lines if this is necessary. In this plan the edges of the table top are shown with dotted lines. The method of showing the cutting plane position for the plan on the multi-view elevation with dot dash line is illustrated in Fig. 47 D. The ends of the line and arrows turn to point in the direction the observer looks in making the drawing. The letters A–A, designating the cutting plane, should be placed at the ends of the arrows as shown and used in the title of the sectional drawings made on this plane. In architecture and interior design floor plans are made through doors and usually no cutting line for the plan is required on elevations. The line of the cutting plane should be shown when it is necessary or helpful in understanding the sectional drawing. Plans at different heights on an object may each require a cutting plane line.

The theory for sectional drawings made on vertical planes (sections) is the same as for the plan example shown in Fig. 47, and described in the preceding paragraph. The only difference is that the plane is vertical instead of horizontal. The development of a section drawing is shown in the pictorial drawings of Fig. 48 I, II and the section in Fig. 48 III.

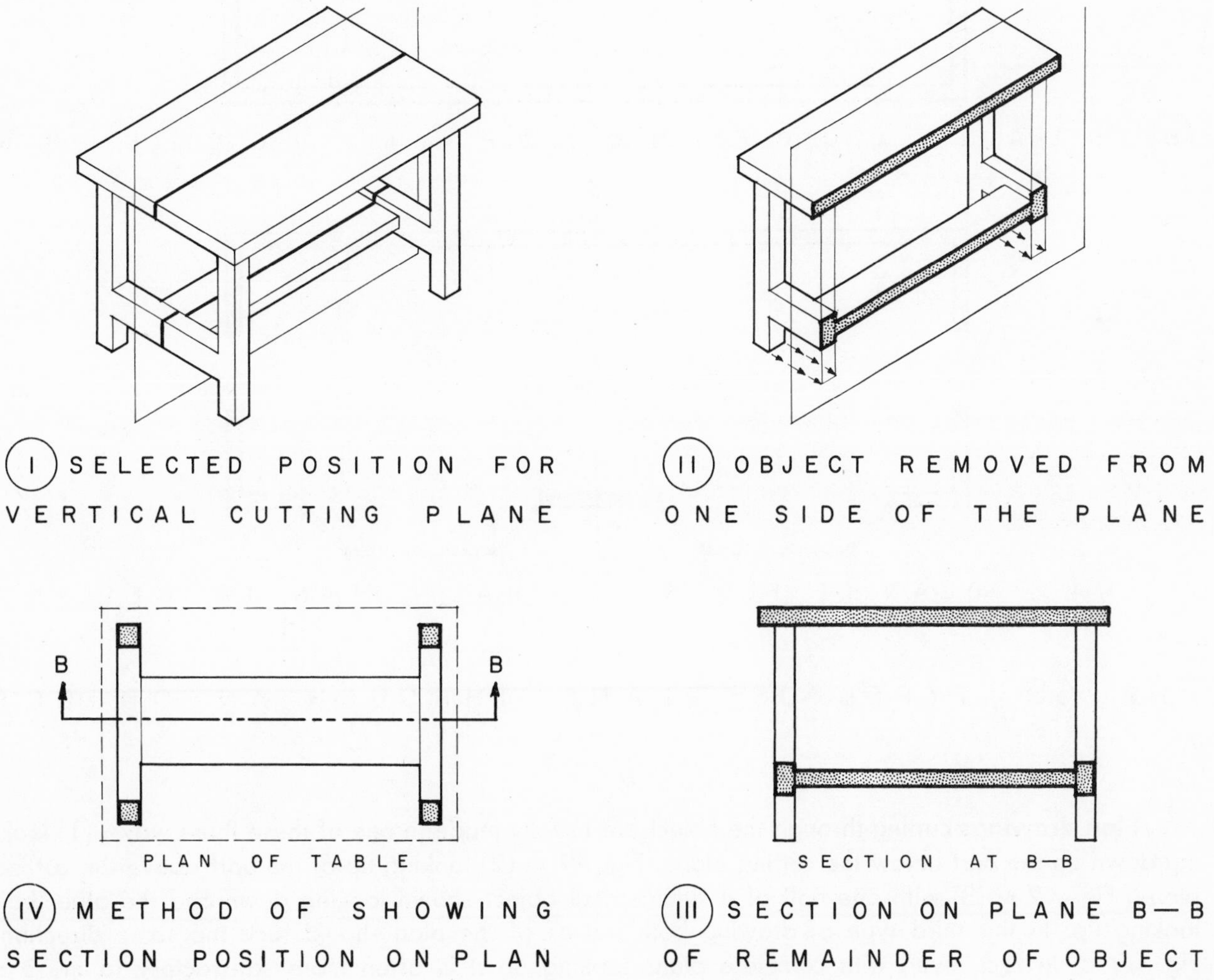

FIG. 48 DRAWING A SECTION THROUGH AN OBJECT

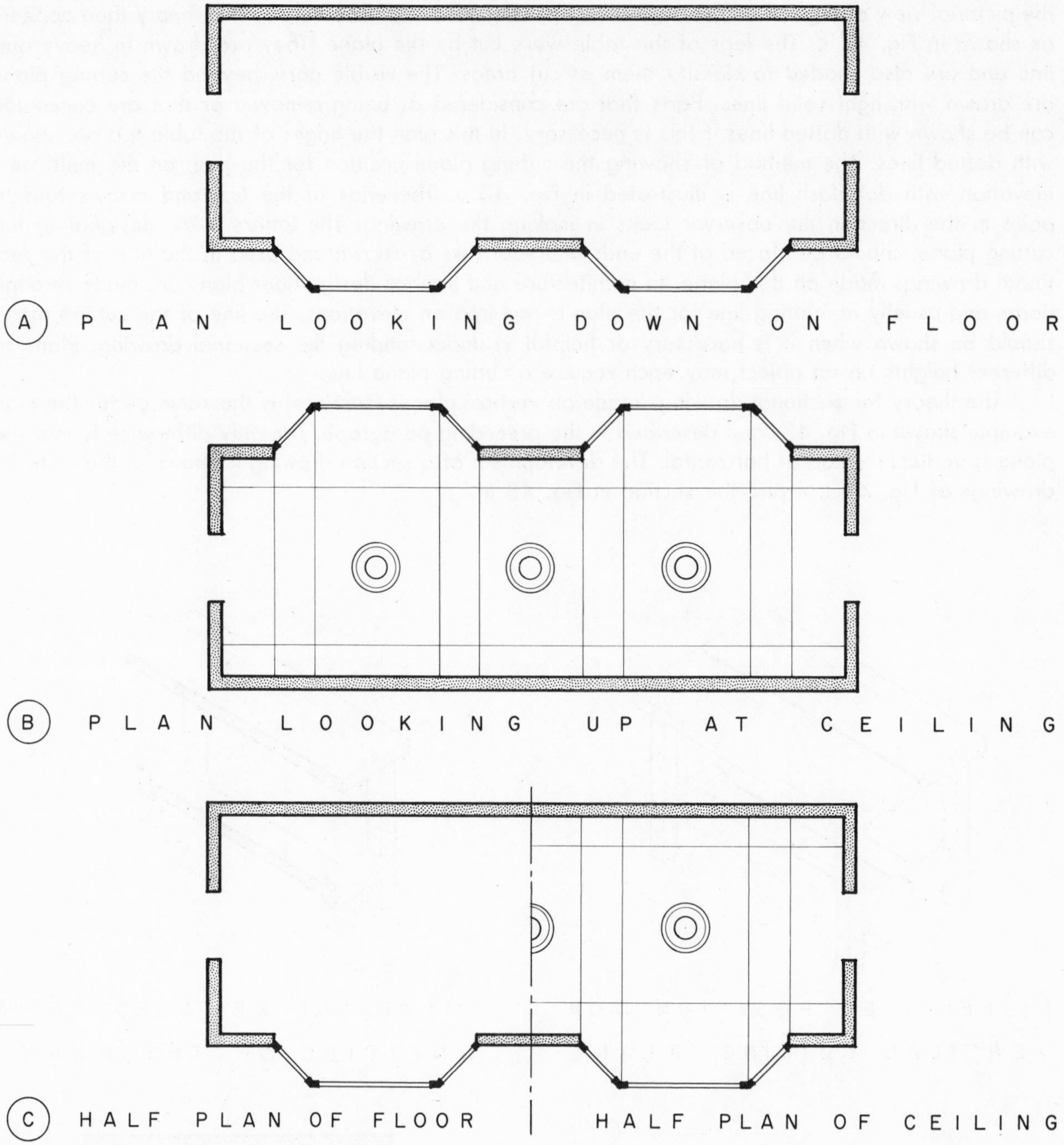

FIG. 49 TYPES OF PLANS THROUGH AN OBJECT

Plan drawings cutting through the object are usually made in one of these three ways: (1) looking down on the part below the cutting plane, Fig. 49 A; (2) looking up at the part above the cutting plane, Fig. 49 B; (3) with one half of a symmetrical object shown looking down and the other half looking up. In this third type of drawing both halves of the plan should face the same direction, Fig. 49 C. In fact, even with complete plans looking up it is often more satisfactory to make a reflected or mirror plan that is turned the same way as the plans looking down. The different features of the two plan types are more easily related to each other when both face the same way.

(I) TRANSVERSE SECTION OF A COUCH

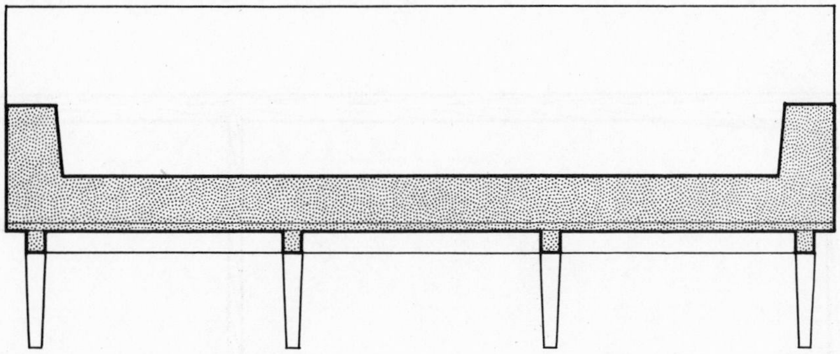

(II) LONGITUDINAL SECTION OF A COUCH

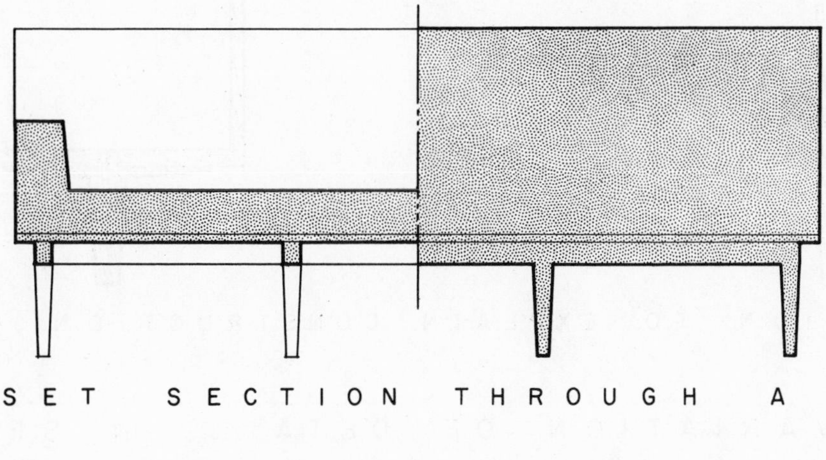

(III) OFFSET SECTION THROUGH A COUCH

FIG. 50 TYPES OF ENTIRE SECTION DRAWINGS

Sections are classified according to the direction of the cutting plane, Figs. 50 I, II, III. (I) A transverse section shows the width of the object. (II) A longitudinal section shows the length of the object. (III) An offset section uses two or more parallel positions of the cutting plane to show parts of the object which would not be shown on one continuous plane, or on one continuous drawing. Offset sections should be used only when some definite advantage is gained by their use. They are more difficult to work out and understand than continuous plane sections. The transition between planes is sometimes hard to explain clearly in the drawing of an offset section.

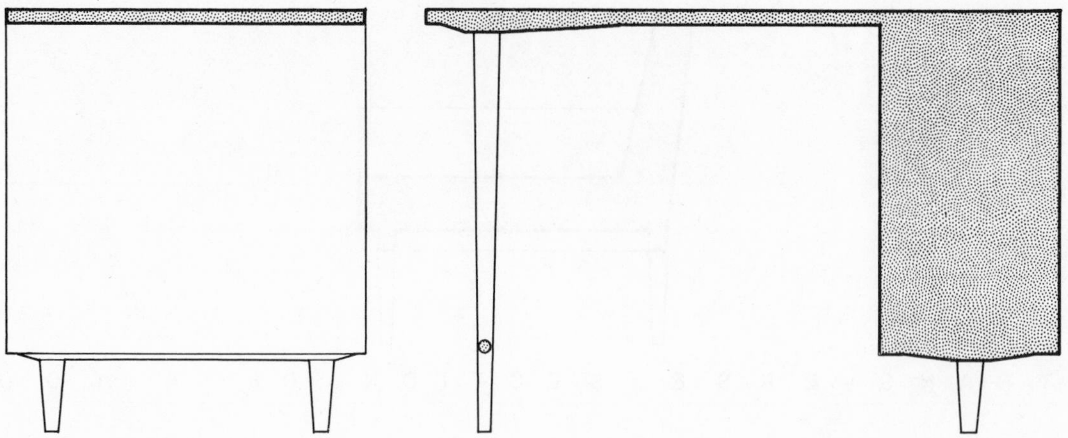

(A) SECTIONS TO EXPLAIN DESIGN OF A DESK

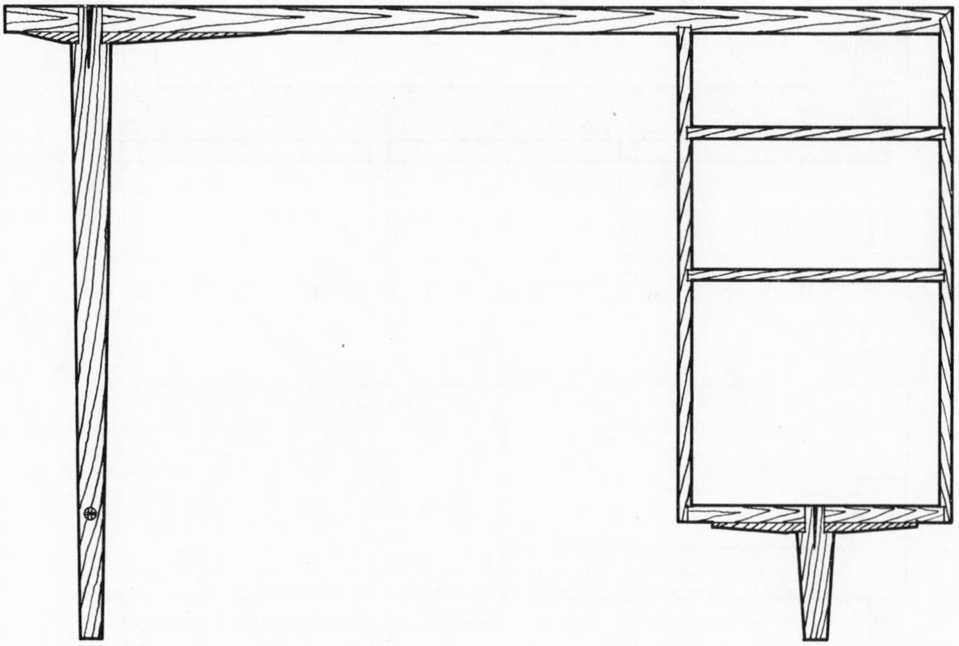

(B) SECTION TO EXPLAIN CONSTRUCTION OF DESK

FIG. 51 VARIATION OF DETAIL IN SECTIONS

The amount of detail shown in a cut area of a sectional drawing depends on the purpose of the drawing and the wishes of the designer. If the purpose of the drawing is to show the visible shapes and surfaces of the object, it is often satisfactory to silhouette the cut areas and leave them blank or uniformly shaded. This procedure keeps the drawing as simple as possible and avoids confusing distractions from the objective of the drawing, Fig. 51 A. If it is considered advisable or necessary to show the details of the cut areas, these parts of the drawing should be surrounded with a heavy outline to separate the visible from the hidden parts of the object, Fig. 51 B. This clear separation of areas makes the drawing seem much more simple and easy to understand. The really skillful draftsman and designer has the knack of making drawings that separate into divisions at a glance and are readily interpreted.

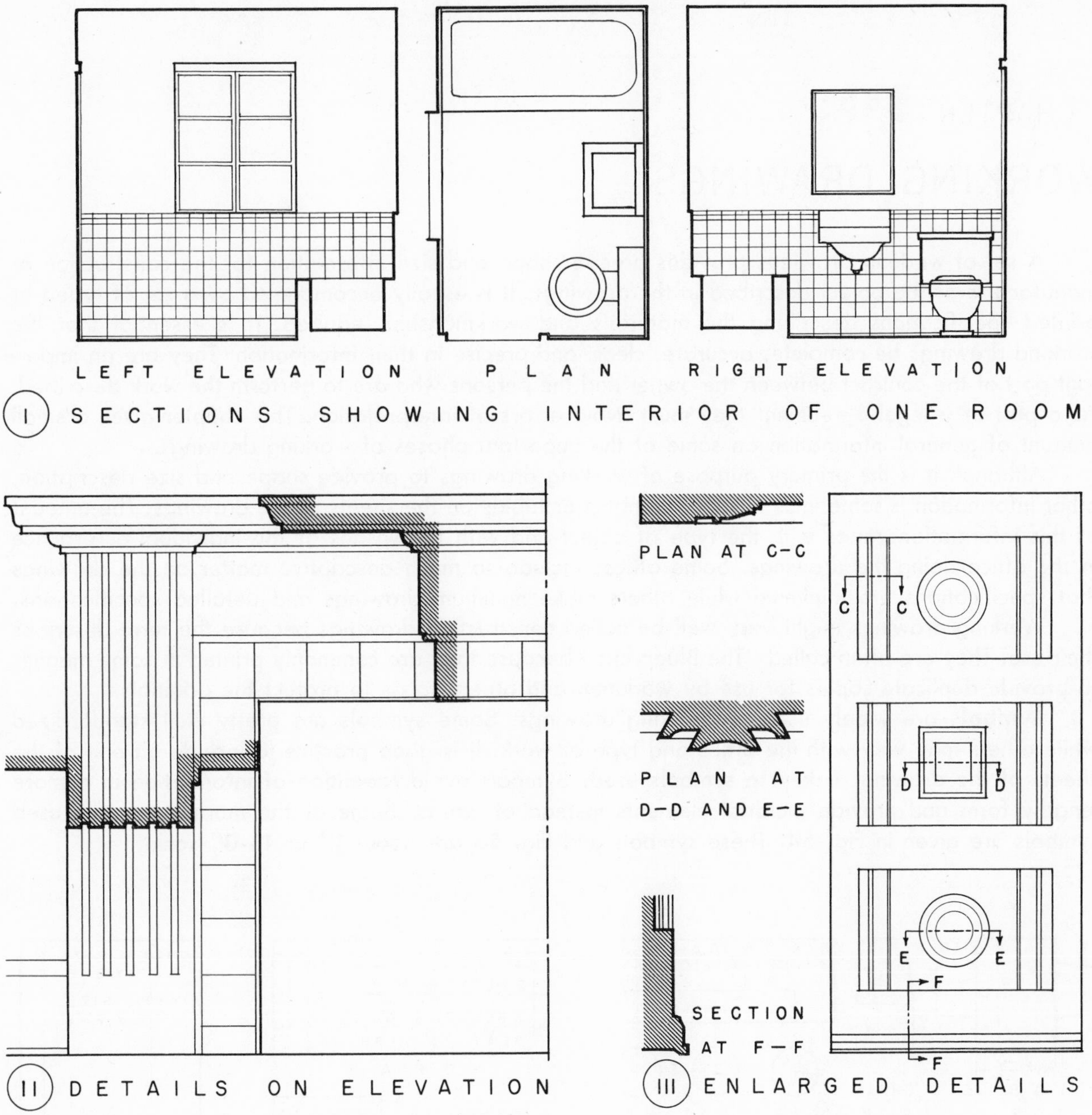

FIG. 52 SOME TYPES OF PART SECTION DRAWINGS

Part sectional drawings show a portion, not all of the object. One room in a building may be singled out for special sectional drawings of its floor (ceiling) and walls, Fig. 52 I. In this type of interior drawing it is often more satisfactory to show the visible surfaces as seen from within the room, but to omit any thicknesses to adjoining rooms and avoid showing any of the enclosed cut areas that would not be visible. If the thickness and structural details of the walls are shown, the visible surface should be emphasized with a heavy outline separating it from the hidden part.

Part sectional drawings either on horizontal or vertical planes are sometimes used over the elevation drawing of an object to explain molding shapes, projections, etc., Fig. 52 II. It is sometimes better to make these part sections as separate drawings that may be either at the same scale as the elevation or enlarged in size, Fig. 52 III.

CHAPTER 10

WORKING DRAWINGS

A set of working drawings provides precise shape and size information for the construction or manufacture of the object described in the drawings. It is usually accompanied by a set of typed or printed specifications describing the materials and workmanship required. It is essential that the working drawings be complete, accurate, clear, and precise in their information. They are an important part of the contract between the owner and the persons who are to perform the work described. As a part of a legal agreement they must avoid errors of interpretation. This chapter gives a small amount of general information on some of the important phases of working drawings.

Although it is the primary purpose of working drawings to provide shape and size description, other information is sometimes included in notes or tables on the sheets of the drawings. The amount of this information varies with the type of object and with the wishes of the individual or practice in the office doing the drawings. Some offices include so much descriptive matter on the drawings that specifications are minimum while others make minimum drawings and detailed specifications.

Working drawings might very well be called construction drawings because the term describes their use. They are often called "The Blueprints" because they are commonly printed in some manner to provide duplicate copies for use by workmen and others so as to protect the originals.

Symbols are widely used on working drawings. Some symbols are pretty well standardized while others may vary with the office and type of work. It is good practice to include on one of the sheets of the drawings a key to symbols used. Symbols avoid repetition of information in a more lengthy form and provide pictorial elements instead of words. Some of the more commonly used symbols are given in Fig. 54. These symbols and Fig. 53 are about $\frac{1}{4}'' = 1'\text{–}0''$ scale.

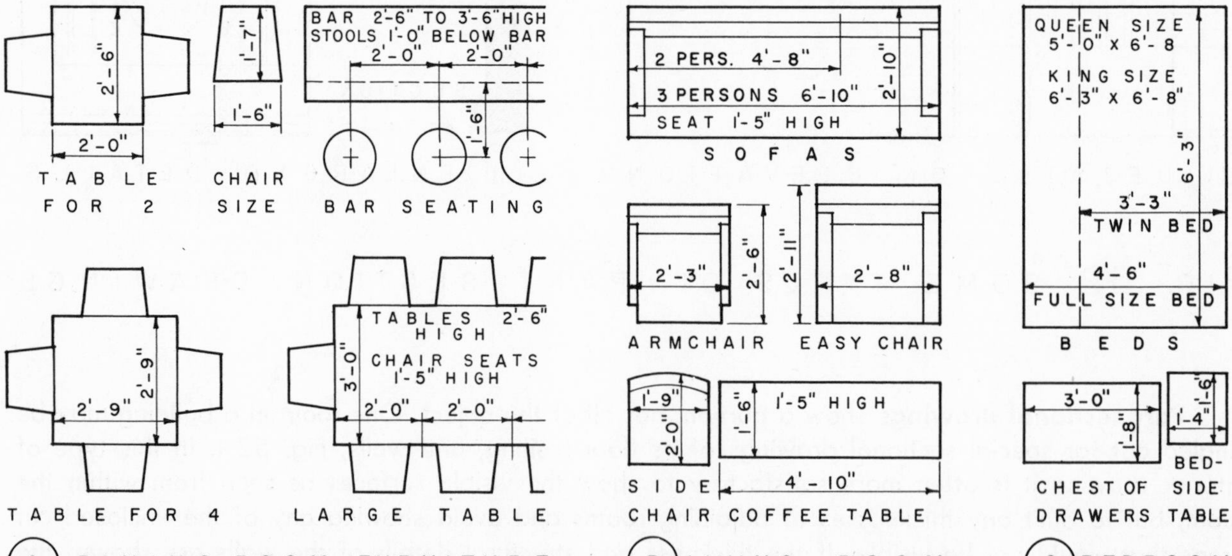

FIG. 53 AVERAGE SIZES FOR COMMON FURNITURE

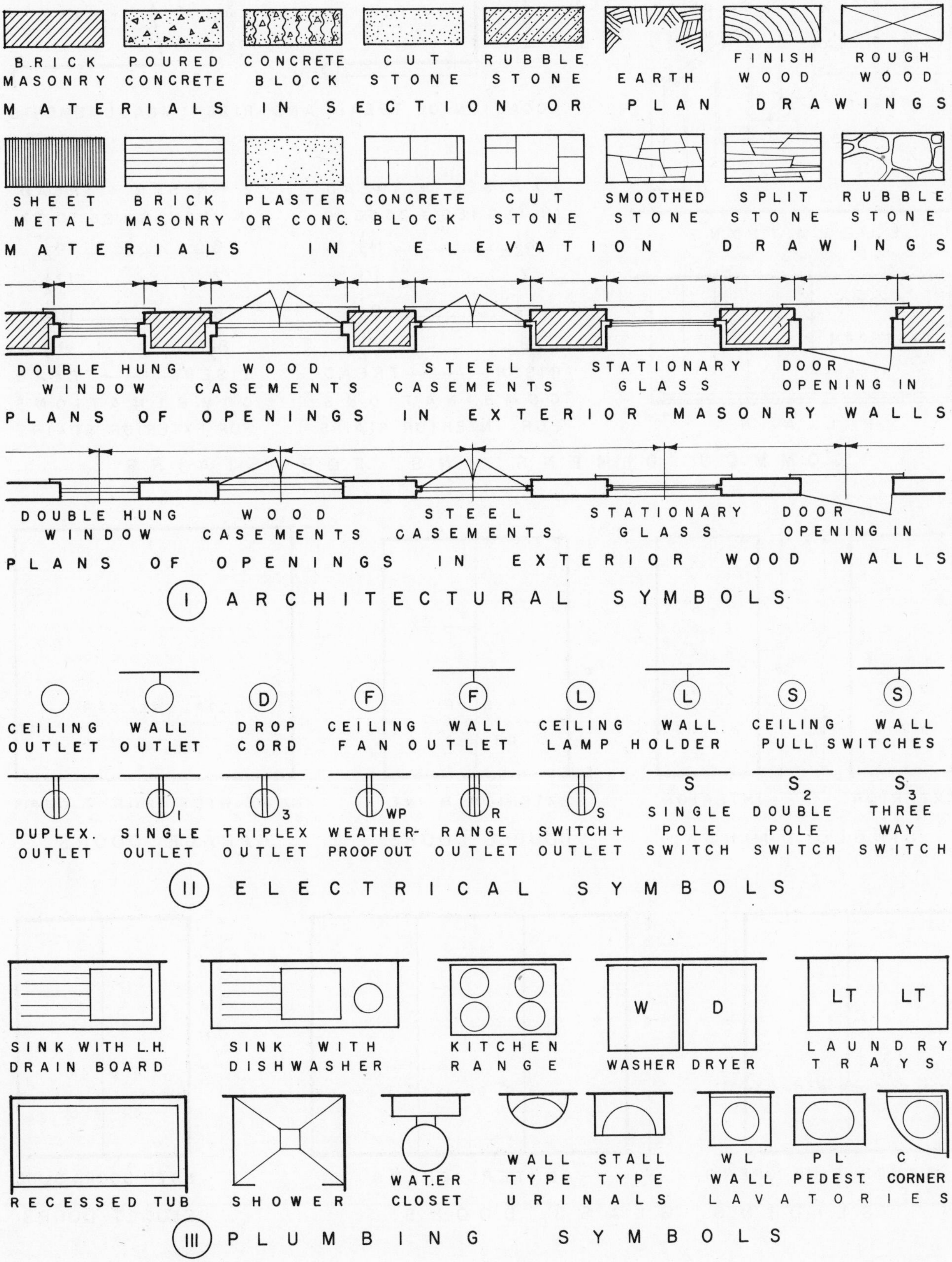
BRICK MASONRY
POURED CONCRETE
CONCRETE BLOCK
CUT STONE
RUBBLE STONE
EARTH
FINISH WOOD
ROUGH WOOD
MATERIALS IN SECTION OR PLAN DRAWINGS
SHEET METAL
BRICK MASONRY
PLASTER OR CONC.
CONCRETE BLOCK
CUT STONE
SMOOTHED STONE
SPLIT STONE
RUBBLE STONE
MATERIALS IN ELEVATION DRAWINGS
DOUBLE HUNG WINDOW
WOOD CASEMENTS
STEEL CASEMENTS
STATIONARY GLASS
DOOR OPENING IN
PLANS OF OPENINGS IN EXTERIOR MASONRY WALLS
DOUBLE HUNG WINDOW
WOOD CASEMENTS
STEEL CASEMENTS
STATIONARY GLASS
DOOR OPENING IN
PLANS OF OPENINGS IN EXTERIOR WOOD WALLS
I ARCHITECTURAL SYMBOLS
D
F
F
L
L
S
S
CEILING OUTLET
WALL OUTLET
DROP CORD
CEILING FAN OUTLET
WALL
CEILING LAMP HOLDER
WALL
CEILING PULL SWITCHES
WALL
1
3
WP
R
S
S
S2
S3
DUPLEX. OUTLET
SINGLE OUTLET
TRIPLEX OUTLET
WEATHER-PROOF OUT.
RANGE OUTLET
SWITCH + OUTLET
SINGLE POLE SWITCH
DOUBLE POLE SWITCH
THREE WAY SWITCH
II ELECTRICAL SYMBOLS
W
D
LT
LT
SINK WITH L.H. DRAIN BOARD
SINK WITH DISHWASHER
KITCHEN RANGE
WASHER DRYER
LAUNDRY TRAYS
RECESSED TUB
SHOWER
WAT.ER CLOSET
WALL TYPE
STALL TYPE
URINALS
WL WALL
PL PEDEST.
C CORNER
LAVATORIES
III PLUMBING SYMBOLS

FIG. 54 COMMONLY USED SYMBOLS FOR DRAWINGS

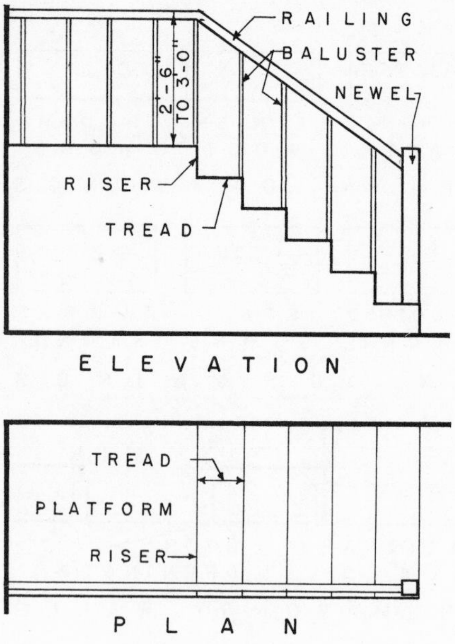

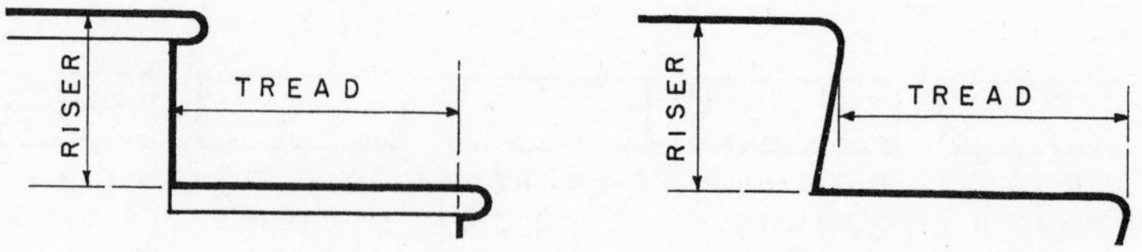

LOCATION OF TREAD AND RISER MEASUREMENTS

2 x RISER + TREAD IN INCHES = 24 TO 26

RISER	TREAD
$6\frac{1}{2}$	$11\frac{1}{2}$
7	10
$7\frac{1}{2}$	$9\frac{1}{2}$
8	$8\frac{1}{2}$

RISER — TREAD COMBINATIONS FOR INTERIOR STAIRS

2 x RISER + TREAD IN INCHES = 26 TO 27

RISER	TREAD
6	$14\frac{1}{2}$
7	$12\frac{1}{2}$
8	$10\frac{1}{2}$
$8\frac{1}{2}$	$9\frac{1}{2}$

RISER — TREAD COMBINATIONS FOR EXTERIOR STAIRS

COMMON DIMENSIONS FOR STAIRS

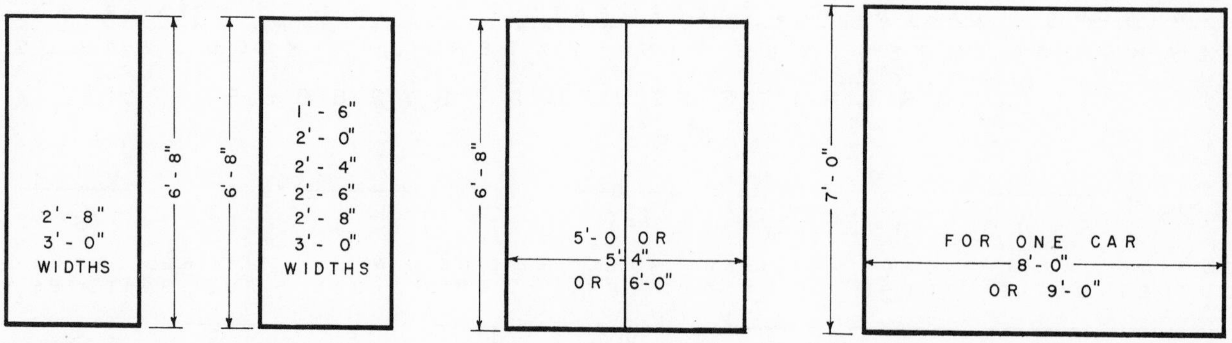

EXTERIOR INTERIOR

SINGLE DOORS

EXTERIOR & INT.

DOUBLE DOORS

16'-0" WIDE FOR 2 CARS

GARAGE DOORS

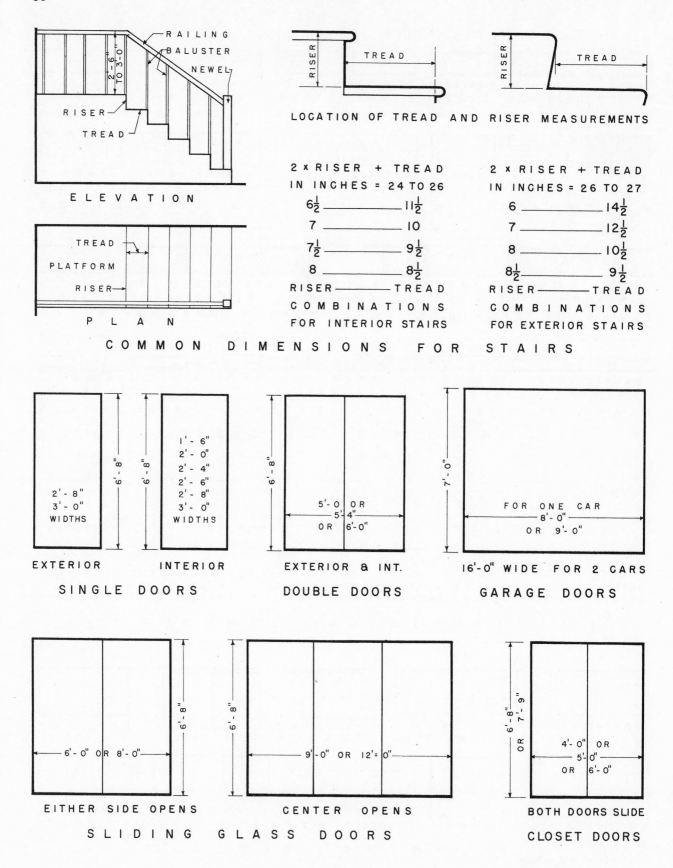

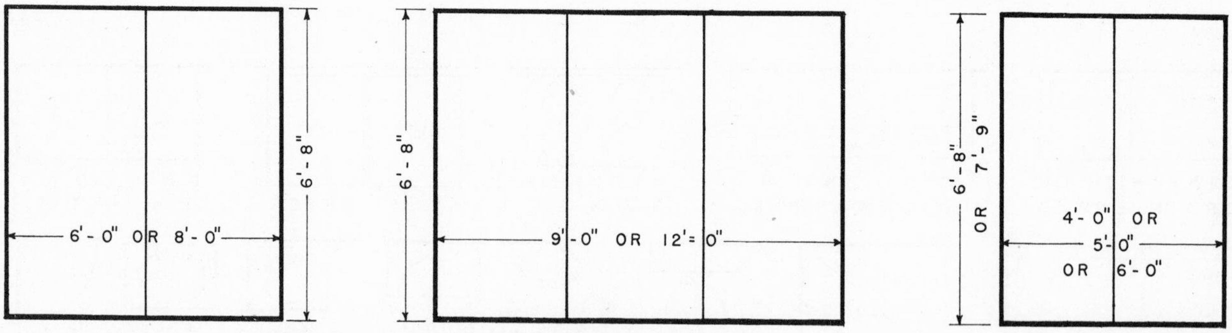

EITHER SIDE OPENS CENTER OPENS

SLIDING GLASS DOORS

BOTH DOORS SLIDE

CLOSET DOORS

FIG. 55 SIZES OF COMMON GRAPHIC ELEMENTS

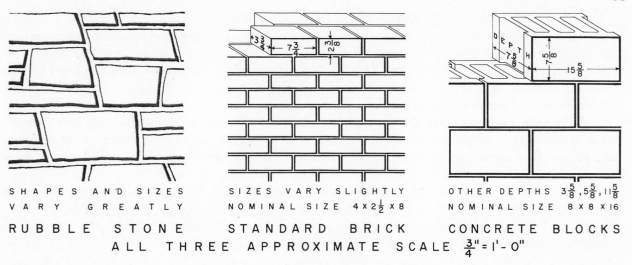

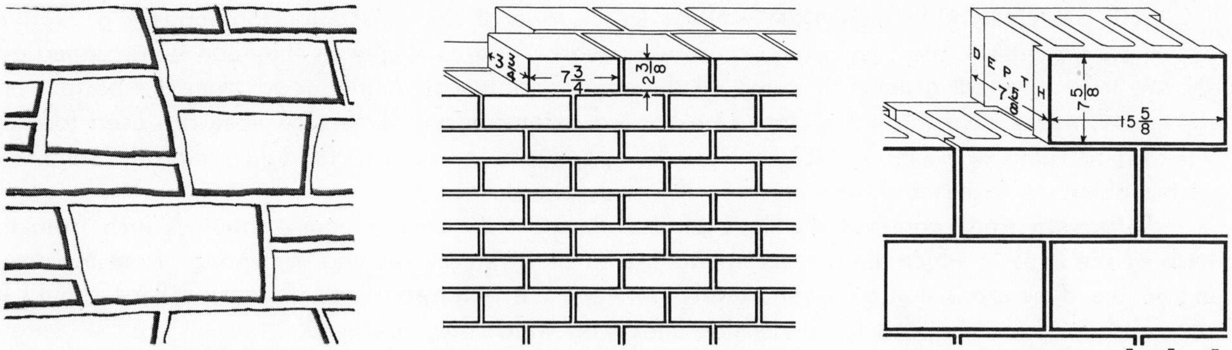

SHAPES AND SIZES VARY GREATLY

RUBBLE STONE

SIZES VARY SLIGHTLY NOMINAL SIZE $4 \times 2\frac{1}{2} \times 8$

STANDARD BRICK

OTHER DEPTHS $3\frac{5}{8}, 5\frac{5}{8}, 11\frac{5}{8}$ NOMINAL SIZE $8 \times 8 \times 16$

CONCRETE BLOCKS

ALL THREE APPROXIMATE SCALE $\frac{3}{4}$" = 1'-0"

FIG. 56 SIZES OF COMMON MASONRY UNITS

Sizes of elements of buildings and of objects that are associated with buildings are a very important part of graphics. The sizes of a very few of the most common pieces of furniture have been given on the two preceding pages. Pages 60 and 61 give sizes of some of the most common building elements for exteriors and interiors.

Some sizes such as the height of a dining table, height of a chair seat, heights of railings and doors, and sizes of brick, concrete blocks, and steps of stairs are pretty well standardized. People expect to see these objects at certain sizes. Such objects having set sizes are valuable in design as indicators of size for a wall, a building, a monument, the interior of a room, and other objects that may not have definite set sizes. These elements of set size suggest the size, or give design scale, to the object of which they are a part and to surroundings of the object. They are very important in graphical representation, and care should be taken to assure that they are drawn at their correct sizes on design and other drawings.

Even some of these elements with generally accepted sizes have their size variations and should not be used without consideration for the object on which they are applied and for conditions affecting their use. When there is great danger from a fall, as in a high building, a railing may be made 4 feet high to provide safety and a sense of security. Where there is no danger involved the railing may be $2\frac{1}{2}$ feet or less in height. Doors vary to suit the requirements of use. In a hospital, doors to patients' rooms may be wider than the sizes given here for single doors to provide space for the entrance of carts with patients. In a fire station a greater door height than the 7 feet required for a passenger car is necessary for fire trucks.

Rustic stonework varies a great deal in dimensions that may depend on the available material and also on sizes that can be handled by the masons. Stones are seldom less than 2 inches or more than 6 to 8 inches thick. They are seldom over $1\frac{1}{2}$ to $2\frac{1}{2}$ feet long. Flagstones for paving and walks usually have a large exposed horizontal area and are thin in the vertical direction. Stones for walls may have relatively thin edges exposed and large flat surfaces concealed.

Cut stones for veneering may be 3 or 4 feet high and several feet long. They may require a derrick for moving and setting in place.

Monumental buildings such as memorials, state capitols, and religious edifices may have larger elements than those in residential and utilitarian structures. They are sometimes expected to be grand and impressive in appearance. This effect may be accomplished partly by the general design and partly by the larger than normal sizes of elements of the structure.

THE DIMENSIONING OF DRAWINGS. This is one of the most important phases of working drawings. Dimensions must be given accurately, clearly, and as simply as they can be arranged and shown. It is universal practice to have all dimensions, notes, and titles read from the bottom and right only, never from the left or top. Lines called extension and dimension lines are used to show where dimensions apply on the object, Figs. 57 A, B. These lines are made lighter than the solid lines of the object to avoid confusion between the two sets of lines.

Extension lines continue the lines of the object. They should begin about $\frac{1}{32}$ inch from the ends of the lines to which the measurements are to be given and extend far enough from the drawing so the dimensions can be given clearly between the extension lines. Extension lines should be drawn about $\frac{1}{8}$ inch beyond the dimension lines with which they are used.

Dimension lines are the lines on which dimensions are given. They are terminated with arrows which have their points ending exactly on the extension lines to which measurements are given. Dimension lines can be drawn in either of two ways: (1) as continuous lines with the numerals for the dimensions placed just above the lines, Fig. 57 A; or (2) with a part of the center of the line omitted so that the dimension can be given centered on the line, Fig. 57 B. The first method is commonly used for architecture and structural engineering, the second for mechanical engineering. One method should be used consistently throughout a set of drawings.

Dimensions are given in various ways to suit the convenience of the type of work and the accepted practice in the profession for which the drawings are made. (A) In architecture and structural engineering, dimensions are given in feet and inches with the foot (′) and inch (″) signs after the numerals and a dash always placed between the numerals for feet and inches, thus $5'-2\frac{1}{2}''$, Fig. 57 A. Some offices give any dimension of a foot or more in feet and inches, 1′–0″, etc. Others continue measurements in inches beyond one foot with an arbitrary maximum for distances that can be given in inches only. This is convenient in giving spacings of joists and other structural elements. (B) In mechanical engineering all dimensions are given in inches only and the inch sign is omitted, Fig. 57 B. A note to that effect should be given with the scale or as a part of the title.

Fractions are given either as common or decimal fractions. Common fractions are given as half, fourths, eighths, sixteenths, thirty-seconds, and sixty-fourths. Other fractional divisions are seldom used. Common fractions should be given with a horizontal line separating numerators and denominators ($\frac{3}{16}$) and with the numerals about two thirds the size of other numerals. There is less chance of error in reading fractions when the horizontal division is used.

Multiple dimension lines are sometimes necessary on the same side of an object because dimensions should not be given across the object when it can be avoided. Multiple dimension lines should be arranged so that they cross extension lines only where the measurements terminate. In order to avoid confusion and make the simplest arrangement of dimensions, the smaller measurements are kept near the object and larger ones progressively farther away as shown in Fig. 57 C. All dimensions that are either necessary or useful should be provided on the drawing. Give enough dimensions so that other persons are not required to add or subtract to obtain necessary measurements. Unnecessary repetition of measurements is often confusing, not helpful. Avoid useless repetition. It is good practice to locate dimensions between views where their relation to two views can be seen for both, Fig. 57 D. Base line dimensioning is sometimes advisable or necessary. This is especially true for a mechanical contrivance where measurements must be exact from some working surface. In this system distances in one direction are given from the same line, Fig. 57 E.

Small spaces on the drawings may require special treatment in dimensioning, Fig. 57 F.

Circles are dimensioned in various ways for different professions. The method for mechanical engineering is shown in Fig. 57 G. Either the diameter or radius may be given depending on which will be most useful in laying out the construction of the object. In some work it is desirable to give the dimension for a circle in the view where it appears as a circle. When the diameter is given the abbreviation DIA. accompanies the numerals of the size when the circle view is not shown. The letter R is used with the numerals for a radius, Fig. 57 G.

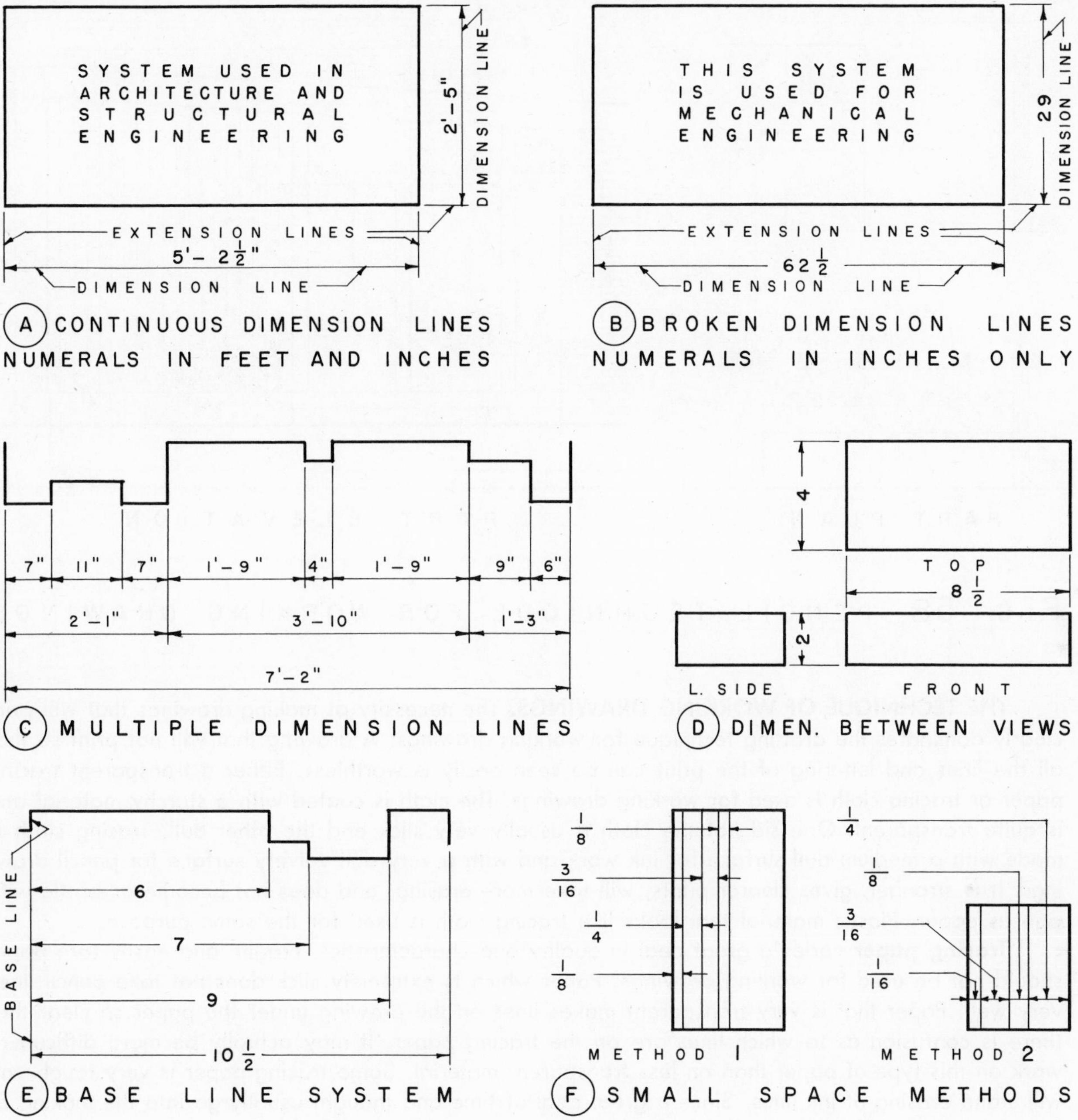

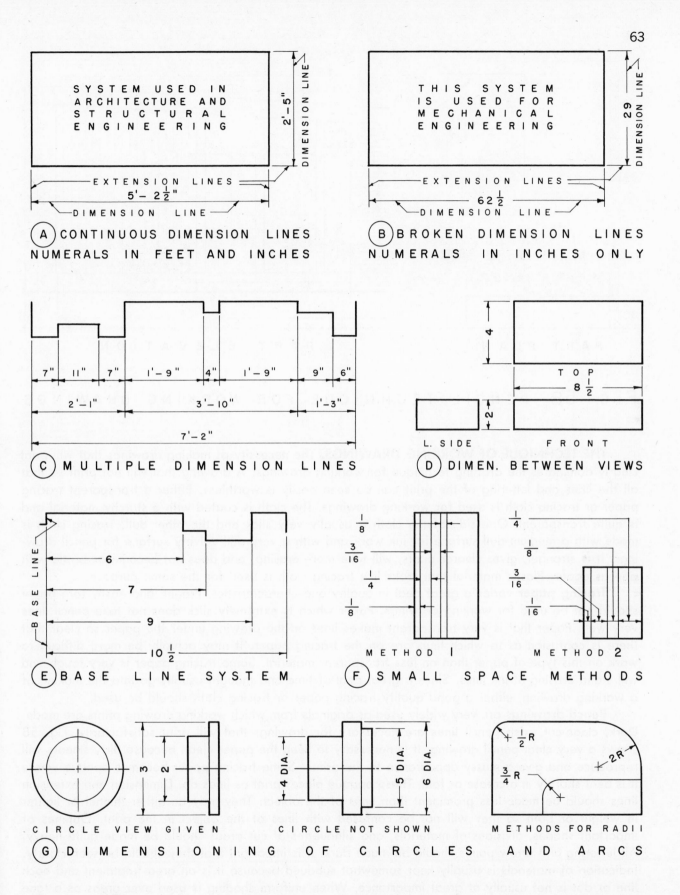

FIG. 57 THE DIMENSIONING OF DRAWINGS

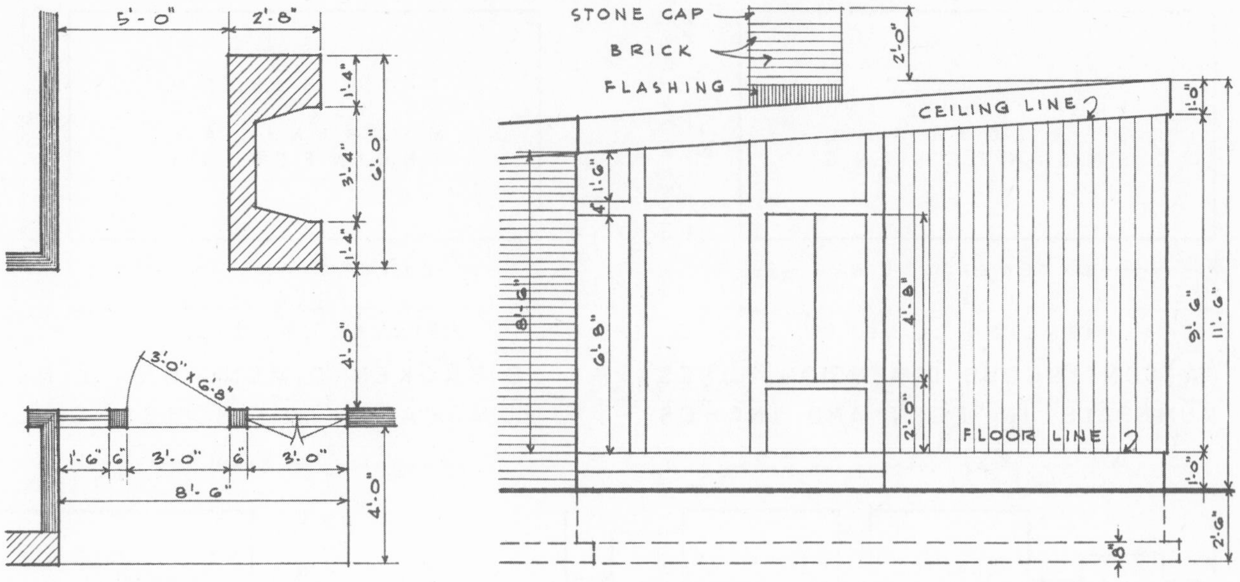

PART PLAN PART ELEVATION

FIG. 58 PENCIL TECHNIQUE FOR WORKING DRAWINGS

THE TECHNIQUE OF WORKING DRAWINGS. The necessity of making drawings that will print clearly dominates the drafting technique for working drawings. A drawing that will not print so that all the lines and lettering of the print can be seen easily is worthless. Either a transparent tracing paper or tracing cloth is used for working drawings. The cloth is coated with a starchy material and is quite transparent. One side of the cloth is usually very slick and the other dull. Tracing cloth is made with a medium dull surface for ink work and with a very dull velvety surface for pencil drawings. It is stronger, gives clearer prints, will take more erasing, and does not become as brittle with age as paper. Plastic material that looks like tracing cloth is used for the same purpose.

Tracing paper varies a great deal in quality and characteristics. Fragile and easily torn paper should not be used for working drawings. Paper which is extremely slick does not take pencil lines very well. Paper that is very transparent makes lines on the drawing under the paper so clear that there is confusion as to which lines are on the tracing paper. It may actually be more difficult to work on this type of paper than on less transparent material. Some tracing paper is very tough and will stand erasing of ink lines. Since a great deal of time and thought usually go into the making of a working drawing, either a good quality tracing paper or tracing cloth should be used.

Pencil drawings are very widely used as originals from which working drawing prints are made. Dark, clean-cut, crisp pencil lines are necessary for drawings that will print satisfactorily. Fig. 58 shows a very clear pencil drawing. It is necessary to keep the paper clean because dirty smears will reproduce and give a mussy appearance to the prints. Some tracing paper becomes opaque where it is bent sharply in a crease or fold. These opaque places print as lines do. Dimension and extension lines should be made less prominent than lines of the object. They may be either thinner or lighter in weight or both so they will not be confused with lines of the object in the print. Outlines of important shapes, divisions of materials, and silhouettes of cut areas should be made quite heavy. All lettering and arrow points should be made dark. It is important that they should be seen clearly. Indication of materials is usually kept somewhat subdued because it is an area treatment and each line or dot is not usually of great importance. When uniform shading is used over areas as a tone symbol for a material the shading can be applied on the back of the paper or cloth. This procedure has these advantages: (1) lines surrounding the areas are not smeared by application of the tone, therefore print more clearly; (2) erasures and changes can be made more readily.

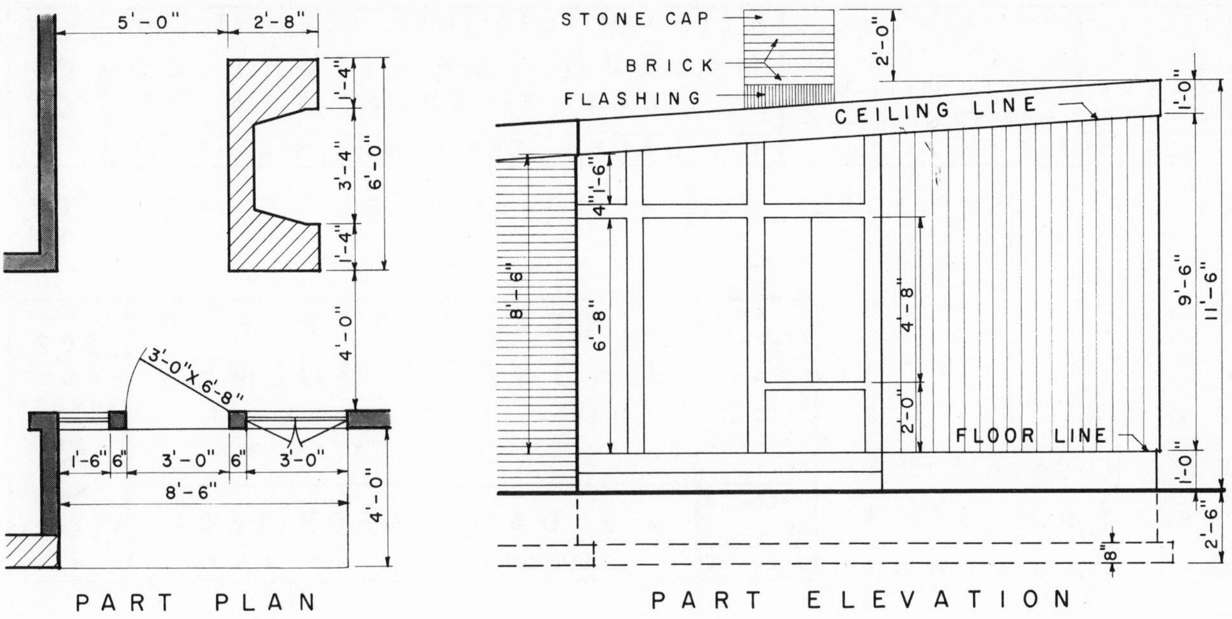

FIG. 59 INK TECHNIQUE FOR WORKING DRAWINGS

Ink drawings either on tracing paper or tracing cloth are used in some offices. It is usually necessary to make a complete preliminary drawing on scrap paper and trace it in ink. Changes are more easily made on pencil drawings than on ink ones. Ink drawings give clearer, brighter prints, Fig. 59. Ink technique provides a more positive variation of darkness of line by the use of diluted and colored inks. Tones can be applied to either the front or back of tracing cloth with a small brush and diluted or colored ink. Use a moist brush. Avoid getting the cloth very wet. Wet spots on tracing cloth become opaque and wrinkled if the water penetrates. Sometimes the surface of tracing cloth repels the ink as though it were oily. Such a condition can be overcome by dusting and rubbing the surface of the cloth with a powder sold for that purpose, or with powdered chalk. The powder should be removed with a clean dusting cloth before inking.

Colors are frequently used on ink drawings and less often on pencil drawings to secure variations of line weight. Whenever possible the draftsman should make sample lines and have them printed as he will have the drawings printed in order to check on the reproduction from colors. Colors sometimes produce surprising results. Yellow prints the same as black on blueprints. It is sometimes used for tones because it does not hide lines on the original. Red ink is sometimes used for dimension and extension lines because it prints lighter than black. The colors help to separate different uses of lines on the originals, and if carefully selected give variations of tones on the lines of the prints, thus producing prints that are more easily read. Colored ink that is too dark can be diluted by adding water to it.

Unnecessary repetition is preferably avoided on working drawings. Needless duplication of the same repeating element in all its details often adds nothing to the clearness of the drawings and causes additional work and expense in making the drawings. The following are examples of ways to avoid repeating details: (1) Continuous bands of details may be drawn completely for a short distance and the remainder drawn more simply or omitted with a note "Continue details." (2) One of a series of units may be drawn completely and all others shown in outline form only with a note stating that the details apply to all the outlined areas. (3) A symmetrical object can be drawn completely on one side of the center line and outlined on the other side.

In all cases where only part of the drawing is finished in detail notes and arrows should be used to make entirely clear where the details are required on the object.

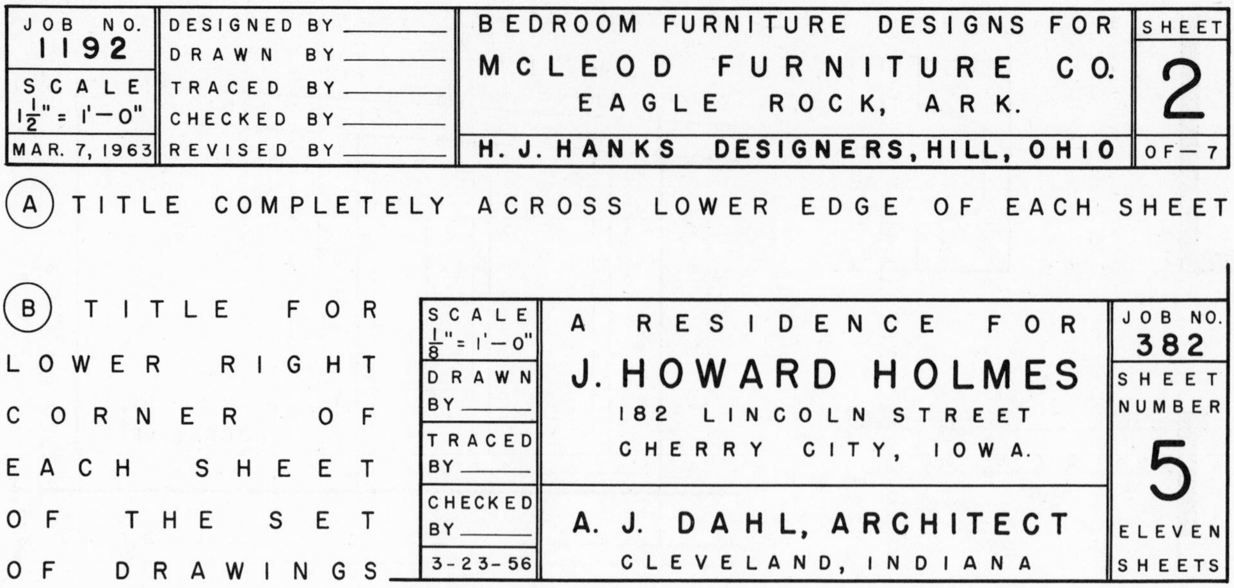

FIG. 60 TITLES FOR WORKING DRAWING SHEETS

The title is an important part of a sheet of working drawings. Usually the set of drawings consists of several sheets and some of the title is repeated on each sheet. Necessary variations are made for items applicable to each individual sheet. The title is usually in a box form in the lower right corner, or extended completely across the bottom of each sheet, Fig. 60. Some of the material usually repeating on each sheet and some of the material that may vary are listed here.

MATERIAL ON EACH SHEET

1. Name of object.
2. Name and address of client.
3. Name, address, and profession of office.
4. Total number of sheets in the set.

MATERIAL THAT MAY VARY

5. Sheet number in the set.
6. Date completed.
7. Names of authors of drawings.
8. Scale on the sheet.

The sheet number is usually located in the lower right corner so that it is easily found. The total number of sheets is given to allow a check for completeness of a set. The first sheet of a set may also include a tabulation of all drawings made for this job. In large offices it is often desirable to give complete listing of types of work done by different individuals on each drawing. This may include sketches, drawing, tracing, computations, checking, and other items necessary or important for the particular job. The scale can be given in the title block when all drawings on a sheet are at the same scale. When the scale "varies" that word may be put under scale in the title block and the scale of each individual drawing given with its subtitle.

The set of drawings should include any and all drawings that are necessary to explain the shapes and dimensions of the object shown. It should include multi-view drawings consisting of two or more complete views. Auxiliary drawings, sections, and plans through the object may be necessary. Details at a larger scale are sometimes made to more clearly explain parts of the object that are not sufficiently large and clear on the multi-view drawings. These details may be either sectional drawings, exterior views, or a combination of the two types. Their positions should be clearly designated on the complete views as shown for the sectional details of Fig. 52.

One of the parallel line pictorial drawing types may be used in a set of working drawings to give a three-dimensional explanation of forms that are difficult to understand in the two-dimensional multi-view drawings.

THE REPRODUCTION OF DRAWINGS. The printing from the original drawings made on transparent paper or cloth is usually done by a commercial blueprinter. Prints can be made in different ways with considerable variety in the results, Fig. 61. In all cases the tracing is placed over a light-sensitive paper and run through a machine that has a strong light shining on the tracing and through it onto the paper it covers. The printing paper is then developed either by use of liquids or vapors.

Blueprints are called negative prints because they have white lines and blue background thus reversing the tone relation of the original drawings. After being exposed they are run through one or more chemical solutions and finally dried. By first making a Van Dyke negative print, which has a dark brown background and transparent white lines, and using it for the printing, blue-line prints can be made. They reverse the blue and white of the common blueprint. They are more satisfactory for use where drawing on the prints is required since they have white background areas.

Direct positive prints are reproductions giving the same tone relations as the original drawings in one step instead of requiring an intermediate negative (Van Dyke) as in blue-line printing. Black and white prints have black lines and a white background. Ozalids have colored lines. Both are developed with ammonia vapor.

Minor distortions of the original drawing shapes and sizes may appear in any type of prints. Warping may be caused by wetting and shrinking of the printing paper or in other ways. Sometimes the length of the print will be changed in the printing process through defective equipment. Minor variations can be expected in prints. However, appreciable distortion of shape or change of dimension should not occur in good prints. The drawings and/or specifications often contain a statement that where dimensions are given they should be followed. Taking sizes from prints with a scale should be avoided.

Discoloration of prints often occurs when they are brought in contact with perspiration, acid, cement, lime, or other substances. Fortunately it is usually an easy and relatively inexpensive matter to replace prints that are damaged.

Photostat prints are not contact prints. They can be made either smaller or larger than the original. They can be made either as negative prints reversing the tone relation of the originals, or, by using an intermediate negative, as positive prints duplicating the tones of the original. Photostats are expensive and are seldom used for working drawings. Their big advantage is change of size.

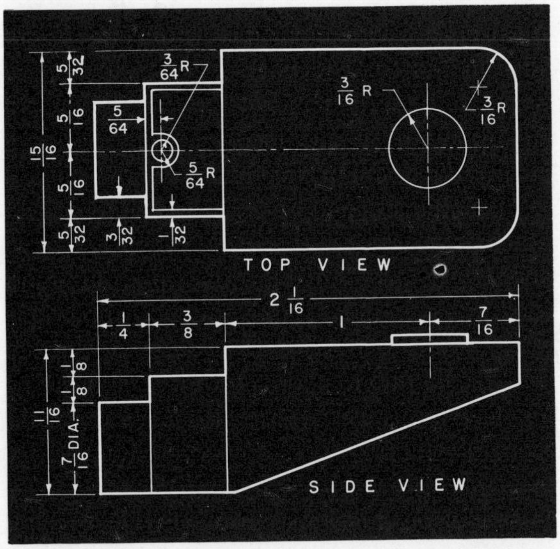

(I) NEGATIVE PRINT

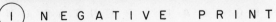

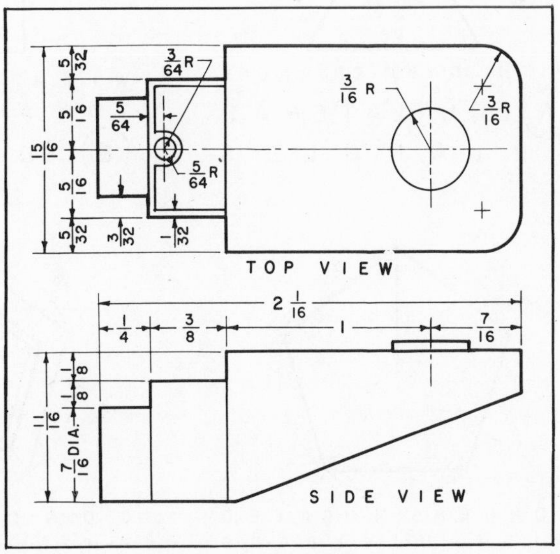

(II) POSITIVE PRINT

FIG. 61 TYPES OF REPRODUCTIONS OF DRAWINGS

CHAPTER 11

GEOMETRIC SHAPES

The simple lines, areas, and solids of geometry are the principal basic forms of design. It is essential that the designer should be able to draw them easily, accurately, and quickly. The simpler geometric forms can be constructed easily when T-square, triangles, instruments, and drafting board are used.

The equilateral triangle can be constructed in four different positions by using the 30° x 60° triangle on the T-square, Fig. 62 A.

A square can be drawn in two ways: (1) by first drawing a circle with diameter equal to a side, then drawing tangents to the circle with T-square and triangle, Fig. 62 B; or (2) with one side given, by drawing the diagonal then constructing the square on its diagonal. Squares can be constructed at any angle by using one of these methods and drawing perpendiculars as shown in Fig. 66 E or F.

The rectangle, which is the most widely used geometic area, has no set proportions. It can vary from almost square to a long thin shape that approaches a straight line.

A pentagon can be drawn in a circle by drawing a vertical line through the center of the circle to locate the top point on the circumference, then stepping off the other corners with the

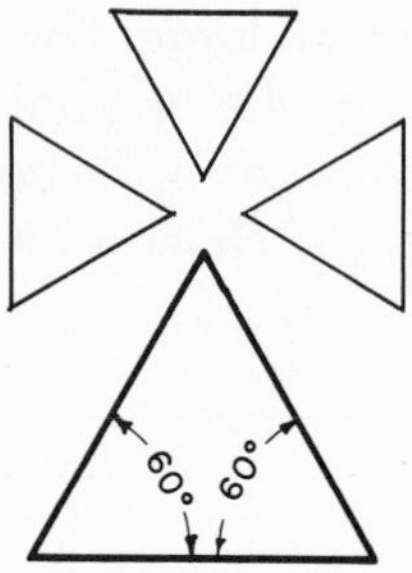

WITH 30°x 60° TRIANGLE

(A) EQUILATERAL TRIANGLES

WITH TANGENTS TO A CIRCLE

FROM ONE SIDE AND A DIAGONAL

(B) SQUARES DRAWN BY TWO METHODS

CORNERS LOCATED WITH DIVIDERS

CONCENTRIC PENTAGONS

CORNERS LOCATED WITH PROTRACTOR

(C) CONSTRUCTION OF A REGULAR PENTAGON

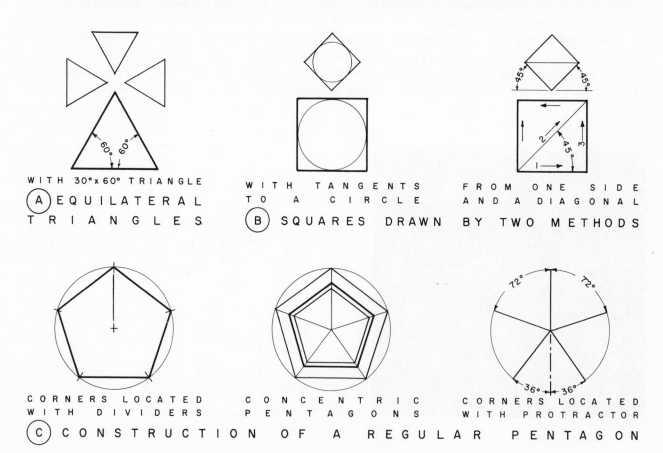

FIG. 62 CONSTRUCTION OF PLANE FIGURES

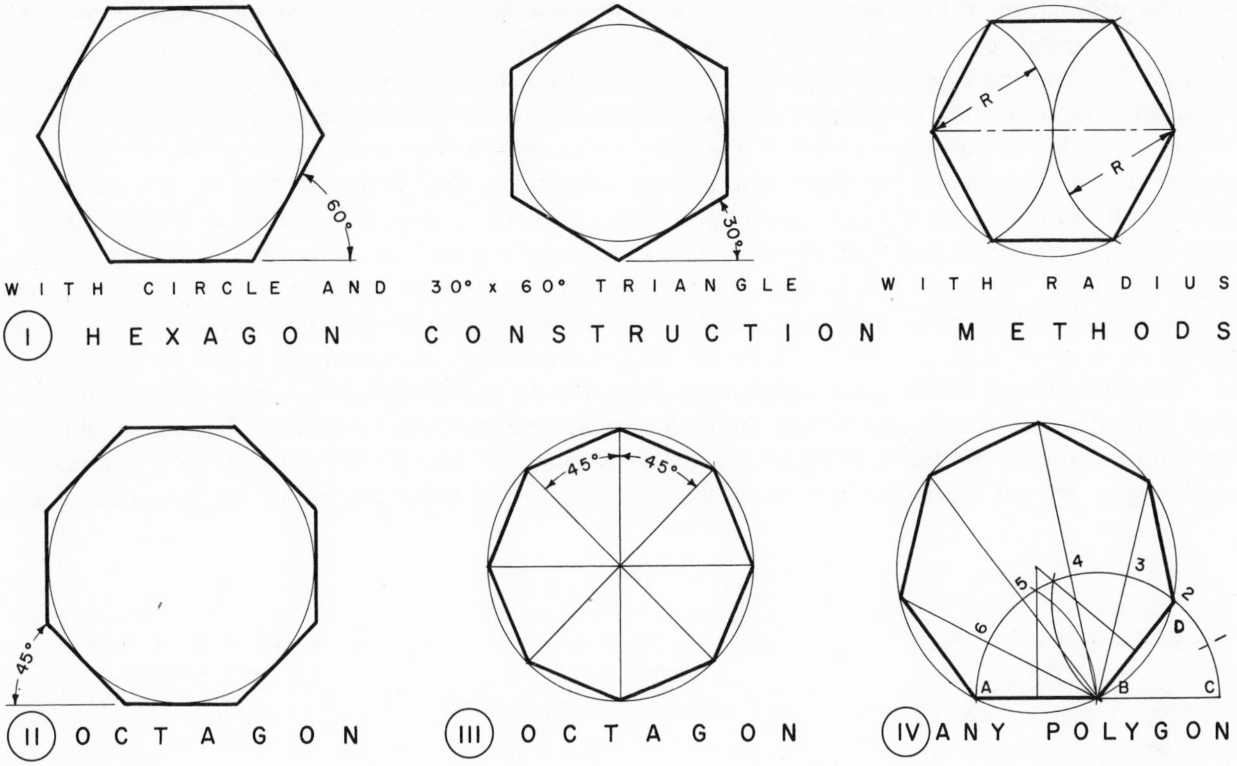

FIG. 63 CONSTRUCTION OF REGULAR POLYGONS

dividers, by trial and error until five equal divisions are secured. A larger or smaller pentagon can be constructed from this by drawing lines from the center through the corners, then drawing lines parallel to the sides of the first pentagon between these radiating lines, Fig. 62 C. An adjustable triangle or other protractor can be used to locate the corners of a pentagon or other polygon by drawing through the center of a circle.

A hexagon can be constructed around a circle by drawing 60° lines tangent to the circle with horizontal tangents at bottom and top, or with 30° tangent lines to make points at top and bottom and vertical lines at both sides, Fig. 63 I. The hexagon can be constructed in a circle by using the radius of the circle as the length of a side of the hexagon.

The octagon can be drawn around a circle with two horizontal and two vertical sides. The four slanting sides are drawn with the 45° triangle, Fig. 63 II. A horizontal, a vertical, and two 45° lines through the center of the circle locate the eight corners on the circumference of the circle. This construction gives corners at the top, bottom, and two sides as shown in Fig. 63 III.

Any regular polygon can be drawn about a given side A–B in the following manner, Fig. 63 IV. Draw a semicircle of which A–B is a radius and A–C a diameter. Divide the semicircle into the same number of equal parts as the number of sides of the required polygon. Seven divisions have been used in the example. Through the second division draw a second side B–D of the polygon. From the two sides A–B and B–D locate the center of the polygon by drawing the perpendicular bisectors of the sides. Draw the circumscribing circle. The remaining corners of the polygon can be located on the circle by drawing radial lines from B through the divisions on the semicircle. The distance A–B can be used to locate the corners of the polygon as an alternate method.

Any regular polygon can be inscribed in a circle by locating with dividers by trial and error the required number of points on the circle for the corners of the polygon. The corners can also be located on the circumference of the circle by drawing from its center angles equal to 360° divided by the number of sides of the polygon.

The projection of line spacing from one multi-view drawing to another on simple geometric solids is illustrated for a cylinder, cone, and hexagon in Fig. 64. In these illustrations the top view is drawn first and the required number of divisions laid out in top view with dividers on the circular top views and with scale or dividers on the polygon top view. The divisions are then drawn from the top views to the correct positions in the front views. When lines are spaced correctly around a cylinder or cone they make the object seem to be smoothly curved. If the spacing is inaccurate, the surface will appear to be warped. Slanting surfaces such as those at the sides of the hexagonal prism are foreshortened and have closer line spacing in front view than where the area is projected from top view in true size. This change of spacing helps to explain the change of planes and the directions of the planes. The projection of equal spaces in this manner is useful in locating the positions of decorative motifs as well as for the spacing of the straight lines that are a part of the design.

Warped surface solids in whose surfaces there are no straight lines have only curved line divisions. The vase and sphere are two examples that have circular cross sections on horizontal planes. These forms can be divided into equal spaces by drawing vertical planes through their centers at equal angles around the circumference of the top view and plotting points on the intersections of

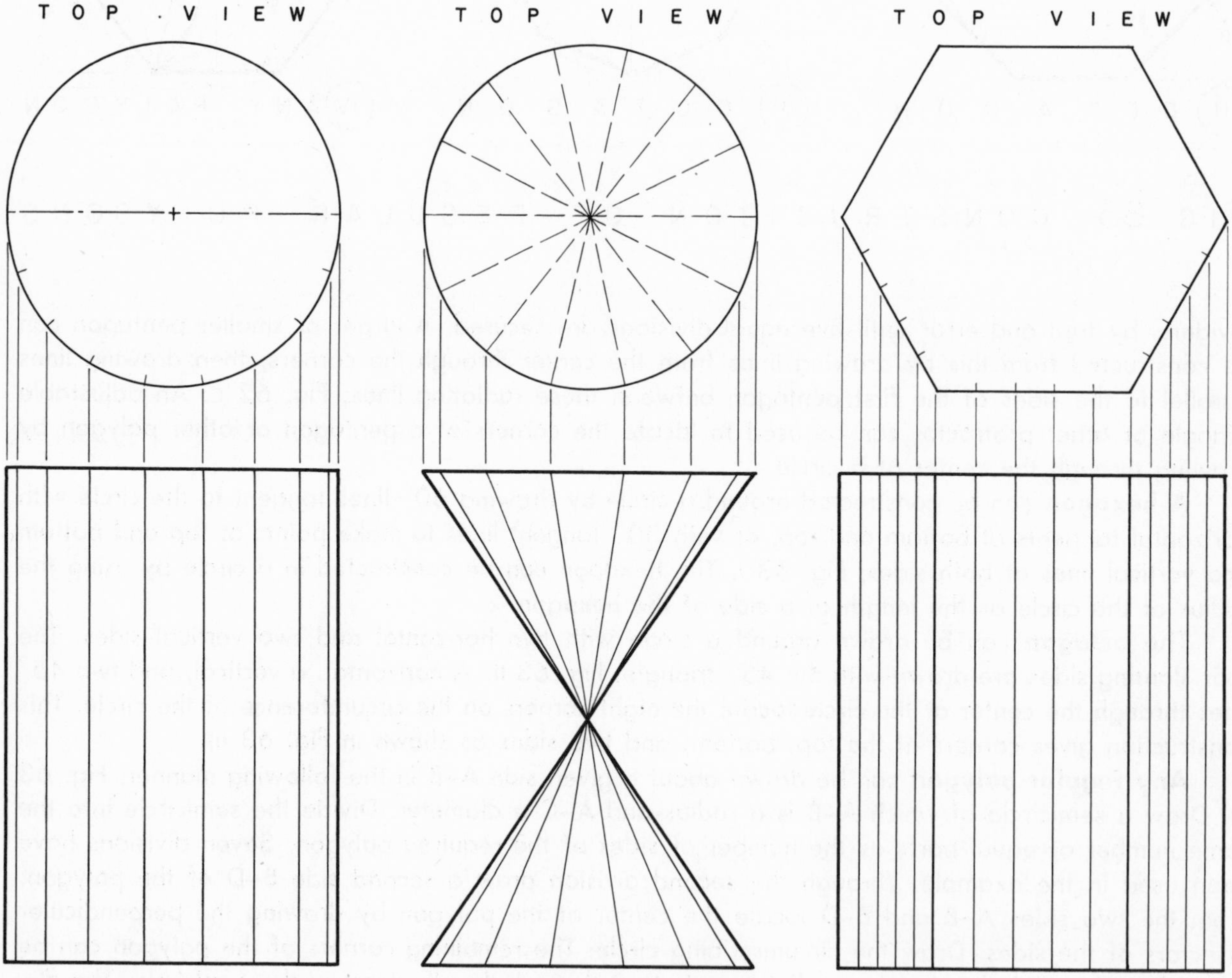

FIG. 64 LINE SPACING ON GEOMETRIC SOLIDS

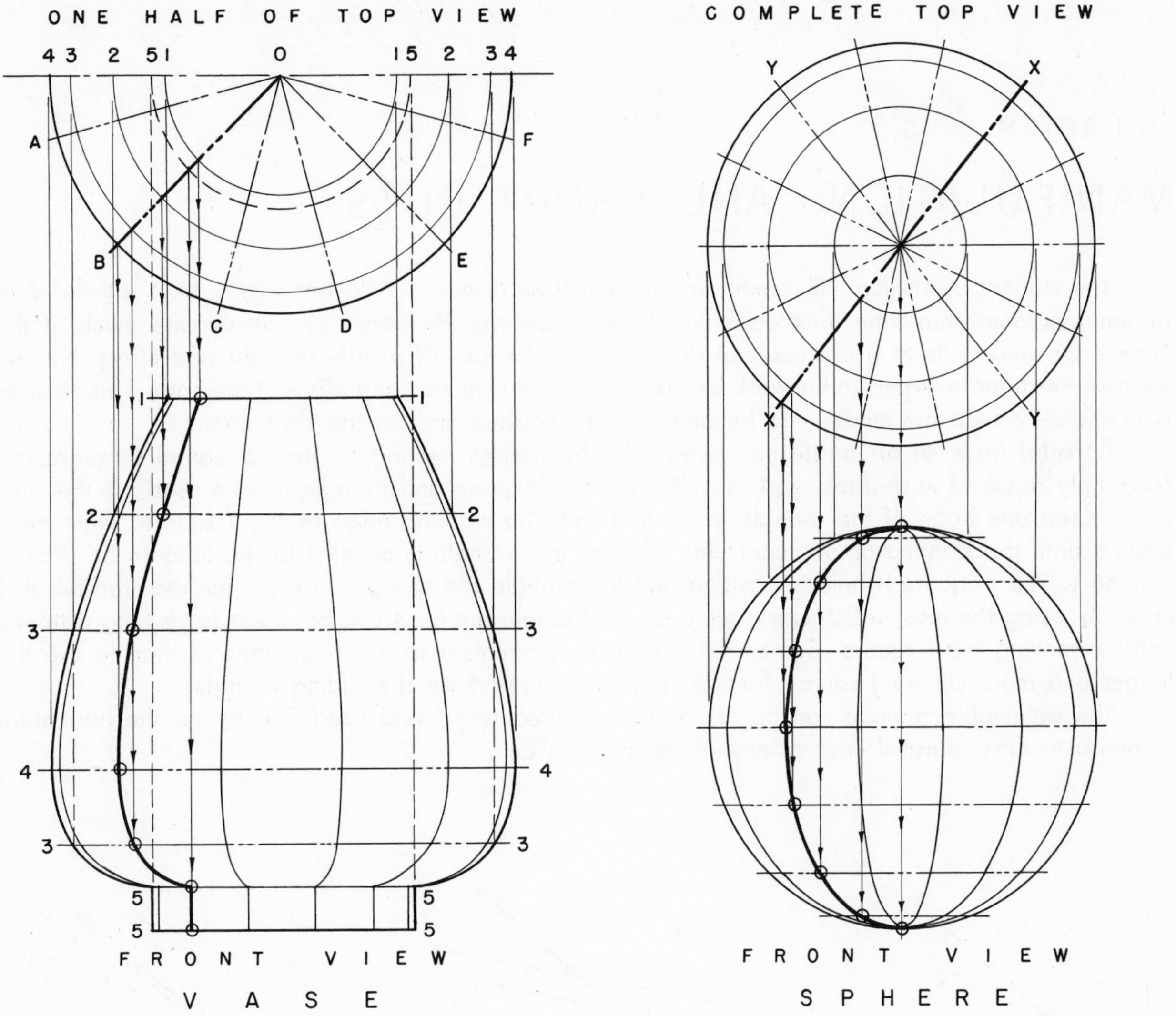

FIG. 65 LINES ON WARPED SURFACE SOLIDS

these planes with the surfaces of the object. In the example of the vase in Fig. 65 points have been located on the 45° plane represented by line B–O in the top view. Horizontal lines have been drawn across the front view wherever it is thought that points will be most useful in drawing the intersection of plane B–O with the surface of the vase. These lines, 1–1, 2–2, etc., represent the front views of horizontal planes through the vase. Their circle intersections are drawn in the top view and labeled 1, 2, etc. These circles must be the diameters cut in the front view by the same planes.

A vertical drawn from the intersection of B–O with circle 1 in top view to line 1–1 in front view locates a point on the intersection of plane B–O with the surface of the vase. The intersections of the other circles give additional points. The curve is then drawn through the points located. Any number of points can be located with this system and the intersections of any number of planes can be located. The same circles 1, 2, etc. and their corresponding planes in front view are used for all vertical cutting planes A–O, B–O, C–O, etc.

It will be observed that the left side of the curve cut by plane X–X on the sphere is visible and the right side is hidden on the back of the sphere in front view. When planes X–X and Y–Y are at the same angle from opposite sides, their complete curves will coincide in front view.

CHAPTER 12

MANIPULATIONS AND SHORT CUTS

The student draftsman will remain an amateur if he draws in awkward ways, takes a great deal of time, accomplishes little, and does unpolished drawings. However, he can acquire much of the knowledge and skills of a professional draftsman by the use of a little thought and effort. He can become much more expert in his work by using correct techniques and efficient methods. This chapter is intended to help the amateur to become a more finished and precise draftsman.

Parallel lines at an angle not given with the triangle resting on the horizontal T-square are frequently required in drafting work, Fig. 66 A. The T-square and triangle can be used for this purpose. Keep one edge of the triangle in contact with the working edge of the T-square. Twist them around until the slanting or perpendicular edge of the triangle is parallel to the lines to be drawn, Fig. 66 B. The T-square is held in position and the triangle slid along it to draw the required parallel lines. By using the most satisfactory angle of the triangle the lines can be made for a long distance without moving the T-square. Sometimes it is more convenient to use two triangles than to use the longer and more clumsy T-square for the stationary support for the sliding triangle.

The adjustable triangle can be set at the required angle and used directly on the horizontal T-square to draw parallel lines at any angle, Fig. 66 C.

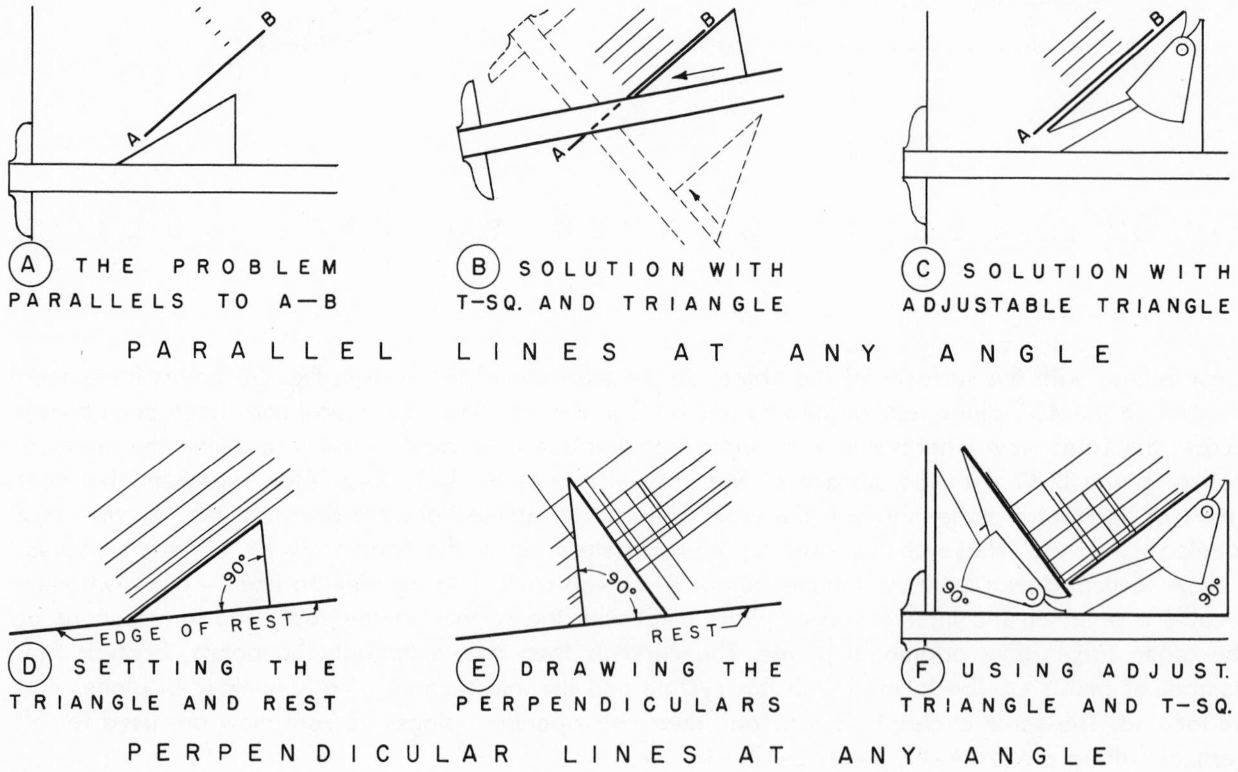

FIG. 66 OTHER USES OF T-SQUARE AND TRIANGLES

Perpendicular lines at any angle require the use of two triangles or a triangle and T-square. When a set of lines is to be drawn at a given odd angle and it is required to draw both perpendiculars and parallels to the given line direction, place the triangle on a rest of T-square or another triangle with a 90° angle on the rest. Twist the triangle and its touching rest so that the acute angle side of the moving triangle lines with the direction given, Fig. 66 D. By sliding the moving triangle the parallels to the given direction can be drawn. By rotating the moving triangle on its 90° corner to bring the other side of the 90° angle in contact with the rest, the same side of the triangle first used will now draw the perpendiculars when the triangle slides along the rest, Fig. 66 E. Remember three things: (1) the moving triangle must be turned on its 90° corner; (2) the two sides of the 90° angle must be used on the stationary rest; (3) the same side of the triangle must be used for both groups of lines. Considerable ingenuity and foresight are required to have the triangles turned so that they cover the required area of the drawing with as little moving of the rest as possible.

The adjustable triangle will also draw perpendiculars to lines at any angle. It is used on the horizontal T-square and set for the given lines. When turned on its 90° angle it will then draw the perpendiculars to the given lines while resting on the horizontal T-square, Fig. 66 F.

The location of center lines with triangles is a routine procedure for an experienced draftsman. The most common problem is to find the center lines of a rectangle that has vertical and horizontal sides. From the bottom corners A and B of the rectangle draw 45° lines to intersect at C, Fig. 67 I. The vertical line through C is the center line of the rectangle. Lines at 45° from the top corners accomplish the same result. Lines at 45° from two corners D and B at one vertical side of the rectangle meet in point E. The horizontal line through E is the other center line of the rectangle. The 45° triangle is ordinarily used for this operation because it is the best for the purpose. However any other angle can be used if the lines drawn from the two corners make identical angles with the line connecting these corners, Fig. 67 II. The diagonals of a rectangle can be drawn to locate its center at their intersection. This is the simple method of geometry. It is accurate on almost square rectangles and loses accuracy on long thin rectangles.

To find the center line of a space between two vertical or horizontal lines L–M and N–O, draw X–Y perpendicular to the given lines and from the corners X and Y draw intersecting 45° lines to locate a point on the required center line, Fig. 67 III.

The center line between two parallel lines at any angle can be located by the following procedure, Fig. 67 IV. Draw V–W perpendicular to the lines. Place one side of the 90° angle of a 45° triangle on a rest of triangle or T-square and adjust so the perpendicular to the rest is parallel to the given lines R–S and T–U. Slide moving triangle to draw the diagonal of one corner. Reverse the triangle to draw the diagonal of the second corner and locate a point Z on the center line at the intersection of the two diagonals. Use the edge of the moving triangle that is perpendicular to the rest to draw the center line through Z.

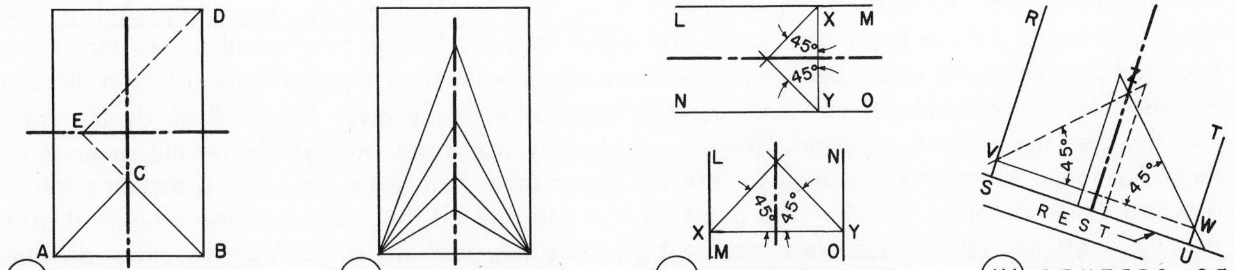

(I) CENTER LINES OF RECTANGLE

(II) ANY=ANGLES CAN BE USED

(III) CENTERS OF PARALLEL LINES

(IV) CENTERS OF OBLIQUE LINES

FIG. 67 THE LOCATION OF CENTER LINES

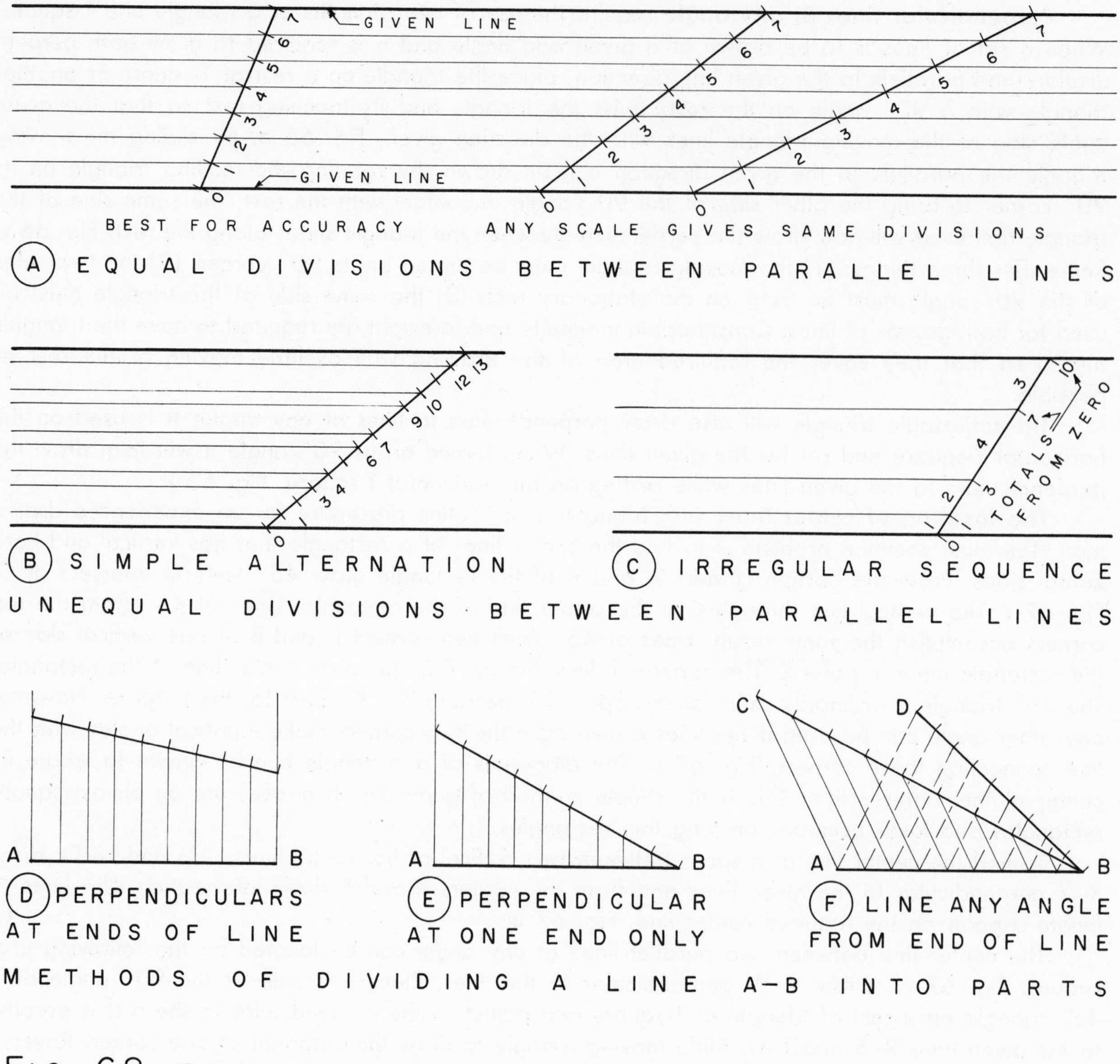

FIG. 68 THE DIVISION OF SPACES AND LINES

The division of a space between two parallel lines by using the scale is one of the most useful manipulations that a draftsman can learn. It enables him to do easily, accurately, and speedily work that would take a great deal longer by other methods. Given two parallel lines Fig. 68 A. Required to divided the space between these lines into a number of equal divisions. Seven divisions are used for the example. If the scale used perpendicular to the given lines will divide the space exactly, then the problem is solved. However, this rarely works out. Almost always the space is too large for some scales and too small for others. Use a scale that gives too large a distance for the required seven divisions. Put the zero point on one line and tilt the scale until the seventh division exactly meets the second line. Now mark out precisely the positions of each of the seven divisions and draw through these points parallel to the given lines to make the required divisions. Note that different scales can be used to obtain the same results. However the scale that is most nearly perpendicular to the given parallel lines will give slightly more accurate results.

Simple unequal divisions can also be laid out in the same manner as equal divisions. A simple alternation of small and large spaces is shown in Fig. 68 B. Here the ratio of size is 1 to 2.

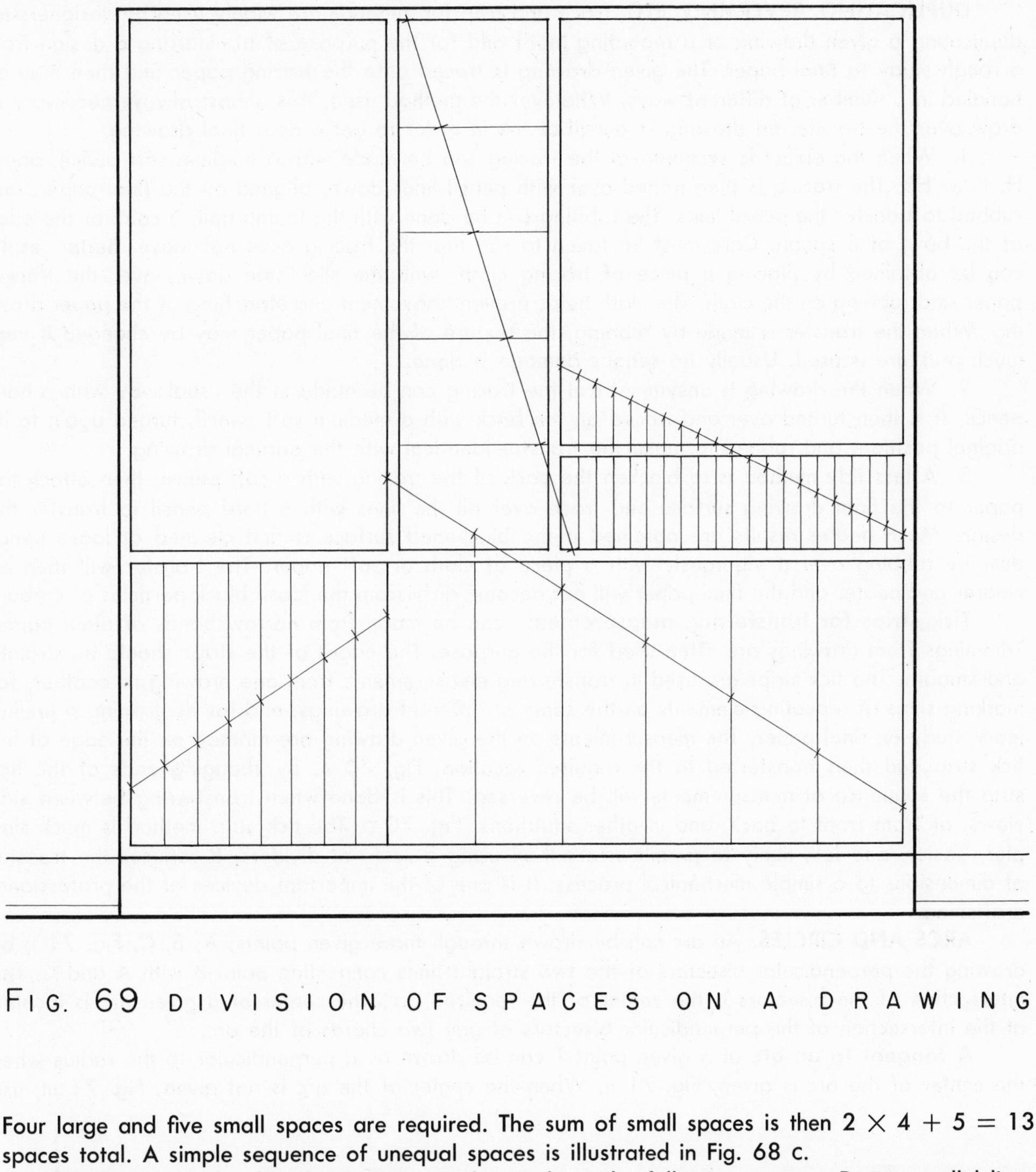

FIG. 69 DIVISION OF SPACES ON A DRAWING

Four large and five small spaces are required. The sum of small spaces is then $2 \times 4 + 5 = 13$ spaces total. A simple sequence of unequal spaces is illustrated in Fig. 68 C.

The division of a line into parts can be made in the following manner. Draw parallel lines perpendicular to the given line A–B at its end points A and B, Fig. 68 D. The space between the two parallel lines is divided and the divisions extended to line A–B by drawing construction lines parallel to the two lines through points A and B. Only one perpendicular to the line to be divided is necessary for this manipulation, Fig. 68 E. One end of the line A–B can be used as a pivot point and the scale revolved until the required division touches the perpendicular at the other end of the line. In the example B has been used as the pivot point and the perpendicular to A–B has been drawn through A. The line A–C drawn at the end of the line to be divided need not be a perpendicular, Fig. 68 F. It can be drawn at any angle and the result will be the same if the lines from the division points are drawn parallel to A–C. It is usually more convenient to draw the construction line perpendicular to the line to be divided when using drafting equipment. The perpendicular also provides favorable construction line intersections for maximum accuracy.

DUPLICATING, REVERSING, ETC. Trace and transfer methods are widely used by designers for duplicating a given drawing or a repeating motif and for the purpose of transferring a design from a rough study to final paper. The given drawing is traced onto the tracing paper and then may be handled in a number of different ways. Whatever the method used, it is almost always necessary to draw over the transferred drawing in pencil or ink in order to get a neat final drawing.

1. When the object is symmetrical the tracing can be made with a medium soft pencil, about H, F, or HB. The tracing is then turned over with pencil lines down, aligned on the final paper, and rubbed to transfer the pencil lines. The rubbing can be done with the thumb nail, a coin, or the edge of the bowl of a spoon. Care must be taken to see that the tracing does not move. Better results can be obtained by placing a piece of tracing cloth, with the slick side down, over the tracing paper and rubbing on the cloth. The cloth helps prevent movement and stretching of the paper drawing. When the transfer is made by rubbing, the texture of the final paper may be changed if very much pressure is used. Usually no serious damage is done.

2. When the drawing is unsymmetrical the tracing can be made in the usual way with a hard pencil. It is then turned over and traced on the back with a medium soft pencil, turned again to its original position, and rubbed to make the transfer identical with the original drawing.

3. A less tidy method is to blacken the back of the tracing with a soft pencil, then attach the paper to the final drawing surface and trace over all the lines with a hard pencil to transfer the design. Much neater results are obtained if the blackened surface is first cleaned of loose pencil dust by rubbing over it vigorously with a piece of cloth or soft paper. The transfer will then be clearer and neater and the final paper will not become dirty from the loose black particles of carbon.

Tick strips for transferring measurements can be made from narrow bands of plain paper. Trimmings from drawings are often used for the purpose. The edges of the strips should be straight and smooth. The tick strips are used in transferring measurements from one drawing to another, for marking sizes of repeating elements on the same or different drawings, and for duplicating a preliminary study on final paper. The measurements on the given drawing are marked on the edge of the tick strip and then transferred to the required location, Fig. 70 A. By changing ends of the tick strip the sequence of measurements will be reversed. This is done when transferring between side views, or from front to back, and in other situations. Fig. 70 C. The tick strip method is much simpler, easier, and less likely to permit errors than using a scale or dividers. It reduces the transfer of dimensions to a simple mechanical process. It is one of the important devices of the professional draftsman.

ARCS AND CIRCLES. An arc can be drawn through three given points, A, B, C, Fig. 71 I, by drawing the perpendicular bisectors of the two straight lines connecting point B with A and C. The intersection of the bisectors is the center of the required arc. The center of a given arc is located at the intersection of the perpendicular bisectors of any two chords of the arc.

A tangent to an arc at a given point *T* can be drawn as a perpendicular to the radius when the center of the arc is given, Fig. 71 II. When the center of the arc is not given, Fig. 71 III, use

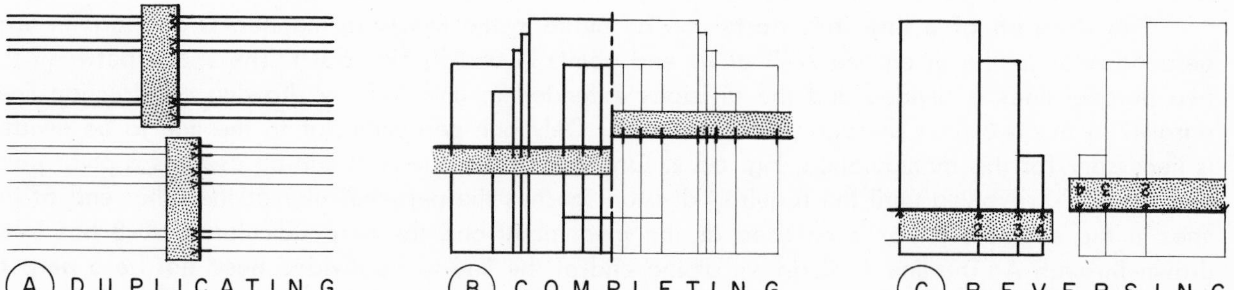

(A) DUPLICATING (B) COMPLETING (C) REVERSING

FIG. 70 TICK STRIP USED FOR TRANSFERRING SIZES

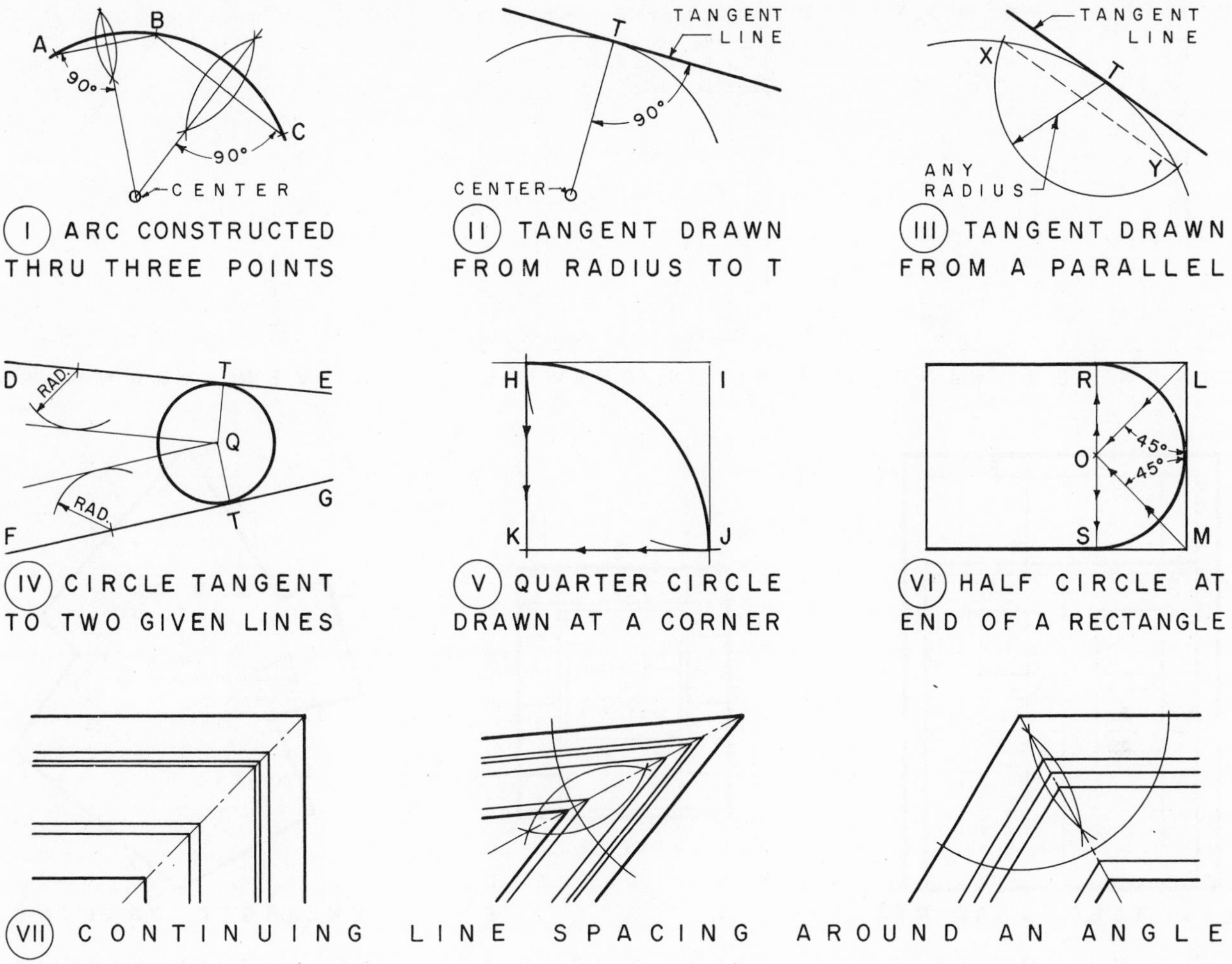

FIG. 71 DRAFTING PROBLEMS OF ARCS AND ANGLES

the point of tangency T as a center and lay off equal distances on each side of it with the compass to locate points X and Y. The required tangent will be parallel to the line X–Y.

A circle tangent to two given lines D–E and F–G, which are not perpendicular or parallel to each other, can be drawn in the following manner, Fig. 71 IV. With the radius of the required circle and a center on each of the given lines draw an arc on the side toward the other line. Draw tangents to these arcs parallel to the lines used as centers for the respective arcs. The parallels meet in point Q, which is the center of the required circle.

A quarter circle at a right angled corner requires for its construction the location of the two tangent points and the center, Fig. 71 V. With the required radius and the corner I as a center, draw arcs to intersect the two sides of the corner at H and J. Draw lines through H and J parallel to the sides of the corner to intersect in K, the required center. The quarter circle terminates at H and J the points of tangency of the arc and straight lines.

A semicircle at the end of a rectangle is constructed as follows, Fig. 71 VI. Draw the 45° bisectors of the corners L and M of the rectangle to locate the required center O. Through O draw the line R–S parallel to L–M to locate the ends of the required semicircle at R and S.

To continue a set of lines around any angle draw the bisector of the angle as shown in Fig. 71 VII, and change direction of the lines on the bisector. When the angle is 90°, the 45° triangle can be used to draw the bisector. The compass is used to locate bisectors of other angles, as shown in the last two examples of VII.

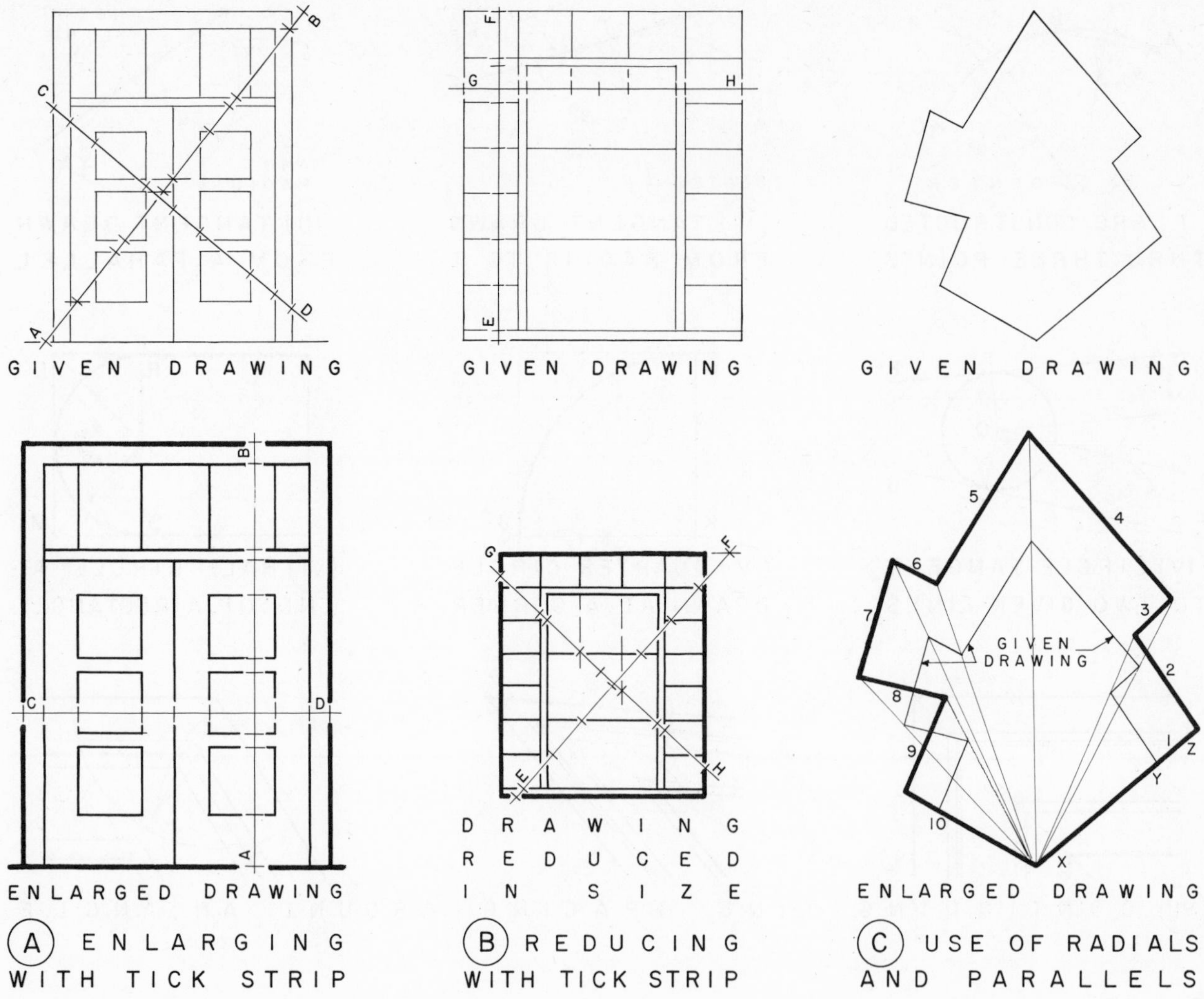

FIG. 72 ENLARGING AND REDUCING DRAWINGS

ENLARGING AND REDUCING THE SIZE OF A GIVEN DRAWING. This is a very common procedure for a draftsman. If the given multi-view or paraline drawing is made to scale, the popular method is to use the scale to measure from it and a larger or smaller scale to measure on the new drawing. This is a relatively simple procedure and easy to use. However it requires many measurements and gives many chances of error in reading, remembering, and transferring correctly. Furthermore the amount of change of size is limited by the available scales.

Simple numerical changes of size of a multi-view or paraline drawing can often be made speedily with the dividers. An enlargement to two times the scale of the given drawing can be made by setting the dividers to the given sizes and using the measurements two times on the enlarged drawing. When making a drawing one half the size of the original, the dividers should be adjusted to one half the given sizes to give correct measurements for the smaller drawing. Other simple relations of size can be handled in the same manner. When the scale relations become complex the amount of effort required is excessive. The dividers method is a more mechanical system than using the scale. It is less likely to cause error in measurements. Both methods require a great deal of detailed work and are limited to simple size relations. The proportional dividers is very convenient for changing the scale of a drawing. It can be adjusted for a wide range of sizes.

The tick strip method of enlarging and reducing multi-view drawings any amount desired is a very convenient device. With one dimension the height A–B of the enlarged drawing established and marked on the tick strip, the strip is slanted to fit these marks between the correct lines of the given drawing, Fig. 72 A. Each of the heights is marked on the edge of the tick strip where it crosses the lines. The tick strip is then used vertically to transfer the heights to the enlarged drawing. The widths should be marked on the second tick strip, which is placed at 90° to the position of the first tick strip on the given drawing. The widths C–D are then transferred to a horizontal line on the enlarged drawing.

When the size of the drawing is reduced, the tick strips E–F and G–H are used vertically and horizontally on the given drawing and slanted to give the sizes on the final drawing, Fig. 72 B.

In using this method the draftsman should be sure the main dimensions of the new drawing are correct. The remainder of the construction is a mechanical process that can be done speedily.

Radial and parallel lines can be used to enlarge or reduce the size of a given straight line drawing of any type as shown in Fig. 72 C. This method is particularly good for lines at odd angles. The change of size can be any desired amount.

Choose a corner X that will be common to both the given and the new drawing. All lines of the given drawing that radiate from X will coincide with the same lines of the new drawing as far as the lengths extend on both of the drawings. When the length of any one of these lines radiating from X is established for the new drawing all other lines are determined by drawing radiating and parallel lines. Radial construction lines from the common corner X through intersections of the given drawing pass through the same intersections on the new drawing. All of the lines of the new drawing are drawn parallel to those of the given drawing. In Fig. 72 C, X–Y is the line of the given drawing and X–Z is the length chosen for the new drawing. The relative lengths of X–Y and X–Z determine the relative sizes of the two drawings. In the example of Fig. 72 C, X–Z has been made $1\frac{1}{3}$ times the length of X–Y. The new drawing is therefore $1\frac{1}{3}$ times the size of the given drawing. The lines of the enlarged drawing have been numbered in the order in which they were drawn. The radiating lines have not been numbered. They were drawn as they were needed to determine ends of lines of the enlarged drawing.

These last two methods of using radials and parallels and of using tick strips to enlarge and reduce the sizes of drawings are devices that an expert draftsman would use automatically and accurately. Both methods have the advantage of allowing any size ratio between the drawings.

Irregular forms can usually be most efficiently reduced or enlarged in size by using two cross section grids. The grids must be made identical in pattern but varied in size to suit the two drawings. There are two methods of making the grids: (1) with uniform spacing, Fig. 73 I, and (2) with spacing varied to produce intersections at important points on the drawings, Fig. 73 II. The first method requires judgment in locating intersections of drawing and grid. It is often quite satisfactory. The second method locates points with greater accuracy, but requires more thought and effort.

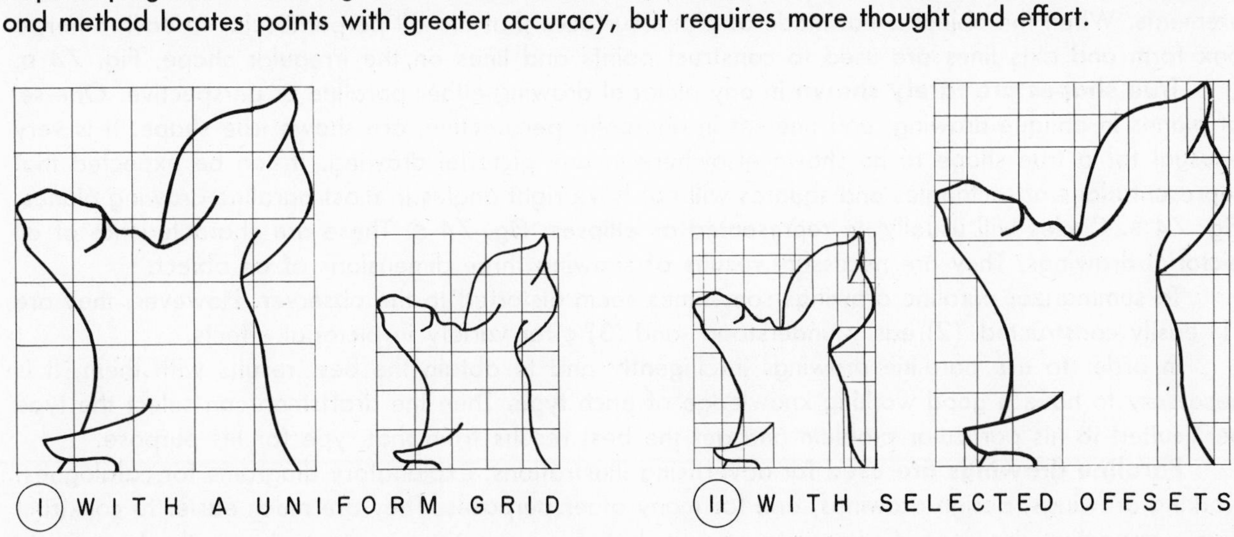

(I) WITH A UNIFORM GRID (II) WITH SELECTED OFFSETS

FIG. 73 ENLARGING AND REDUCING IRREGULAR SHAPES

PART THREE

Paraline Drawing

CHAPTER **13**

CHARACTERISTICS OF PARALINE DRAWINGS

A pictorial drawing gives a three-dimensional view of an object from which it is easy to visualize the forms represented. The term paraline drawing includes all the parallel line pictorial drawing types. As the name indicates, all divisions of this group use parallel lines in the drawings to represent the parallel lines of the objects.

There is an impression of distortion in any paraline drawing because the more distant parts of the object are drawn the same size as the nearer parts, Fig. 74 A. The eye expects more distant parts to appear smaller as they do in an actual object, a perspective drawing, or a photograph. The amount of distortion varies with the shape of the object and the specific arrangement of drawing used. It does not prevent these drawings from being easily understood. It merely makes them seem more or less warped or out of proportion.

Axis lines are used for scale measurements in all paraline drawings. Three adjacent planes, which are perpendicular to each other, meet in a corner of an object and are visible in all types of paraline drawings. The three edges formed by the intersections of the planes of the object that meet at a corner are called axis lines, Fig. 74 B. These planes and edges are those of a box.

Paraline drawings are easy to construct because measurements are laid out to scale on the axis lines and all lines parallel to them. Lines in other directions can seldom be used for scale measurements. When the object is not made of plane surfaces that are all perpendicular to each other, a box form and axis lines are used to construct points and lines on the irregular shape, Fig. 74 D.

True shapes are rarely shown in any pictorial drawing either paraline or perspective. One set of planes in oblique drawing, and one set in one-point perspective, are shown true shape. It is very unusual for a true shape to be shown elsewhere in any pictorial drawing. It can be expected that representations of rectangles and squares will not have right angles in most paraline drawing planes, Fig. 74 B. Circles will usually be represented as ellipses, Fig. 74 C. These are characteristics of all pictorial drawings. They are necessary results of showing three dimensions of an object.

To summarize: paraline drawings sometimes seem distorted to the observer. However, they are (1) easily constructed, (2) easily understood, and (3) offer variety in pictorial effects.

In order to use paraline drawings intelligently and to obtain the best results with them, it is necessary to have a good working knowledge of each type. Then the draftsman can select the type best suited to his particular problem and get the best results from that type for his purpose.

Paraline drawings are used for advertising illustrations, explanatory diagrams for catalogues, working drawings, design drawings, and for many other purposes. They are much easier to construct than perspective drawings. Contrary to popular belief, perspectives are not always the best drawings for representing the shapes of an object. Some irregular objects are not explained as clearly in perspective as in the most suitable type of paraline drawing.

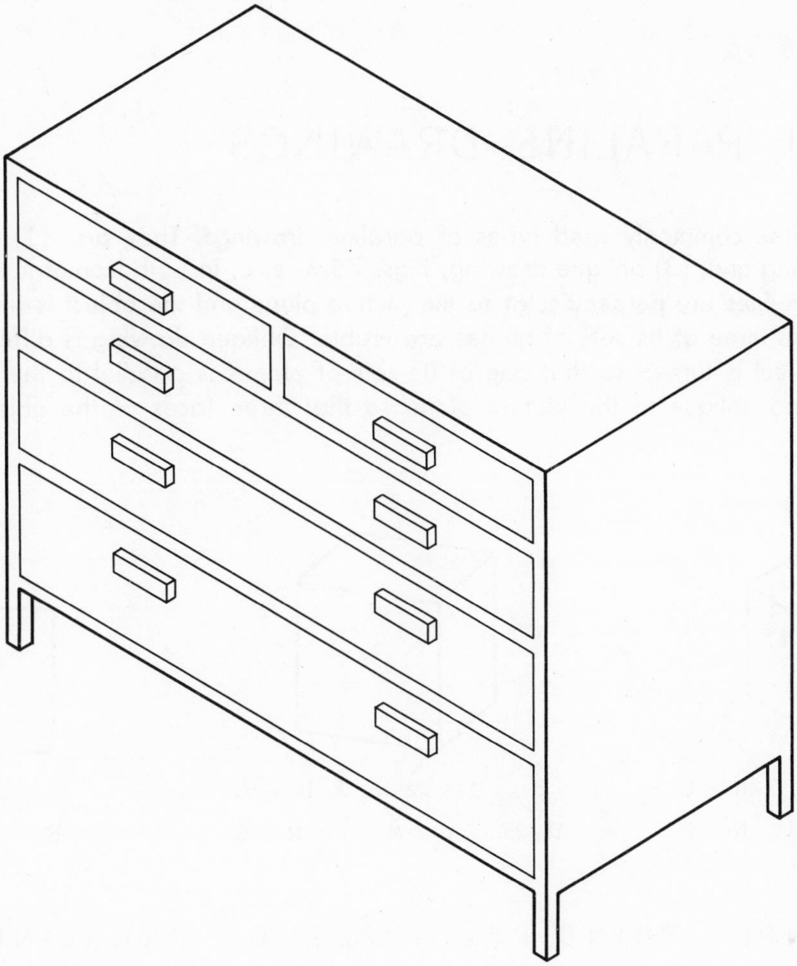

(A) TYPICAL PARALINE DRAWING

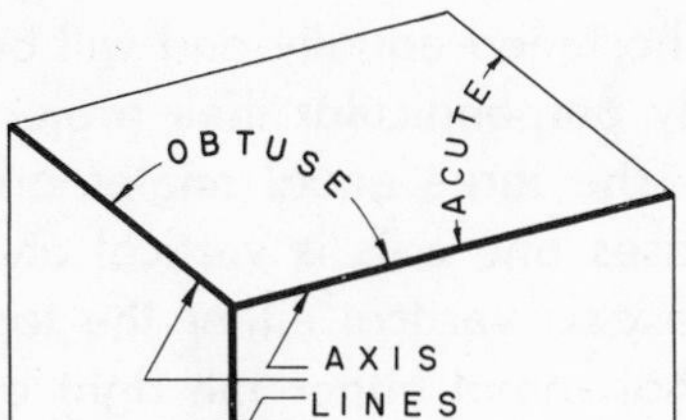

(B) 90° ANGLES APPEAR ACUTE OR OBTUSE

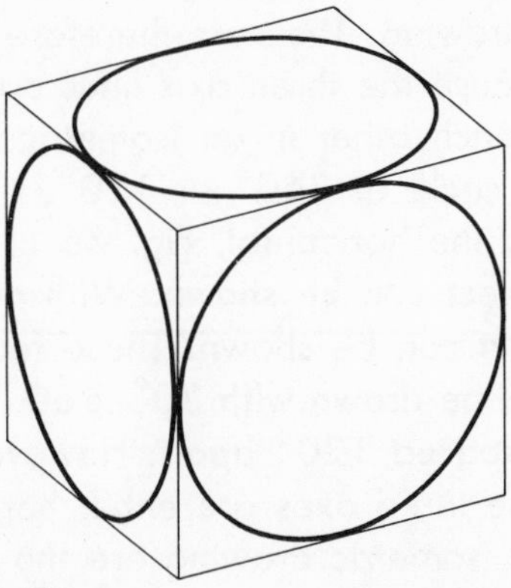

(C) CIRCLES USUALLY APPEAR ELLIPTICAL

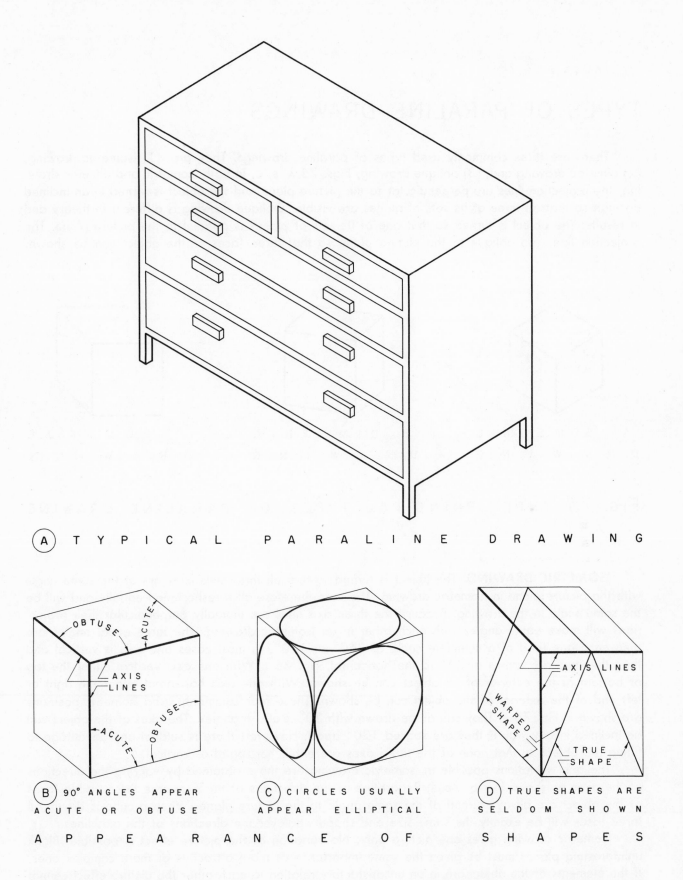

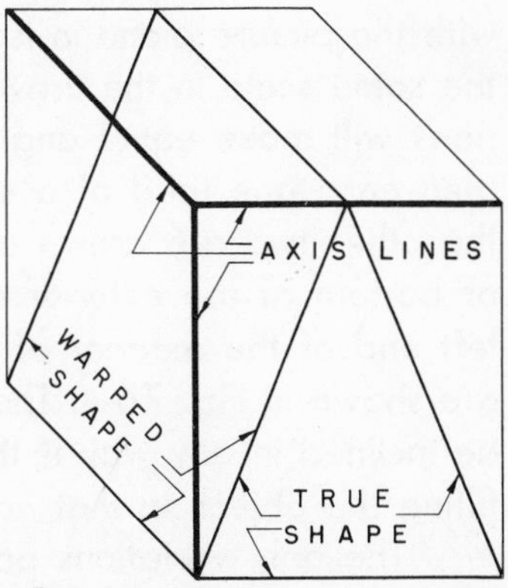

(D) TRUE SHAPES ARE SELDOM SHOWN

APPEARANCE OF SHAPES

FIG. 74 CHARACTERISTICS OF PARALINE DRAWINGS

CHAPTER 14

TYPES OF PARALINE DRAWINGS

There are three commonly used types of paraline drawings. They are: (1) isometric drawing, (2) dimetric drawing and, (3) oblique drawing, Figs. 75 A, B, C. In both isometric and dimetric drawing, the projection lines are perpendicular to the picture plane and the object is turned in an inclined position so that all three of its sets of planes are visible. Oblique drawing is different in theory and in results. The object is turned so that one of its sets of planes is parallel to the picture plane. The projection lines are oblique to the picture plane so that three faces of the object can be shown.

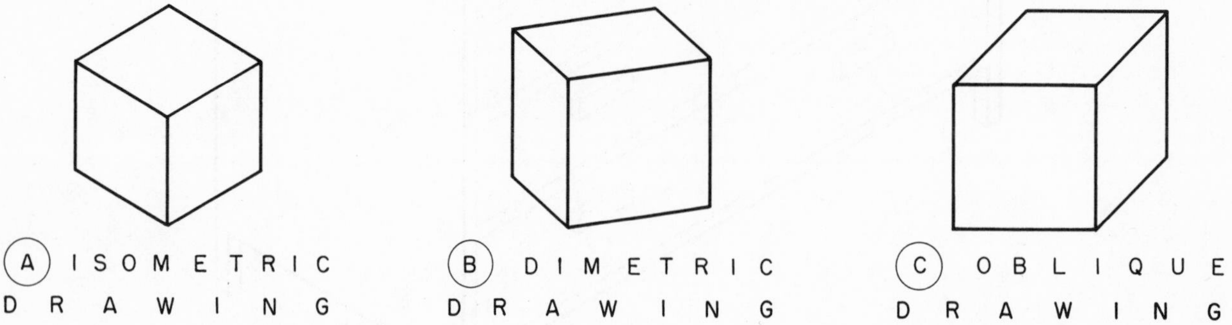

FIG. 75 THREE PRINCIPAL TYPES OF PARALINE DRAWING

ISOMETRIC DRAWING. The object is turned so that all three axis lines are at the same angle with the picture plane in isometric drawing. They are therefore all foreshortened equally and will be the same scale in the drawing. Because the three axis lines are mutually perpendicular their projections will make equal angles with each other in an isometric drawing. The three equal angles are then each one third of a complete circle of 360° or 120°. In most cases one axis is vertical and the other two are drawn at 30° to the horizontal, Fig. 76 I. With one axis vertical either the top or bottom of the exterior of an object can be shown. With one axis horizontal either the right or left end of the exterior of the object can be shown. These four commonly used isometric positions are shown in Fig. 76 II. They can all be drawn with 30° x 60° triangles. The axes of the object can be inclined in any way if they are spaced 120° apart. However, there is seldom any advantage to tilting the object so that none of the three axes are either horizontal or vertical.

The only variations possible in isometric drawing are those obtained by varying the directions of the axes as shown in Fig. 76 II. Regardless of the directions of the axes, the three visible faces of the object are always turned at the same angle to the picture plane. When a cube is drawn all three faces will be exactly the same size and shape whatever the directions of the axis lines.

Isometric drawing gives one picture only. No variation of the picture effect is possible. Blank uninteresting planes must be given the same importance as more attractive or more complex ones. If the elements of the object are in an unsatisfactory relation to each other the picture effect cannot be improved in an isometric drawing. Another paraline type can be used to avoid the difficulty.

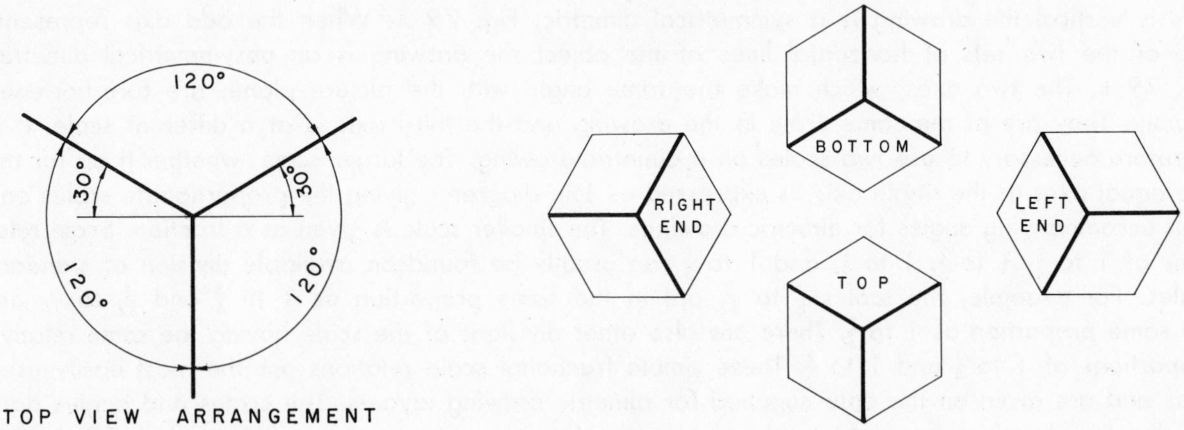

(I) SPACING OF AXES (II) POSITIONS WITH 30° × 60° TRIANGLE

FIG. 76 COMMON POSITIONS OF THE AXES IN ISOMETRIC

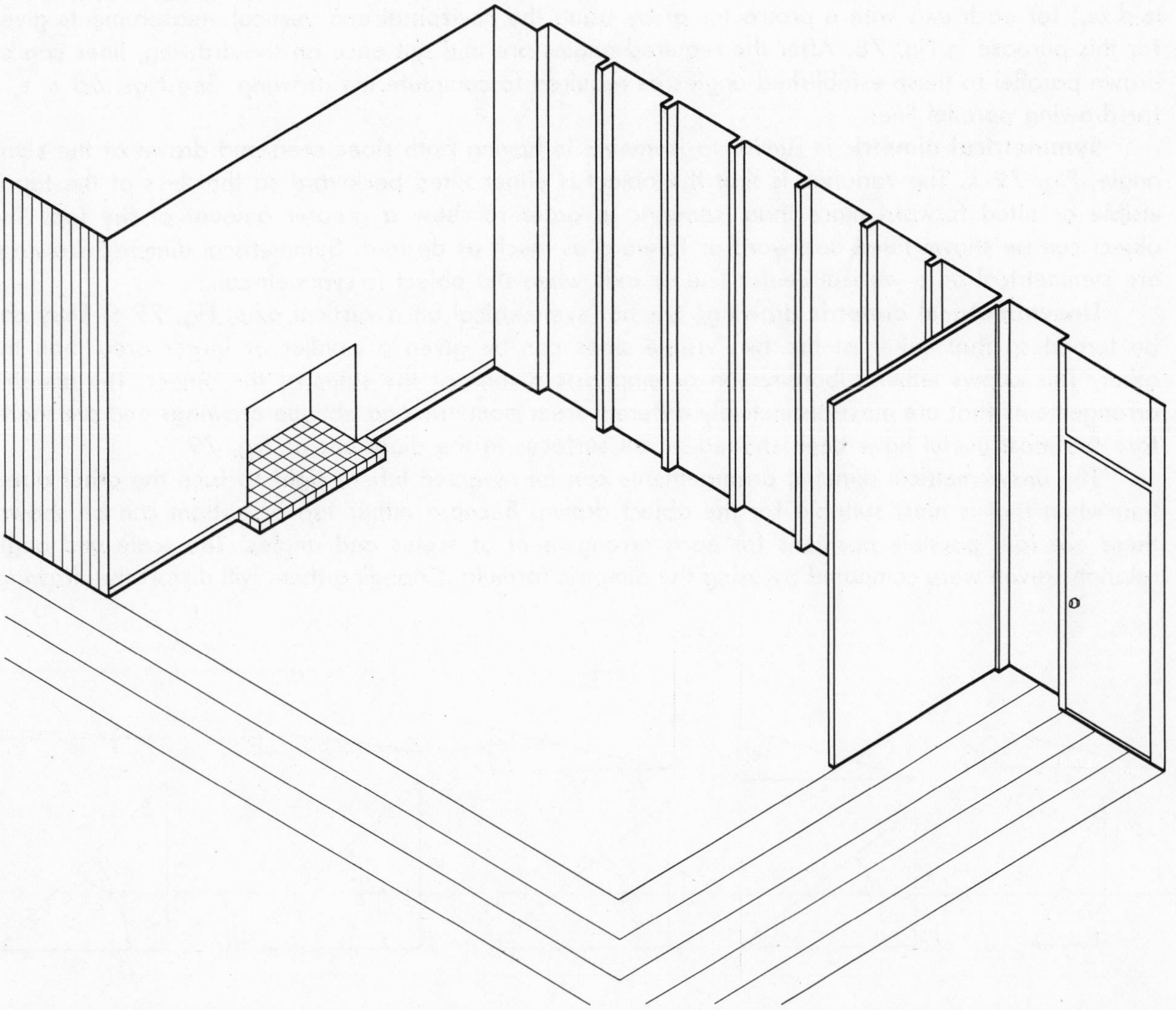

FIG. 77 ISOMETRIC DRAWING OF A ROOM

DIMETRIC DRAWING. The object is turned so that two of its axes make the same angle and the third axis makes a different angle with the picture plane in dimetric drawing. When the odd axis is vertical the drawing is a symmetrical dimetric, Fig. 79 A. When the odd axis represents one of the two sets of horizontal lines of the object the drawing is an unsymmetrical dimetric, Fig. 79 B. The two axes, which make the same angle with the picture plane, are foreshortened equally. They are at the same scale in the drawing and the third axis is at a different scale. It is therefore necessary to use two scales on a dimetric drawing. The larger scale, whether it be for the two equal axes or the single axis, is expressed as 1 in diagrams giving the proportionate scales and their accompanying angles for dimetric drawings. The smaller scale is given as a fraction. Scale relations of 1 to $\frac{3}{4}$, 1 to $\frac{2}{3}$, 1 to $\frac{1}{2}$, and 1 to $\frac{1}{3}$ can usually be found on available division of standard scales. For example, the scales $\frac{1}{8}$ to $\frac{3}{32}$ are in the same proportion as 1 to $\frac{3}{4}$ and $\frac{3}{32}$ to $\frac{1}{16}$ are the same proportion as 1 to $\frac{2}{3}$. There are also other divisions of the scale having the same relative proportions of 1 to $\frac{3}{4}$ and 1 to $\frac{2}{3}$. These simple fractional scale relations are the most easily used ones and are given on the data supplied for dimetric drawing layouts. The scales and angles data for dimetric drawings were obtained by using the formula $\cos a = (-\sqrt{2H^2 - V^2})/2H$. In this formula a = one of the two equal angles between projections of the axes, H = one of two equal scales, V = third scale. The angle A made by each of the two equal axes with a horizontal line in a symmetrical dimetric is a − 90°. One of the axes with the horizontal in unsymmetrical dimetric is also a − 90° and the other is 90° − 2A.

When an adjustable triangle is not available for use, the angles for dimetric drawings can be laid out for each axis with a protractor or by using the horizontal and vertical measurements given for this purpose in Fig. 78. After the required angles are laid out once on the drawing, lines can be drawn parallel to these established angles as required to complete the drawing. See Figs. 66 A, B, C for drawing parallel lines.

Symmetrical dimetric is similar to isometric in having both sides seen and drawn at the same angle, Fig. 79 A. The variation is that the object is either tilted backward so that less of the top is visible or tilted forward more than isometric in order to show a greater amount of the top. The object can be shown tilted backward or forward as much as desired. Symmetrical dimetric drawings are symmetrical on a vertical center line or axis when the object is symmetrical.

Unsymmetrical dimetric drawings are not symmetrical on a vertical axis, Fig. 79 B. They can be turned so that either of the two visible sides can be given a smaller or larger area than the other. This allows either subordination or emphasis of one of the sides of the object. The dimetric arrangements that are most distinctively different from isometric and oblique drawings and are therefore the most useful have been shaded on all surfaces in the diagrams of Fig. 79.

The unsymmetrical dimetric arrangements can be reversed left to right to face the other direction when that is most suitable for the object drawn. Because either top or bottom can be shown, there are four possible positions for each arrangement of scales and angles. The scale and angle relations given were computed by using the dimetric formula. Changing them will distort the drawing.

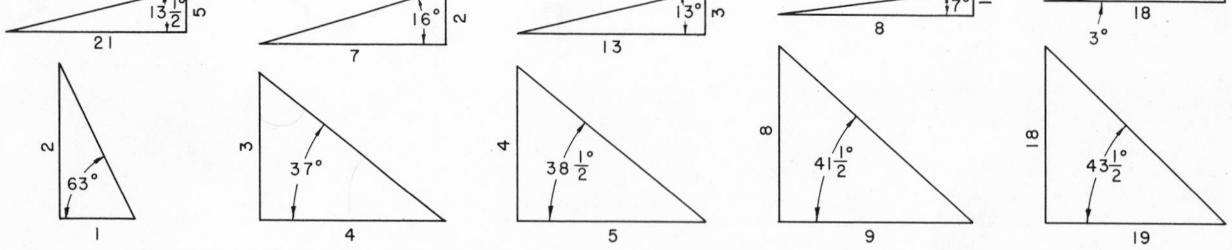

FIG. 78 MEASUREMENTS FOR SOME DIMETRIC ANGLES

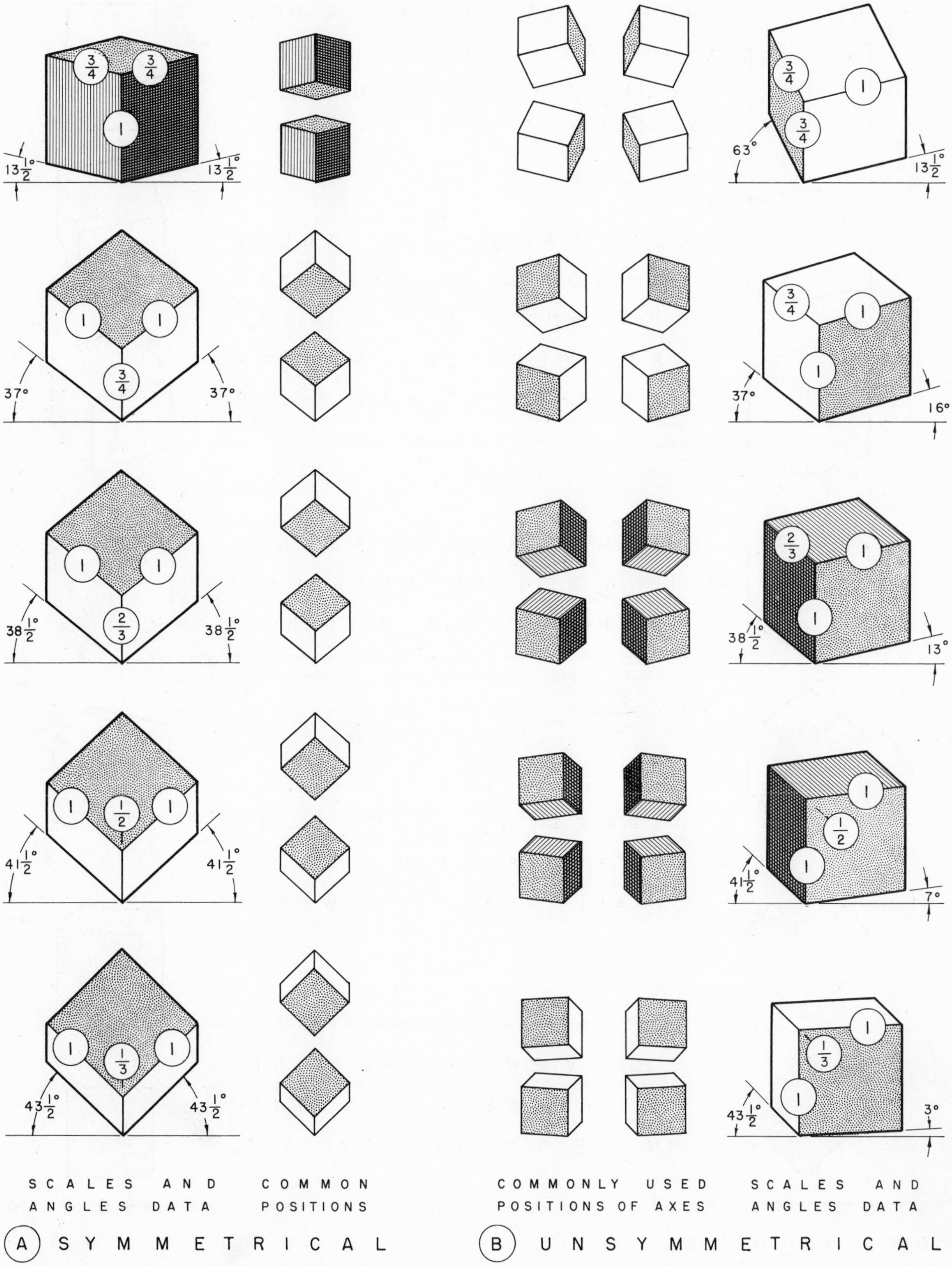

FIG. 79 DIMETRIC SCALES - ANGLES - AXIS POSITIONS

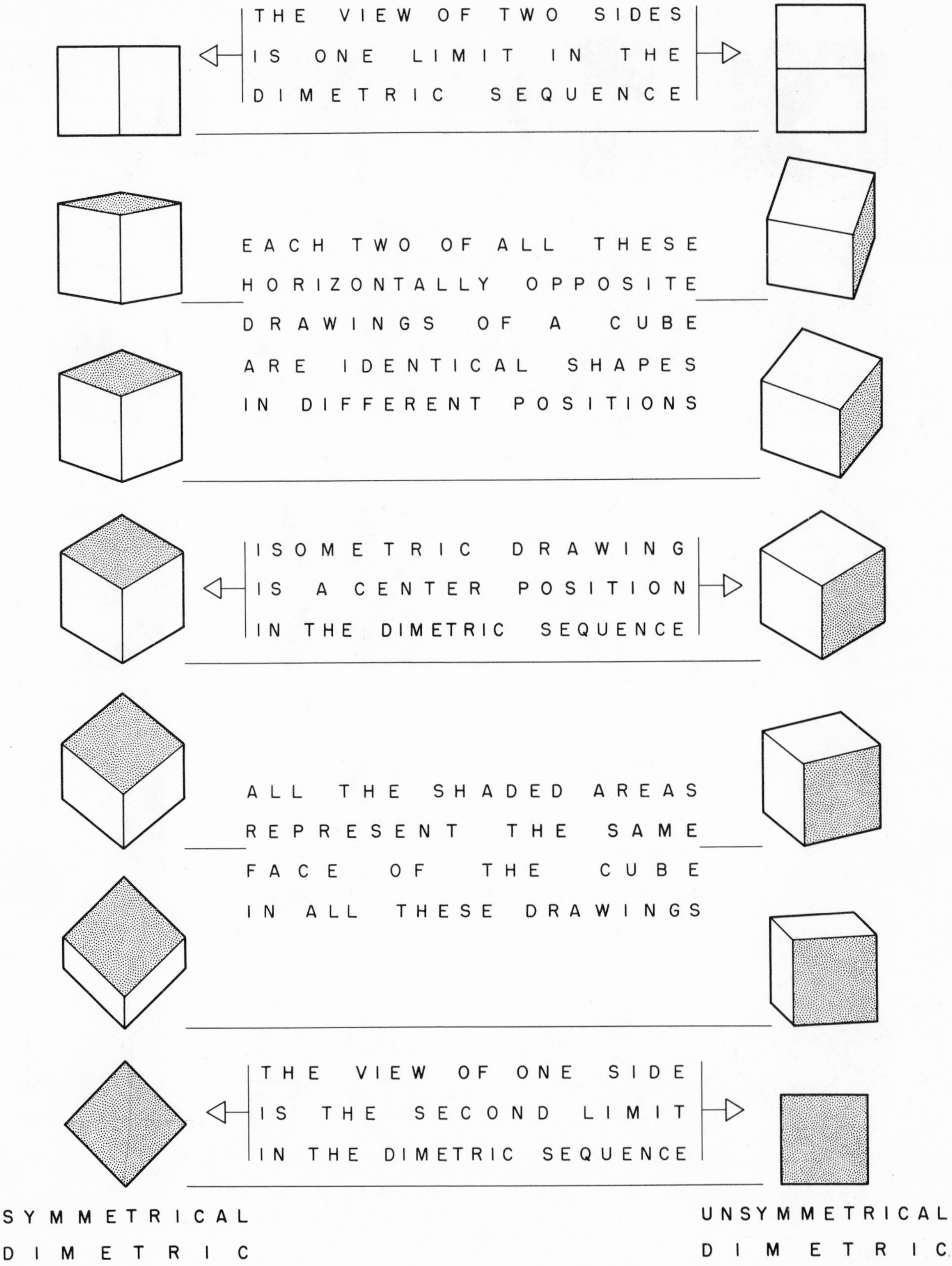

THE VIEW OF TWO SIDES IS ONE LIMIT IN THE DIMETRIC SEQUENCE
EACH TWO OF ALL THESE HORIZONTALLY OPPOSITE DRAWINGS OF A CUBE ARE IDENTICAL SHAPES IN DIFFERENT POSITIONS
ISOMETRIC DRAWING IS A CENTER POSITION IN THE DIMETRIC SEQUENCE
ALL THE SHADED AREAS REPRESENT THE SAME FACE OF THE CUBE IN ALL THESE DRAWINGS
THE VIEW OF ONE SIDE IS THE SECOND LIMIT IN THE DIMETRIC SEQUENCE
SYMMETRICAL DIMETRIC
UNSYMMETRICAL DIMETRIC

FIG. 80 THE SEQUENCE OF DIMETRIC POSITIONS

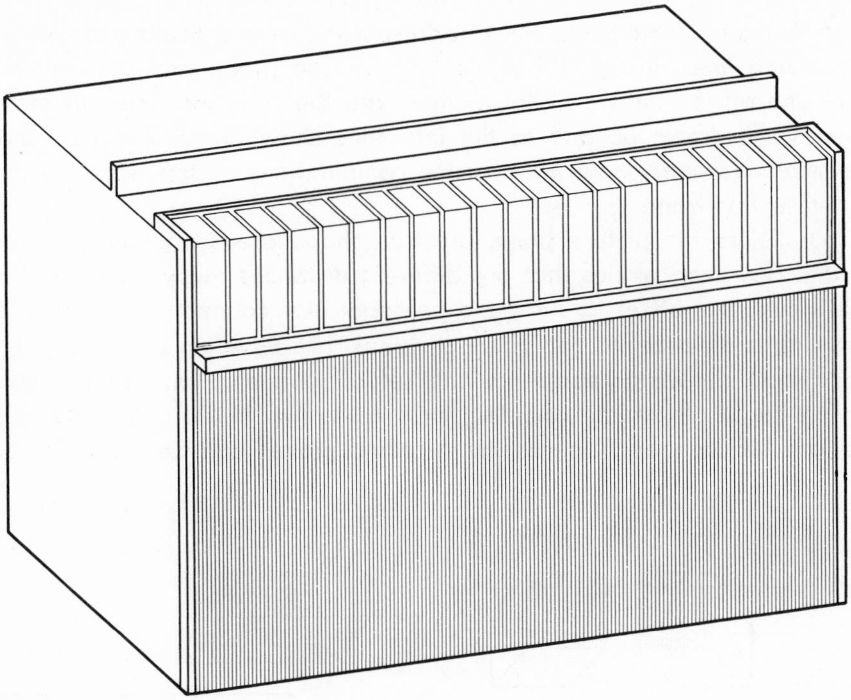

(A) ONE SET OF VERTICAL PLANES EMPHASIZED

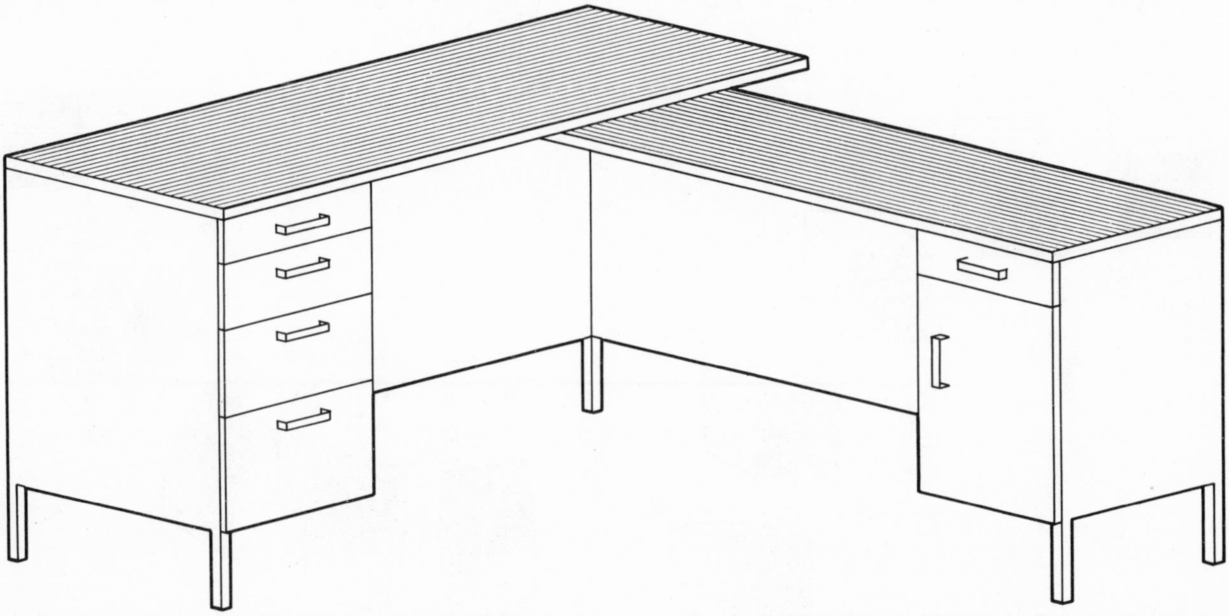

(B) HORIZONTAL AREA SUBORDINATED

FIG. 81 EXAMPLES OF DIMETRIC DRAWING

OBLIQUE DRAWING. One set of planes of the object is always presented in its true shapes in oblique drawing. From these true shape areas parallel lines can be drawn at any angle to represent the perpendiculars to them. These lines, which represent the perpendiculars to the true shape planes, are called the *receding lines.* In Fig. 82 A the front is true shape and the lines where sides, top, and bottom meet and all the lines parallel to them are the receding lines. In the large illustration these receding lines are drawn up and to the left, thus showing the left side and the top of the object. The four small drawings show the possible combinations of top, sides, and bottom that can be shown attached to this front.

All planes parallel to the picture plane are true shape areas and all are drawn at the same scale on a drawing. However, planes that are different distances away, although connected directly in front and side views, are offset to show the perpendicular connecting surfaces, Fig. 82 B.

Oblique drawing is divided into two major divisions: (1) elevation oblique, and (2) plan oblique.

Elevation oblique drawing represents one set of vertical planes of the object in their true shapes. By varying the angle of the receding lines as shown in Fig. 82 C the proportions of the oblique drawing can be changed. One of the receding planes can be subordinated and the other

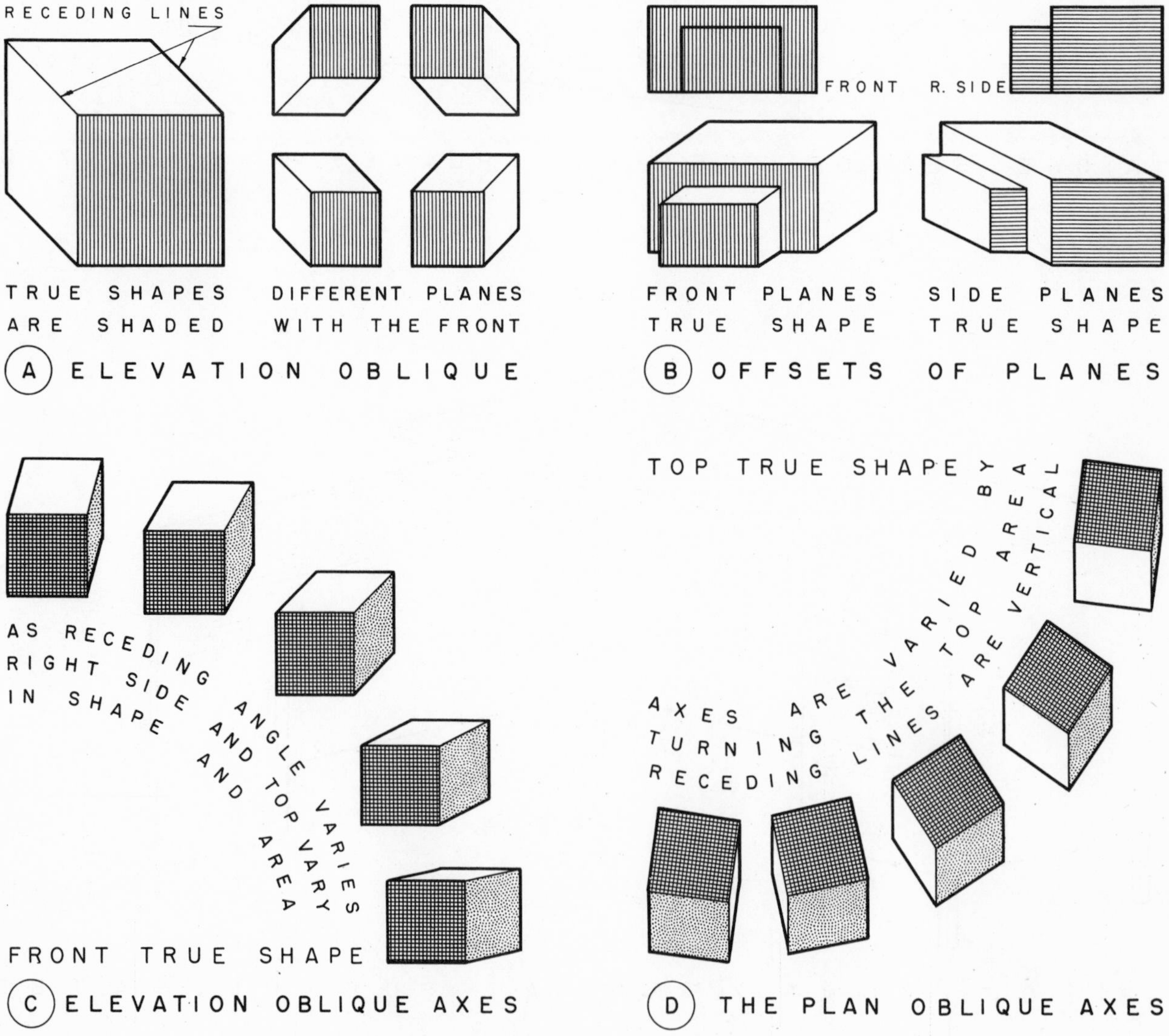

FIG. 82 PICTORIAL VARIETY IN OBLIQUE DRAWINGS

emphasized. Both can be made of equal importance by using a 45° angle for the receding lines.

Plan oblique drawing represents the horizontal planes of the object in their true shapes. In making a plan oblique drawing the vertical lines of the object are the receding lines of the drawing. The receding lines are kept vertical and the plan areas turned to various angles to change the pictorial effect as shown in Fig. 82 D.

The scale of the receding lines can be made the same as that of the two axis lines of the true shape areas. This simplifies the construction of the drawing by using one scale for all three axes and is called *cavalier oblique*. However, the proportions do not seem correct. The object seems to be too long in the direction away from the observer, Fig. 83 I. When appearance is important, better proportions are obtained by using $\frac{3}{4}$ or $\frac{2}{3}$ scale on the receding lines, Fig. 83 II. These two scale ratios are equally good. Use the one that can be found at correct size on the drafting scale for the drawing to be made. Because there are several scale ratios giving proportions of 1 to $\frac{3}{4}$ and 1 to $\frac{2}{3}$, these scale relations can be easily found and used. *Cabinet oblique* drawings are made with the receding lines at $\frac{1}{2}$ the scale of the other two axes, Fig. 83 III. Their proportions seem too thin for most purposes.

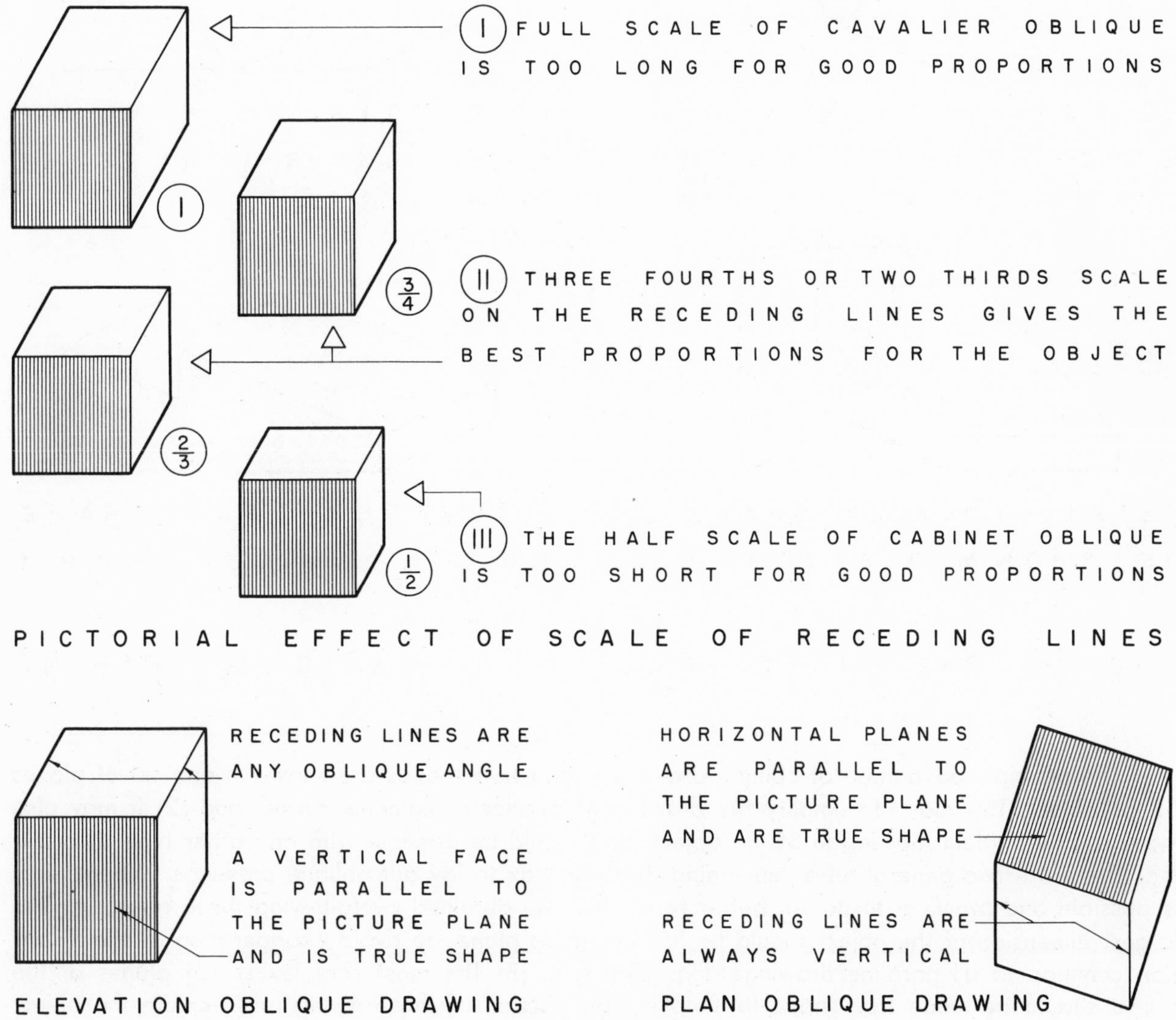
I FULL SCALE OF CAVALIER OBLIQUE IS TOO LONG FOR GOOD PROPORTIONS
I
3/4
II THREE FOURTHS OR TWO THIRDS SCALE ON THE RECEDING LINES GIVES THE BEST PROPORTIONS FOR THE OBJECT
2/3
III THE HALF SCALE OF CABINET OBLIQUE IS TOO SHORT FOR GOOD PROPORTIONS
1/2
PICTORIAL EFFECT OF SCALE OF RECEDING LINES
RECEDING LINES ARE ANY OBLIQUE ANGLE
A VERTICAL FACE IS PARALLEL TO THE PICTURE PLANE AND IS TRUE SHAPE
ELEVATION OBLIQUE DRAWING
HORIZONTAL PLANES ARE PARALLEL TO THE PICTURE PLANE AND ARE TRUE SHAPE
RECEDING LINES ARE ALWAYS VERTICAL
PLAN OBLIQUE DRAWING

FIG. 83 DIRECTION AND SCALE OF RECEDING LINES

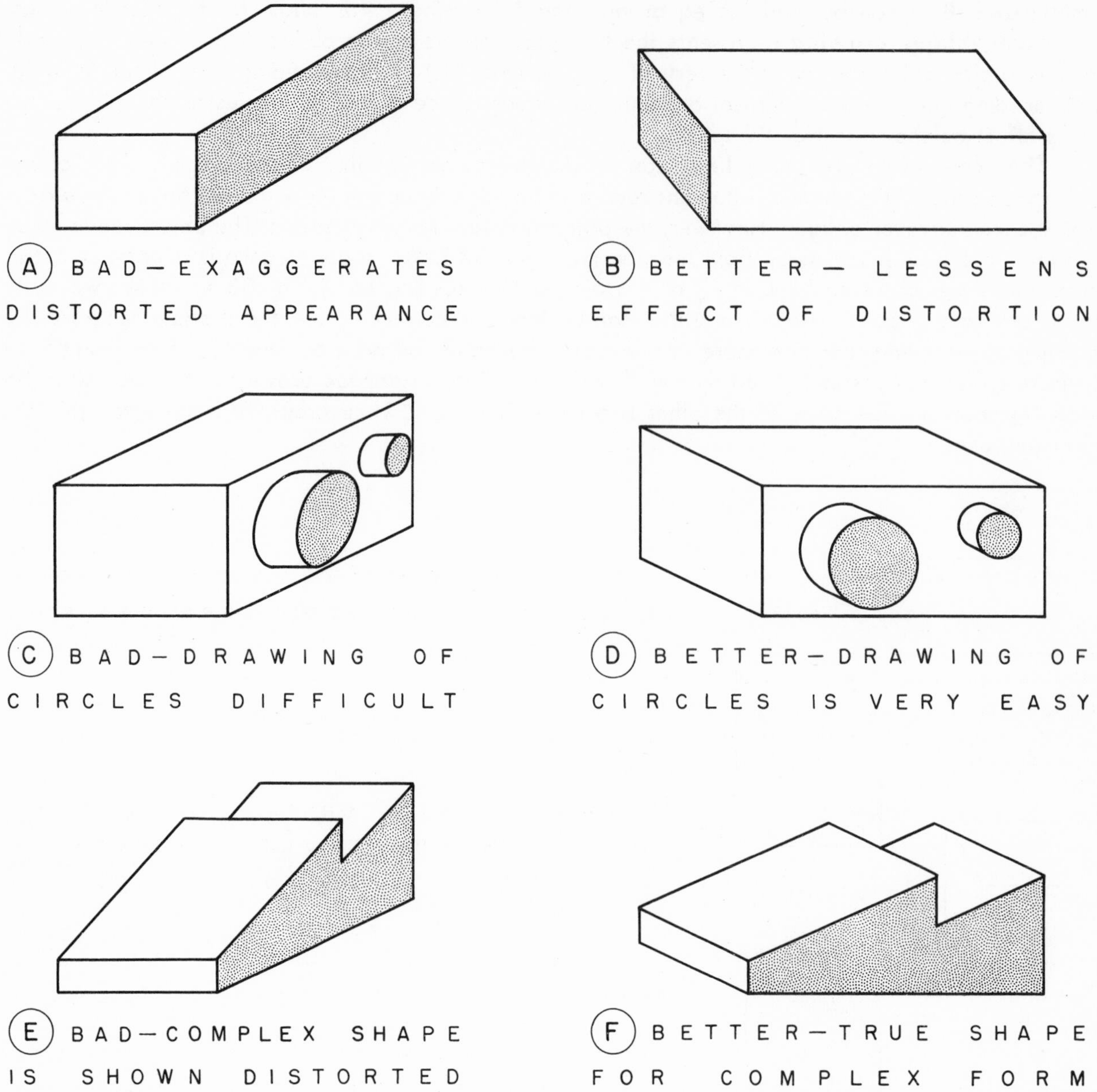
(A) BAD—EXAGGERATES DISTORTED APPEARANCE
(B) BETTER — LESSENS EFFECT OF DISTORTION
(C) BAD—DRAWING OF CIRCLES DIFFICULT
(D) BETTER—DRAWING OF CIRCLES IS VERY EASY
(E) BAD—COMPLEX SHAPE IS SHOWN DISTORTED
(F) BETTER—TRUE SHAPE FOR COMPLEX FORM

FIG. 84 PREFERRED PRACTICE IN OBLIQUE DRAWING

The principal advantage of oblique drawing is that true shapes are shown in one set of planes of the object. This may (1) simplify the drawing of circular or complex forms, and (2) it may also more clearly explain the design of the object than would be possible with any other type of drawing. There are two general rules concerning the best way to lay out oblique drawings. Whenever it is possible and practical to do so, better results will be obtained by following these rules. (A) The largest dimension of the object should be in true shape planes to avoid exaggeration of the distortion common to all paraline drawings, Figs. 84 A, B. (B) The most complex set of planes of the object should be made true shape to simplify construction of the drawing and explain the object clearly, Figs. 84 C, D, E, F. When used correctly for shapes for which it is adapted, oblique drawing is a very valuable member of the paraline drawing group.

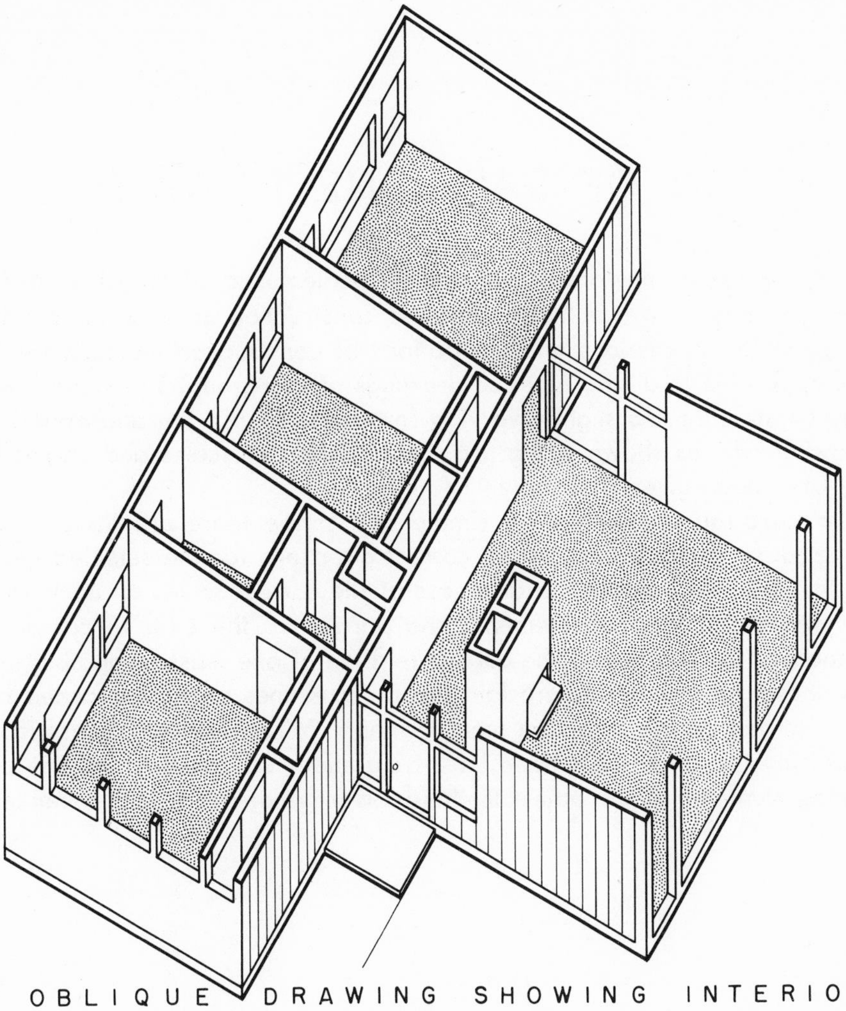

(I) PLAN OBLIQUE DRAWING SHOWING INTERIOR SPACE

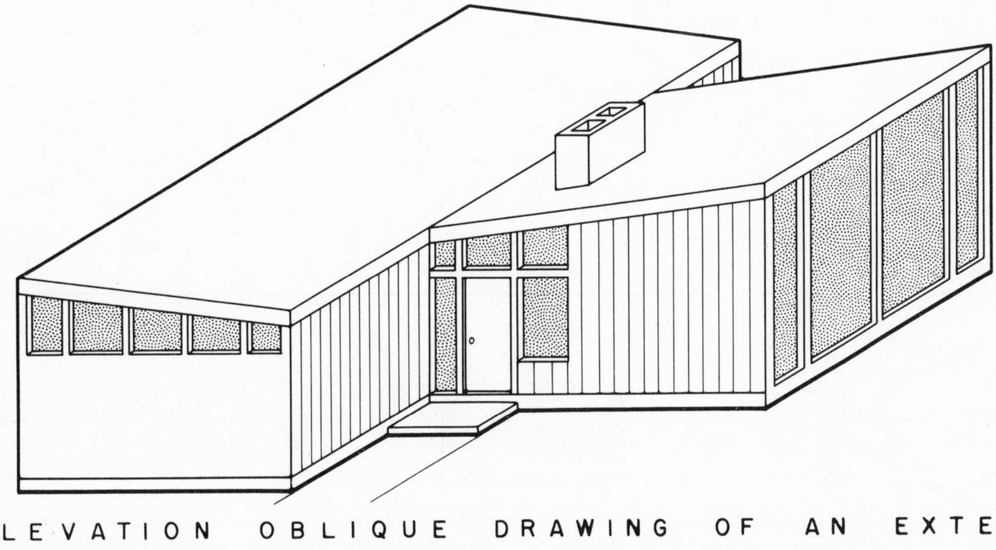

(II) ELEVATION OBLIQUE DRAWING OF AN EXTERIOR

FIG. 85 EXAMPLES OF OBLIQUE DRAWING

CHAPTER 15

CONSTRUCTION OF PARALINE DRAWINGS

The angles at which axis lines are drawn and the scales used on the axes vary in the different types of paraline drawings. However the methods of construction of drawings are the same for all three types. The following discussions and illustrations of construction methods for details of paraline drawings are applicable to all the types of drawings of this group. The student will find it necessary to adapt the constructions to slightly varying forms and to use the appropriate scales on each axis for each drawing type as shown in Fig. 86. Explanations of scales and angles for oblique and dimetric drawing have been given in Chapter 14.

In making a paraline drawing of a simple box shape there are three steps as shown in Fig. 86. Step One, draw the axis lines in the correct directions for the selected type, making them of indefinite length; step Two, lay out the distances at the correct scales on each of the three axes; step Three, draw lines from the measurements and parallel to the axes to complete the drawing.

The offset method is used to find the correct relation of one mass to another in paraline drawing. Figure 87 A shows how distances are laid out on axis lines and then carried by lines parallel to the axes to the correct positions for the measurements. When part of a mass is concealed as in Fig. 87 B it is advisable to draw the hidden lines as a check on construction. The offset method is a process of adding elements of the object in their correct relation to each other until the drawing is completed.

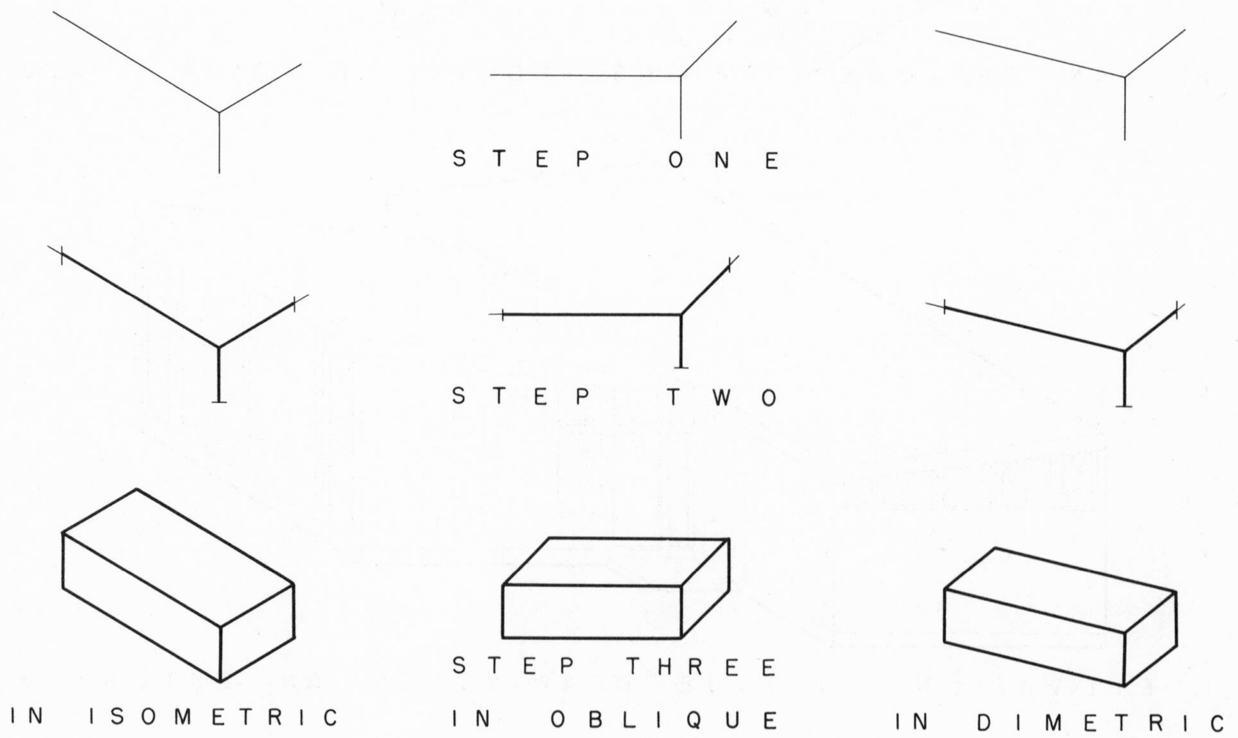

FIG. 86 CONSTRUCTING A PARALINE DRAWING

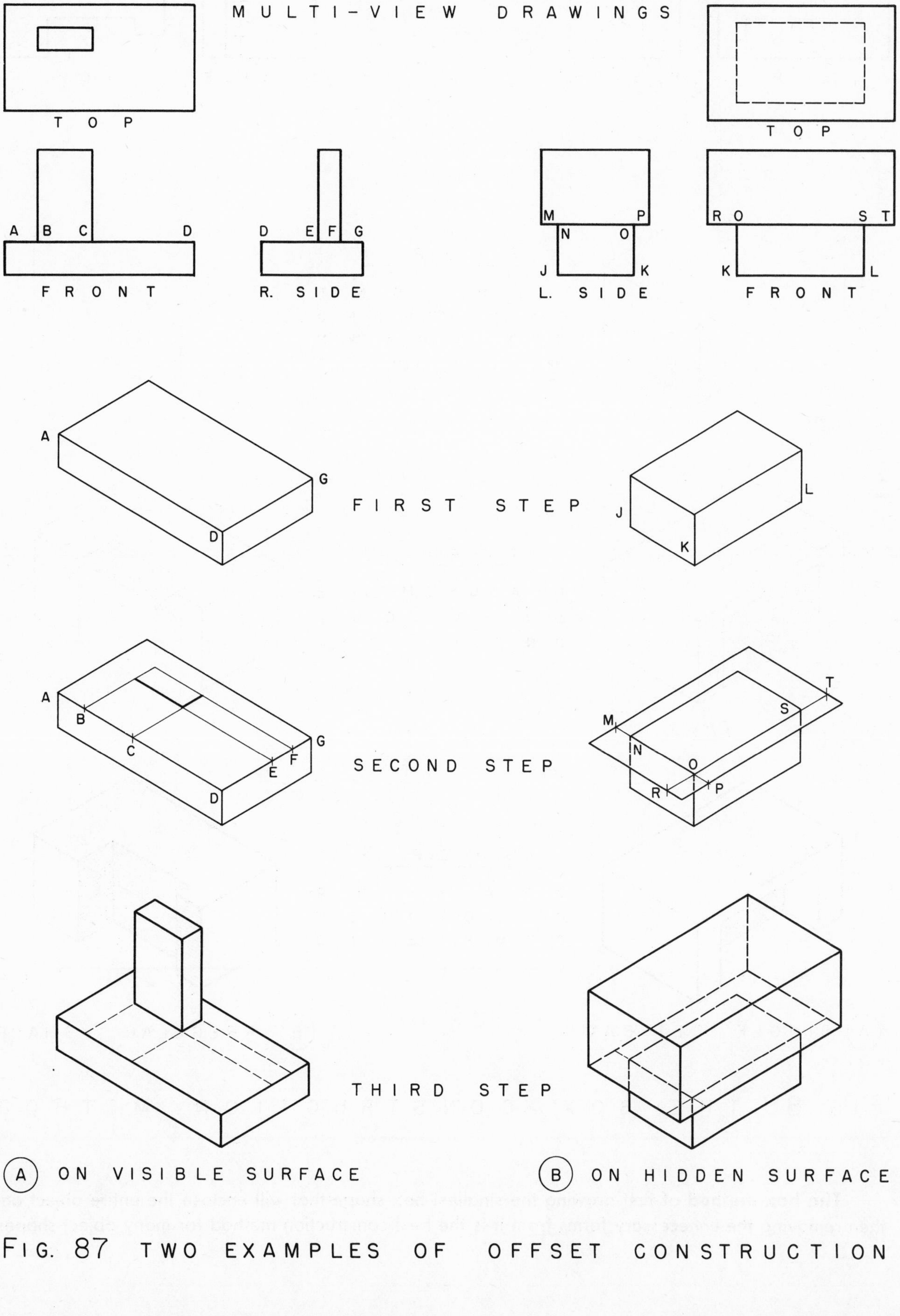

FIG. 87 TWO EXAMPLES OF OFFSET CONSTRUCTION

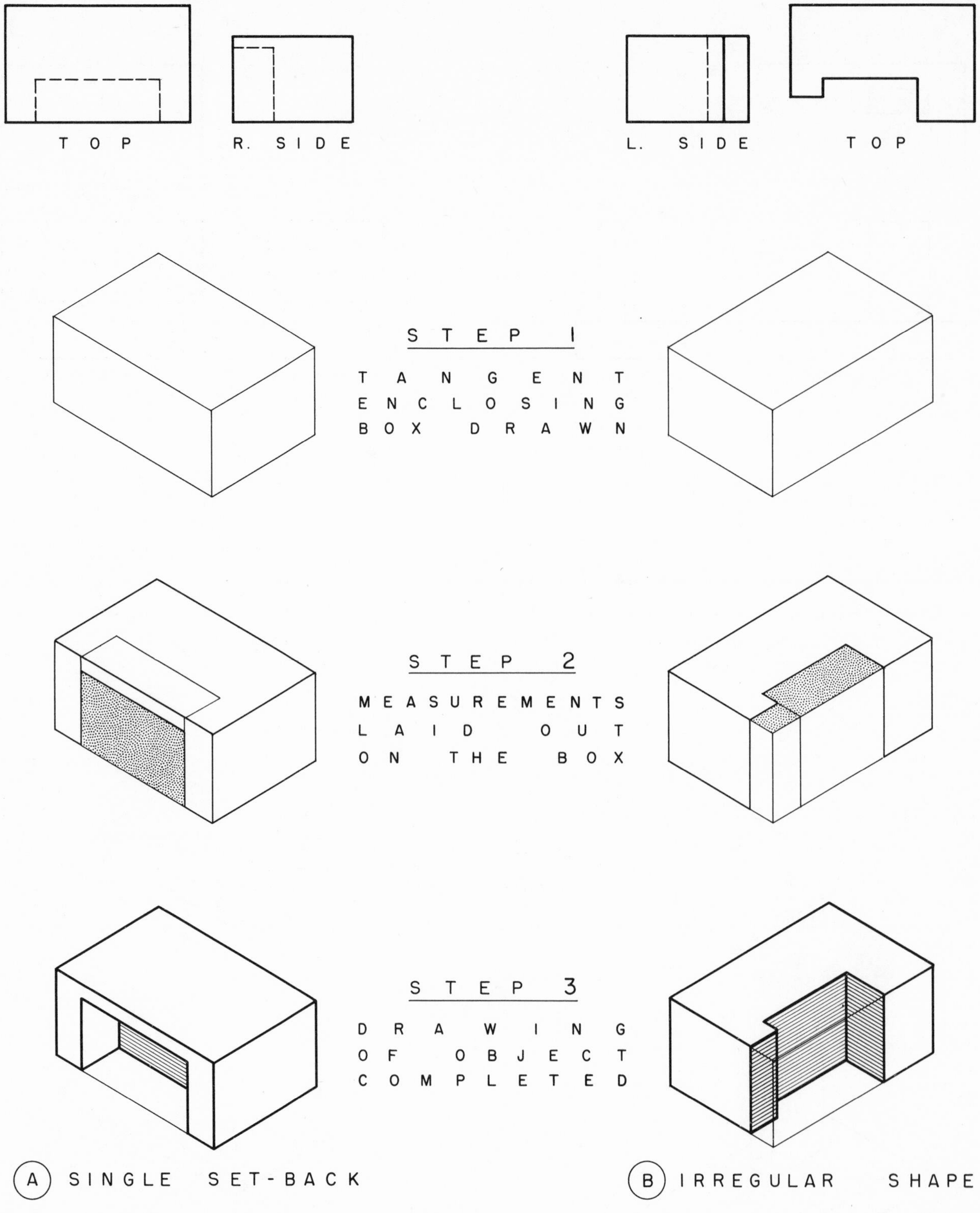

FIG. 88 THE BOX CONSTRUCTION METHOD

The box method of first drawing the smallest box shape that will enclose the entire object and then removing the unnecessary forms from it is the best construction method for many object shapes.

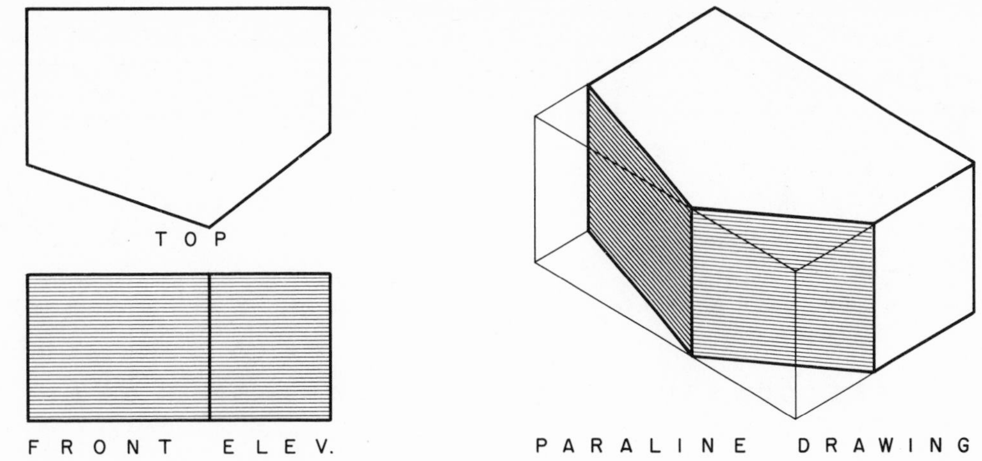

C) OBLIQUE WALL PLANES ON AN OBJECT

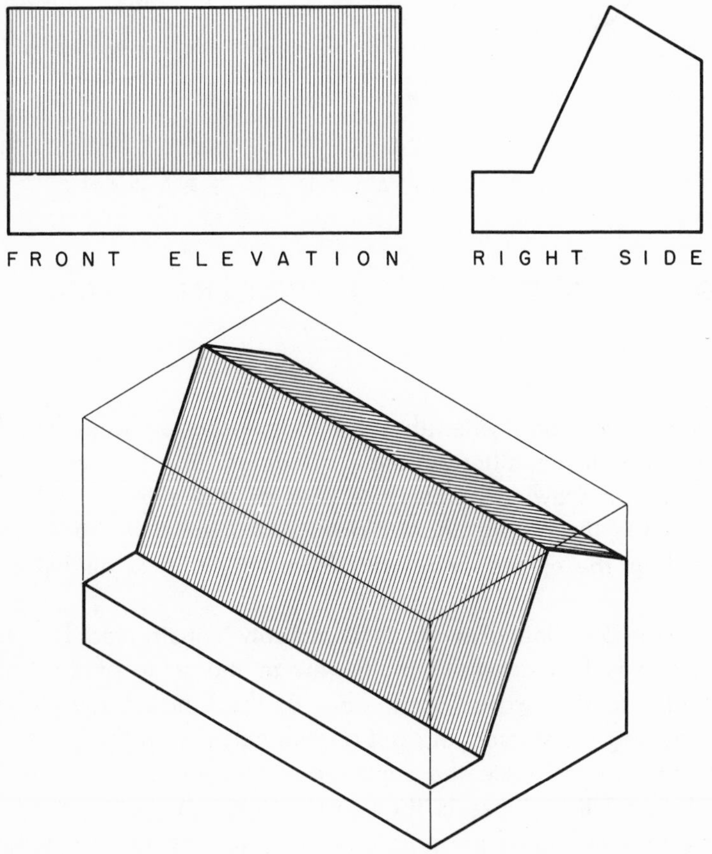

D) INCLINED PLANE SURFACES

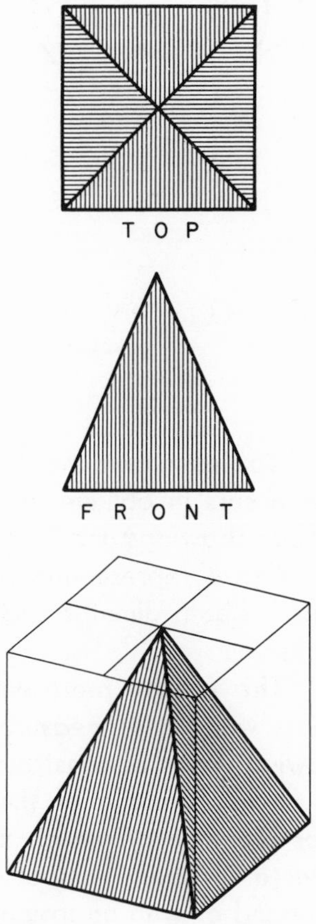

E) PYRAMID

FIG. 89 OBLIQUE SHAPES IN PARALINE DRAWING

Its applications are shown for a single set-back area in Fig. 88 A; for an irregular plan shape in Fig. 88 B; for oblique vertical planes in Fig. 89 C; and for inclined planes in Fig. 89 D.

(A) WHEN BOTH DRAWING AXES OF AREA ARE SAME SCALE

(B) REDUCED SCALE ON ONE OF THE AXES

ELLIPSE CONSTRUCTION FOR PARALINE DRAWING

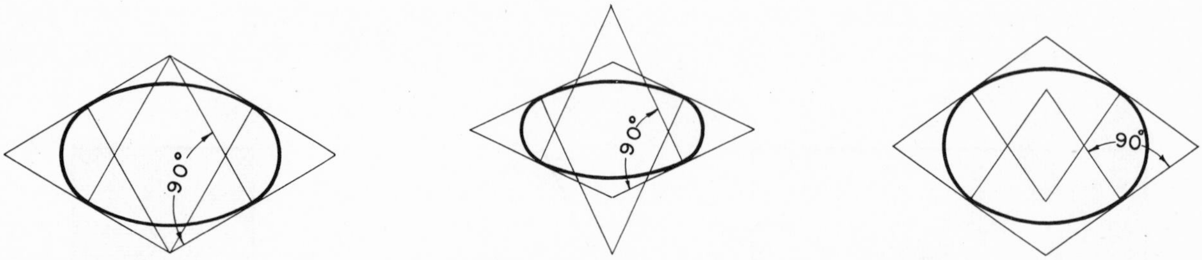

(C) ISOMETRIC SHAPE

(D) THIN OVAL SHAPE

(E) WIDE OVAL SHAPE

FOUR—CENTER OVALS FOR PARALINE DRAWING

FIG. 90 REPRESENTING CIRCLES IN PARALINE DRAWING

Circles in paraline drawing appear as circles only when they are in true shape planes, Fig. 90 A. This occurs in oblique drawing but not normally in other paraline drawings. In all other planes of oblique drawings and in isometric and dimetric drawings circles are seen as true ellipses. In isometric the ellipses representing circles in any of the three coordinate planes are always the same proportions. In both dimetric and oblique drawings the ellipses may vary from very thin to almost circular forms.

The ellipse representing a circle in a paraline drawing is commonly constructed by plotting points with offset measurements. The circle is first drawn in multi-view at the scale of the paraline drawing. Pairs of construction lines parallel to the two adjacent sides of the tangent square around the circle are drawn on the multi-view drawing to intersect in right angled corners on the circle. These lines are then drawn on the paraline drawing to locate the same points on the ellipse, Fig. 90 A. After a sufficient number of points is located the ellipse is then drawn through these points either freehand or with an irregular curve. If one axis line of the paraline drawing is reduced in scale, the measurements in that direction for the ellipse construction must be reduced the same amount. One method of reducing the scale for the small scale axis direction is shown in Fig. 90 B.

Four-center ovals are sometimes used in paraline drawing when the draftsman has difficulty getting a smooth freehand ellipse. However, the four-center oval is only an approximation of an ellipse and should not be used when precision of appearance is important. The four-center oval construction will work only when the representation of the square around the ellipse has equal sides in the paraline drawing—that is, when the same scale is used in both of the axis directions of the construction of the square and the figure is a rhombus in paraline drawing. The shape of the four-center oval is most satisfactory when the corresponding ellipse is almost circular and least satisfactory when the ellipse is very thin. Extreme precision in drawing the construction to locate centers, setting the radii on the compass, and drawing the arcs is necessary in order to make a good four-center oval. The perpendicular bisectors of the four sides of the diamond shape (rhombus) representing the square around the circle in the paraline drawing, Figs. 90 C, D, E, intersect at the four centers of the oval. They also define the beginning and end of each arc. In isometric drawing two centers always fall on the corners of the short diagonal of the rhombus, Fig. 90 C. Furthermore the perpendicular bisectors of the sides can always be drawn with the 30° x 60° triangle whenever one axis of the drawing is horizontal or vertical (not necessarily one of the two used). For other proportions of the rhombus two of the centers lie either outside the rhombus for thin ovals, Fig. 90 D, or all four are within the rhombus for almost circular ovals, Fig. 90 E.

Irregular curves are constructed in paraline drawings by the method of plotting points by offsets as used in Fig. 90 A for the ellipse representing the paraline drawing of a circle. Either a uniform cross section can be used over the entire area, Fig. 91 I, or construction lines can be used to intersect at selected points, Fig. 91 II. The first method requires good judgment in locating points on the curve because lines rarely cross at intersections of construction lines.

Curves that do not lie in one of the three coordinate planes can be located on a paraline drawing by plotting points on section planes through the curves. In Fig. 91 III horizontal planes through the object are used to plot points on the curved form.

Dimensioning on a paraline drawing is most satisfactory in appearance when the extension lines, dimension lines, arrowheads, and numerals are all a part of the plane of the drawing for which the dimension is given. The extension and dimension lines parallel the axis lines of the drawing. The numerals and arrows are shaped to conform to the paraline drawing forms, Fig. 91 IV.

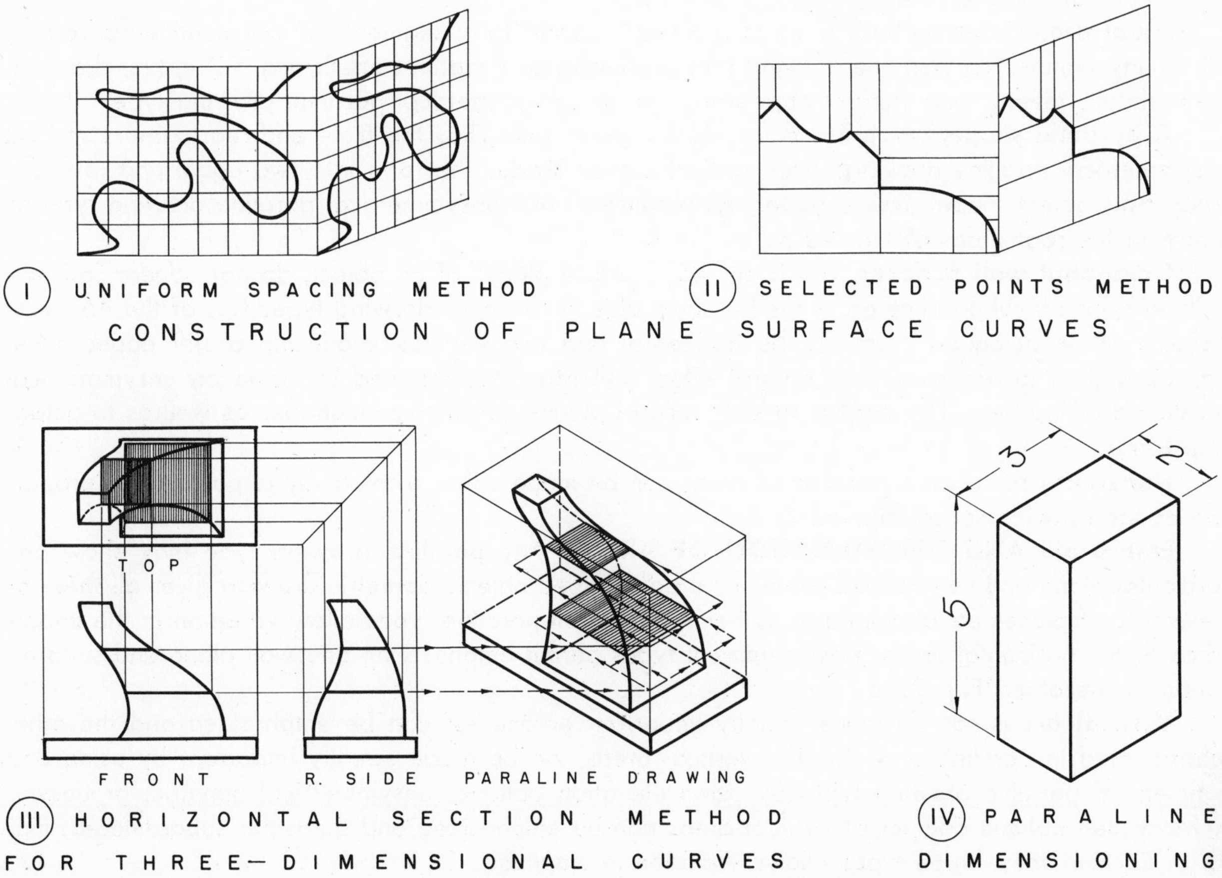

FIG. 91 CURVES AND DIMENSIONS IN PARALINE DRAWING

CHAPTER 16

SELECTING A PARALINE DRAWING TYPE

Unsatisfactory relations of lines and areas in the representation of an object may appear in any type of pictorial drawing. Some of these pictorial defects are unpredictable chance relations. They can usually be improved by varying the perspective, dimetric, or oblique setup. Other pictorial defects result from the use of a type of drawing basically unsuited to the object drawn. The following paragraphs should help the delineator to choose a type of paraline drawing that will be best for each specific object.

SYMMETRICAL FORMS. A drawing type in which the two visible wall planes of an object are turned at the same angle to the observer is said to be symmetrical. The three symmetrical paraline drawing types are isometric drawing, symmetrical dimetric drawing, and 45° plan oblique drawing. They are practically never satisfactory for representing a symmetrical object, or an object that has prominent symmetrical details. Symmetrical forms are shown most effectively in (1) unsymmetrical dimetric, (2) elevation oblique, and (3) unsymmetrical plan oblique (not 45°). These are the three unsymmetrical paraline drawing types, Fig. 92 A.

Equal projections on both sides of a forward corner form segments of one continuous vertical line in any symmetrical paraline drawing thus producing an unnatural effect, Fig. 92 A, first drawing. These details give a more natural appearance in any unsymmetrical paraline drawing type.

A pyramid shape, which has equal slopes on all sides, has the front and rear corners vertical in symmetrical paraline drawings. This vertical corner divides the form into two equal and reversed areas. This object shape gives a better appearance in any unsymmetrical paraline drawing type as shown in the roof areas of Fig. 92 A.

Octagonal wall surfaces, which are 45° vertical planes of an object, do not appear satisfactorily in symmetrical paraline drawings for some objects. In these drawing types two of the 45° wall surfaces of an octagonal form will be horizontal and two vertical, producing a stiff appearance, Fig. 92 B, first drawing. A more natural effect will often be obtained by using an unsymmetrical paraline drawing type. This applies to 45° vertical planes on other plan shapes as well as to octagonal forms.

Horizontal areas of a paraline drawing can be made either a relatively large or small proportion of the drawing space, Fig. 92 C.

EMPHASIS AND SUBORDINATION OF AREAS. Any paraline drawing type may show one horizontal plane and two vertical planes of a box shaped object. Isometric drawing gives all three of these sets of planes equal emphasis. Other symmetrical paraline types allow variation in the importance of the horizontal areas. Unsymmetrical types permit emphasis on one wall plane and subordination of the other, Fig. 92 D.

Vertical areas can be made equally important or one set can be emphasized and the other subordinated in paraline drawing. The vertical areas can be made equally important by using any symmetrical paraline drawing type. By using elevation oblique, unsymmetrical dimetric, or unsymmetrical plan oblique one set of vertical areas can be emphasized and the other subordinated, Fig. 92 D. Each of these three types allows variation in emphasis.

Unusual shapes that lie in one set of planes may be difficult to visualize and understand when warped from their true forms in isometric, dimetric, or perspective drawings. They can sometimes be more easily understood in oblique drawings, Fig. 92 E.

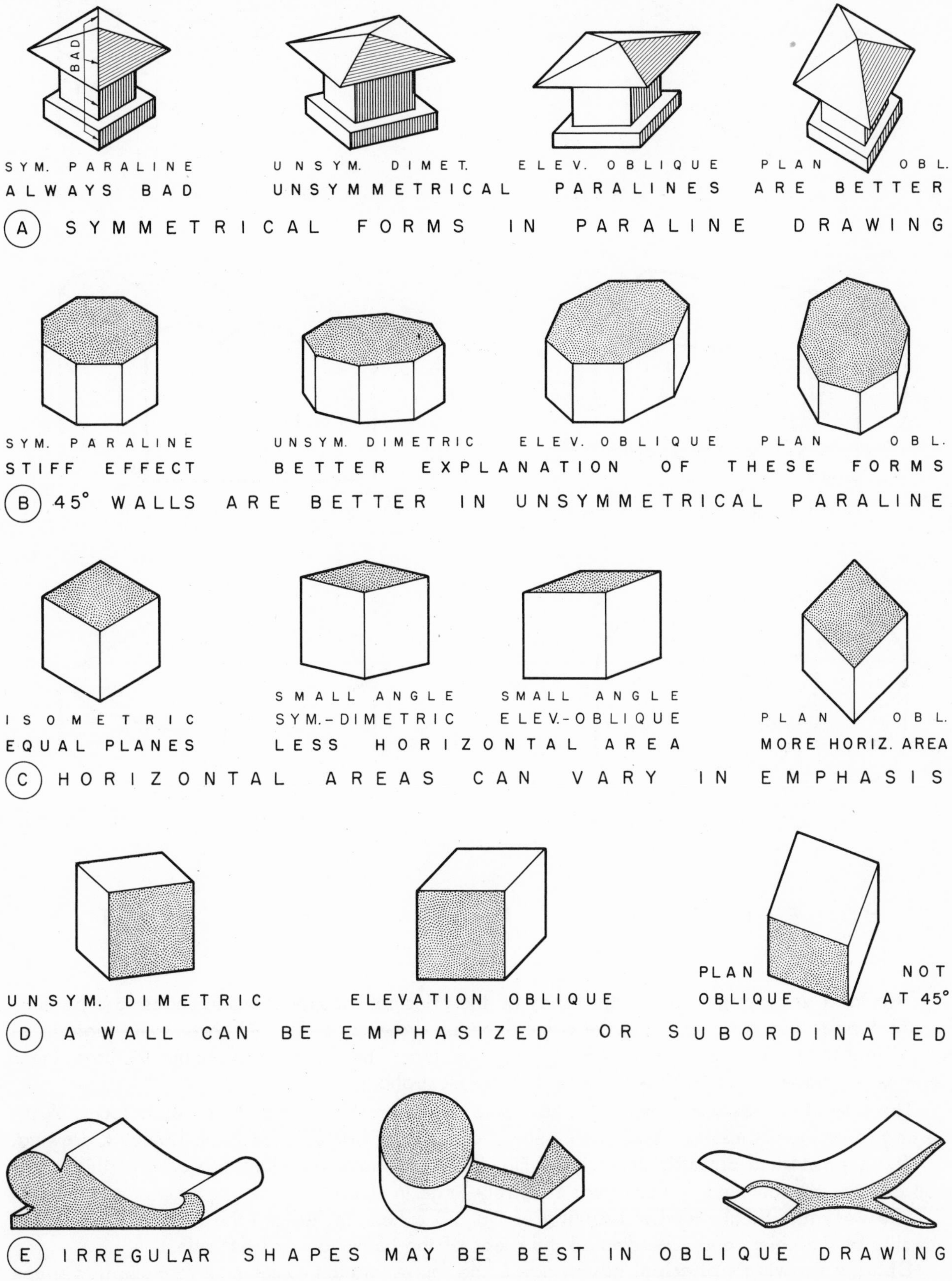
BAD
SYM. PARALINE
ALWAYS BAD
UNSYM. DIMET.
ELEV. OBLIQUE
PLAN OBL.
UNSYMMETRICAL PARALINES ARE BETTER
(A) SYMMETRICAL FORMS IN PARALINE DRAWING
SYM. PARALINE
STIFF EFFECT
UNSYM. DIMETRIC
ELEV. OBLIQUE
PLAN OBL.
BETTER EXPLANATION OF THESE FORMS
(B) 45° WALLS ARE BETTER IN UNSYMMETRICAL PARALINE
ISOMETRIC
EQUAL PLANES
SMALL ANGLE
SYM.-DIMETRIC
SMALL ANGLE
ELEV.-OBLIQUE
LESS HORIZONTAL AREA
PLAN OBL.
MORE HORIZ. AREA
(C) HORIZONTAL AREAS CAN VARY IN EMPHASIS
UNSYM. DIMETRIC
ELEVATION OBLIQUE
PLAN OBLIQUE
NOT AT 45°
(D) A WALL CAN BE EMPHASIZED OR SUBORDINATED
(E) IRREGULAR SHAPES MAY BE BEST IN OBLIQUE DRAWING

FIG. 92 CHOOSING THE BEST PARALINE TYPE

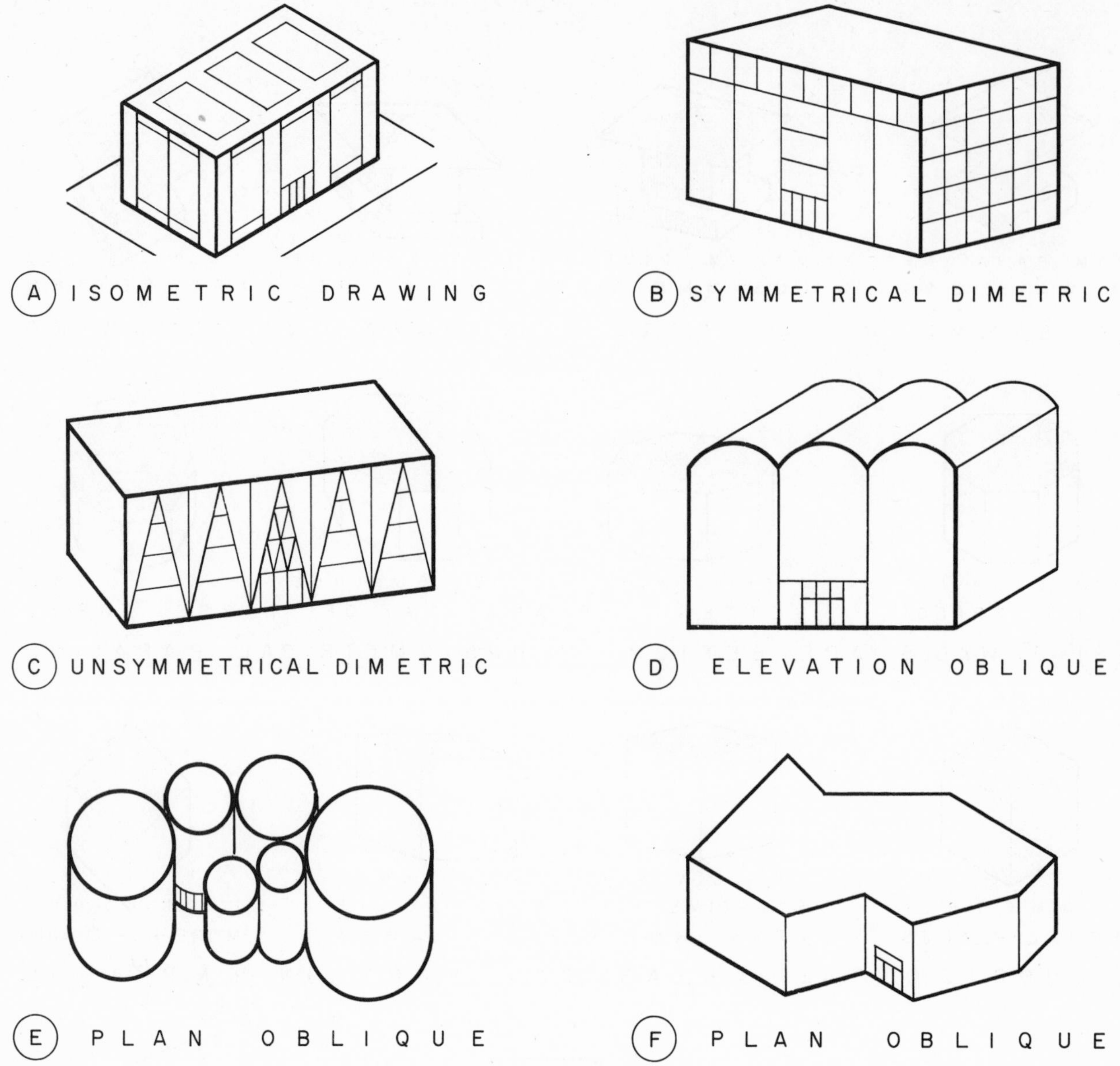

FIG. 93 SELECTING A PARALINE DRAWING TYPE

The form and design of an object may be the principal considerations in choosing a paraline drawing type to use in representing the object. The six drawings of Fig. 93 show some features of designs that may influence the selection of a paraline type. These drawings explain the basic ideas presented on pages 98 and 99 with more detailed illustrations.

The isometric drawing of Fig. 93 A has some details on each of the three visible faces. When one or two of these faces are bare there seems to be much wasted area in an isometric drawing.

The symmetrical dimetric drawing of Fig. 93 B has made the blank top area of this object small and the two detailed vertical areas relatively large in size.

The unsymmetrical dimetric drawing of Fig. 93 C has emphasized the area of the detailed right side of the object and subordinated the areas of the blank top and left side.

Oblique drawing's principal advantage is the representation of complex forms in true shape areas where they may be easier to draw and also sometimes easier to understand, Figs. 93 D, E, and F.

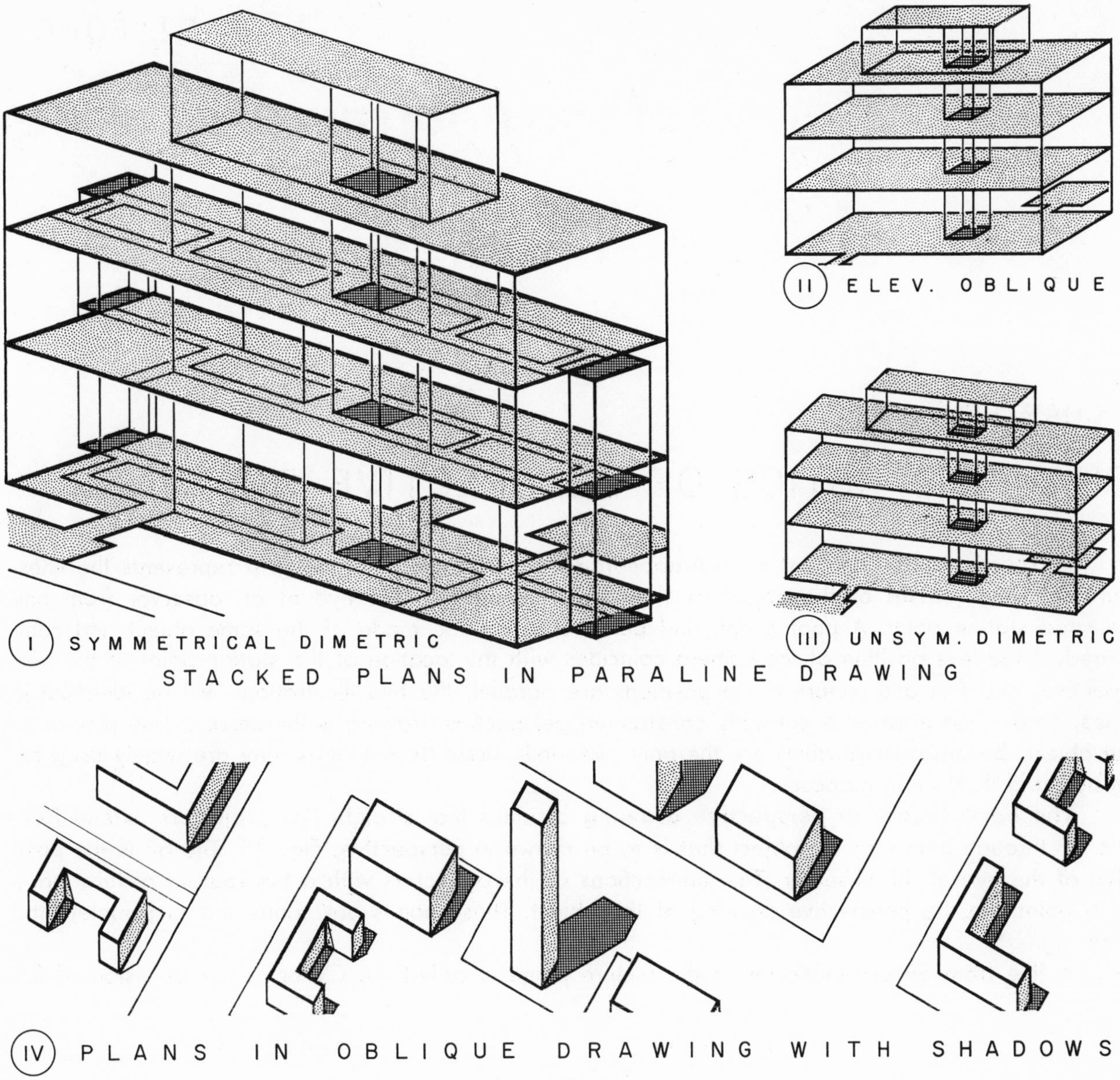

FIG. 94 STACKED AND THREE DIMENSIONAL PLANS

Vertical relations of horizontal planes of an object can frequently be shown effectively and clearly by using vertically connected paraline plans, Figs. 94 I, II, and III. The paraline plans are compressed vertically and the sequence is easier to comprehend as a unit than the much more extended orthographic plans. Continuous vertical elements in a building such as stairs, elevators, stacked toilet rooms, and structural features can be shown to connect the paraline floor plans and explain the general scheme for a multi-floor building. This type of three dimensional drawing should supplement the orthographic plans to explain relations of volumes, areas, and the structural system. It cannot usually satisfactorily replace the orthographic plans.

A three-dimensional plan can be made from a single orthographic plan by turning the plan at an angle and making a plan oblique drawing of it. This is especially effective when a number of relatively small three dimensional objects are spread out horizontally as in city planning projects. The addition of shadows usually adds clearness to the three dimensional effect of this type of drawing, Fig. 94 IV.

PART FOUR

Perspective Drawing

CHAPTER 17

CHARACTERISTICS OF PERSPECTIVE DRAWINGS

Perspective gives the most natural appearance of any type of drawing. It represents the lines, surfaces, and masses of the object as they would appear to the eye of an observer from one selected station point. A photograph and perspective can be made of the same object and compared. If the lens position of the camera coincides with the location of the station point of the perspective, and film and picture plane positions are parallel, the two illustrations will be identical in lines, areas, and masses. A correctly constructed perspective drawing is therefore a true picture of an object. Because perspectives are the only pictorially accurate drawings they are widely used for design and illustration purposes.

The basic theory of perspective drawing assumes that straight line projectors extend from the SP through points on the object that is to be drawn in perspective, Fig. 95. The SP is the position of the eye of the observer. The intersections of the projectors with a transparent picture plane give points on the perspective drawing of the object. These points are connected to complete the drawing.

A line from SP perpendicular to the picture plane is called the CV or center of vision of the

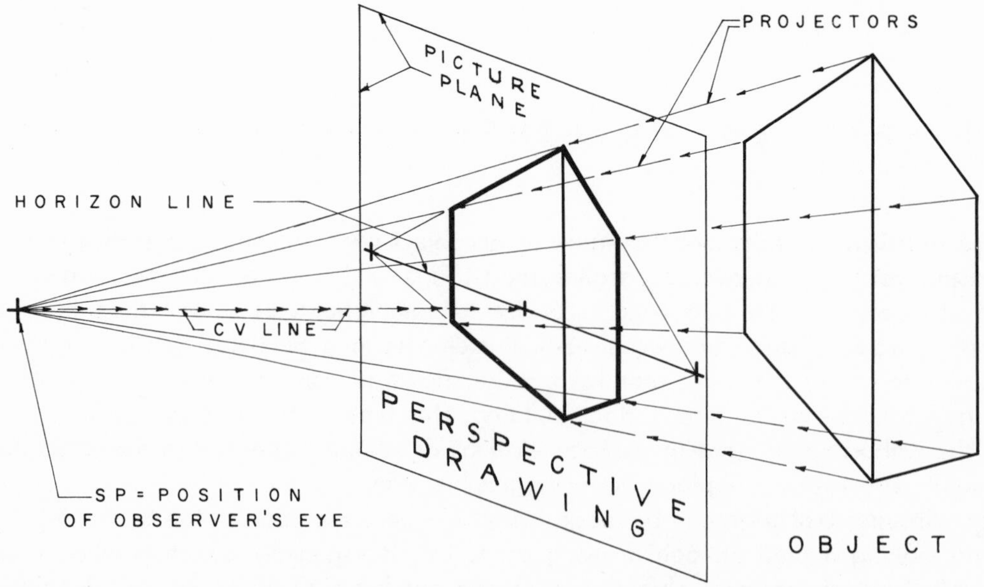

FIG. 95 BASIC THEORY OF PERSPECTIVE DRAWING

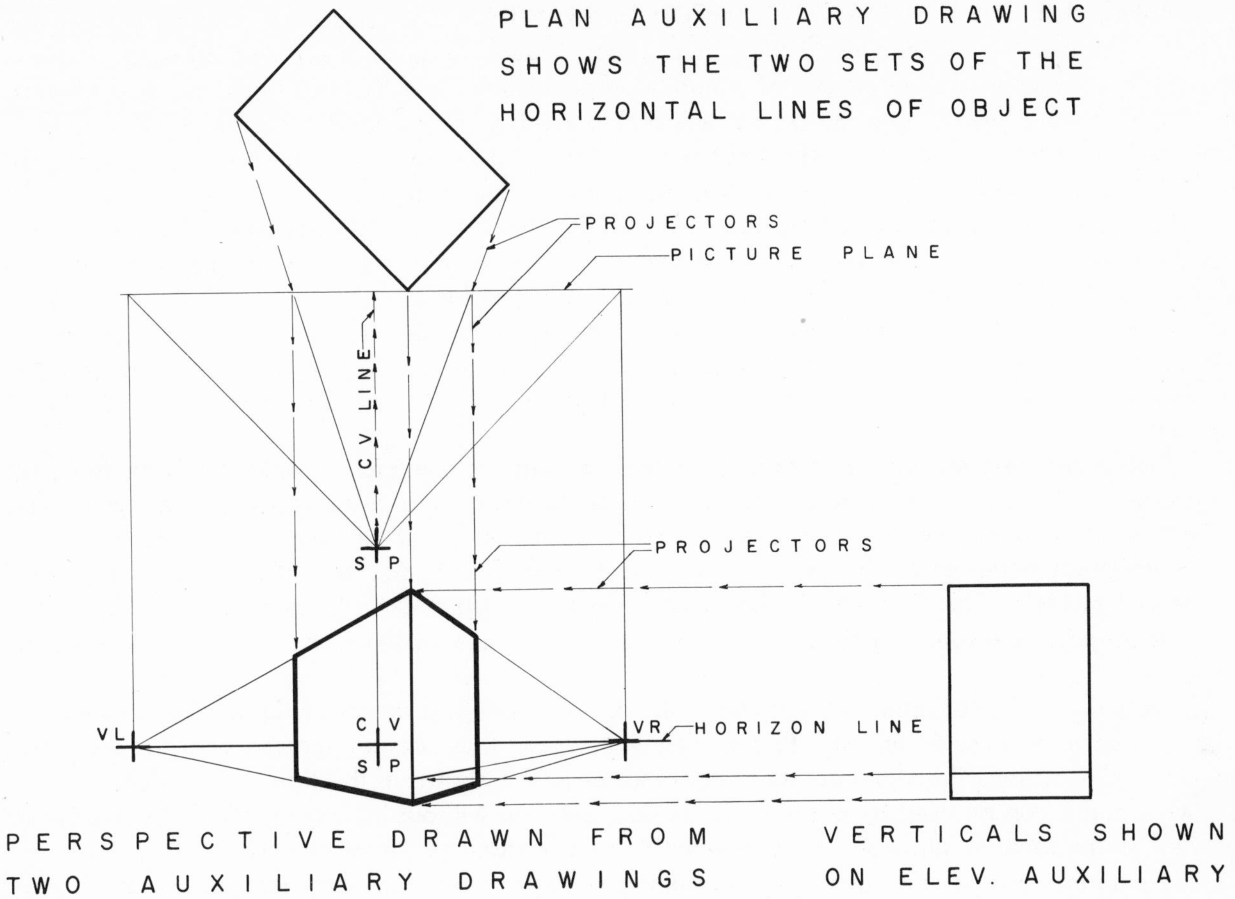

FIG. 96 AUXILIARY DRAWINGS IN PERSPECTIVE

perspective. In one-point and two-point perspective this CV line intersects the vertical picture plane at a point on the horizon line. The horizon line is then a horizontal line on the picture plane at the height of the SP, Fig. 95.

A sketch perspective can be made on a window glass or other transparent vertical picture plane. The object sketched is viewed through the transparent plane and the sketch made using a single eye, which remains in one fixed position for the drawing.

Because such a sketch perspective is a relatively crude drawing, and the object is not always available for use in this manner, drafting methods based on the above theory are used to construct perspective drawings. Perspectives of objects which are not available and of designs of proposed objects which do not actually exist can be made by these methods.

Mechanical methods of constructing perspective drawings have several variations. All of these methods accomplish the same result of a true picture of the object if they are used correctly and accurately. Multi-view orthographic drawings are usually required to give shape and size information for the construction of the perspective. In some methods they are also used as auxiliary drawings for a part of the construction where they are employed in locating the positions of perspective lines. It is therefore essential that the draftsman have a clear understanding of multi-view drawings before he attempts to make perspective drawings.

The auxiliary plan of Fig. 96 is used to trace the ends of the two sets of horizontal lines of the object to the picture plane, and then down vertically to the perspective drawing. The auxiliary elevation is used to trace the heights horizontally into perspective position directly when they are in the picture plane.

THERE ARE THREE TYPES OF PERSPECTIVE DRAWING. Each type has a different relation between the lines of the object and the picture plane. Figure 97 gives a paraline drawing of a box shape. This shape has the three sets of mutually perpendicular lines that are found on most objects. In this figure the lines of one horizontal set are labeled X, the second set of horizontal lines is labeled Y, and the lines of the vertical set are labeled Z. In perspective drawing any one of these sets of lines may be parallel, perpendicular, or oblique to the picture plane.

Parallel lines that are parallel to the picture plane remain parallel in perspective. The vertical lines of Figs. 98 A and B and the one set of horizontal lines of Fig. 98 A are parallel to the picture plane and are actually drawn parallel in the perspective drawings.

A set of lines that is either perpendicular or oblique to the picture plane vanishes to a vanishing point in perspective. The names of the three types of perspective drawings are derived from the number of vanishing points required for each type for the X, Y, and Z groups of parallel lines, Fig. 98.

One-point perspective has two sets of lines parallel to the picture plane and the third set perpendicular to it. Because a set of lines not parallel to the picture plane converges to a vanishing point this arrangement requires only one VP and is called one-point perspective, Fig. 98 A.

Two-point perspective requires two VPs, one for each of the two sets of lines that are oblique to the picture plane. The third set of lines, usually vertical, is parallel to the picture plane, Fig. 98 B.

Three-point perspective has all three sets of lines oblique to the picture plane, thus requiring three VPs. Fig. 98 C.

Every line in any direction not parallel to the picture plane has its vanishing point in perspective. Although some of these additional VPs are sometimes useful they are not necessary for practical perspective construction. The standard vanishing point or points shown in the three illustrations of Figs. 98 A, B, and C can be used to locate a line in any direction without having its VP. This construction as well as the location and use of additional VPs will be discussed in later pages.

A person standing in a room can from one position see parts of the room as one-point, two-point, and three-point perspectives merely by looking in different directions. When the center of vision of the observer is horizontal and perpendicular to a wall the room will be seen as a one-point perspective. When looking horizontally at a corner of the room it will be seen in two-point perspective. When looking up or down at a corner of the room it will appear as in three-point perspective.

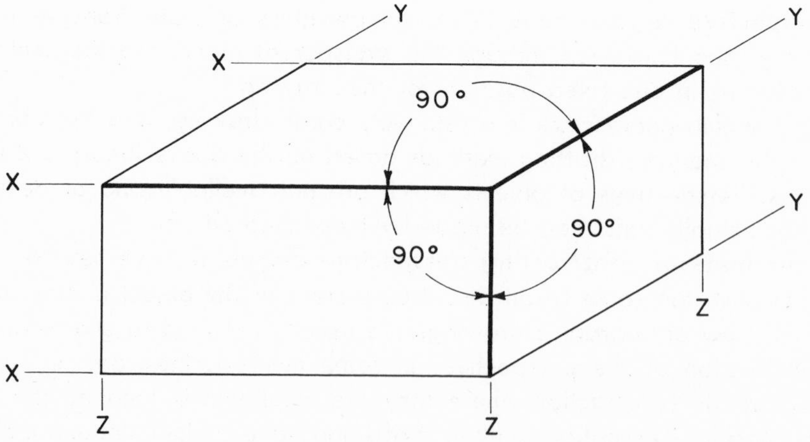

THESE ARE THE BASIC LINES OF PERSPECTIVE DRAWING

FIG. 97 THE THREE SETS OF PERPENDICULAR LINES

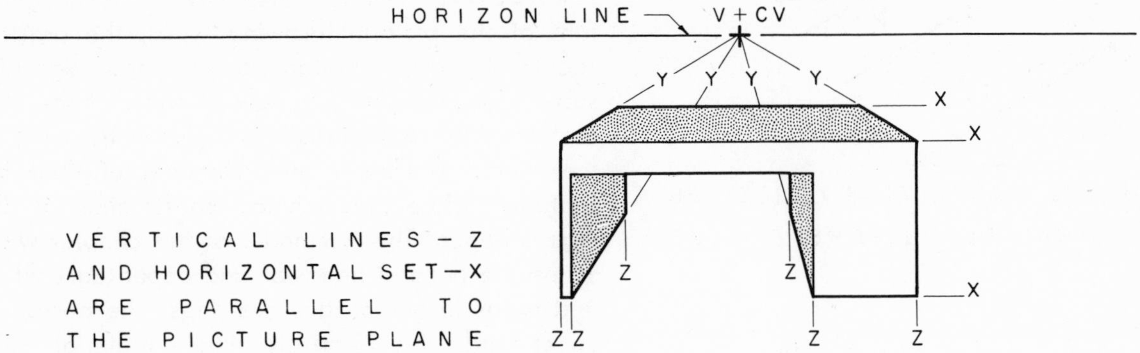

(A) ONE—POINT PERSPECTIVE HAS 1 VP

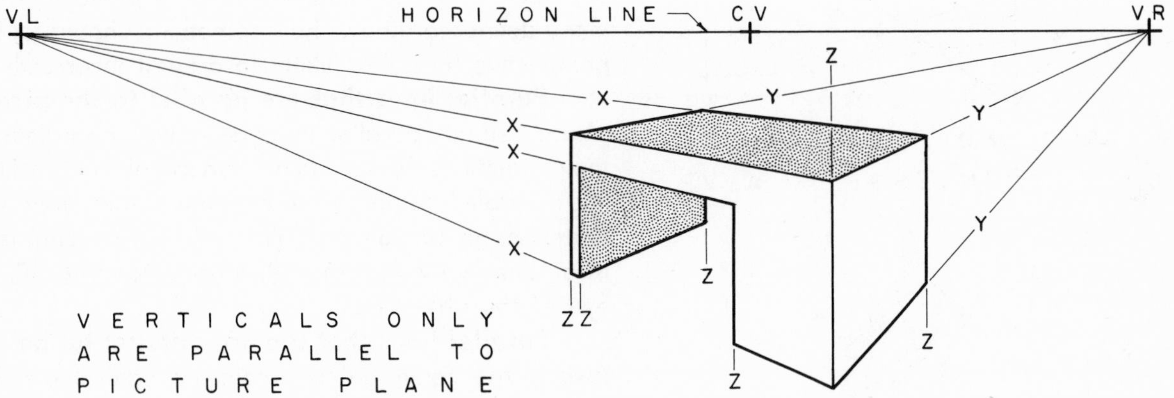

(B) TWO—POINT PERSPECTIVE HAS 2 VPS

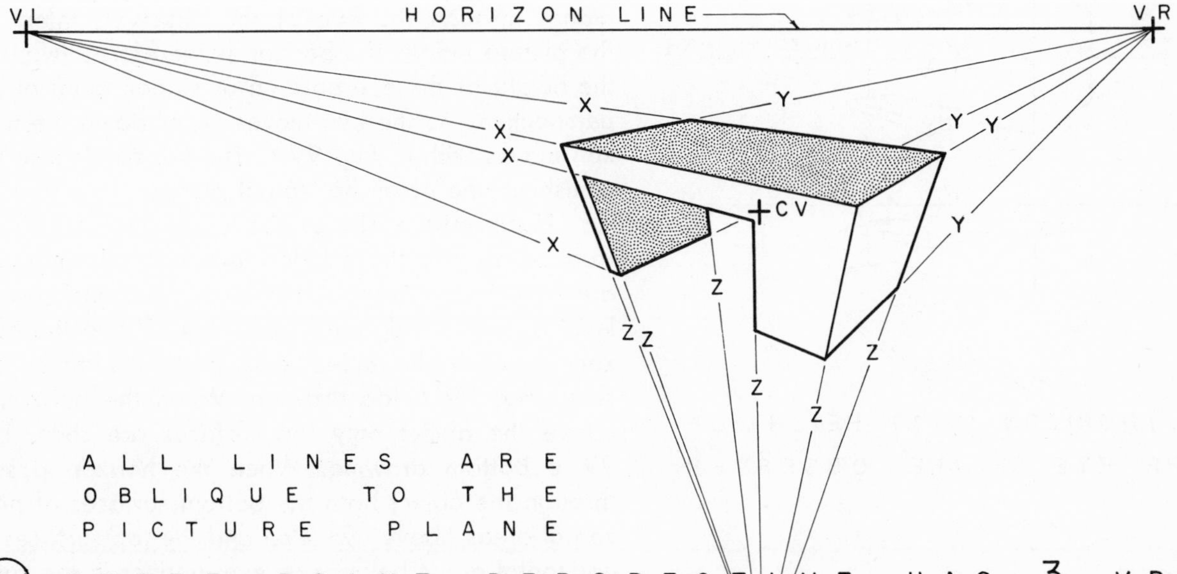

(C) THREE—POINT PERSPECTIVE HAS 3 VPS

FIG. 98 THE THREE TYPES OF PERSPECTIVE DRAWING

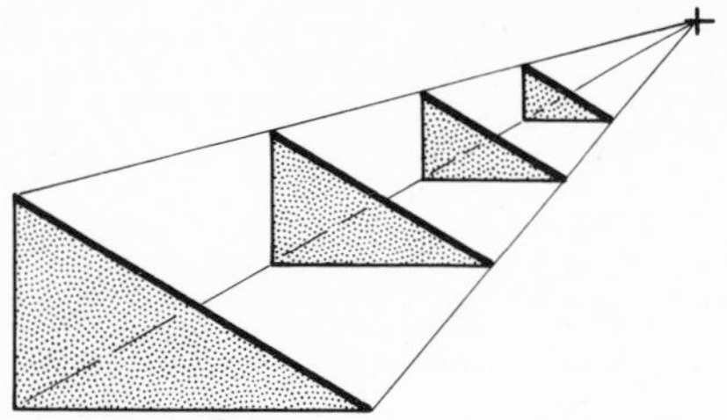

(A) LINES PARALLEL TO PICT. PL. ARE PARALLEL IN PERSPECTIVE

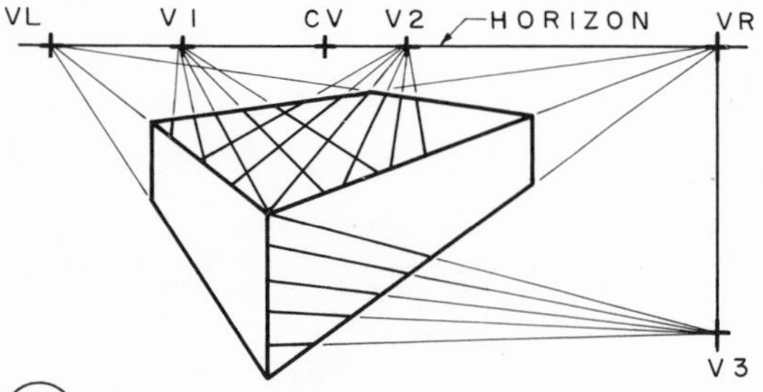

(B) LINES NOT PARALLEL TO PICT. PL. CONVERGE TO A V.P.

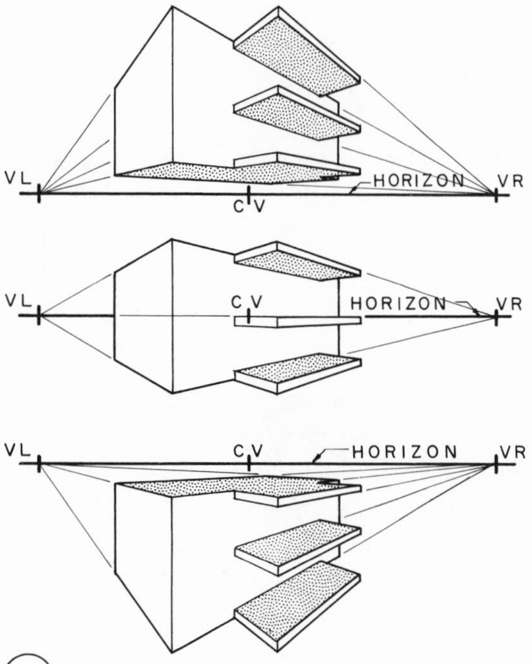

(C) HORIZON IS AT HEIGHT OF THE EYE OF THE OBSERVER

FIG. 99 LINES AND AREAS IN PERSPECTIVES

CHARACTERISTICS OF LINES AND AREAS IN PERSPECTIVE. Because perspective is the most important of the pictorial drawing types, the draftsman should obtain a thorough working knowledge of the subject. A preliminary survey of some of the important pictorial characteristics of perspectives will give the reader a clearer understanding of their basic features before the technical construction of drawings is begun. The remainder of this chapter will describe the general behavior and appearance of lines and areas in perspective drawings. The person who understands this relatively simple material will be better able to visualize the appearance of perspective drawings as he constructs them. This should remove some of the doubts and uncertainties from perspective construction and help to prevent errors. If the delineator knows how something should look in perspective he is less likely to draw it incorrectly.

Parallel lines that are parallel to the picture plane remain parallel in perspective regardless of their direction. Thus vertical, horizontal, and inclined lines parallel to the picture plane retain their true directions in perspective, Fig. 99 A. The lengths of these lines vary with their distances from the SP, the eye of the observer.

Parallel lines that are not parallel to the picture plane converge to a common vanishing point. Each set of parallel lines has its vanishing point, Fig. 99 B. The vanishing points of all horizontal lines are on the horizon.

The horizon is located where the horizontal plane, through the eye of the observer, intersects the picture plane. The horizon is therefore always at the height of the eye position or station point of the perspective. As the eye moves up or down the horizon moves with it, Fig. 99 C. The horizon is also the vanishing line of all horizontal planes.

Horizontal surfaces above eye level are visible from below and those below eye level (the horizon) are seen from above. A surface at eye and horizon level is seen in edge view as a line. When the horizon is below the object only bottom surfaces are seen, Fig. 99 C top drawing. When the horizon is above the object only top surfaces are seen, Fig. 99 C bottom drawing. When the horizon passes through the object both the bottom surfaces of horizontal areas above eye level and the top surfaces of horizontal areas below eye level appear in the same drawing, Fig. 99 C center drawing. This last condition never occurs in paraline drawing.

The more distant parts of an object are smaller in a perspective drawing. Areas that are actually equal in size on the object are larger near the observer and decrease in size as they get farther away. Vertical lines that represent equal heights are longer near the observer and become shorter as the distance away increases. Lines to a vanishing point when divided into equal segments on the object show progressively smaller segments as the line approaches its vanishing point, Fig. 100 D. Obviously then, a scale cannot be used on all lines of a perspective drawing.

Scale size occurs in a perspective drawing only where the lines of the object lie in the picture plane, Fig. 100 E line C–D. Because the projectors converge to the station point, lines behind the picture plane are reduced in size at the picture plane by the decreasing space between the projectors as shown by line E–F. Lines in front of the picture plane are increased in size because the projectors from the object diverge and become farther apart on their way to the picture plane, line A–B.

True shapes are seldom shown in perspective drawings. Areas that parallel the picture plane retain their true shapes in perspective, Fig. 99 A and 100 F. Areas that are not parallel to the picture plane are drawn as they would appear from the station point. A square that is not parallel to the picture plane can be seen as a straight line or an irregular four-sided figure. This figure may be very thin, almost square, or any form between a straight line and a square, Fig. 100 F. In most cases a circle that is not parallel to the picture plane will appear as an ellipse in the perspective drawing. The proportions of the ellipse vary with the angle from which it is seen, Fig. 100 F. A perspective drawing shows the lines and areas of the object depicted as they must be to appear correctly from the SP of the drawing, not as they actually are.

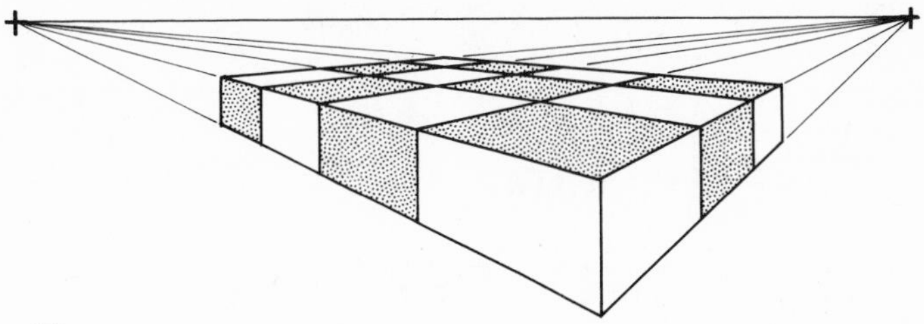

(D) MORE DISTANT LINES AND AREAS ARE SMALLER

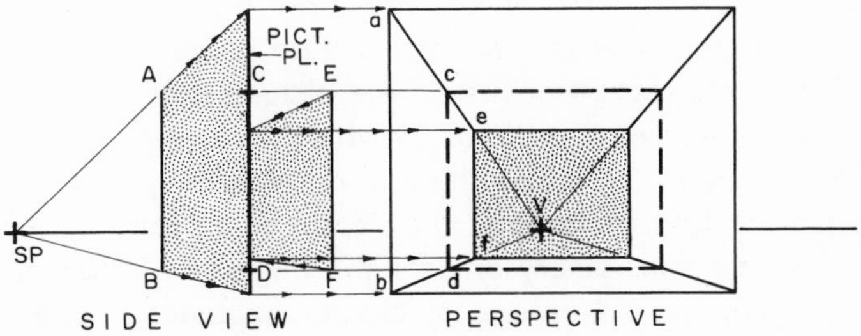

(E) SCALE SIZES OCCUR AT THE PICTURE PLANE ONLY

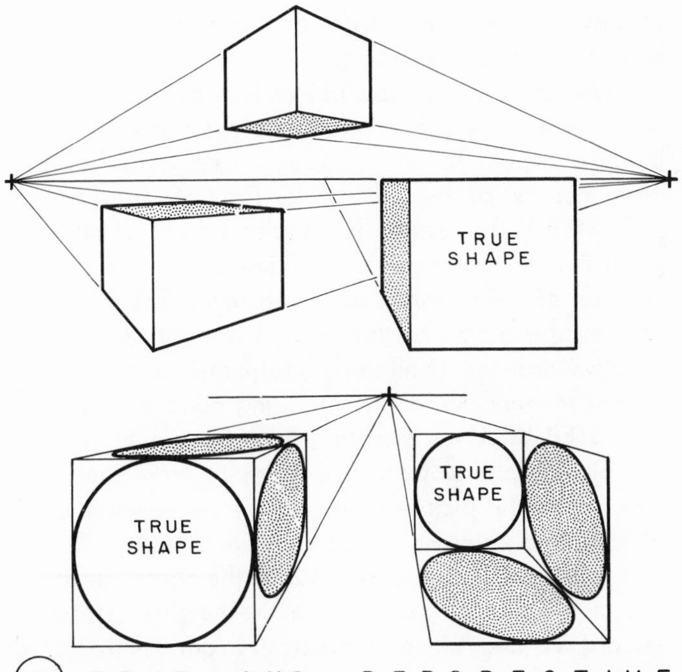

(F) TRUE AND PERSPECTIVE SHAPES MAY VARY GREATLY

FIG. 100 SIZES AND SHAPES IN PERSPECTIVE DRAWING

CHAPTER 18

TWO-POINT PERSPECTIVE

Two-point perspective is used for approximately nine-tenths of all perspective work. For this reason it is presented first in this text. The method employed throughout this chapter is widely used in offices and schools. It is called the Common Method and also the Office Method. When ease of use and understanding are important it is a very good method. Any method of perspective drawing locates intersections with the picture plane of imaginary lines from the SP to points on the object. These intersection points on the picture plane are connected to make the perspective of the object. There are several methods by which this construction is accomplished. Just as there is "No royal road to geometry," so also there is no extremely easy method of doing perspective drawing. Although persons with a thorough knowledge of perspective may prefer another method, the common method is a very satisfactory one for the beginner. Other methods are described in Chapter 21.

For the advantage of clearer explanation the development of a simple exterior and interior example of perspective drawing has been divided into three steps in Fig. 101.

STEP I. The plan is drawn with the sides at an oblique angle. A line called the *center of vision* (CV) is drawn from the center of the plan. It represents a horizontal line through SP and perpendicular to the picture plane. The plan position of the station point is located at a reasonable distance from the object on this line. The horizontal line representing the plan view of the vertical picture plane is drawn through the corner of the object. The drawing now shows a plan of object, picture plane, station point, and center of vision.

An elevation of the object is drawn below the station point and to one side of the plan. At some chosen height as related to the elevation the horizon line is drawn and extended indefinitely below the plan for the perspective drawing. The plan and elevation are called auxiliary drawings. They must be at the same scale. They are used to locate points and lines of the perspective drawing.

STEP II. To locate the vanishing point of all horizontal lines of the object in the direction of line A–B, Fig. 101, from SP draw a line parallel to A–B to meet the picture plane at X. Point X is the plan position of the required vanishing point. The perspective position of the vanishing point VR is located at the intersection of the vertical through X and the horizon. VR is the vanishing point in the perspective drawing of all horizontal lines parallel to A–B. The second vanishing point VL is located in a similar manner. VL is the vanishing point of the perspectives of all horizontal lines parallel to A–C.

STEP III. Lines radiating from SP are traced from points on the plan of the object to intersect the picture plane. Lines are dropped from these points of intersection, and from the near corner which is in the picture plane, to the perspective drawing. These lines provide the horizontal spacing of lines and points in the perspective drawing. The height is carried over horizontally from the elevation to the vertical line A1–A2 of the corner in the picture plane. This line is scale height because it lies in the picture plane. From the heights established here at points A1 and A2, lines are drawn toward VL and VR to complete the perspective of the exterior and away from VL and VR for the interior.

The perspective position of the SP or eye position is located on the vertical through the plan of SP at its intersection with the horizon. This point is also called CV or center of vision here because it represents the line from SP perpendicular to the picture plane as well as the SP.

If the student is confused as to which vanishing point to use he should remember the following. Any horizontal line that is parallel to SP–Y in plan will go to the vanishing point located by that construction line and the vertical from Y to the horizon.

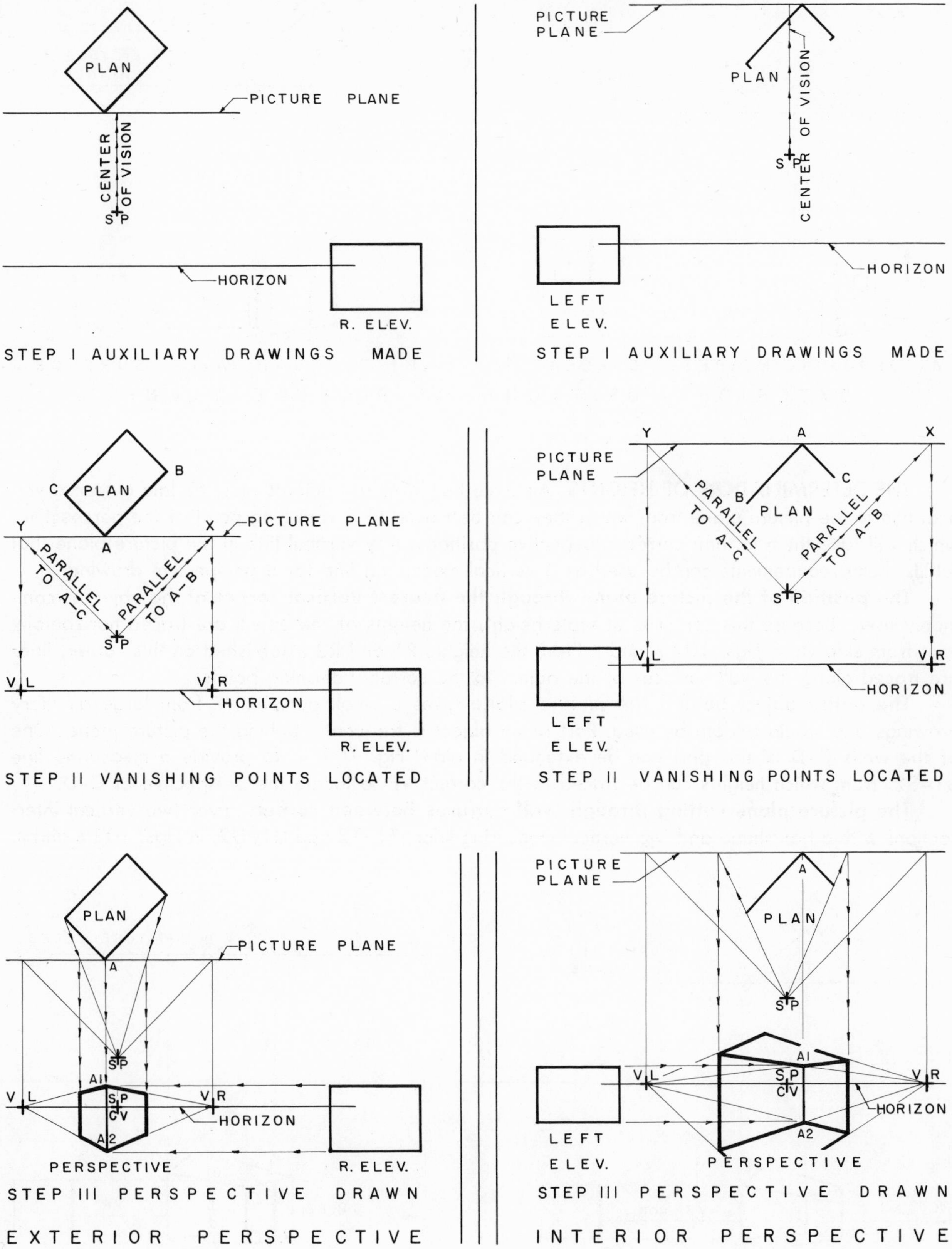

FIG. 101 ELEMENTARY TWO-POINT PERSPECTIVE

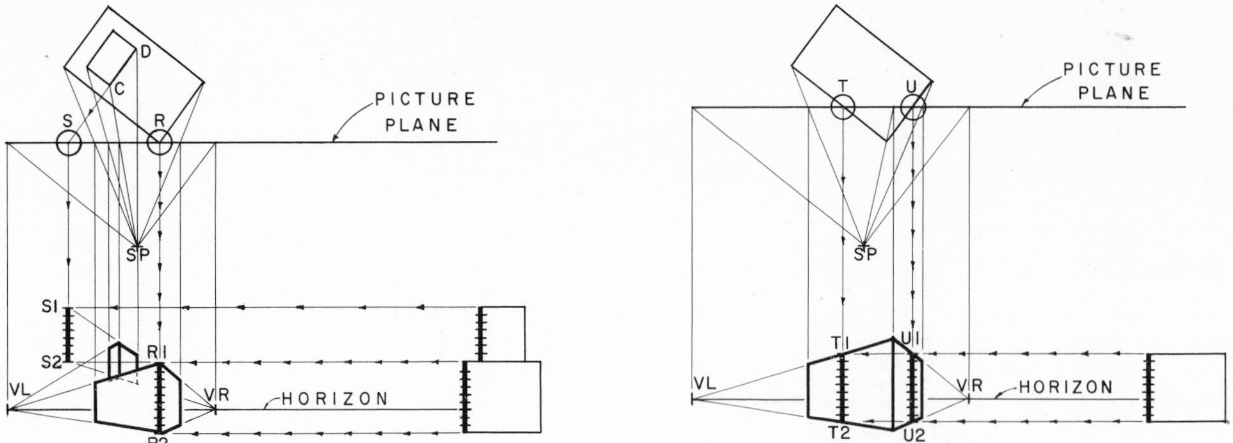

(A) THROUGH NEAREST CORNER (B) THROUGH WALL SURFACES

EXTERIOR POSITIONS OF PICTURE PLANE

THE DETERMINATION OF HEIGHTS. All scale height measurements must be laid out on a vertical line in the picture plane from which they can be traced to a vanishing point of the perspective, which will take them to their correct perspective positions. Any vertical line in the picture plane that fulfills these requirements can be used as a vertical measuring line for a perspective drawing.

The position of the picture plane through the nearest vertical corner of the object is commonly used. Because this corner is at scale height, the heights of the object are traced horizontally to it from side view, Figs. 102 A and I. From the heights R1 and R2 established on this corner, lines are traced along the wall surfaces of the object to the correct vanishing points.

The entire object behind the picture plane gives a small perspective from large auxiliary drawings and would seldom be used. Part of an object is frequently behind the picture plane. One of the walls C–D of this part can be extended in plan, Fig. 102 A, to provide a measuring line S1–S2, from which heights can be traced to the correct VP to locate the perspective of C–D.

The picture plane cutting through wall surfaces between corners gives two vertical intersections with a box shape and two vertical measuring lines, T1–T2 and U1–U2, in Figs. 102 B and II.

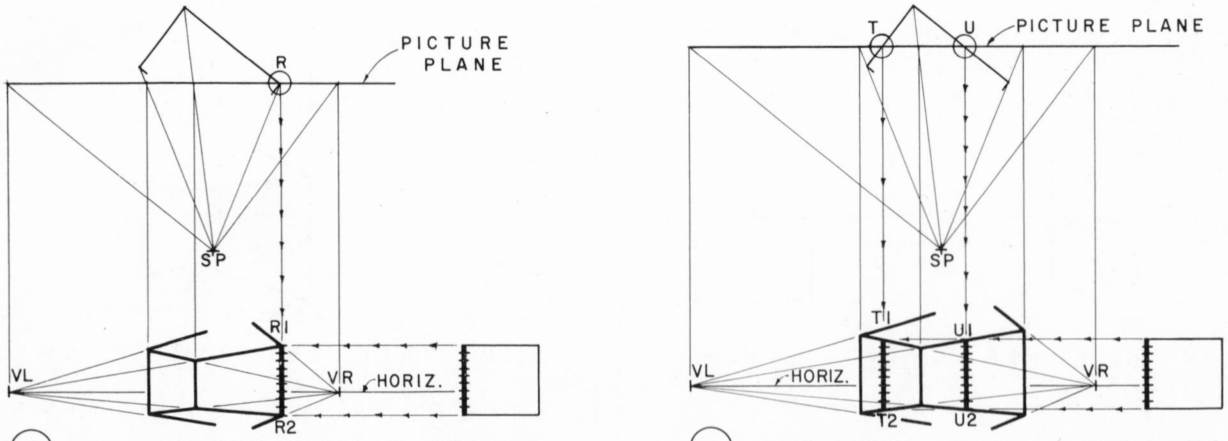

(I) AT NEAREST VISIBLE CORNER (II) THROUGH WALL SURFACES

INTERIOR POSITIONS OF PICTURE PLANE

FIG. 102 HEIGHT CONSTRUCTION IN TWO-POINT PERSPECTIVE

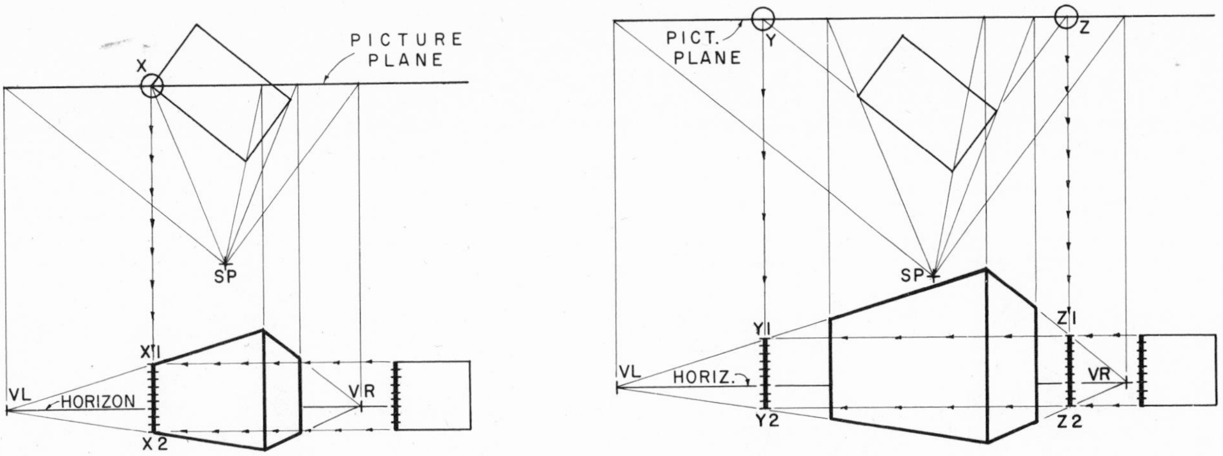

(C) FARTHEST VISIBLE CORNER (D) BEHIND THE ENTIRE OBJECT

EXTERIOR POSITIONS OF PICTURE PLANE

The picture plane through the farthest visible vertical corner of an object provides a perspective larger than the auxiliary drawing. For interior perspective it provides height measurements in a position from which they can be traced along both wall surfaces, Fig. 103 III. The exterior requires tracing lines away from one VP to meet the nearest wall corner and then toward the other VP to locate heights on the other wall, Fig. 103 C.

The object in front of the picture plane requires that either of the two visible wall surfaces be extended in plan to meet the picture plane in an imaginary intersection at Y or Z, which will provide a vertical measuring line in the perspective drawing for the height construction. Both of these imaginary intersection lines Y1–Y2 and Z1 and Z2 are shown in the perspectives of Figs. 103 D and IV. Lines are traced from the VP through the height points on these lines to perspective positions. This procedure enlarges the measurements and the perspective. Both walls can be extended and two height lines located for the simple box shape. More complex shapes can have a vertical measuring line for each wall surface.

The object in front of the picture plane gives a large perspective from a small plan and elevation. Extreme enlargements may become inaccurate.

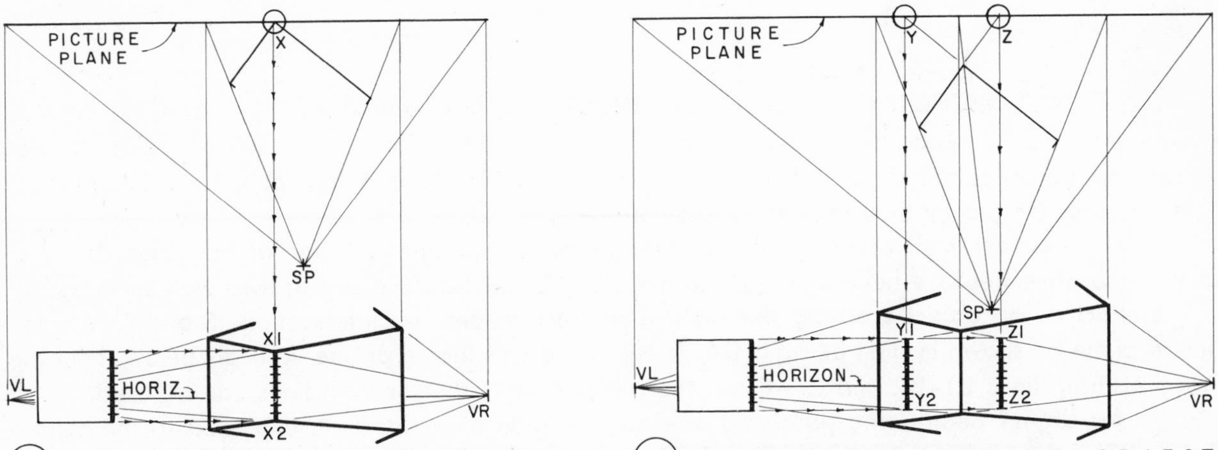

(III) AT FARTHEST CORNER (IV) BEHIND THE ENTIRE OBJECT

INTERIOR POSITIONS OF PICTURE PLANE

FIG. 103 HEIGHT CONSTRUCTION IN TWO-POINT PERSPECTIVE

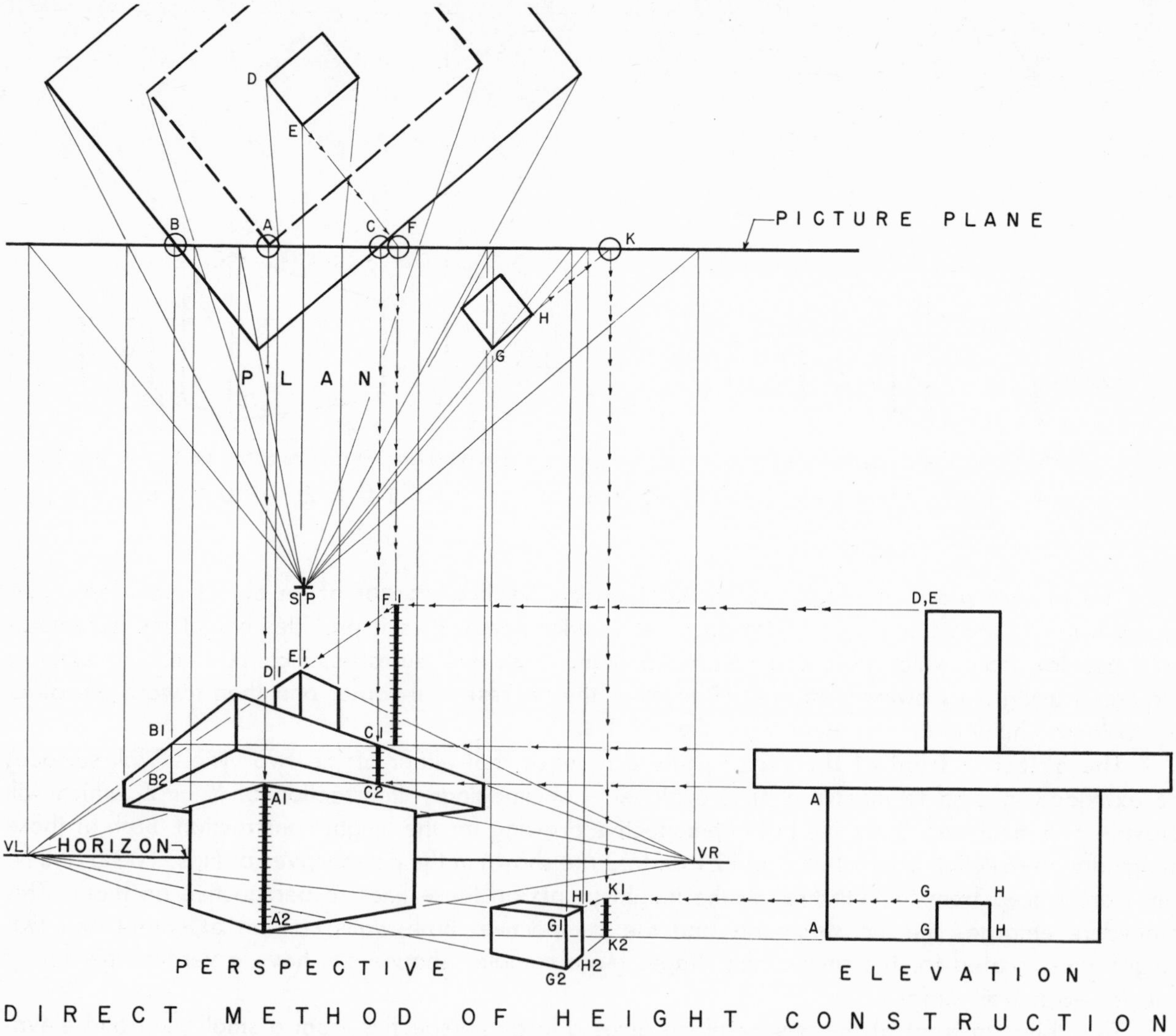

FIG. 104 HEIGHTS IN TWO-POINT PERSPECTIVE

THE DIRECT METHOD OF HEIGHT CONSTRUCTION. This method has been used on the two preceding pages for separate explanations of height construction for each of several different relations of the object to the picture plane. On this page, Fig. 104 shows four of these relations illustrated as they frequently may appear on a single perspective.

1. The nearest wall corner in the picture plane is a popular position of the object for two-point perspective because heights on this corner A1–A2 are traced along its two wall surfaces.

2. Part of an object crossing the picture plane provides two intersections B and C with the picture plane as shown in plan of Fig. 104. These two points locate on the verticals below them the two measuring lines B1–B2 and C1–C2 in the perspective. Either or both lines can be used.

3. An object behind the picture plane has the plan of a side D–E extended to the picture plane at F. A vertical is drawn from F to meet the horizontal line from the elevation of D–E at F1. From F1 a line is drawn to VL to locate the perspective height of line D–E at D1–E1.

4. An object in front of the picture plane in Fig. 104 has side G–H extended in plan to meet the picture plane at K and locate on the vertical measuring line below K the points K1 and K2, from which the scale heights are traced into the perspective.

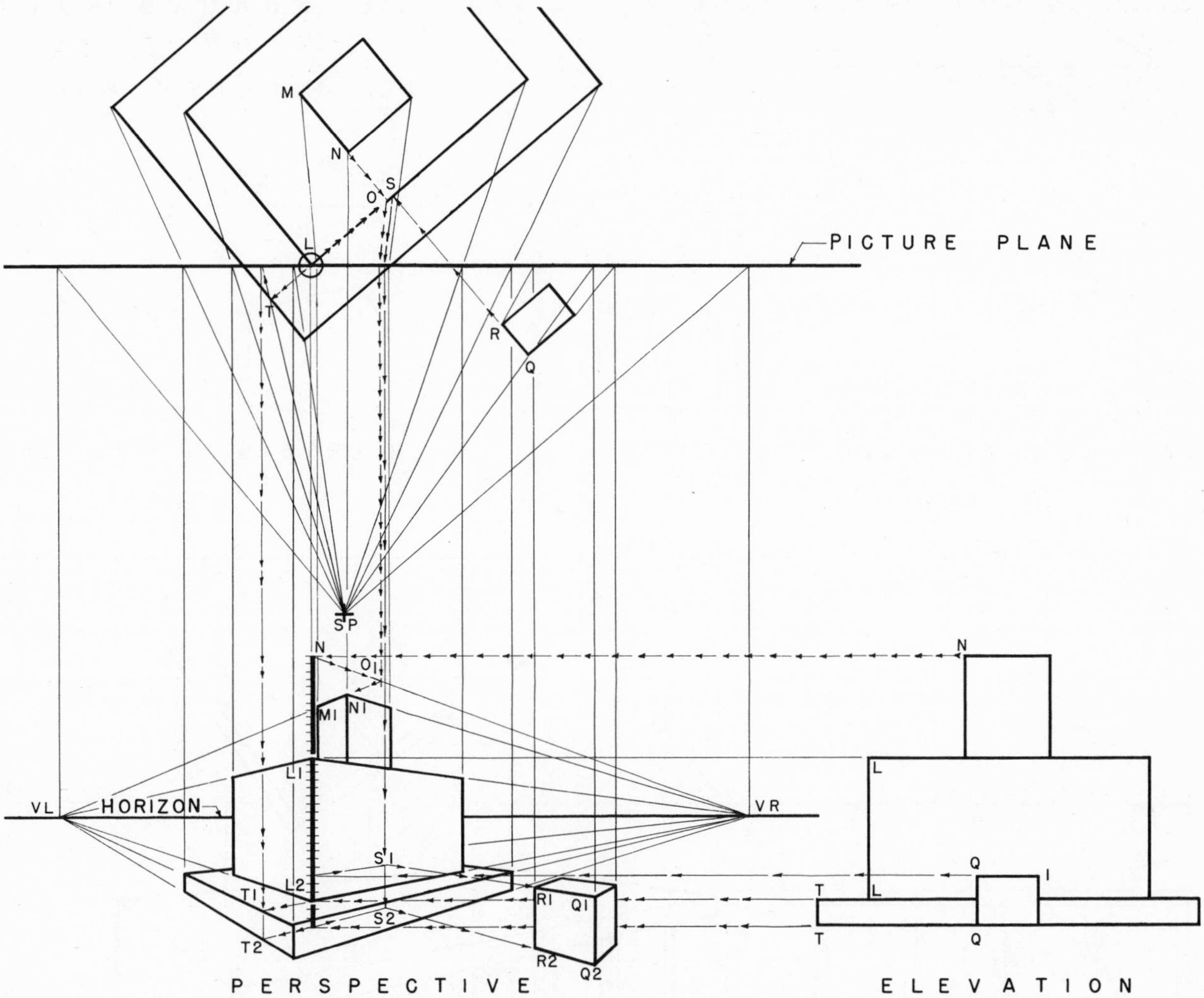

INDIRECT METHOD OF HEIGHT CONSTRUCTION

FIG. 105 HEIGHTS IN TWO-POINT PERSPECTIVE

THE INDIRECT METHOD OF HEIGHT CONSTRUCTION. All heights are laid out in the perspective to scale on a single height line L1–L2, which is in the picture plane. This line may be the main vertical corner of the object, which may be extended as shown in Fig. 105.

Heights for lines on surfaces meeting in the height line are traced directly to one of the VPs and into perspective position. Heights of other surfaces are traced around corners of the object or around imaginary corners to get them into correct perspective position from the height line.

Lines that are used to trace a height to perspective position must be, (1) lines to vanishing points, (2) must intersect at a corner in plan, and (3) must lead to the line where the height is located. The construction can go around any number of corners of the plan or imaginary corners for construction if the tracing lines follow these requirements. Remember to follow only the two line directions that lead to the vanishing points of the perspective.

An object behind the picture plane has side N–M extended in plan to meet the line from L (the vertical measuring line) at O. The height construction for line N–M follows the route L to O to N–M in plan. In perspective the construction for the height of line N–M follows the perspective of this same route from N on the heightline to O1 to N1–M1, the required line.

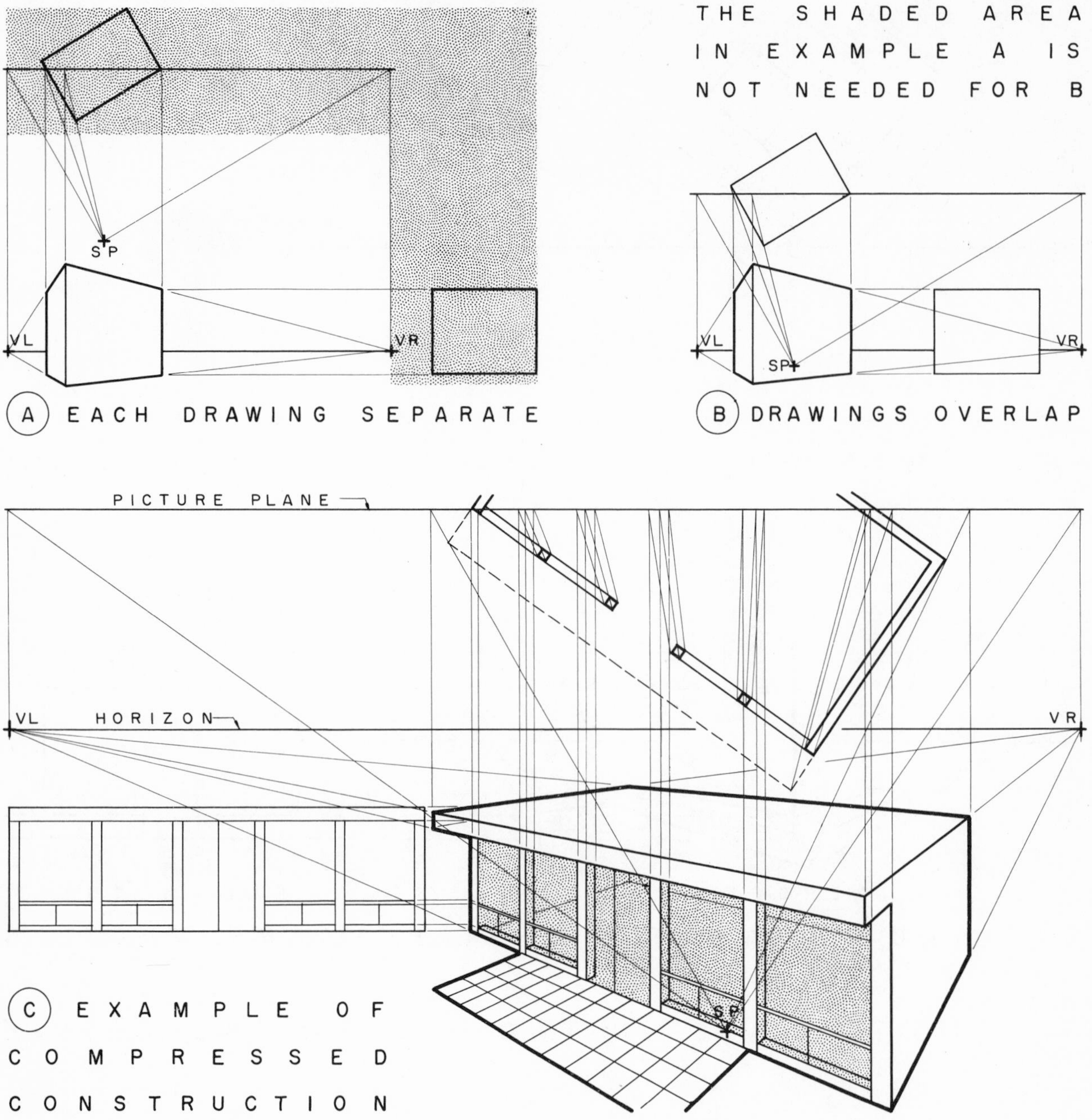

FIG. 106 SPACE SAVING IN EXTERIOR PERSPECTIVE

The preceding explanations of two-point exterior and interior perspective have used illustrations in which the plan, elevation, and perspective drawings have been separated to make the construction of the perspective drawings as clear as possible. Experienced draftsmen frequently overlap the auxiliary and perspective drawings for perspective construction. Figs. 106 and 107 show this procedure. The perspectives are made close to the plans of the object with the plan positions of the station points falling within the perspective drawings. The elevations are placed near the perspectives with one VP in or beyond the elevation to save space horizontally. Perspective drawings usually take a lot of space and the compressing of construction is often necessary to keep the drawings on the board.

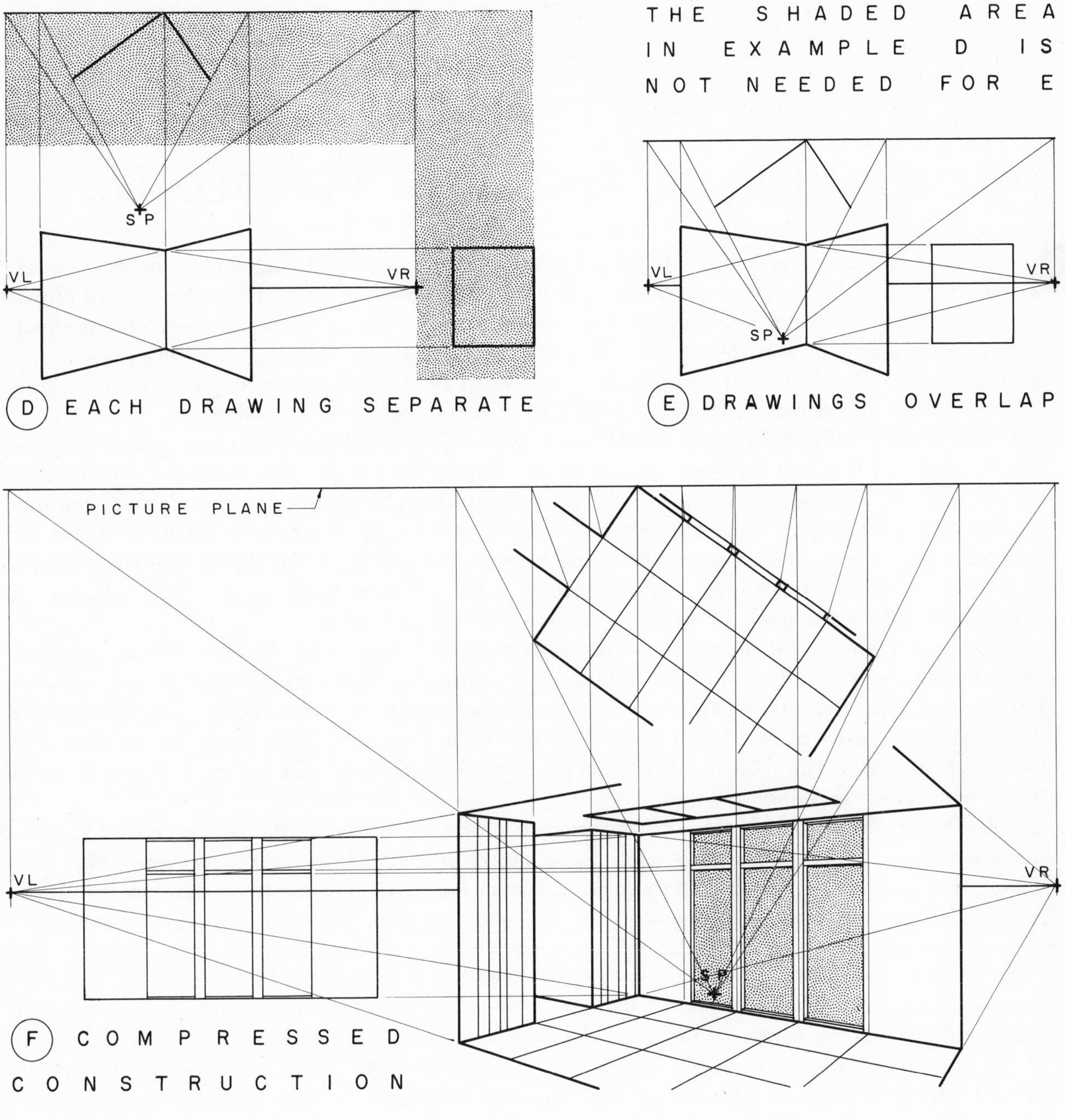

FIG. 107 SPACE SAVING FOR INTERIOR PERSPECTIVE

An elevation has been included as an auxiliary drawing in each explanation of perspective construction given in this text. It makes the height construction visually clear and helps to remove some of the uncertainties of the draftsman concerning heights. Furthermore it lessens the chances of error in height measurements. Any elevation or section view that gives the required heights can be used for this purpose. If the auxiliary drawing of the elevation clearly explains the design of the object, the construction from it is more easily understood.

Although it is helpful, an elevation is not an essential part of the construction of a perspective drawing. Heights can be laid out directly on the vertical measuring lines of the perspective. The ground line can be used as a base line from which the heights are measured.

CHAPTER 19

THE VARIABLES IN TWO-POINT PERSPECTIVE

How is it possible to obtain the perspective view of the object that the delineator wishes to have? That is one of the major problems of the person who is learning to use perspective drawing. There are only three things that can be varied in a perspective setup to change the pictorial effect. A change of any one, or two, or all three of these will change the appearance of the perspective. It is necessary for the designer to learn how to use each of these variables singly or in combinations in order to obtain the most effective illustrations from his perspective drawings.

THE THREE VARIABLES THAT CONTROL THE PICTORIAL EFFECT. Place some object on a desk. The three things that can be done to change the view of that object are the three items that can be changed in a perspective setup to vary the pictorial effect. The observer can look at the object (1) from different angles, (2) from different heights, and (3) from different distances. These three variations are the only ones that can be made to change the view of the object. The three variables in perspective are the three ways that the location of the station point can be changed to view the object from different angles, different heights, and different distances.

Only one thing, the variable under consideration, has been changed in the perspective setup of the sequence of illustrations explaining the effect of that variable on the perspective pictures in Figs. 108 I, II, and III. Thus any variation in perspective effect in a single sequence of these drawings is the result of one factor alone. In Fig. 108 I that factor is the angle of the object with the picture plane; in Fig. 108 II it is the height of the horizon line; and in Fig. 108 III it is the distance from object to station point.

I. The angle of the object with the picture plane as shown in plan can be varied to change the proportions of the two visible sides of an object seen in a perspective drawing, Fig. 108 I. Usually one face of the object is more important than the other. The angle of view can be adjusted to give the required amount of emphasis on the important side. It is more satisfactory composition if the two major areas are not equal in the perspective. It should be observed that in each of these three illustrations the plan is at a different angle with the picture plane. The station point for each drawing has been kept on the line of the center of vision. This line is perpendicular to the picture plane and through the center of the plan of the object. The SP should never be moved to one side of the plan to change the perspective. This will change the angle of view in the easiest way. However, it causes a distorted perspective that does not represent the true proportions of the object.

II. The height of the horizon in a perspective drawing determines whether the object is seen from above, from below, or from somewhere within its height, Fig. 108 II. The horizon carries with it wherever it is moved the perspective positions of the vanishing points of all horizontal lines. When an elevation is used as an auxiliary drawing the horizon is drawn in the chosen relation to the object on this drawing. Thus the draftsman is able to see a graphical representation of the height of the observer in relation to the object before drawing the perspective.

III. The distance from the object to the station point determines whether the object is viewed from very close, from far away, or from a middle distance, Fig. 108 III. When the SP is very near to the object the vanishing points are close to the perspective drawing. Lines to the VPs slant sharply. Horizontal areas appear large. There is a great contrast in size between near and distant parts of the object. When the station point is far from the object the vanishing points are far from the perspective. Line to the VPs become more nearly horizontal. There is little contrast in size of near and distant parts of the object. Horizontal surfaces that are visible become thin and small.

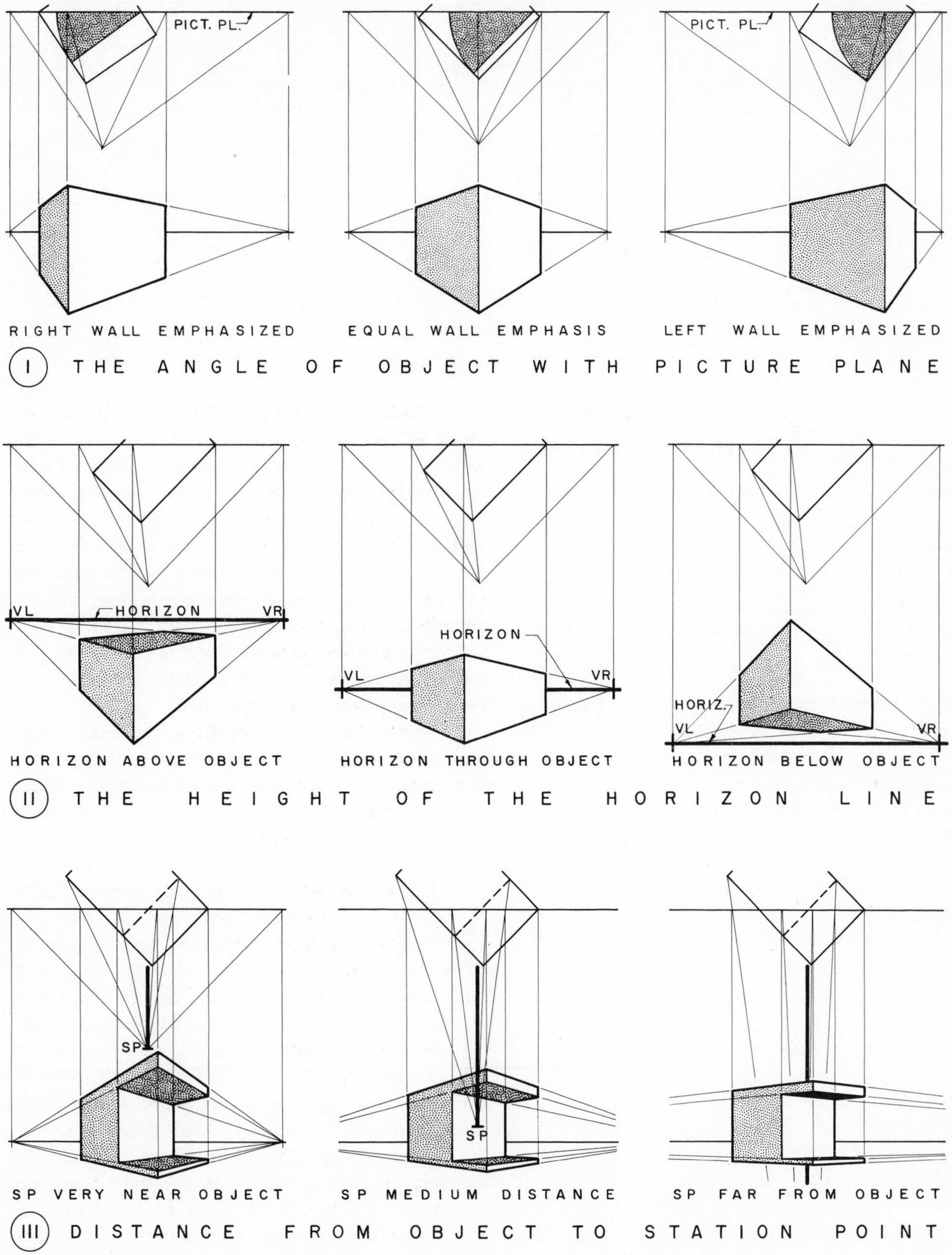

FIG. 108 THE THREE VARIABLES IN PERSPECTIVE

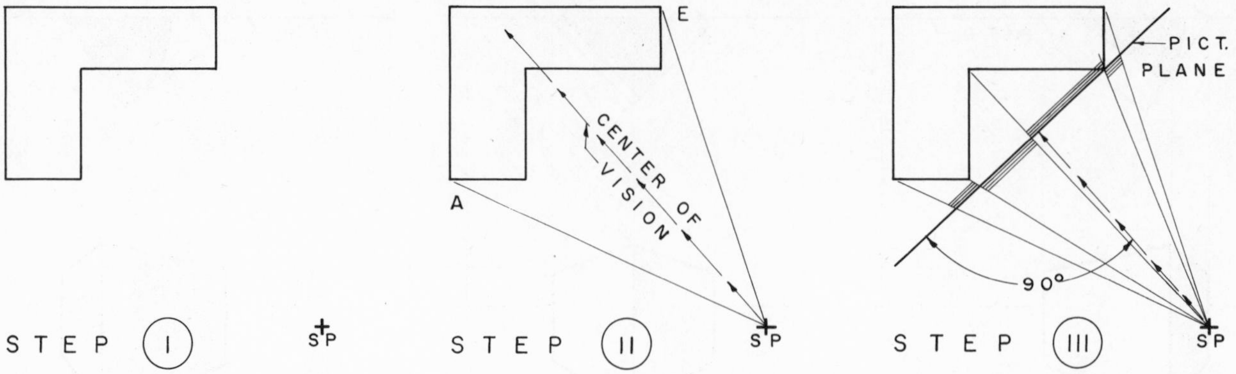

THREE STEPS IN EVALUATING A PROPOSED SP FROM A SINGLE MULTI-VIEW PLAN

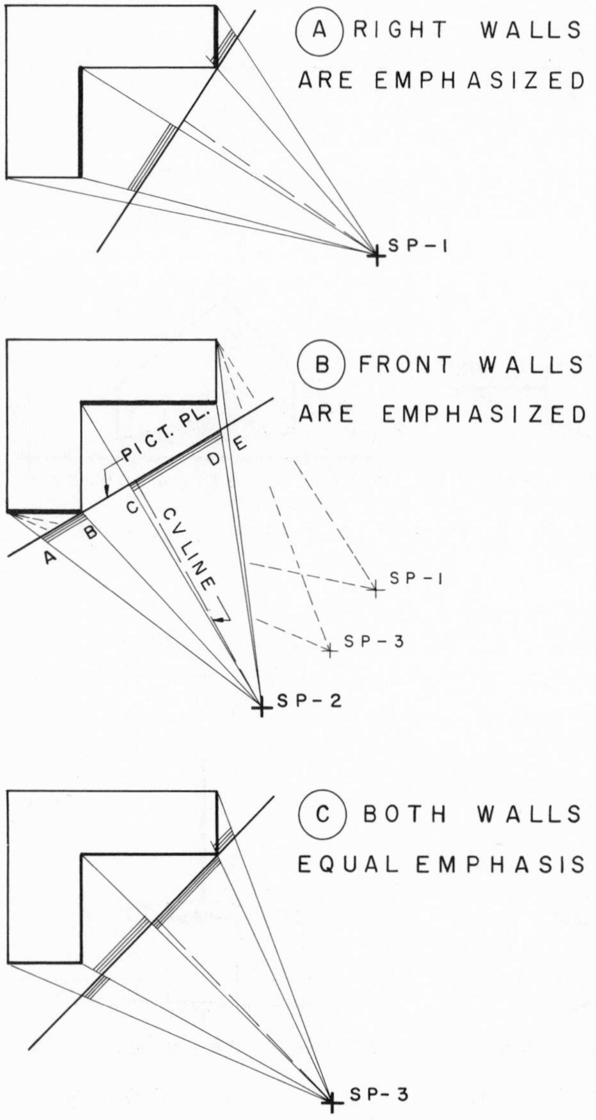

FIG. 109 SELECTING AN SP

SELECTING THE PLAN POSITION OF A STATION POINT. Because the plan position of the SP determines which wall areas will be visible and how much width each will occupy in the perspective its location is very important. The appearance of these vertical areas of the perspective from proposed SPs in order to choose a SP for a final perspective can be judged from a single block plan without actually constructing the perspectives. This preliminary work will increase the probabilities of obtaining a satisfactory perspective drawing with the minimum amount of drafting.

Three steps in the drafting process of testing a trial SP are given across the top of Fig. 109. The center of vision line should bisect the angle A–SP–E in step II and the picture plane line must be at 90° to the center of vision as shown in step III.

Three trial SPs are shown for the same plan in Fig. 109 B. To avoid confusion of lines one construction has been drawn in detail and the other two suggested with dotted lines. These two have been drawn in detail in Figs. 109 A and C in order to give a clear comparison of the three.

In actual practice the studies of proposed SPs can usually all be made and evaluated satisfactorily on the plan sheet of paper with a black drafting pencil. If this procedure becomes confusing, each study of a proposed SP can be made on the same sheet of paper with a different colored pencil, or studies can be made on tracing paper over the plan. More complex objects offer problems other than those in Fig. 109. Two or more masses of the object, and columns or large openings require study of alignment of these features.

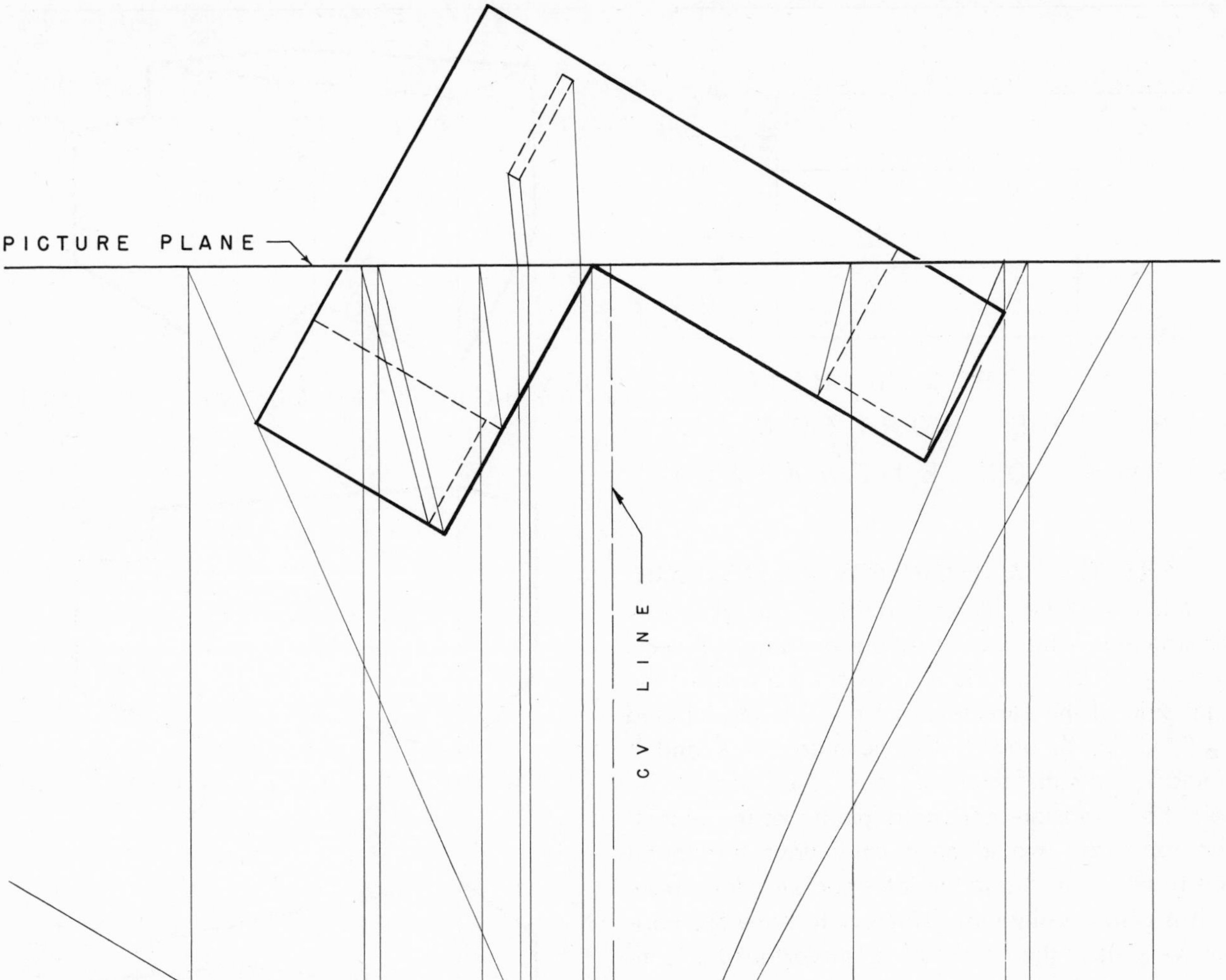

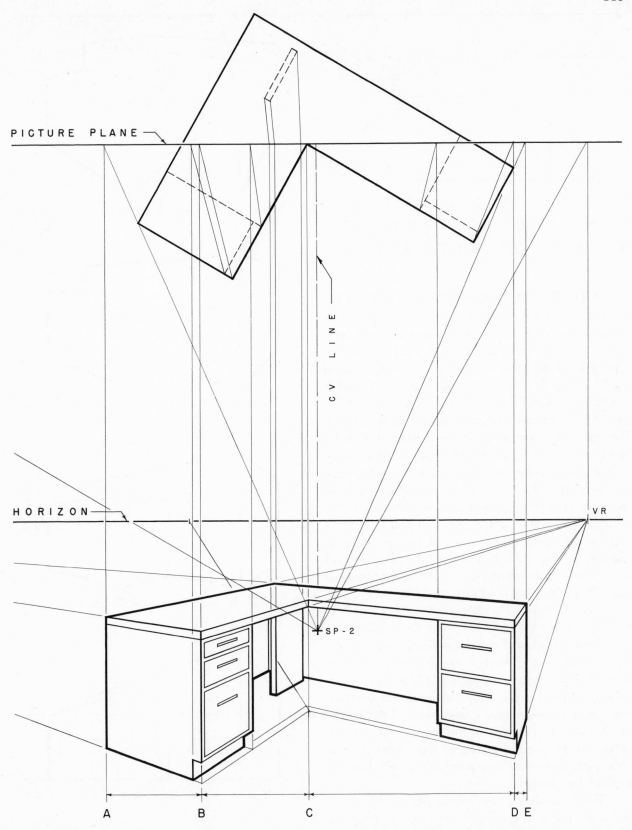

FIG. 110 PERSPECTIVE DRAWING FROM DIAGRAM 109 B

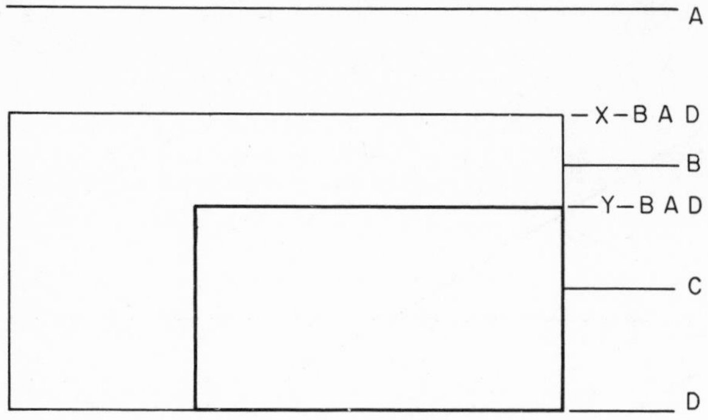

FIG. 111 PROPOSED HEIGHTS FOR THE HORIZON AS SHOWN ON ELEVATION

SELECTING A HEIGHT FOR THE HORIZON. A satisfactory height for a horizon can be partly determined from an elevation drawing. Several possible horizon positions have been drawn at the right side of the elevation of Fig. 111 and labeled A, B, C, D, X, and Y. The positions at X and Y would be unsatisfactory because they are at the height of important horizontal planes of the object. The top plane would be a continuous horizontal line from height X and the intermediate plane from Y. It is also usually unsatisfactory to have the horizon very near the height of an important horizontal plane so that it appears almost as a continuous straight line in the perspective. Position D is satisfactory for some purposes as shown in the perspective of Fig. 112 D. It simplifies shadows and foreground for rendering and provides emphasis of top silhouette. The positions at A, B, and C are some of the most satisfactory ones. Figs. 112 A, B, and C show perspectives from these positions.

Two additional considerations when choosing a height for a horizon are sometimes helpful in obtaining a good perspective. (1) A more interesting perspective is usually obtained with the horizon either above or below the center of the height of an object. (2) When the horizontal pattern either on the ground or top of the object is complex and important an aerial view will help to explain the design.

Block studies of the simple masses of an object can be drawn quickly in perspective. They are often helpful in selecting a setup for a large perspective. The sequence of Fig. 112 is a simple group of such studies.

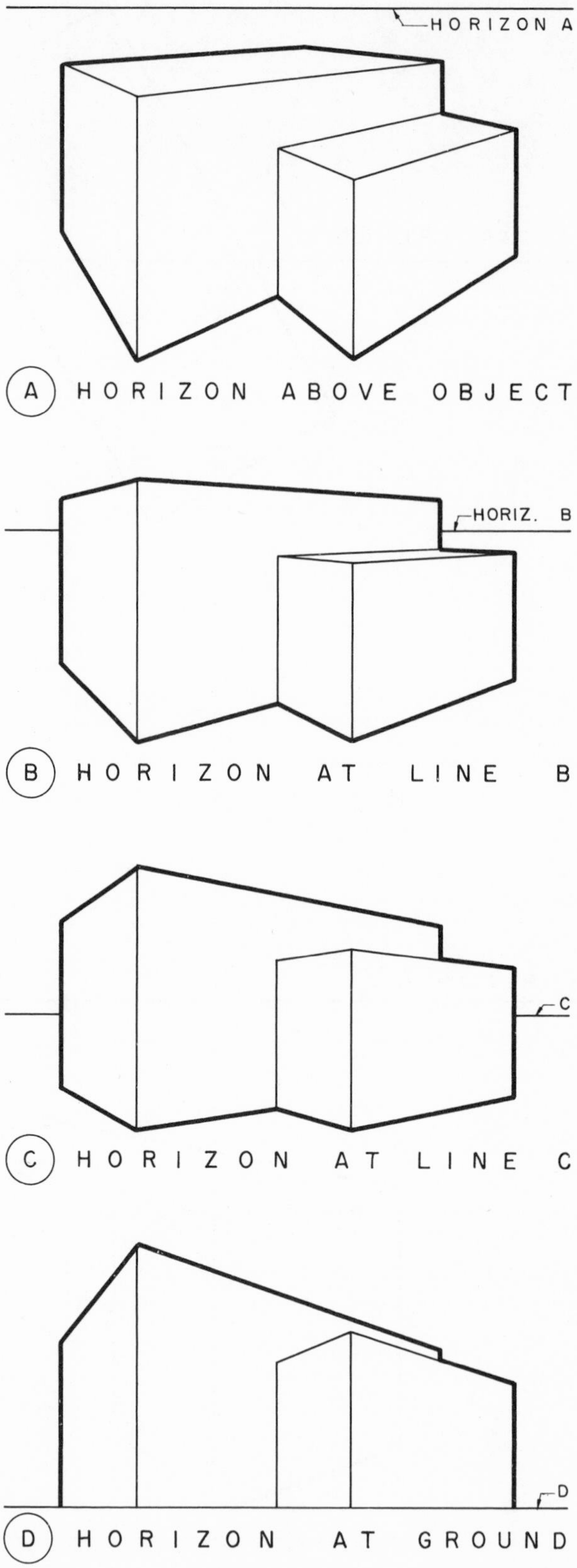

FIG. 112 SELECTING HORIZON FROM AN ELEVATION

SELECTING THE DISTANCE FROM OBJECT TO STATION POINT. How can the designer determine the distance away from the object for his station point? There is no one answer that will be best for all objects and under all conditions. The perspective should look right for the object depicted. It should also give the effect that will best satisfy the requirements of its use and purpose.

The estimated angle of clear vision of the human eyes has often been used to provide a minimum distance of SP from the object in making a perspective drawing. Such an arbitrary rule is likely to limit the imagination of the designer delineator, thus producing standardized and mediocre results. Furthermore it may eliminate consideration of special conditions that make a very large or very small angle of view appropriate and advantageous. The angle of vision of the human eyes is a rather speculative matter. We see most clearly a tiny area on which the eyes concentrate. Persons with two good eyes are able to see through a horizontal angle of 180°, a complete half circle. The center of this band is seen with both eyes, the edges with one eye only. The extreme edges of this area appear hazy. In between the center and edges of vision are diminishing degrees of clearness of sight with no decided breaks in sharpness.

The angle of vision in plan from the SP to the left and right edges of the object is sometimes used to locate the SP at a minimum or desirable distance from the object, Fig. 109 II, page 118, angle A–SP–E. This angle of vision may vary greatly under different conditions as explained below.

When the observer is within the object, or group of objects, the perspective subject extends all around him. This may be true in a landscape, in a group of buildings, and within some interiors. Under such conditions, and when near a very large object, the delineator may wish to use a very wide angle of view of 60° or slightly more from SP to edges of object for his perspective. In recognition of the variations of acuteness of vision and the extreme shapes at edges of his perspective, he may focus attention on the center of his perspective in presentation and subordinate the edges.

Circular forms and interior details become quite warped in perspectives that are made from close station points. This is especially true of circles in or near the corners of the drawings and of interiors when furniture, lighting fixtures, or other objects of distinctive forms appear in corners or along edges of the perspective drawings. A 45° or 30° maximum angle of vision is sometimes suggested for these objects.

When an object is extremely small it would almost touch the eye of the observer to appear as objects are shown in close up perspective. When it is drawn in this way it may appear unnatural and perhaps even ridiculous. Close up perspectives of ladies' compacts may appear very unreal because they are never viewed from very close by a person with normal vision. The same logic is even more emphatic for watches, jewelry, and other tiny objects. Even a 20° angle of vision may make the SP too close for these subjects. The making of a good perspective requires judgment and imagination in selecting positions of the variables for best results.

When the height of the object exceeds its width the SP should be located to suit the height.

Interior perspectives should, according to some persons, always be made from station points that could be used in the building to see the scene as it is depicted. This limits the amount that can be shown satisfactorily from within a room in a single perspective to a small proportion of the entire room. It does not allow a visual impression of the complete room. In some types of work it is permissible to assume that a part of the walls of the room are removed. The SP is then taken at a sufficient distance so that the entire room can be shown in a single perspective. When this is done the actual limits of the room should not be exceeded in the perspective drawing. These limits may be shown on ceiling or floor, or the lines of the drawing may stop short of the volume of the room.

The purpose of a perspective drawing should influence the selection of a SP. If the purpose is to show the object as it would actually be seen, the choice of a SP is often very limited. If the objective is to explain the forms of the object as clearly as possible, the selection of a SP has no limits. Perspectives have disadvantages over observation of the actual object. A person looking at an object has two eyes with binocular vision and depth perception. He also has the advantage of moving his eyes and head to see through a greater angle and of moving to change his position. The perspective has a fixed picture with one eye from one position.

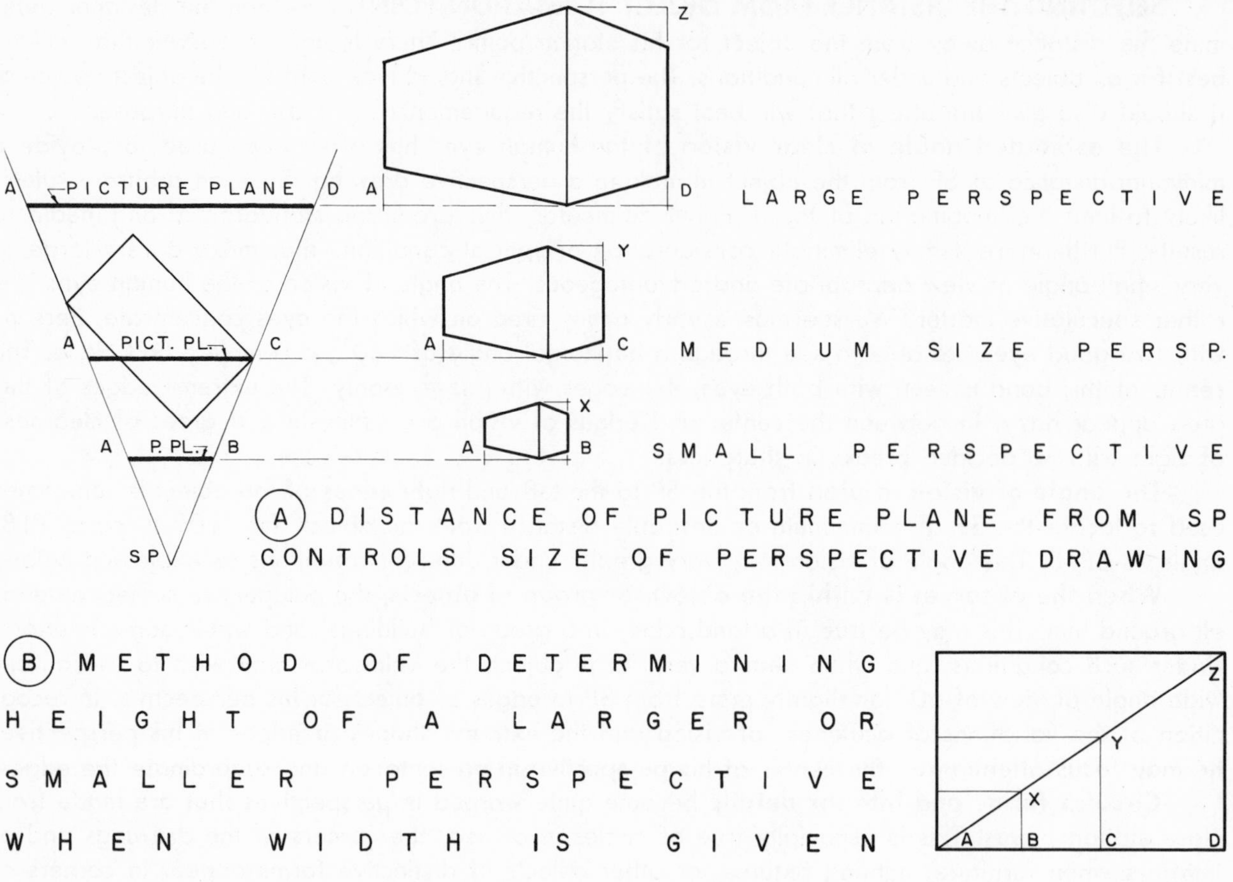

FIG. 113 CONTROLLING THE SIZE OF A PERSPECTIVE

CONTROLLING THE SIZE OF THE PERSPECTIVE DRAWING. The obvious method of obtaining size variations in the perspective drawing of a given object is to change the scale of the auxiliary plan and elevation. This will produce a considerable variation of size and the perspective drawings will be exact duplicates if the setup is not changed in other ways. This method is simple. However it requires a completely new construction for each size variation, does not provide for small changes of size, and is limited by scale ratios to a few sizes.

Parallel positions of the picture plane can be used to control the size of the perspective drawing obtained from a given plan and elevation as suggested by the diagram of Fig. 113 A. The position of the picture plane can be varied by moving it either farther from or nearer to the station point. When the perspective setup is not changed in other ways, and all positions of the picture plane are parallel, the only change in the resulting perspective will be in size. This procedure allows small or large variations in size in the perspectives. The same auxiliary plan, elevation, and station point can be used for constructing perspectives of different sizes. New studies can be made on tracing paper over the first one. The width of the proposed perspective can be determined by extending the lines from the station point through the extreme left and right edges of the plan of the object and measuring the picture plane line between them as shown in Fig. 113 A. When both the height and width of one perspective are given and the widths of other sizes of the same perspective are assumed, their corresponding heights can be determined as shown in Fig. 113 B. This method is based on the fact that diagonals of rectangles having the same proportion are parallel when the corresponding sides of the rectangles are parallel. The method of controlling the size of the perspective precisely by the position of the picture plane is very useful and practical. Extreme enlargements produced by locating the picture plane far beyond the object will magnify inaccuracies.

Enlarging a perspective drawing is sometimes the simplest and best way to produce a larger perspective drawing. Two methods of enlarging a perspective are shown in Fig. 114. In the first method, which is shown in Fig. 114 I, a common point A and line A–B of the two perspectives are used as the beginning of the enlarged drawing, which is superimposed on a copy of the small drawing. Any lines like A–C and A–D that meet at the selected pivot point A will be extended to make the enlarged drawing. Lines that do not coincide for a part of their lengths are parallel in the two drawings. A line drawn from the pivot point A through any corner X or other point on the small perspective will when extended pass through the same point on the large drawing. After the length of one line on the enlarged drawing is determined all other sizes are constructed by the use of radiating and parallel lines. With this method one size of enlargement is as easy as another. There is no advantage to simple fractional relations as there would be when using a scale to make an enlargement or reduction of size of a drawing.

The technique employed when using this method can be varied to suit the way the drawing is located and used. A simple method is to make the large drawing on tracing paper over the small one.

The second method of enlarging a perspective drawing is shown in Fig. 114 II. Its theory is simple. A rectangle is drawn tangent to the given small perspective. Lines of the perspective are extended to the edges of the rectangle. A larger rectangle of the same proportion is made the size selected for the large perspective. The points of intersection on the sides of the small rectangle are transferred to correct positions on the large rectangle. These points can be located by scale when the relative sizes permit. They can be located by methods of proportional enlarging regardless of size relation. The lines of the large perspective are drawn through the points on the tangent rectangle. It is more convenient and more accurate to use vanishing points when they are close enough.

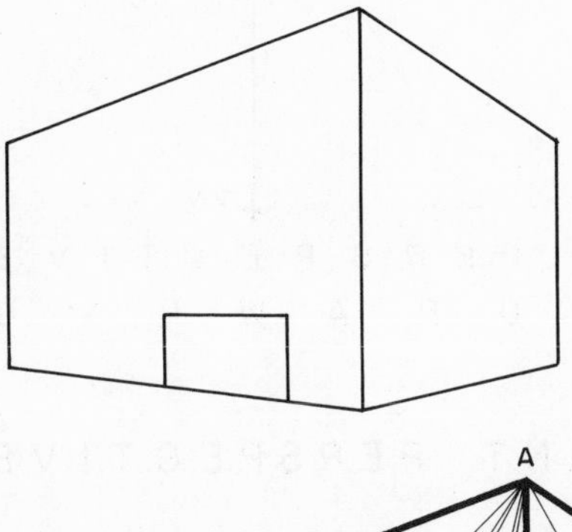

(I) WITH RADIATING AND PARALLEL LINES

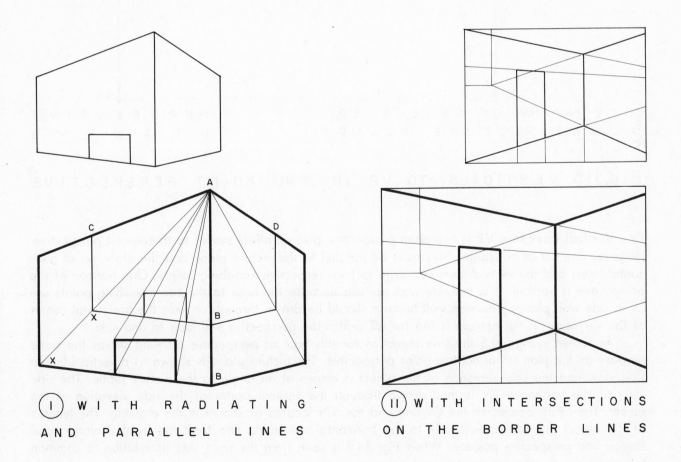

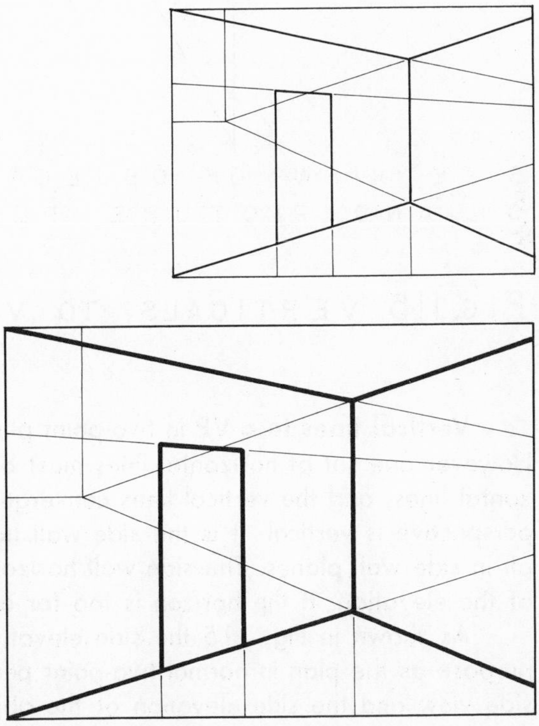

(II) WITH INTERSECTIONS ON THE BORDER LINES

FIG. 114 ENLARGING A PERSPECTIVE DRAWING

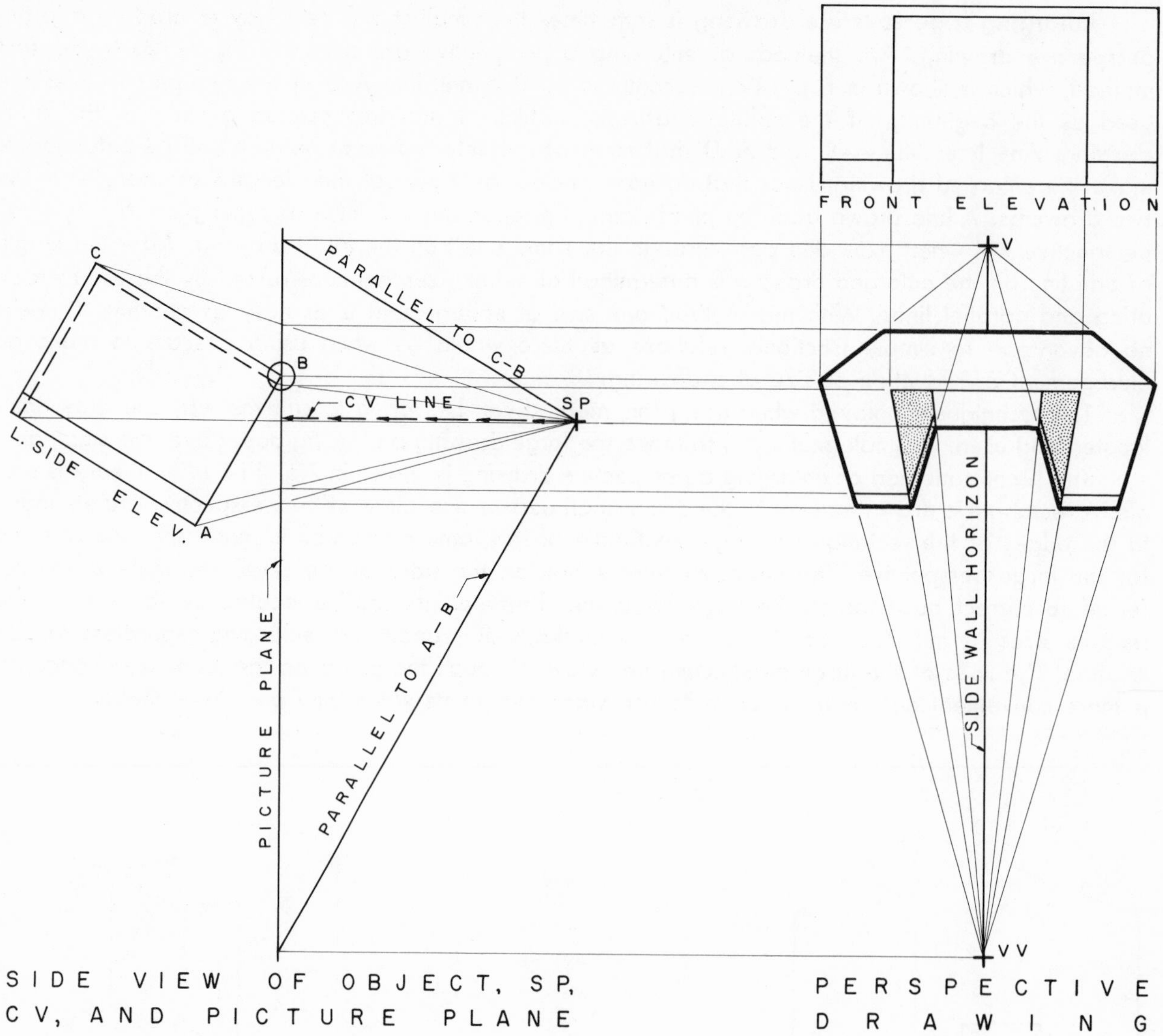

FIG. 115 VERTICALS TO VP IN TWO-POINT PERSPECTIVE

Vertical lines to a VP in two-point perspective give an effect similar to three-point perspective. However one set of horizontal lines must be parallel to the picture plane and the other set of horizontal lines, and the vertical lines converge to their respective vanishing points. One horizon of the perspective is vertical. It is the side wall horizon because the lines to the two vanishing points are all in side wall planes. The side wall horizon should be drawn through or near the horizontal center of the elevation. If the horizon is too far off center the perspective will lean to one side.

As shown in Fig. 115 the side elevation for this type of perspective drawing serves the same purpose as the plan in normal two-point perspective. The picture plane is shown as a vertical line in side view and the side elevation of the object is drawn at an angle to the picture plane. The side view of the horizontal CV is then drawn through the vertical center of the side elevation of the object. The SP is located on the CV line and the VPs located as shown in the drawing. The lengths of the object are carried vertically to the horizontal measuring line from the front elevation and thence into perspective position. When Fig. 115 is seen from the right side its relation to common two-point perspective construction will be more apparent.

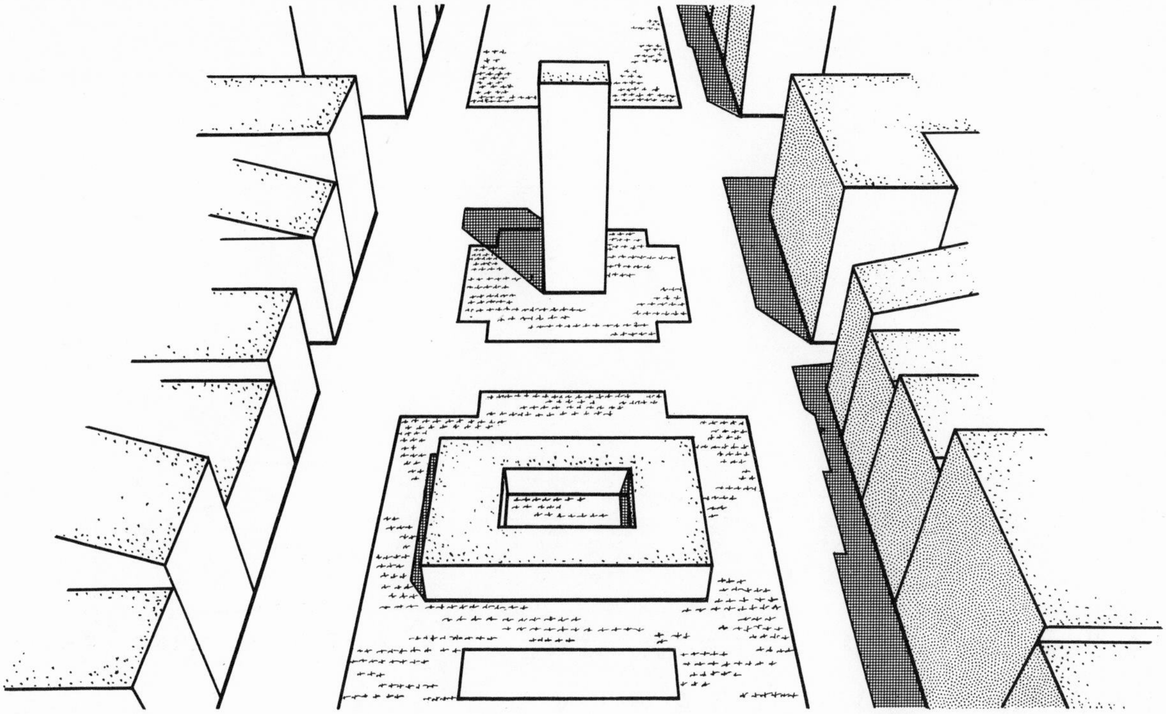

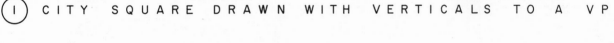

(I) CITY SQUARE DRAWN WITH VERTICALS TO A VP

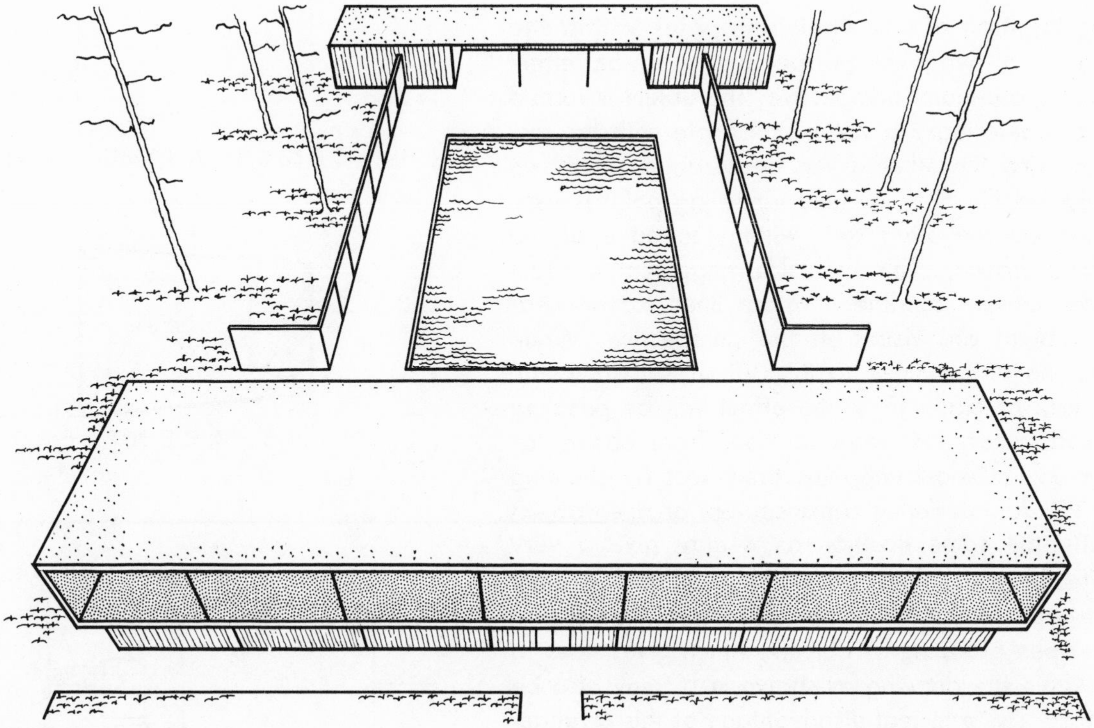

(II) PERSPECTIVE PLOT PLAN WITH VERTICALS TO A VP

FIG. 116 VERTICALS TO A VP IN TWO-POINT PERSPECTIVE

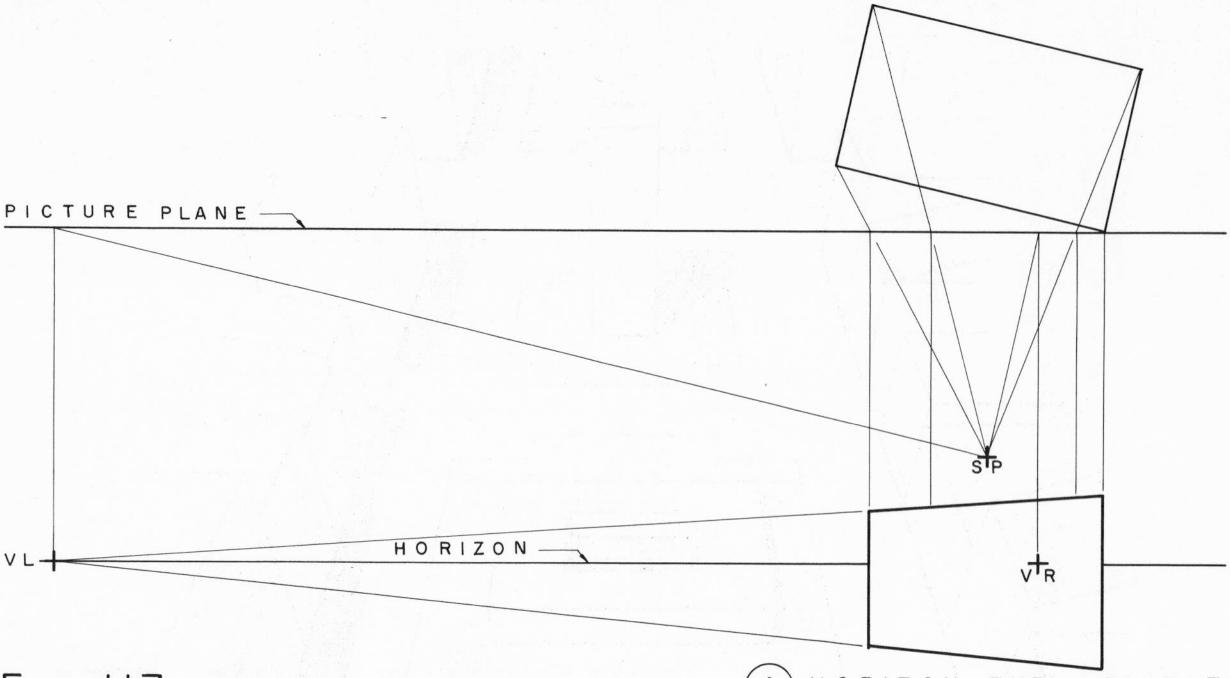

A HORIZON THRU OBJECT

FIG. 117 ONE VP WITHIN THE PERSPECTIVE DRAWING IN TWO-POINT PERSPECTIVE

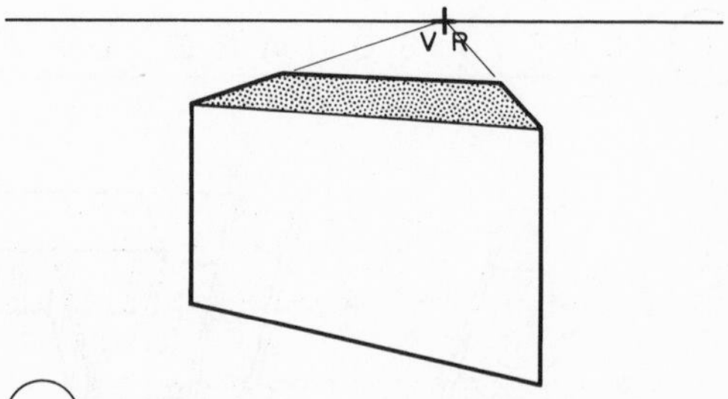

B HORIZON ABOVE OBJECT

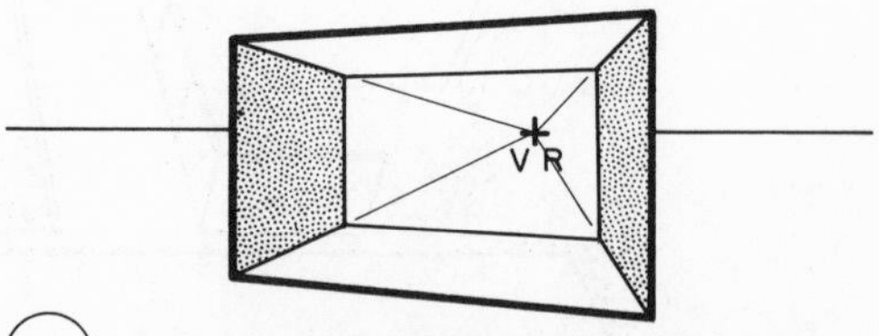

C TRANSPARENT FRONT

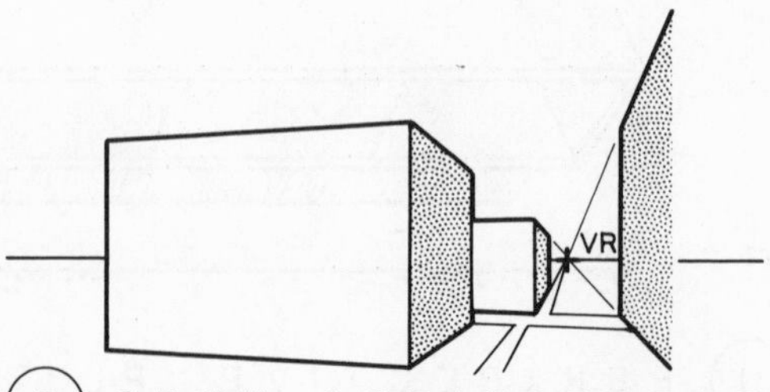

D OPEN ARRANGEMENT GIVING LINES TO THE VR

The location of one vanishing point within the drawing of a two-point perspective gives an effect approaching one-point perspective. The object is turned so that one side make a very small angle with the picture plane and the other a very large angle as shown in the plan of Fig. 117 A. One vanishing point is very far away and the other falls within the edge of the perspective drawing. This special arrangement is effective under certain conditions where lines to the near vanishing point are visible in the perspective. When there are no visible lines to this VP as shown in the opaque box of Fig. 117 A the effect will be puzzling and unsatisfactory. However a view from above, as shown in B, or below improves the effect by showing lines to VR. An interior or a transparent or open object in exactly the same position as A may give a very good effect because there are visible lines of the object that converge to the VP within the drawing as shown in C. An open grouping of objects, which gives lines to the VP within the drawing as shown in D, may also be satisfactory. The principal disadvantage of this arrangement is the somewhat minor difficulty encountered in locating and using the distant vanishing point or in drawing to this point without locating it.

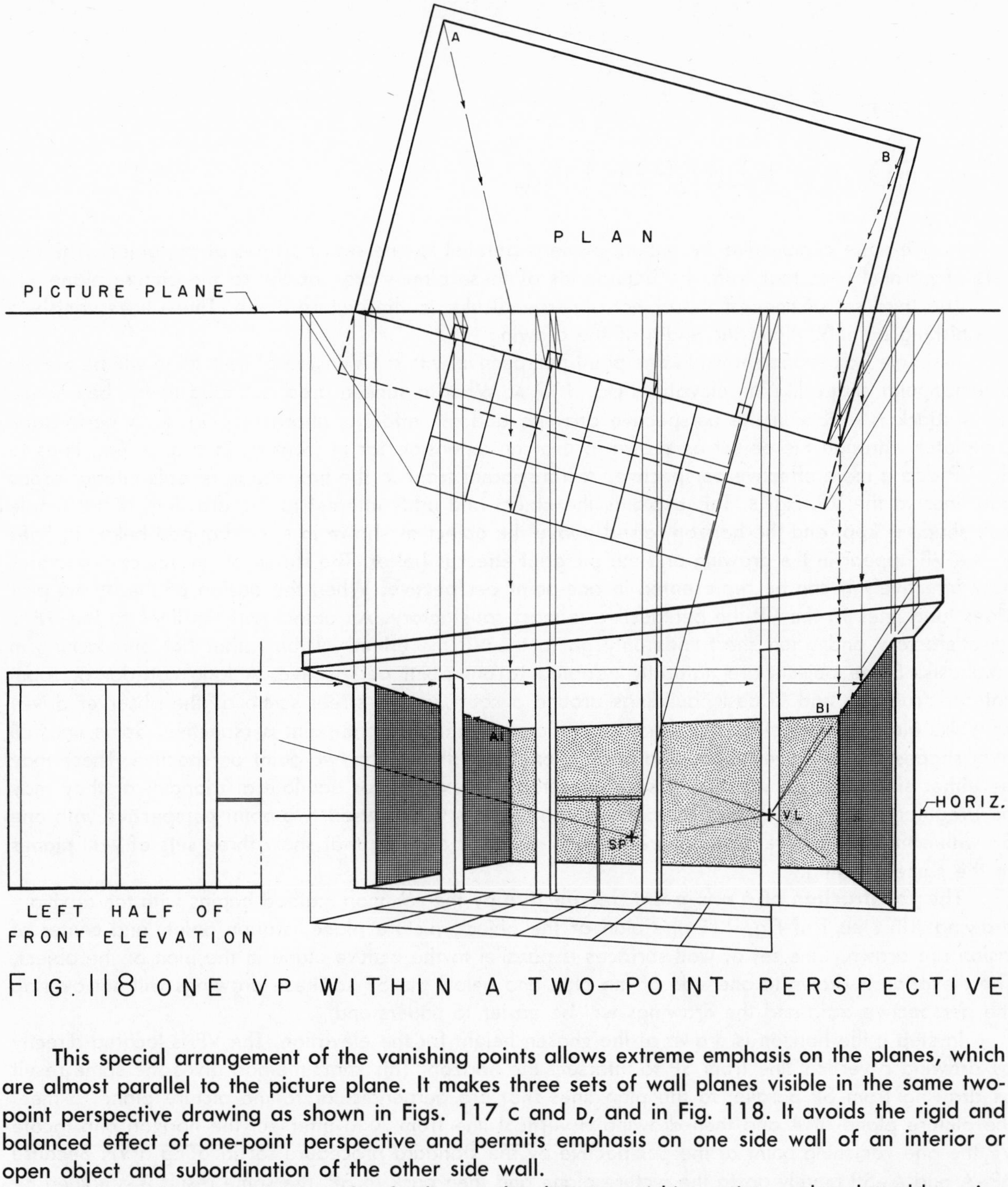

FIG. 118 ONE VP WITHIN A TWO—POINT PERSPECTIVE

This special arrangement of the vanishing points allows extreme emphasis on the planes, which are almost parallel to the picture plane. It makes three sets of wall planes visible in the same two-point perspective drawing as shown in Figs. 117 C and D, and in Fig. 118. It avoids the rigid and balanced effect of one-point perspective and permits emphasis on one side wall of an interior or open object and subordination of the other side wall.

Fig. 118 shows how both ends of a line to the distant vanishing point can be plotted by using the near vanishing point. The line can then be drawn between the two points and will be in the correct direction to the missing distant VP. This construction is emphasized for line A–B. This method is satisfactory when there are only a few lines to the distant VP. It is more accurate for long lines than for short ones. This method is shown in Fig. 159 A also.

When very many lines are drawn to the missing distant VP the scales method explained on pages 172 and 173 will be more satisfactory.

Additional illustrations of this type of perspective are shown on pages 273, 285, and 289.

CHAPTER 20

ONE-POINT PERSPECTIVE

In one-point perspective the picture plane is parallel to one set of planes of the object. The two sets of parallel lines that form the boundaries of these planes are parallel to the picture plane.

The third set of lines of the object is perpendicular to the picture plane. These lines vanish to a vanishing point V within the width of the drawing.

A simple box shape shown in one-point perspective with a CV inside of its outline will be merely a rectangular shape like an elevation, Fig. 119 A. When a sunken area is added to the box shape the setback is visible in the perspective drawing and the effect is improved, Fig. B. A perforation completely through the object as shown in C or an extension far in front as in D give long lines to the VP and a more effective perspective. A transparent front to the box shape reveals interior areas and lines to the VP, Fig. E. This explains the object and adds interest to the drawing. If the simple box shape is kept and the horizon raised above the object as shown in F, or dropped below it, lines to the VP appear in the drawing and the pictorial effect is better. The shape of an object determines how effectively it can be represented in one-point perspective. When the design of the object provides long lines to the VP the perspective is most satisfactory. An object with no lines to the VP is unsatisfactory and when short lines only go to the VP the effect will be rather flat and lacking in emphasis. Some objects are naturally adapted to one-point perspective. A long corridor or room entered from the end, a desk, buildings around a court, and a street scene as the observer drives or walks along the street appear very emphatic and natural in one-point perspective. Some unusual plan shapes are explained more clearly by a one-point than by a two-point perspective. These may be either simple polygonal shapes such as octagon, hexagon, or equilateral triangle, or they may be irregular shapes. One-point perspective and the less widely used two-point perspective with one SP within the perspective drawing are the only types of drawing that show three sets of wall planes in the same drawing.

The construction of a one-point perspective by the common method begins with the auxiliary drawings. In step I of Fig. 119 the plan of the object, picture plane, station point, and center of vision are drawn. One set of wall surfaces is parallel to the pciture plane in the plan of the object. The elevation is drawn to one side of the plan and below the SP so these drawings will not overlap the perspective area and the drawings will be easier to understand.

In step II the horizon is drawn at the chosen height for the elevation. The VP is located directly by drawing a vertical line from SP to intersect the horizon. This short method gives the same result as drawing from SP parallel to the plan lines that are perpendicular to the picture plane to meet the picture plane at A and then drawing a vertical line from A to intersect the horizon and locate VP the one vanishing point of the perspective by the standard procedure for locating a VP. Because SP–A and A–SP merely go to the picture plane and then back to SP, the same result is obtained by drawing a vertical directly from SP to the horizon line. The part of the object that lies in the picture plane is now constructed by drawing verticals from plan and horizontals from elevation to locate points and lines. This part of the perspective drawing is a scale size part elevation of the object.

In step III projection lines are drawn from points in plan toward SP to meet the picture plane and then vertically into the perspective area. They locate the horizontal spacing of points and vertical lines in the perspective. Lines are drawn from corners B, C, D, and E of the scale drawing at the picture plane toward the VP to meet the verticals just drawn. The horizontals from these intersections complete this simple one-point perspective.

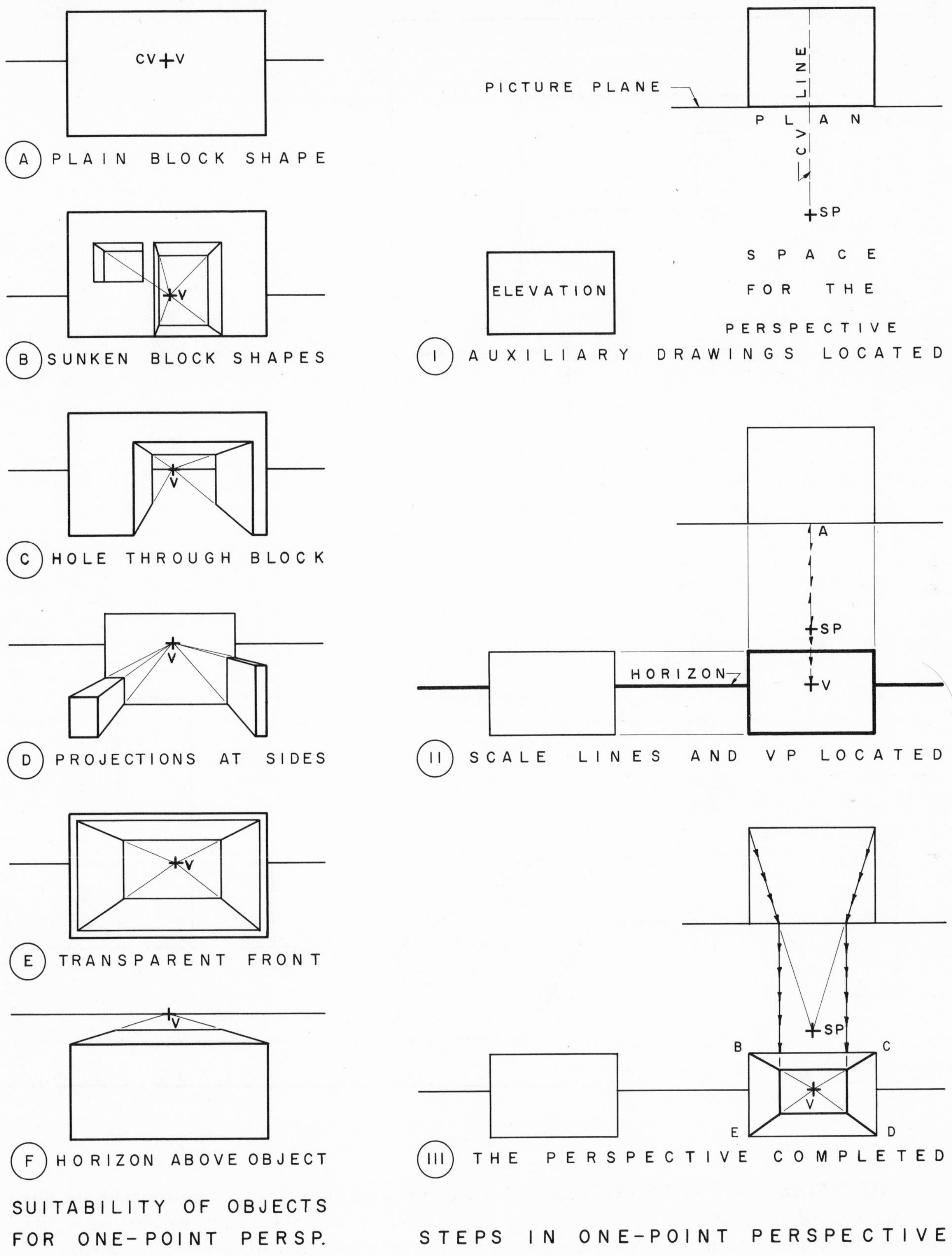
CV+V
A PLAIN BLOCK SHAPE
V
B SUNKEN BLOCK SHAPES
V
C HOLE THROUGH BLOCK
V
D PROJECTIONS AT SIDES
V
E TRANSPARENT FRONT
V
F HORIZON ABOVE OBJECT
SUITABILITY OF OBJECTS FOR ONE-POINT PERSP.
PICTURE PLANE
LINE
PLAN
CV
SP
ELEVATION
SPACE FOR THE PERSPECTIVE
I AUXILIARY DRAWINGS LOCATED
A
SP
HORIZON
V
II SCALE LINES AND VP LOCATED
SP
B
C
V
E
D
III THE PERSPECTIVE COMPLETED
STEPS IN ONE-POINT PERSPECTIVE

FIG. 119 ELEMENTARY ONE-POINT PERSPECTIVE

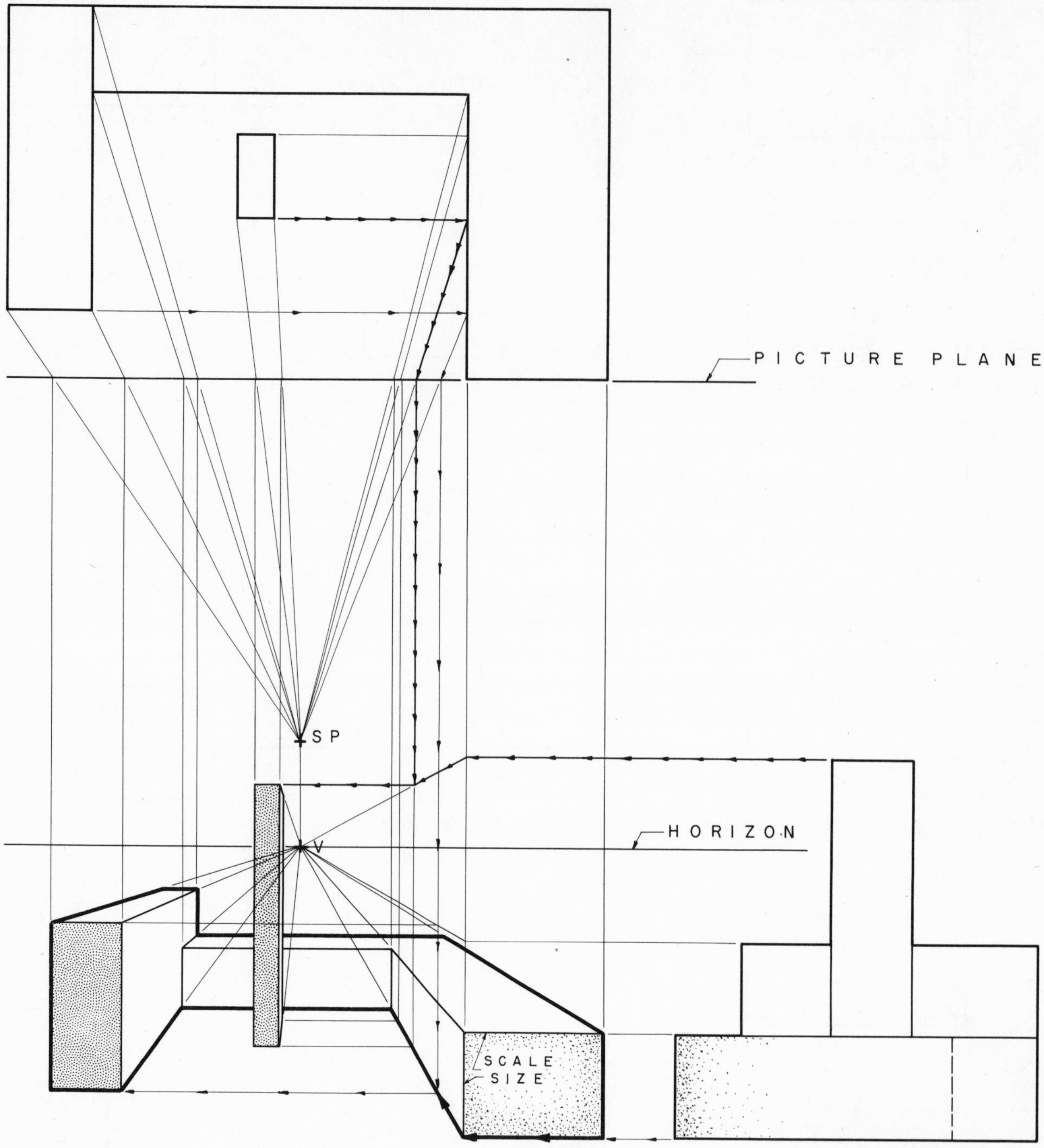

FIG. 120 WALL PLANE HEIGHT METHOD FOR EXTERIORS

THE DETERMINATION OF HEIGHTS. There are two general methods of determining heights in one-point perspective. They are (1) by carrying heights around wall planes into perspective position, and (2) by projecting from a scale silhouette in the picture plane toward or from the V point.

The method of carrying heights around wall planes seems more obvious for interiors than for most exterior perspectives because the walls of the object are usually more nearly adequate to serve for height construction without using imaginary wall planes. The heights are carried from the scale size end wall area of the perspective along the side walls toward V in Fig. 120 and away

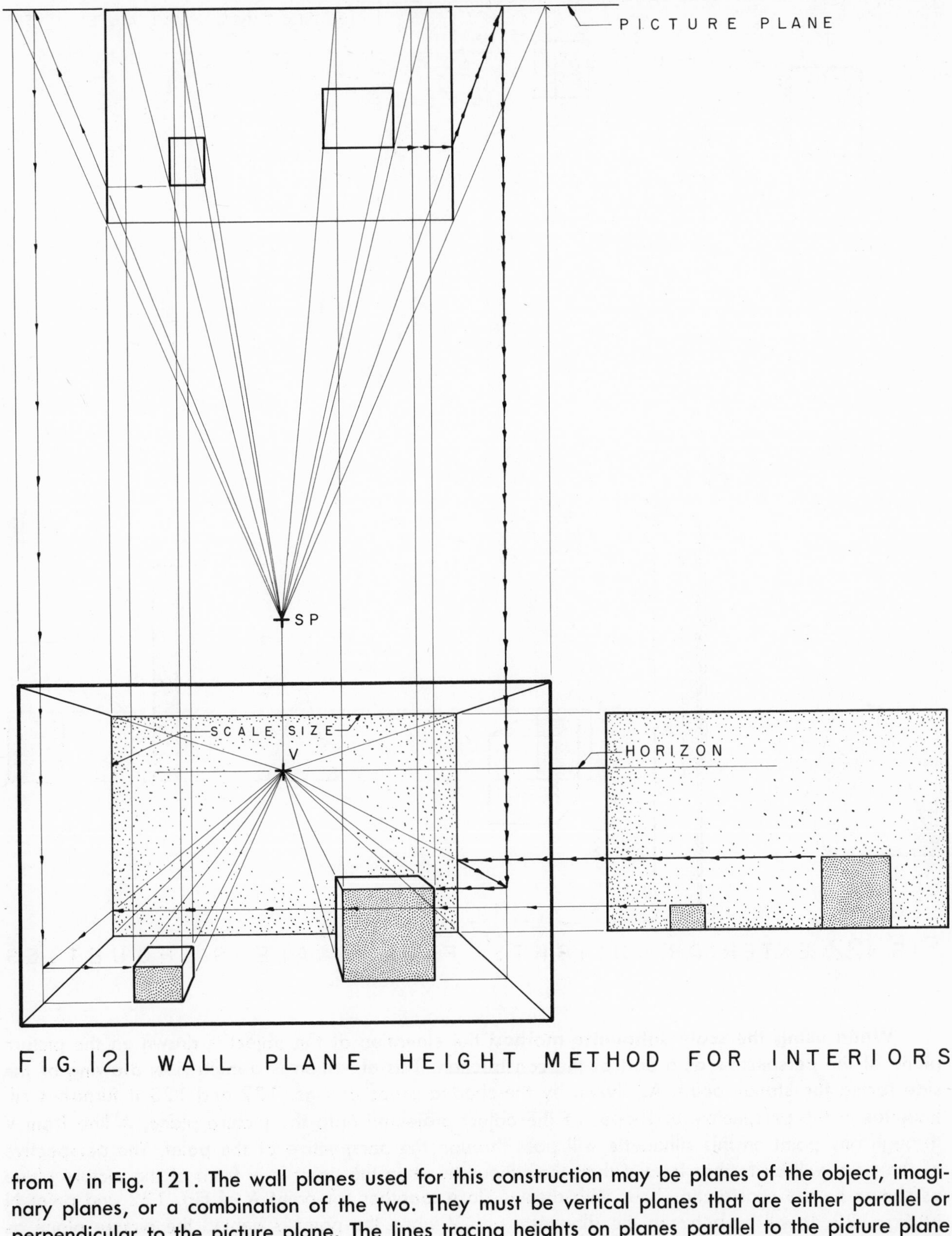

FIG. 121 WALL PLANE HEIGHT METHOD FOR INTERIORS

from V in Fig. 121. The wall planes used for this construction may be planes of the object, imaginary planes, or a combination of the two. They must be vertical planes that are either parallel or perpendicular to the picture plane. The lines tracing heights on planes parallel to the picture plane are horizontal lines. Those on planes perpendicular to the picture plane are drawn either toward or away from the vanishing point V of the perspective drawing. These lines to or from V represent horizontal lines perpendicular to the picture plane in the perspective. The heights can be carried behind the picture plane as shown in Fig. 120 or in front of the picture plane as shown in Fig. 121.

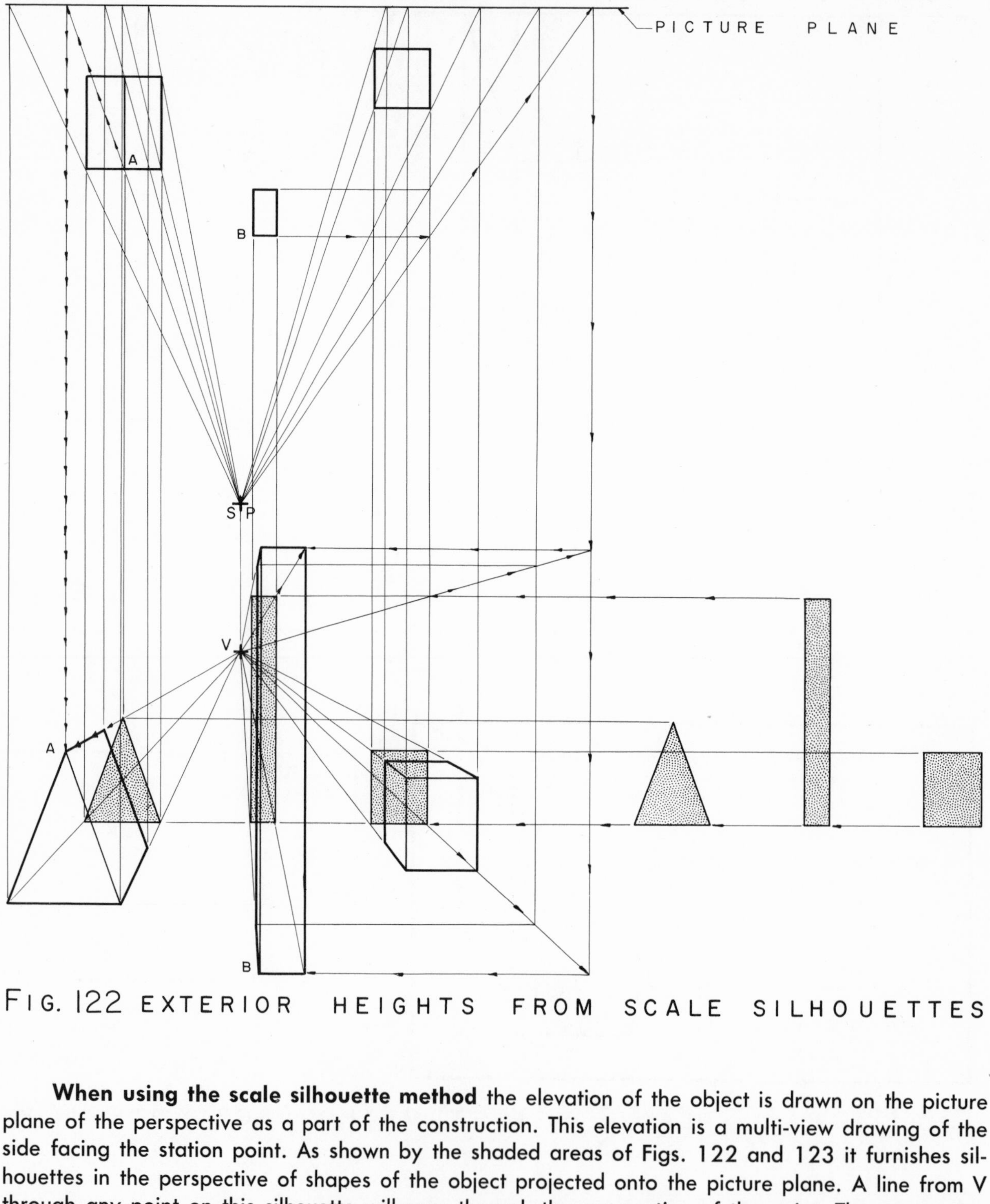

FIG. 122 EXTERIOR HEIGHTS FROM SCALE SILHOUETTES

When using the scale silhouette method the elevation of the object is drawn on the picture plane of the perspective as a part of the construction. This elevation is a multi-view drawing of the side facing the station point. As shown by the shaded areas of Figs. 122 and 123 it furnishes silhouettes in the perspective of shapes of the object projected onto the picture plane. A line from V through any point on this silhouette will pass through the perspective of the point. The perspective of the point will be farther from V than the silhouette when the point is in front of the picture plane as shown by the construction lines with arrows close together for point A of Fig. 122 and point N of Fig. 123. It will be between the silhouette and V when the point is behind the picture plane as shown by point O of Fig. 123. When the point is on the picture plane its perspective position will coincide with its position on the scale silhouette.

The perspective position of the point on the line from V is determined by drawing a line from the plan of the point toward or away from SP, as required by its location, to meet the picture plane.

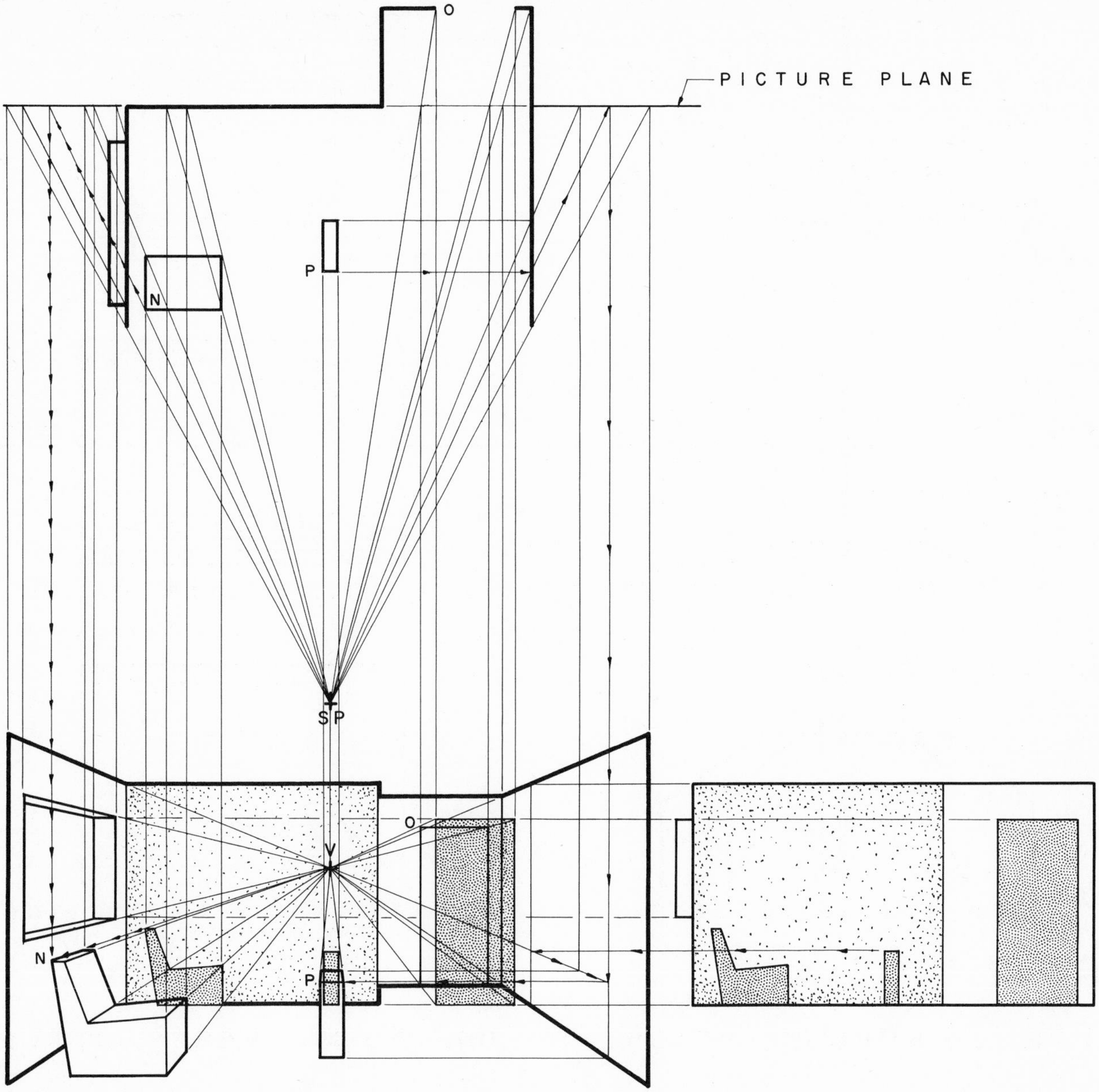

FIG. 123 INTERIOR HEIGHTS FROM SCALE SILHOUETTES

The vertical from this intersection meets the line from V in the required point. Projectors through the top and bottom points of vertical lines of the silhouette give their heights in the perspective.

This method of determining heights in a one-point perspective works very well for points that are far to one side of the station point. As construction nears a vertical line through the SP it becomes increasingly more difficult to locate accurately the intersections of the almost vertical lines from V and the verticals from plan. When the line from V is vertical there is no intersection with the vertical from plan and the point cannot be located by this method. In such cases where the direct construction is inaccurate or impossible an indirect method can be used as shown for point B of Fig. 122 and point P of Fig. 123 by the lines with small arrows spaced far apart. A line or plane of this part of the object is assumed to be moved horizontally to the right or left of the real object. Height construction is made for this new imaginary position and then carried across horizontally to the real position on the perspective.

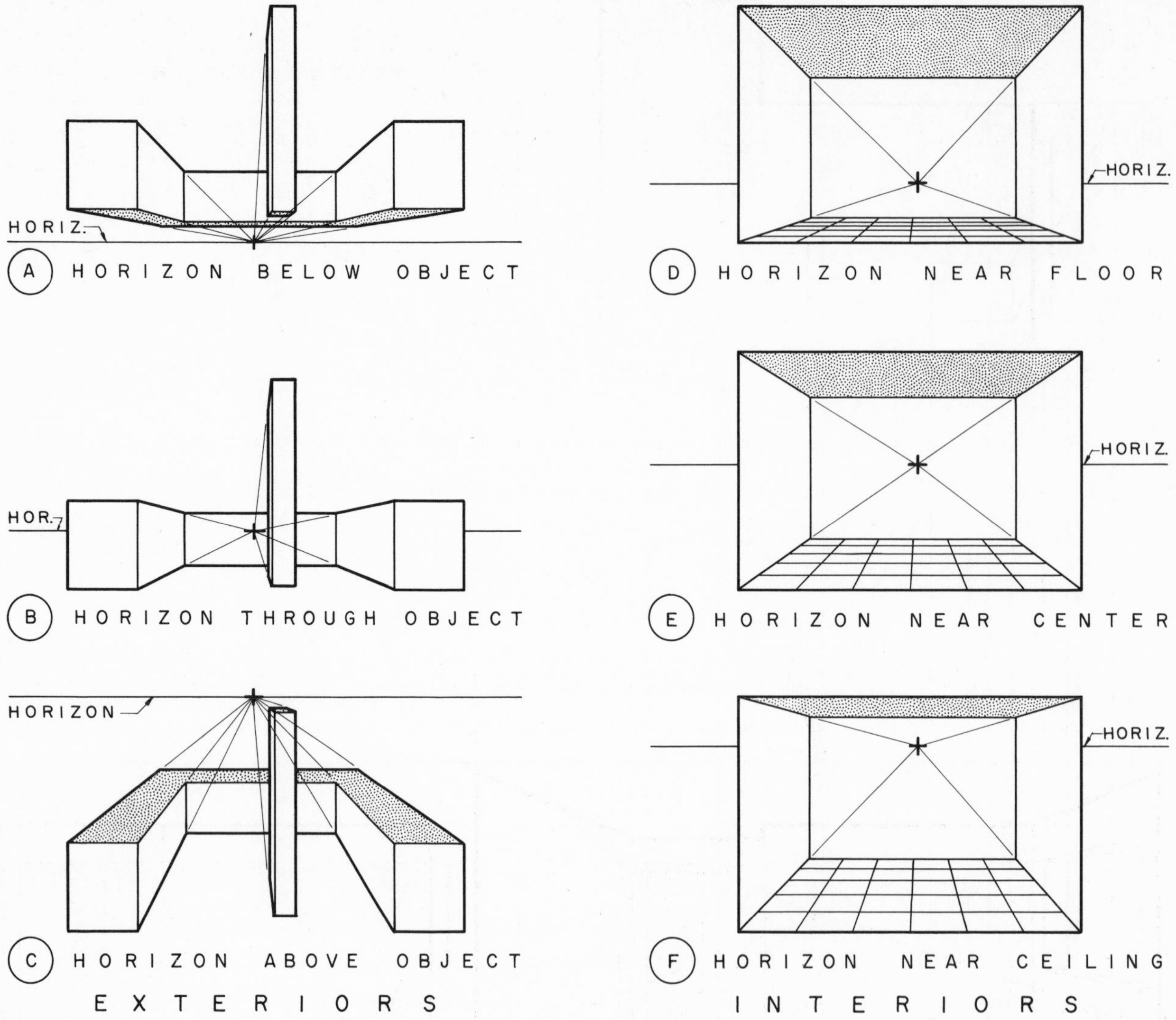

FIG. 124 HORIZON HEIGHT IN ONE-POINT PERSPECTIVE

THE VARIABLES. Less extensive and less spectacular changes are produced by variables in the pictorial effects of one-point perspective than in two-point perspective. The angle of the object with the picture plane cannot be varied in one-point perspective.

The variations of the height of the horizon in one-point perspective can produce in an exterior a view from below, a normal perspective, or a view from above as shown in Figs. 124 A, B, C. In interiors the horizon is almost always located between floor and ceiling, Figs. 124 D, E, F. The variations of height of the horizon are often further restricted by the necessity for showing tops of tables and other pieces of furniture. These are frequently shown from the height of a standing or seated person within the room. Stairways or differences of floor levels sometimes give variations of height of horizon different from those of actual view points within the interior of a single room.

The distance from SP to object does not change the position of the vanishing point because it is located by drawing a vertical from SP to the horizon. However it does change the angle of the projectors from SP to different points on the object. When the SP is close to the object, large areas of horizontal and vertical planes perpendicular to the picture plane appear in the perspective, Figs. 125 I, IV because of the widely diverging projectors in plan. As the distance from SP to object

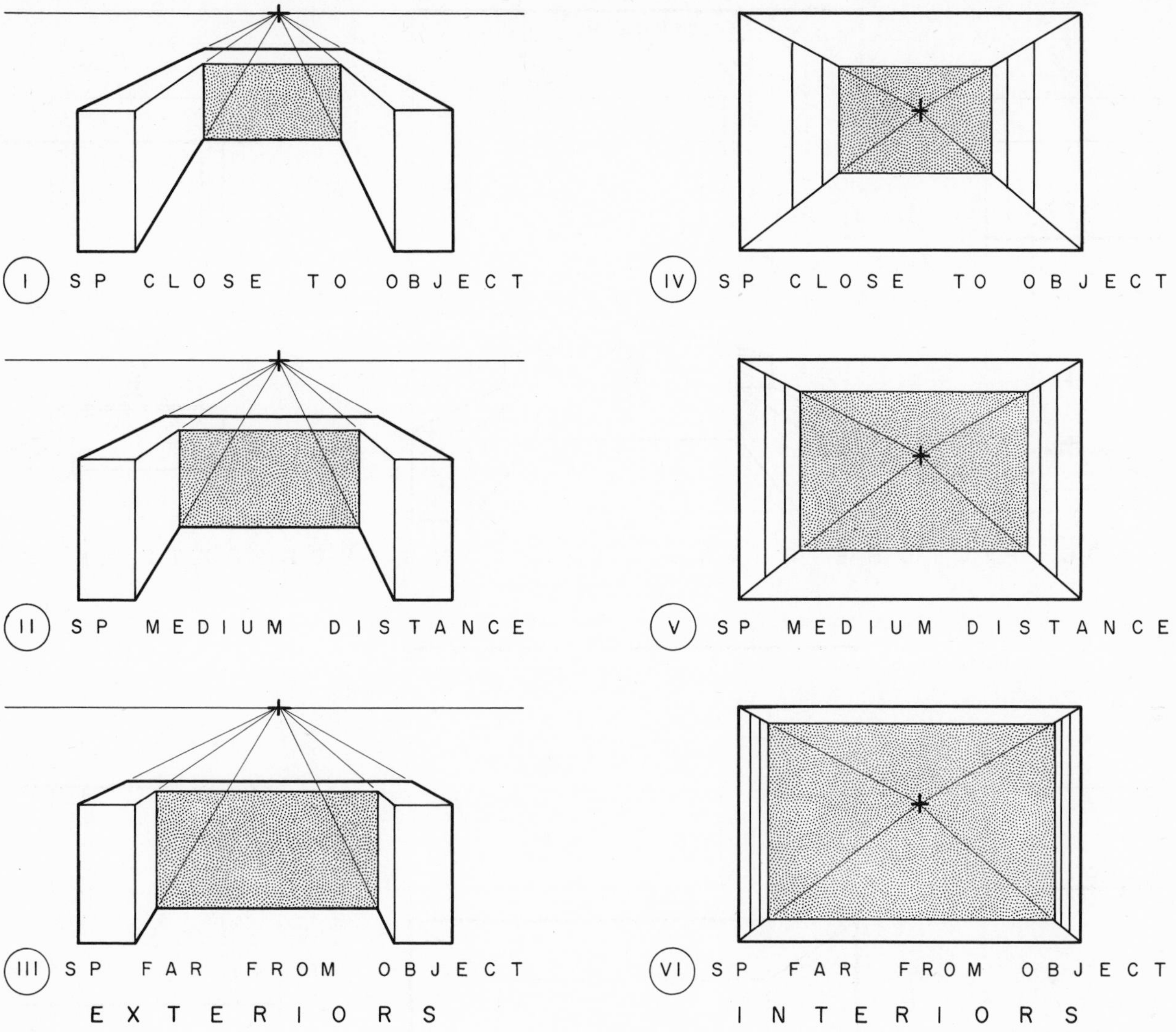

FIG. 125 DISTANCE FROM SP TO THE OBJECT

increases these areas become smaller. When the SP is near the object sizes of near and distant parts of the object vary a great deal, Figs. 125 I, IV. As the SP moves farther away the variation in size between the near and distant parts of the object decreases, Figs. 125 III, VI. A station point near the object gives a perspective with greater contrasts whereas one far away produces a flatter appearance that approaches an elevation. Nearest lines of Fig. 125 are in the picture plane.

The only variation in angle of view in one-point perspective is secured by moving the SP slightly to the right or left of the vertical center line of the plan. Whenever a satisfactory effect can be secured with the SP on center it is better to locate it there. If, however, the effect seems too stiff with a symmetrical object or unsatisfactory in other ways, the SP can be located a little to one side. When the off-center location coincides with the center of interest of the perspective the results are better in avoiding distortion. This is true because the observer will naturally look at the center of interest of the perspective, which will be from the direction of the SP used. The SP should not be moved far off center of the plan. To do so will give a distorted effect. When one-point perspective will not give a satisfactory effect with the SP in the middle fifth of the width of the perspective, better results can probably be obtained with two-point perspective.

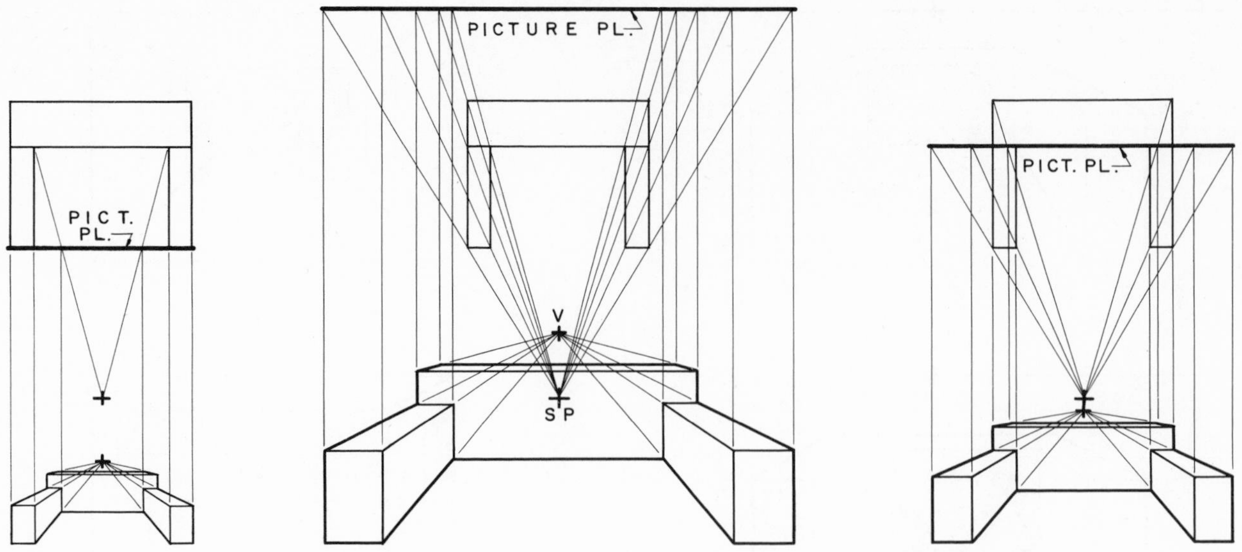

GOOD PICTURE PLANE POSITIONS FOR EXTERIORS

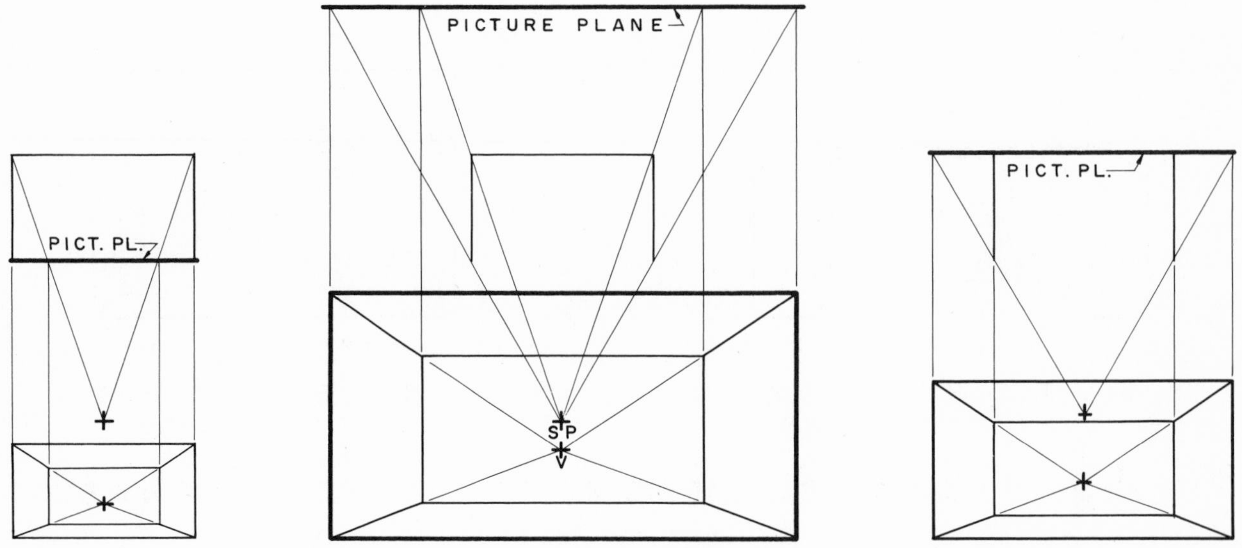

GOOD PICTURE PLANE POSITIONS FOR INTERIORS

FIG. 126 SIZE CONTROL IN ONE-POINT PERSPECTIVE

The position of the picture plane determines the size of the perspective produced in one-point perspective as it does in two-point perspective. The closer the picture plane to the SP the smaller the perspective and the farther the picture plane from the SP the larger the perspective, Fig. 126. The picture plane is often located at either the farthest visible plane of the object or at the nearest plane. However, it can cut through the object at any selected position, be located beyond the object to produce a large perspective, or be placed in front of the object to give a small perspective. When other elements of the perspective setup are not changed, the different positions of the picture plane vary the size of the perspective but have no other effect on it, Fig. 126. Rendered examples of one-point perspectives are shown on pages 257 top, 272, 288 bottom, and 296.

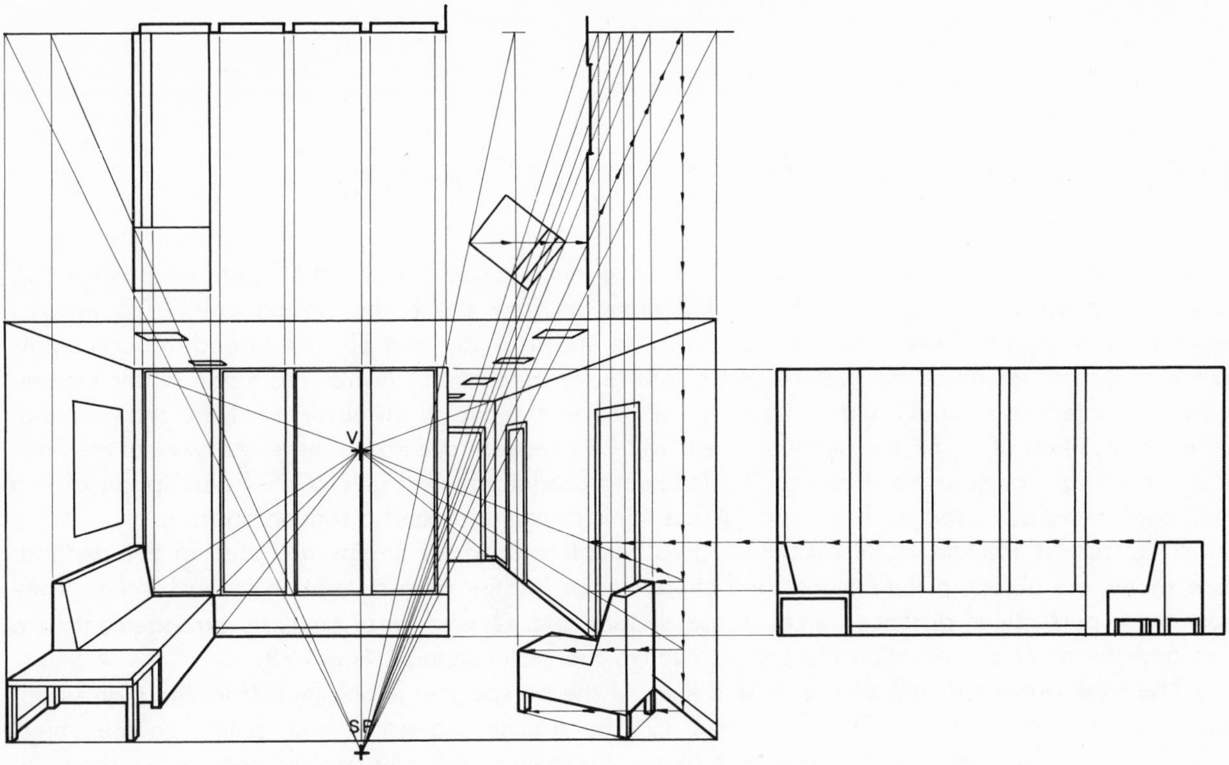

INTERIOR EXAMPLE

EXTERIOR EXAMPLE

FIG. 127 SPACE SAVING IN ONE-POINT PERSPECTIVE

CHAPTER **21**

ADDITIONAL PERSPECTIVE METHODS

Perspective drawing is the process of locating on a plane surface the apparent positions of points of an object as seen from a selected point of view called the station point. The process requires the tracing of lines called projectors. These lines radiate from SP and extend through points on the object to determine their intersections with the picture plane. A drawing made in this manner shows the object as it would appear from the SP. When the eye of an observer of the drawing is at the exact position of its SP the pictorial effect will be precisely accurate. There are several methods of constructing a perspective drawing. The following paragraphs will give a brief description of two additional commonly used methods and discuss their advantages and disadvantages.

THE DIRECT PROJECTION METHOD. Two complete auxiliary setups are used in this method. Each shows the object, picture plane, and station point in their correct relation to each other. They must agree perfectly in distances, sizes, scale, shapes, etc. One of these auxiliary arrangements is a plan and the other an elevation looking parallel to the picture plane, Fig. 128.

The horizontal spacing of points and lines of the perspective is obtained from the plan setup. This is done most directly in Figs. 128 and 129 by tracing projectors from points on the object toward or away from SP to meet the picture plane and thence vertically into the perspective drawing.

The heights in perspective of points of the object are obtained from the elevation parallel to the picture plane. Projectors are drawn from points on the elevation of the object toward or away from the SP as required to meet the picture plane and determine these heights. The heights are carried across from their positions on the elevation of the picture plane by horizontal projectors to

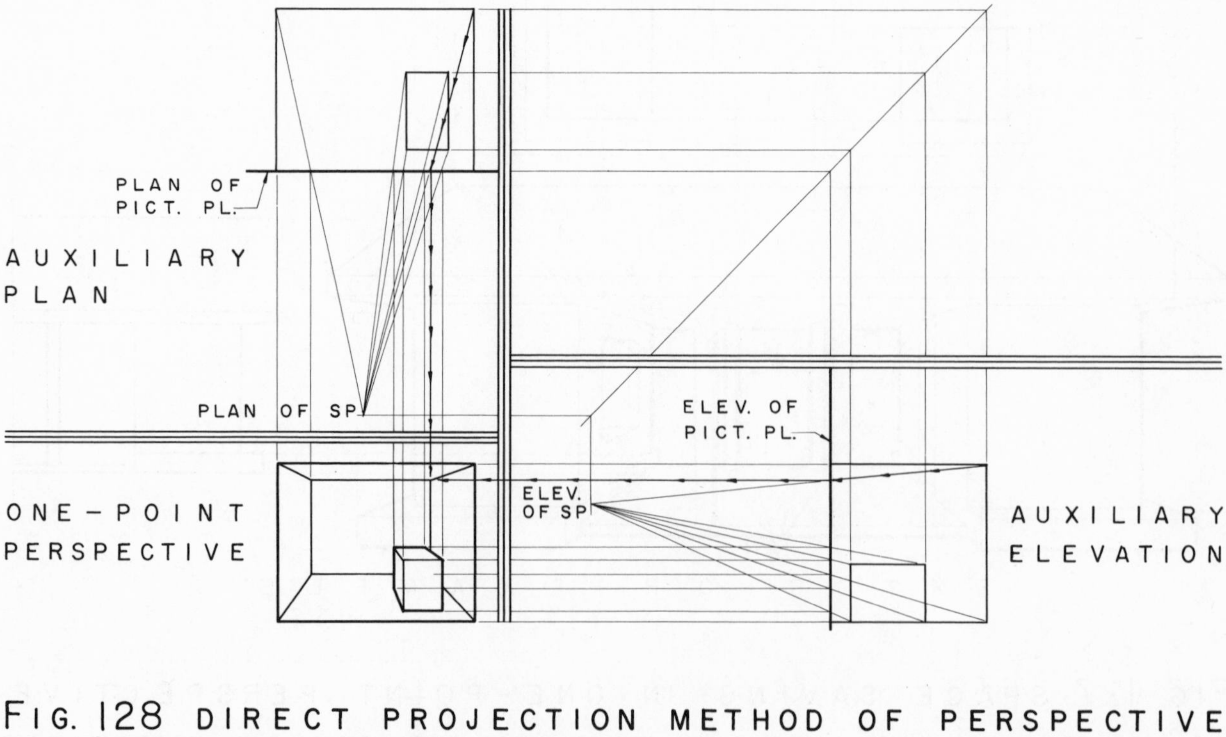

FIG. 128 DIRECT PROJECTION METHOD OF PERSPECTIVE

their correct locations in the perspective. The vertical projectors from the plan of the picture plane meet the horizontal projectors from the elevation of the picture plane to locate points of the perspective. The construction from a point in plan meets the construction from the same point in elevation to locate the perspective position of that point as shown by arrow lines in Figs. 128, 129.

The elevation parallel to the picture plane is an ordinary orthographic elevation or section in one-point perspective, Fig. 128. In two-point perspective this elevation is a view from a corner since the object is oblique to the picture plane, Fig. 129. It is a drawing that would never be made for other purposes and is therefore entirely a part of the perspective construction. When the object is simple, hidden parts of the elevation can be shown with dotted lines. If the object is complex, it may be necessary to use two complete elevations parallel to the picture plane, one on each side of the perspective. One elevation would show the view from the right and the other from the left. Each would include its SP and picture plane.

The theory of the direct projection method as given here is simple. The method does not require the use of vanishing points because the positions of the two ends of a line give its direction. Much of the process is visually apparent in both plan and elevation, allowing an accurate estimate of general perspective effect and also of details from auxiliary drawings. There are, however, several disadvantages. The elevation from a corner is more difficult to construct and understand than the common multi-view drawings. The method uses a lot of drafting space. It requires the drawing of many construction lines. Minor inaccuracies in construction will cause considerable error in directions of short lines when vanishing points are not used. The location and use of vanishing points makes the construction shorter and more accurate.

THE COMMON METHOD. This method of perspective drawing has been used in preceding chapters on perspective. It is also called the office method and the mixed method. It uses the plan construction from the direct projection method and the height construction from the perspective plan method. It makes use of the common orthographic plan and elevation. When blueprints or tracing studies of these drawings are available they can be attached to the board and used for auxiliary drawings. The elevation is really not necessary but it does help to relate the heights and shapes of the elevation to the perspective. A height line can be used instead of an elevation to save space.

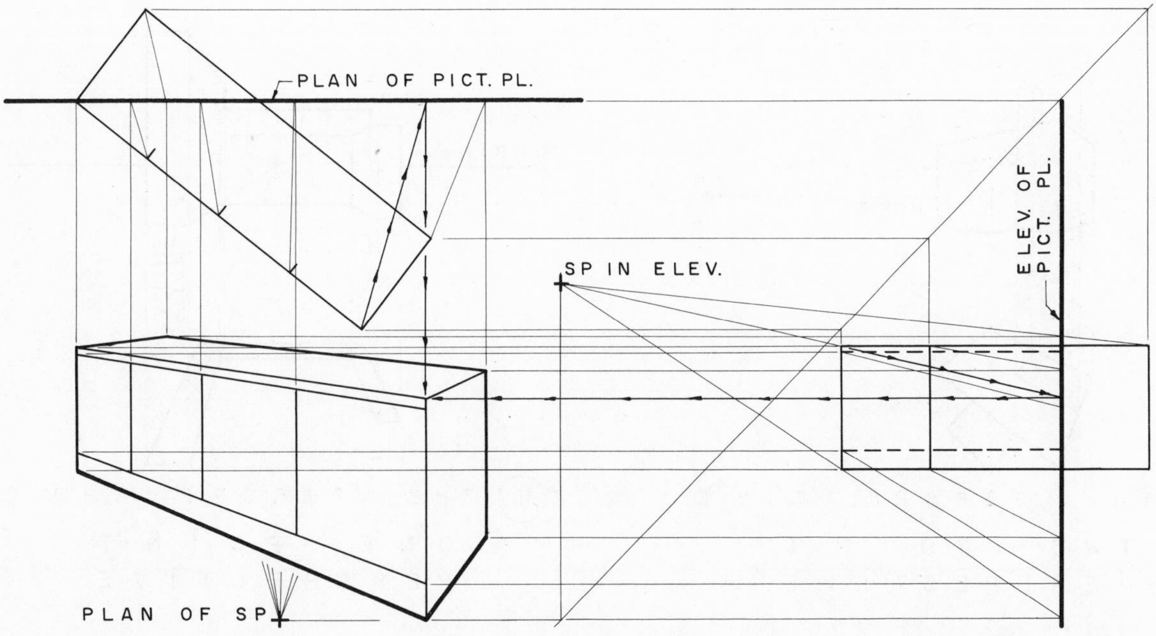

FIG. 129 TWO-POINT PERSPECTIVE BY DIRECT PROJECTION

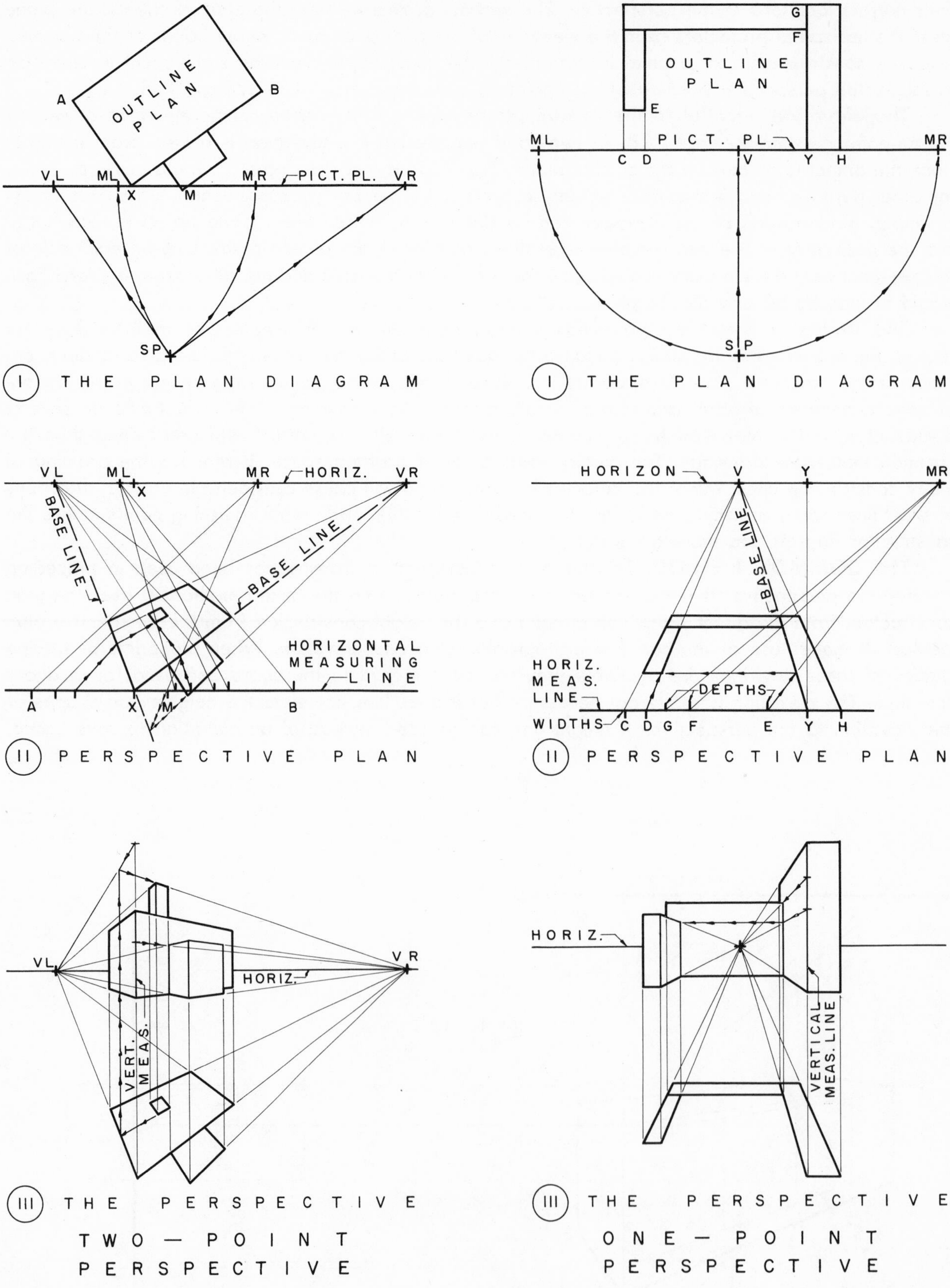

FIG. 130 PERSPECTIVE PLAN METHOD FOR EXTERIORS

THE PERSPECTIVE PLAN METHOD. The construction of a perspective by this method is divided into three steps in the following explanation.

I. The diagram is an orthographic plan drawing showing the outline plan shape of the object, the picture plane, and the SP. The vanishing points and measuring points are located as shown in step I of Fig. 130, and the intersection of the plan and picture plane is marked at X in the two-point and at Y in the one-point perspective. This drawing of the diagram provides the spacing of the vanishing points, measuring points, and a plan location point on the picture plane. These points are transferred to the horizon of the perspective plan. The diagram has no further use.

II. The perspective plan is constructed as shown in Fig. 130 step II. A horizon is drawn and the vanishing points, measuring points, and plan intersection with the picture plane transferred to it. Below the horizon a horizontal measuring line is drawn and the plan intersection with the picture plane is transferred vertically from the horizon to this line. In the two-point perspective this intersection point X is the corner of the plan. Lines are drawn from X to VL and VR. They are the left and right edges of the plan and are also base lines where measurement correction lines to the measuring points end. The measurements for the perspective plan are laid out on the horizontal measuring line. The measurements for the left side are laid out to the left of X and those for the right side to the right of X for the two-point perspective. For a measurement X–M extending in front of X–VR the distance is laid out to the right of X. It is a continuation of the left side measurements beyond X and overlaps the right side measurements. In this case the base line VL–X must be extended beyond X to receive the measurement correction line from MR. Lines to the vanishing points are drawn from the foreshortened measurements on the base lines to make the perspective plan.

III. The perspective is constructed by drawing verticals from the perspective plan and tracing heights from a vertical measuring line. The verticals from perspective plan give the correct spacing of vertical lines in the perspective. The height or vertical measuring line must be a line in the picture plane. In step III it is the nearest corner of the large block shape of the object. Any of the methods of determination of heights which were explained for the common method can be used in the perspective plan method. They are applied through the perspective plan here and the orthographic plan in the common method. The method used in Fig. 130 employs a single true height line.

The perspective plan has been placed low enough in each of the examples of Figs. 130 and 131 to be clear of the perspective drawings. It could have been placed above the object or located on the ground plane and allowed to overlap and partially coincide with the perspective. Any convenient horizontal plane can be used for the perspective plan.

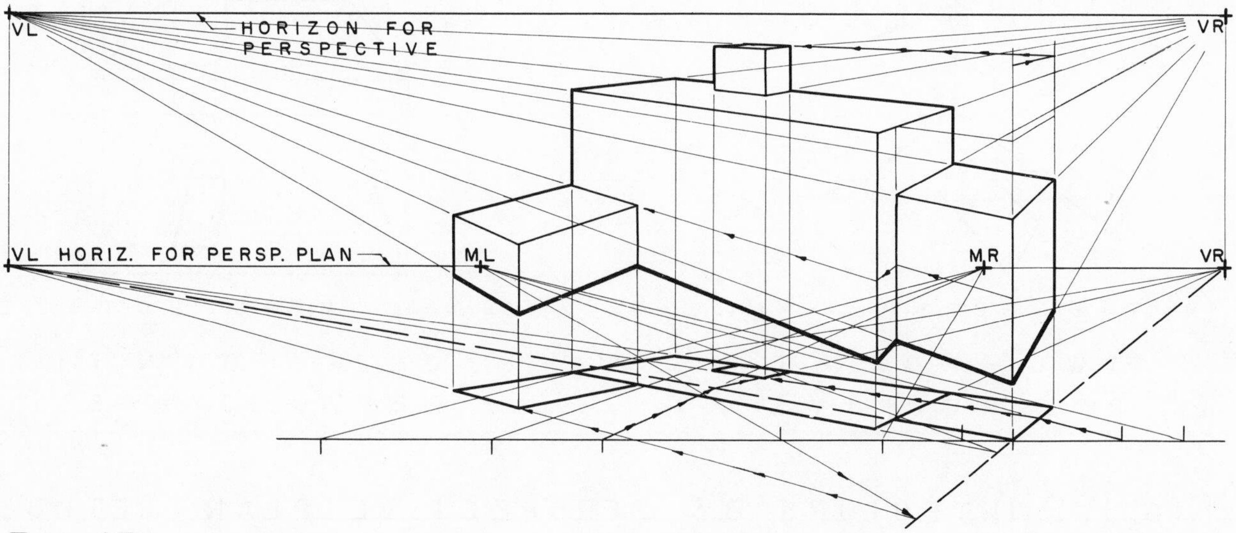

FIG. 131 COMPRESSED PERSPECTIVE PLAN METHOD

VL ML X MR ⌐PICT. PL. VR

A C D E
 L F G

VL‑SP = VL‑ML SP SP‑VR = ML‑VR

Ⓐ T H E P L A N D I A G R A M

ML PICT. PL. H V I J Y MR

 K

 L
 M

SP‑V = ML‑V S P SP‑V = MR‑V

Ⓐ T H E P L A N D I A G R A M

VL ML ⌐HORIZON MR VR

BASE LINE FOR MR BASE LINE FOR ML

 HORIZ. MEAS.
 ─LINE
A C D ⌐X E F G

Ⓑ P E R S P E C T I V E P L A N

ML HORIZON V MR

BASE LINE FOR MR

HORIZ. MEAS.
LINE H I J
 ML K K L M

Ⓑ P E R S P E C T I V E P L A N

VL X HORIZ.⌐ VR

 HEIGHT
 LINE
 X

Ⓒ T H E P E R S P E C T I V E
 T W O ‑ P O I N T
 P E R S P E C T I V E

HORIZ.⌐ V

 HEIGHT
 LINE

Ⓒ T H E P E R S P E C T I V E
 O N E ‑ P O I N T
 P E R S P E C T I V E

Fɪɢ. 132 INTERIORS BY PERSPECTIVE PLAN METHOD

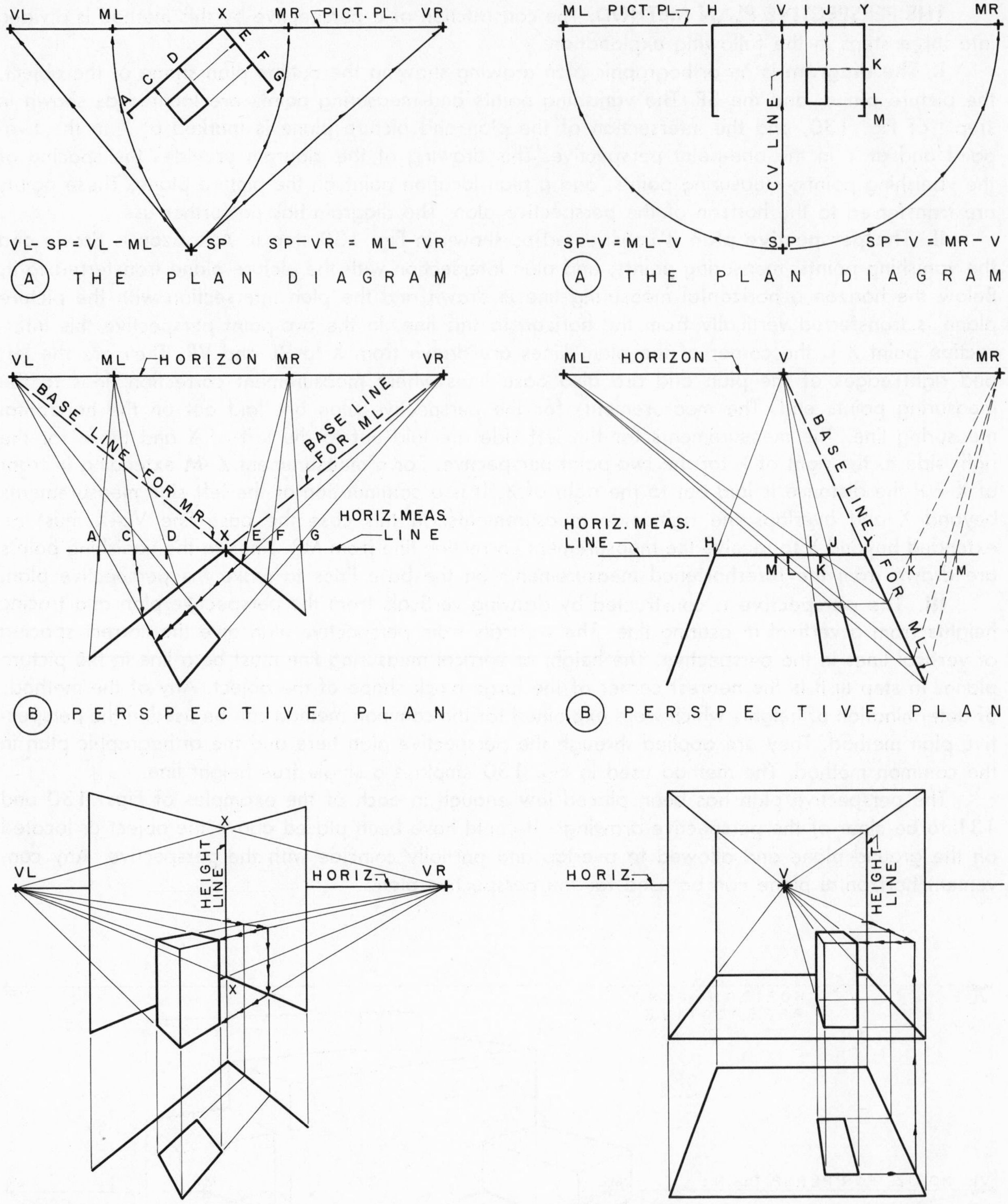

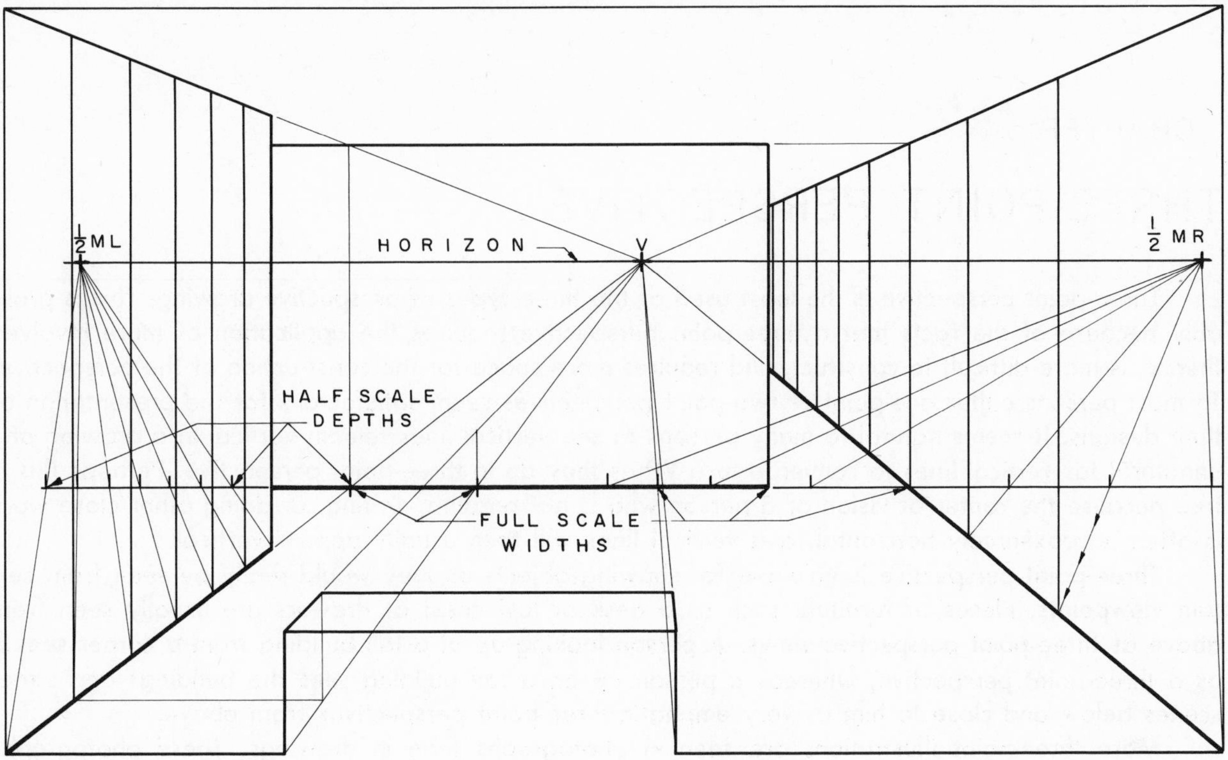

FIG. 133 THE MEASURING POINT METHOD

The interior two-point perspective of Fig. 132 has the farthest visible corner of the walls in the picture plane. This corner is the vertical measuring line from which heights are traced.

In the one-point interior perspective of Fig. 132, either wall line that is drawn to V in the perspective plan can be used for the base line. Either ML or MR can be used for the depth construction. When MR is used the measurements are to the right side of the base line and when ML is used they are to the left side, when the object extends in front of the picture plane as in this example. The measurements to MR are in the reverse order of those to ML.

The perspective plan method can be used to save space on the drafting board. It is preferred by some experienced draftsmen. It does require more theoretical knowledge than either the common method or direct projection method. The developing perspective cannot be analyzed from auxiliary drawings as easily as in either the common method or direct projection method. Variations of position of the picture plane to control the size of the perspective are more confusing in this method.

THE MEASURING POINT METHOD. The construction is worked out more directly on the perspective drawing in this method than in any of the previously described methods. This method applies the perspective plan system of measuring points directly on the perspective drawing omitting the construction of a separate perspective plan. Whenever it is more convenient to do so, measuring points are used for wall planes instead of horizontal planes. The purpose of this method is to save space on the drafting board and work as directly as possible in constructing a perspective drawing. In order to use this method intelligently the draftsman must know a great deal about perspective.

In the example of Fig. 133 the construction has been limited to the area of the perspective itself. The perspective plan has been drawn on the adequately large floor area. A point $\frac{1}{2}$ ML, which is one half the distance from V to ML, has been used for a measuring point for half scale depth measurements so those measurements and $\frac{1}{2}$ MR do not extend beyond the perspective area.

CHAPTER 22

THREE-POINT PERSPECTIVE

Three-point perspective is the least used of the three types of perspective drawing. This is probably because of the facts that a three-point perspective requires the application of more involved theory, is more difficult to construct, and requires more space for the construction of the perspective. To most persons either one-point or two-point perspectives seem satisfactory for the presentation of their designs. It seems natural to many persons to see vertical lines remain vertical in a drawing and unnatural for vertical lines to converge to a VP as they do in three-point perspective. Perhaps this is true because the center of vision of a person who is not reading, writing, or doing other close work is often approximately horizontal, and vertical lines will then usually appear vertical.

Three-point perspective is valuable for showing objects as they would really be seen from certain viewpoints. Pieces of furniture such as a desk or low chest of drawers are usually seen from above as three-point perspective views. A person looking up at a tall building from a corner sees it as a three-point perspective, whereas a person up on a tall building sees the buildings and street scenes below and close to him as very emphatic three-point perspectives from above.

More three-point illustrations are seen in photographs than in drawings. These photographs usually provide interesting and perhaps exciting views. The delineator will find that the three-point perspectives may have the same characteristics and can make his illustrations of suitable subjects more interesting and more alive.

The explanation of the construction of a three-point perspective drawing looking up at a simple block shape has been divided into five parts in Fig. 134. The explanation for each of these parts begins with the same Roman numeral as the title of the drawing of that part.

I. Size and shape information for the object to be drawn is usually provided in as much detail as necessary by multi-view drawings.

II. The relation of the plan to the ground line is selected to give the desired view of the object. From this plan an elevation-parallel-to-picture-plane is constructed. The position of the SP is selected for this elevation. The CV line is drawn from SP through the approximate center of the object. The picture plane is drawn through GL and perpendicular to the CV line.

III. The elevation-parallel-to-picture-plane has been turned with the picture plane line vertical, and from this view and the plan a plan-parallel-to-picture-plane has been constructed. This is a paraline drawing. Its lines are not parallel to the plan lines.

IV. The plan-parallel-to-picture-plane including object, picture plane line, and SP is placed above the area for the perspective. The SP must be on the vertical center line of this plan or the perspective leans to one side. The elevation-parallel-to-picture-plane including object, picture plane line, and SP is placed to the side of the area for the perspective. The SP projection line from any point A in the plan-parallel-to-picture-plane meets the picture plane line in a point X, from which it is traced vertically into the perspective. A SP construction line is traced from point A in the elevation-parallel-to-picture-plane to meet the picture plane line at Y and is then traced horizontally to meet the vertical at the perspective position of A. All points are projected in a similar manner and connected to make the perspective drawing without the use of vanishing points.

V. Greater accuracy in line direction can be obtained in the perspective, especially for short lines, by locating and using the three vanishing points of the perspective. The construction for locating these three points has been emphasized with arrows on the construction lines of step V.

Steps III, IV, and V can be combined on one drawing in practice. They are separated here to make explanations clearer.

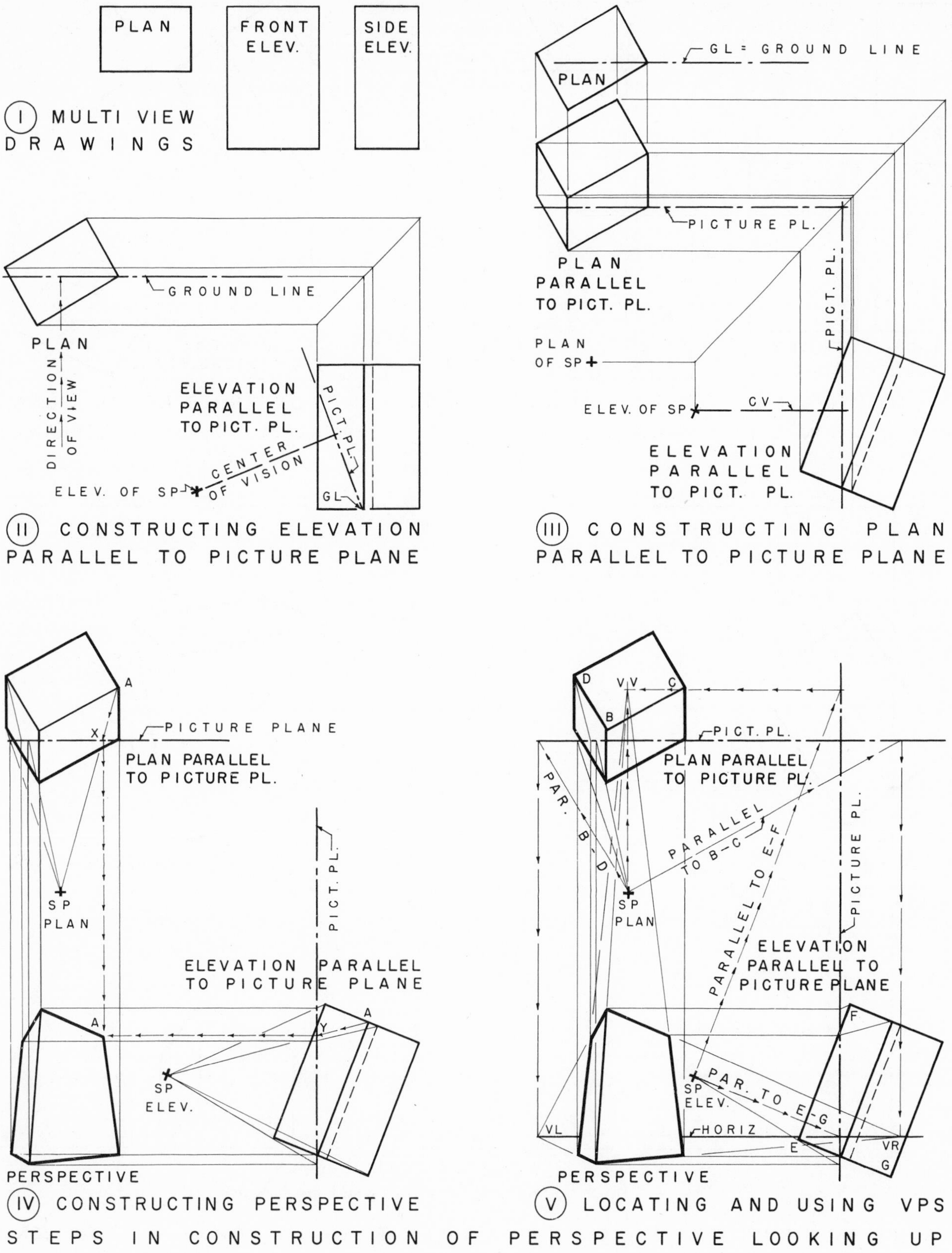

FIG. 134 THREE POINT PERSPECTIVE BY DIRECT PROJECTION

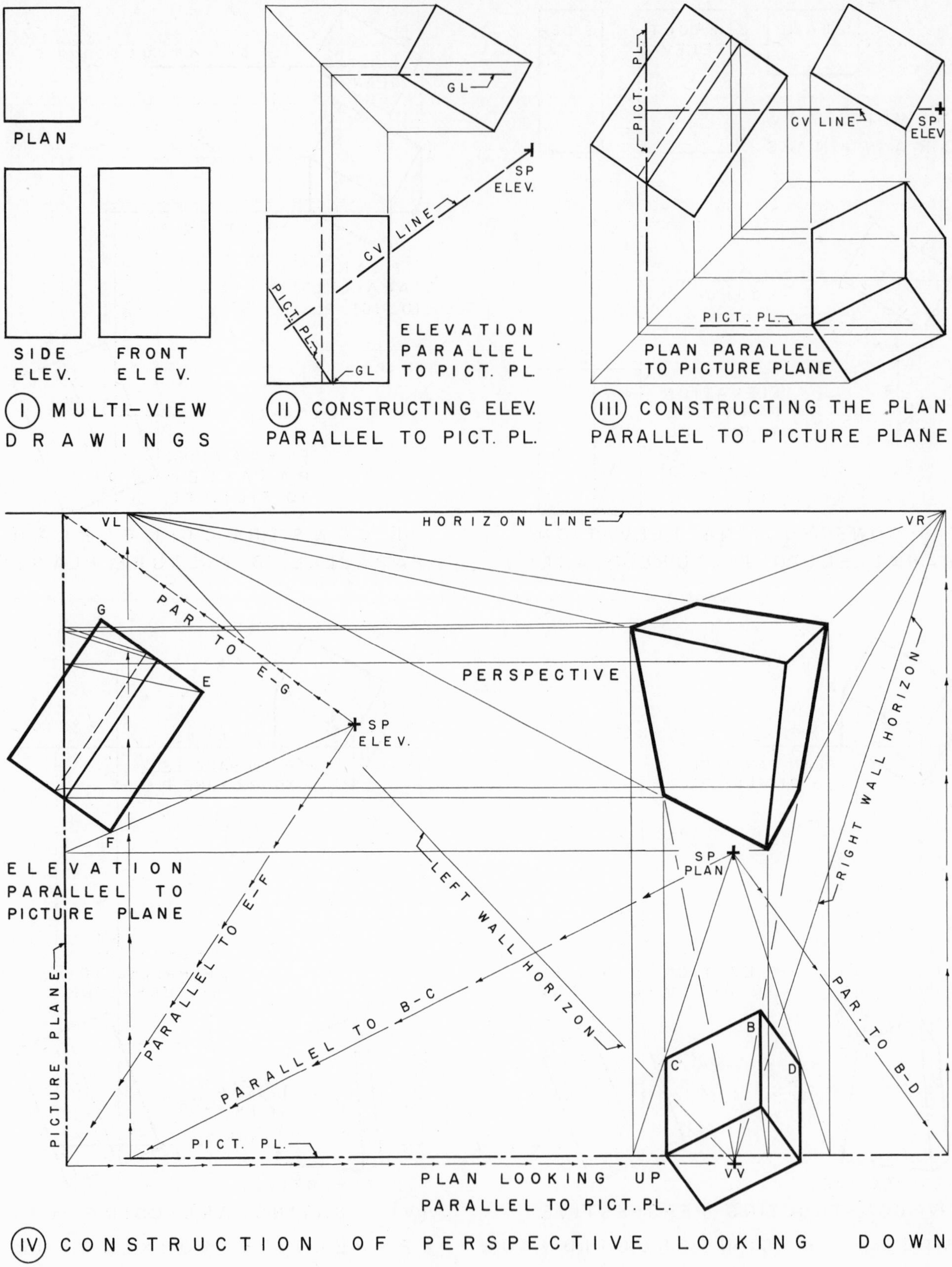
PLAN
SIDE ELEV.
FRONT ELEV.
(I) MULTI-VIEW DRAWINGS
GL
SP ELEV.
CV LINE
PICT. PL.
GL
ELEVATION PARALLEL TO PICT. PL.
(II) CONSTRUCTING ELEV. PARALLEL TO PICT. PL.
PICT. PL.
CV LINE
SP ELEV
PICT. PL.
PLAN PARALLEL TO PICTURE PLANE
(III) CONSTRUCTING THE PLAN PARALLEL TO PICTURE PLANE
VL
HORIZON LINE
VR
PAR TO E-G
G
E
F
PERSPECTIVE
SP ELEV.
ELEVATION PARALLEL TO PICTURE PLANE
PARALLEL TO E-F
LEFT WALL HORIZON
RIGHT WALL HORIZON
SP PLAN
PICTURE PLANE
PARALLEL TO B-C
PAR. TO B-D
B
C
D
PICT. PL.
VV
PLAN LOOKING UP PARALLEL TO PICT. PL.
(IV) CONSTRUCTION OF PERSPECTIVE LOOKING DOWN

FIG. 135 STEPS IN MAKING A THREE-POINT PERSPECTIVE

The construction for a three-point perspective looking down obliquely is shown in the four steps of Fig. 135. In steps II and III the drawings have been crowded together to allow space for a larger perspective. The text on page 144 applies to the construction in the first three steps of Fig. 135 and to step IV where the IV and V of Fig. 134 have been combined. The plan-parallel-to-picture-plane has been made looking up in Fig. 135 in order to avoid hidden and unnecessary lines in it.

In practice all drawings shown in steps I, II, and III can be made on scrap paper. When VPs are not used space is saved by moving the two auxiliary drawings very close to the perspective with the SP within or beyond the perspective. When VPs are used it may be necessary to use one of the methods of drawing to a distant VP, as well as to move drawings close together, see page 149.

THE VARIABLES IN THREE-POINT PERSPECTIVE. Although the variables for three-point perspective are very similar to those for two-point perspective their application is more complex.

A. The angle of the plan is given with the GL because the picture plane is not vertical and cannot be represented by a line in plan. The angle of the plan with the GL determines how much width of the perspective each visible vertical side of the object occupies, Fig. 136 A.

B. The distance of SP from object is first determined in the elevation-parallel-to-picture-plane. A SP near the object will produce an extreme perspective effect with close VPs and extreme slanting of lines. A SP far from the object causes the lines of the object to slant less and looks more nearly like an elevation-parallel-to-picture-plane, Fig. 136 B.

C. The height of the SP is chosen at the same time as the distance from the object because the one drawing and the same SP determine both. The four general height positions of the SP are illustrated in the diagrams of Fig. 136 C. When the height of the SP is changed vertically and not by a new position on the CV line a new CV line and new angle of the picture plane are required.

D. The size of the perspective is controlled over a fairly large range of sizes by the position of the picture plane in front of, through, or behind the object as shown in Fig. 136 D.

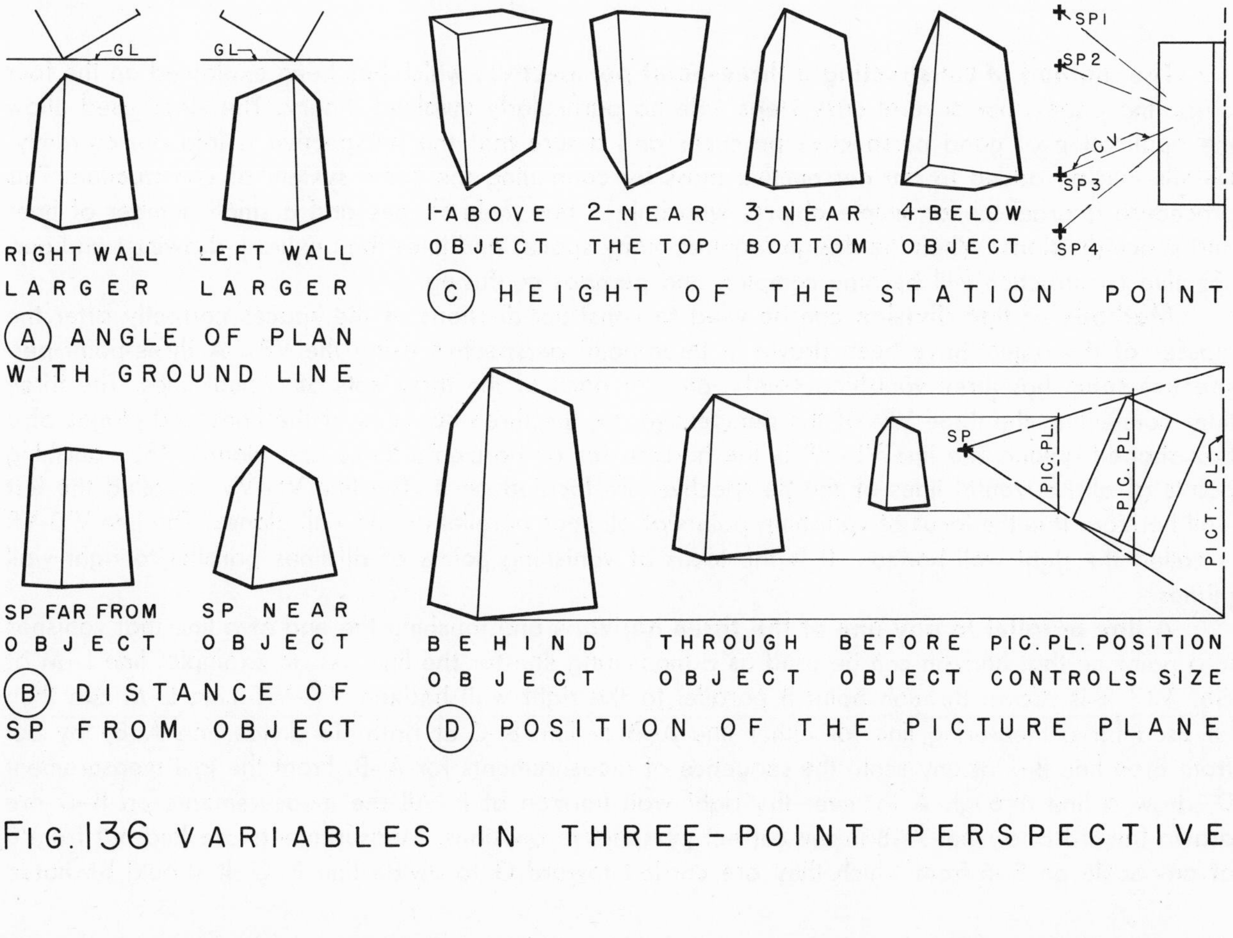

FIG. 136 VARIABLES IN THREE-POINT PERSPECTIVE

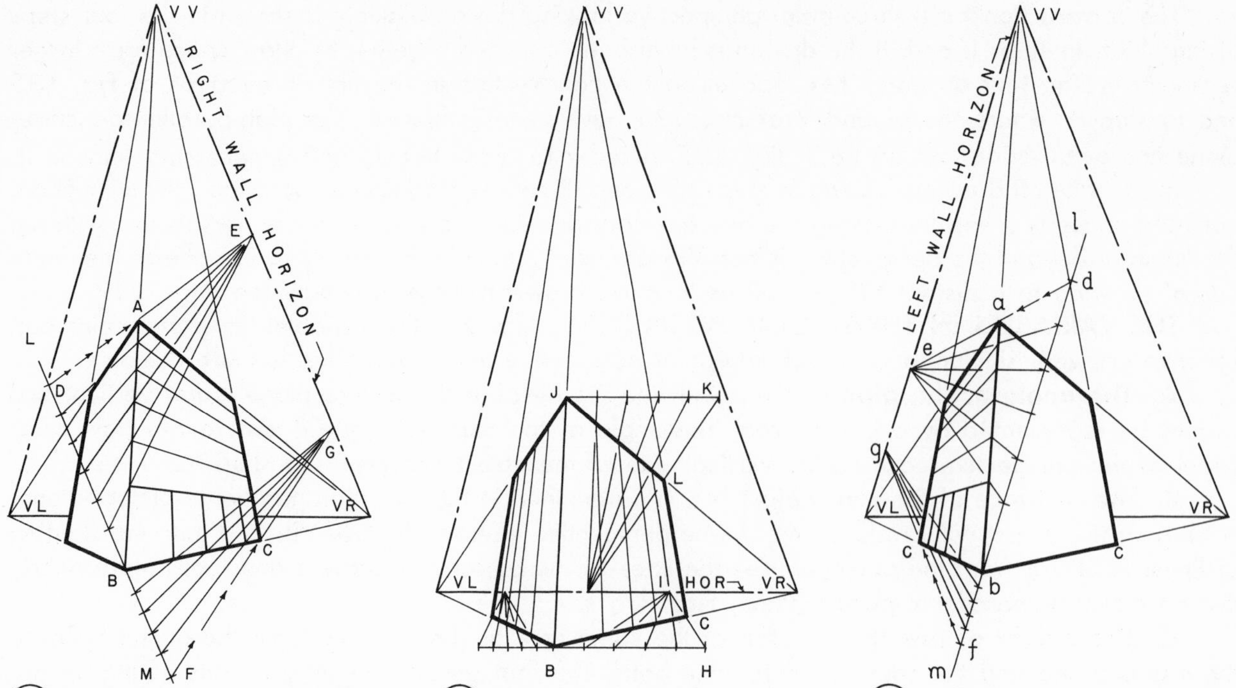

(A) DIVISIONS TO VPS ON RIGHT WALL HORIZON

(B) DIVISIONS TO VPS ON THE HORIZON

(C) DIVISIONS TO VPS ON LEFT WALL HORIZON

FIG. 137 LINE DIVISION FOR THREE-POINT PERSPECTIVE

The method of constructing a three-point perspective, which has been explained on the four preceding pages, has several easy steps with no particularly involved theory. The steps used allow the application of good perspective practices and assure that the perspective is laid out correctly. Details can be added to the perspective mass by continuing the same system of construction. This procedure is practical for simple objects with only a few main shapes and a small number of lines and space divisions. When the design requires many spaces and lines the auxiliary drawings and perspective construction will become complex and perhaps confusing.

Methods of line division can be used to construct divisions of the spaces correctly after the masses of the object have been drawn in three-point perspective using the VPs. A three-point perspective setup has three vanishing points, one for each of the three sets of typical lines. The three lines connecting the three VPs of the perspective are the three horizons of the lines and planes of a box shaped object. The line VL–VR is the horizon for all horizontal lines and planes. The vanishing points of all horizontal lines of the perspective are located on it. The line VL–VV is called the left wall horizon. It is the locus of vanishing points of all lines parallel to left wall planes. The line VV–VR is called the right wall horizon. It is the locus of vanishing points of all lines parallel to right wall planes.

A line parallel to any one of the three horizons and touching the end of a line that vanishes in a point on that horizon can be used as a measuring line for the line. As an example, line L–M of Fig. 137 A is drawn through point B parallel to the right wall horizon VV–VR. Line L–M can then be used for a measuring line for either line A–B or line B–C or both. To divide line A–B, lay out from B on line B–L at any scale the sequence of measurements for A–B. From the last measurement D, draw a line through A to meet the right wall horizon at E. All the measurements on B–D are drawn toward E to meet A–B in the correct perspective divisions. Measurements are laid out from B at any scale on B–F from which they are carried toward G to divide line B–C. It should be noted

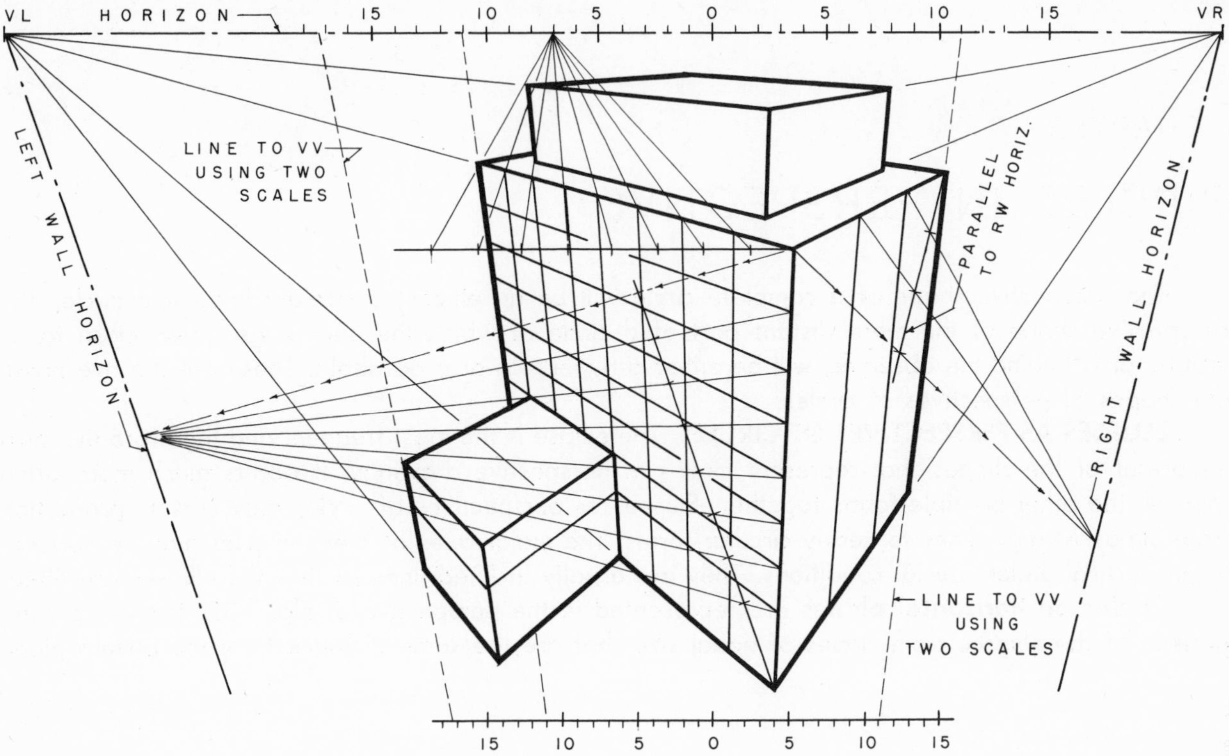

FIG. 138 SPACE SAVING IN THREE-POINT PERSPECTIVE

carefully that the measurements laid out on the measuring line to divide any one line must be the correct sequence, and the correct total for the space they are to occupy.

Either horizon direction can be used for the measuring line for B–C because line B–C has its vanishing point on the horizon as well as on the right wall horizon. The VP for the construction from the measuring line must be on the horizon to which it is parallel. In Fig. 137 B line B–H is parallel to the horizon VL–VR. From H a line is drawn through C to meet the horizon at I, the VP for the construction lines. If line B–C is too nearly parallel to the horizon for good construction, line J–K can be used to divide J–L for the same construction.

Fig. 137 C shows the same construction as Fig. 137 A but drawn to the left wall horizon.

When details are to be added to a three-point perspective by line division methods, the block shape, vanishing points, and horizons can be constructed either at final size or at a smaller size and enlarged. The small drawing can be enlarged by one of the methods shown on page 123. Because the full lengths of all the three horizons are not needed, space can be saved in making the final drawing. This can be done by using a method of drawing to a distant VP as shown in Fig. 138 and explained in detail on pages 172 and 173. In Fig. 138 two horizontal scales are used to give the directions of lines to VV. One scale is used at the top of the perspective and it coinsides with the horizon, because that is a convenient location on this drawing. The other scale should be located near the lower edge of the perspective. The two scale lines must be chosen to give exactly the same scale measurement horizontally between the two wall horizons. The O points on the scales can be either on the vertical through VV as shown, with measurements to both sides, or the O points can both be on either wall horizon. There are several other methods of drawing to distant VPs. This one is relatively simple, sufficiently accurate for a careful draftsman, and requires no special equipment. On this illustration $\frac{3}{16}$ scale was used at the top and $\frac{1}{8}$ scale at the bottom. The engineers chain scale adds other possible scale relations to those of the architects scale if they are needed.

CHAPTER **23**

CIRCLES IN PERSPECTIVE

The perspective shape of a complete circle will be an ellipse, a straight line, or a circle. The perspective shape of the more distant part of a circle of which the near edge is too close to be visible, or is behind the observer, will be either a hyperbola or a parabola. These are the five possible shapes of perspectives of circles.

ELLIPSES AS PERSPECTIVES OF CIRCLES. The ellipse is the most frequent and therefore the most important of the shapes that represent circles in perspective drawings. It occurs much more often than all the other possible forms together. Ellipses as perspectives of circles may vary in proportion from almost straight lines to nearly circular forms. The major axes of these ellipses may be horizontal or vertical under special conditions. They are usually inclined lines so that the ellipses are tilted.

Circles on horizontal planes are represented in the perspective of Fig. 139. It gives a comparison of the ellipses from circles of equal size that are the same distance from the picture plane

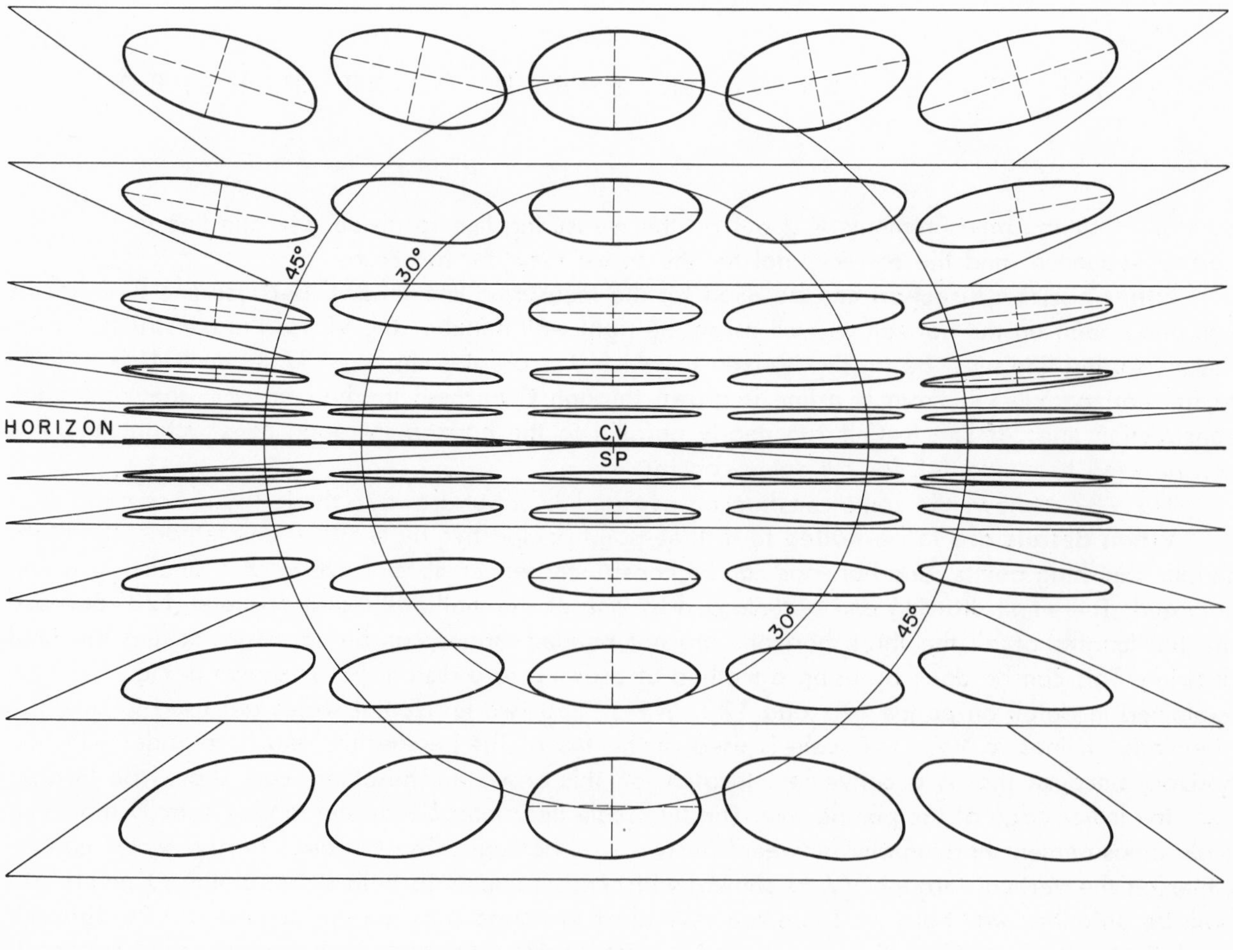

FIG. 139 HORIZONTAL CIRCLES AT DIFFERENT HEIGHTS

but vary in their distances above and below the horizon and in their horizontal distance from CV. The plane through the horizon gives an edge view of the circles. They are represented by straight lines on this plane in the perspective. The vertical line through the SP and CV point of the perspective passes through the centers of a row of ellipses. All these ellipses are turned horizontally. Their major axes are horizontal lines and their minor axes vertical lines. The ellipses to either side of this vertical row have an inclined position. The farther they are located from the vertical line through CV and from the horizon the greater the angle of inclination of the ellipses. The ellipses in the four corners of this drawing are therefore tilted the greatest amount. These shapes on a plane surface must give the correct form when seen from the SP of the drawing. If SP is close to the object the drawing seems distorted unless it is viewed with one eye at this close position. When seen from the normal viewing distance the drawing appears distorted because it gives a decidedly different effect than from the close position. Fig. 139 shows how the shapes which are tilted the most are removed with a 45° cone of vision and even more of them with a 30° cone of vision. The cone of vision has its apex at the SP and its base at the picture plane. It is often more satisfactory to have the SP far from the objects when representing circles at the edges of a perspective drawing.

Fig. 140 shows a photograph of ellipses from circles at different distances from the observer on one horizontal plane below eye level. As the ellipses get farther away from the observer they become closer to the horizon, smaller, thinner in proportion, and more nearly horizontal.

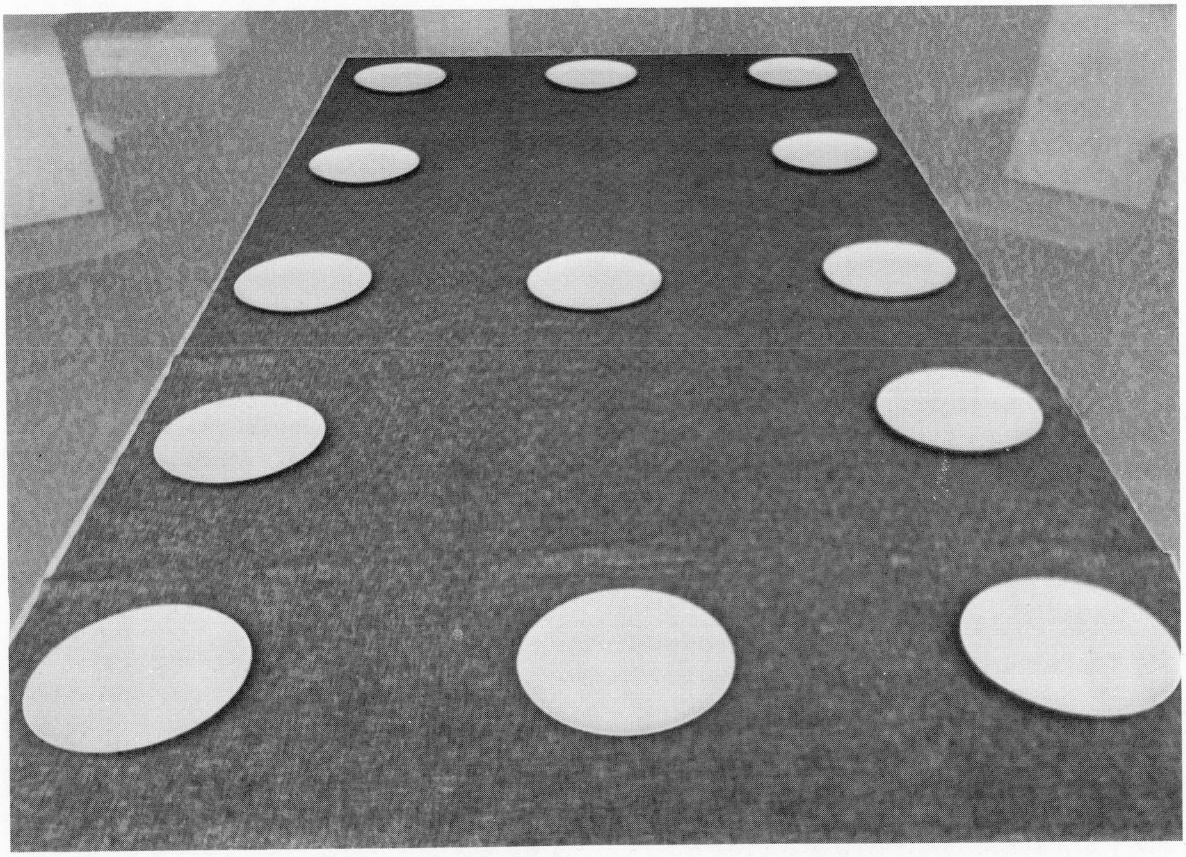

FIG. 140 HORIZONTAL CIRCLES AT DIFFERENT DISTANCES

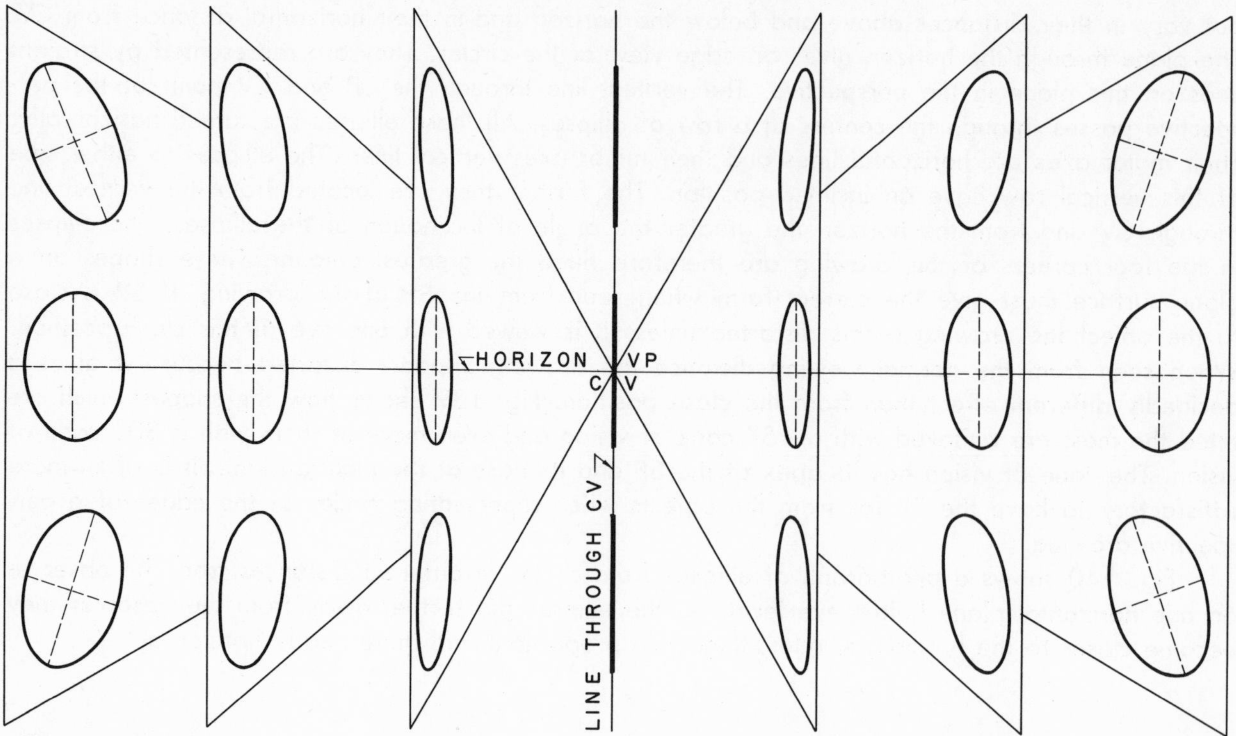

(A) CIRCLES AT SAME DISTANCE FROM PICTURE PLANE

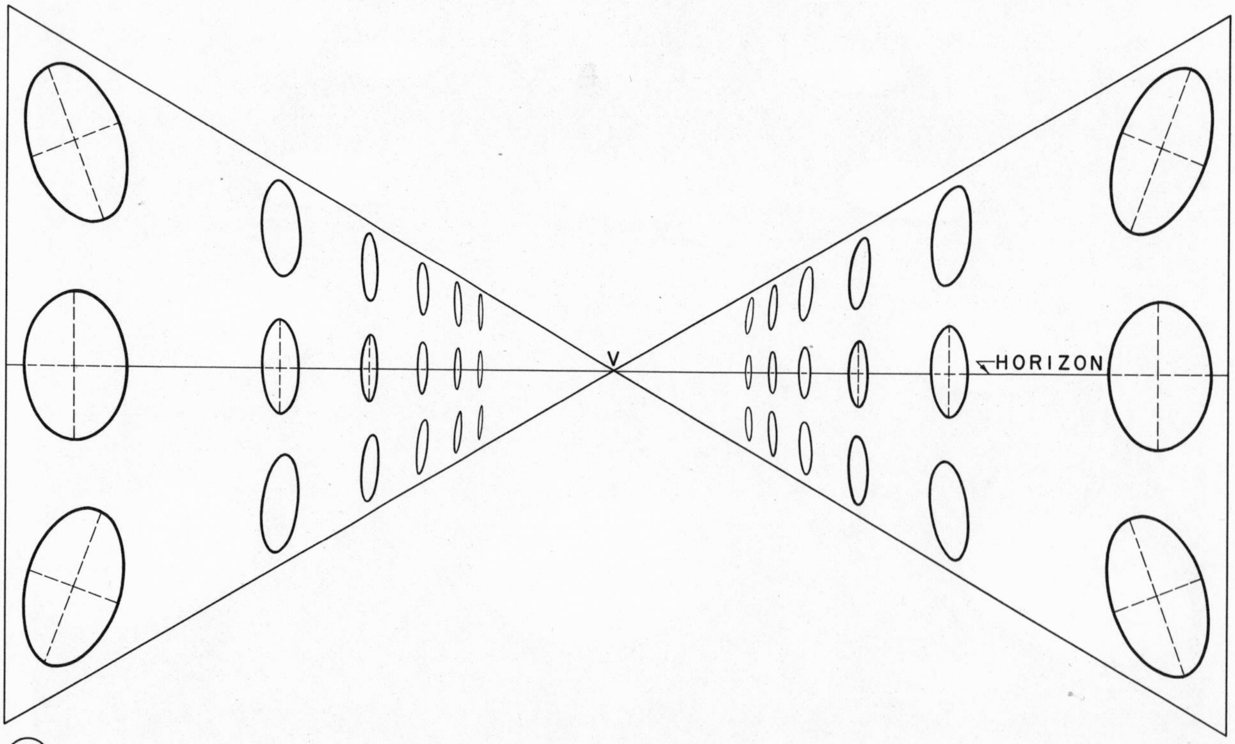

(B) CIRCLES AT VARIOUS DISTANCES FROM PICTURE PLANE

FIG. 141 VERTICAL CIRCLES NOT PARALLEL TO PICT. PL.

Circles on vertical planes that are either perpendicular or oblique to the picture plane are usually seen as ellipses. Fig. 141 A shows the perspective ellipses of three horizontal rows of circles on a number of parallel vertical planes that are perpendicular to the picture plane. All of these ellipses are the same distance from the picture plane and are the same height in the perspective drawing. The ellipses are widest at the right and left edges of the drawing and decrease in width as they get closer to the vertical line through the CV point. At this line they are seen in edge view and are merely straight lines. The circles that center on the horizon have vertical major axes and horizontal minor axes for their perspective ellipses. All the other ellipses have inclined axes. The ellipses in the extreme corners of both Figs. 141 A and B are tilted the most. These ellipses follow the same general rules as horizontal ellipses. As the ellipse approach the vertical line through CV and the horizon their axes become more nearly horizontal and vertical. In Fig. 141 B there are two vertical planes that are perpendicular to the picture plane with circles at varying distances from the picture plane. These ellipses become smaller, thinner, and less inclined as they become farther away.

Figs. 141 A and B are both drawn for one-point perspective with the ellipses on the planes perpendicular to the picture plane. In two-point perspective the ellipses in the corners would tilt and ellipses centered on the horizon would have horizontal and vertical axes. However the circles on the vertical through the CV would be vertical ellipses and not straight lines.

Circles parallel to the picture plane are shown on a number of planes at varying distances in the perspective drawing, Fig. 142. The perspective form is always a circle for circles in this position. The observer may note that the circles that are far removed from his center of vision are seen at an angle and appear slightly elliptical on actual objects. When the eye is close to the perspective at the position of the SP the same effect will be obtained from the perspective drawing. Circles parallel to the picture plane usually occur in one-point perspectives only.

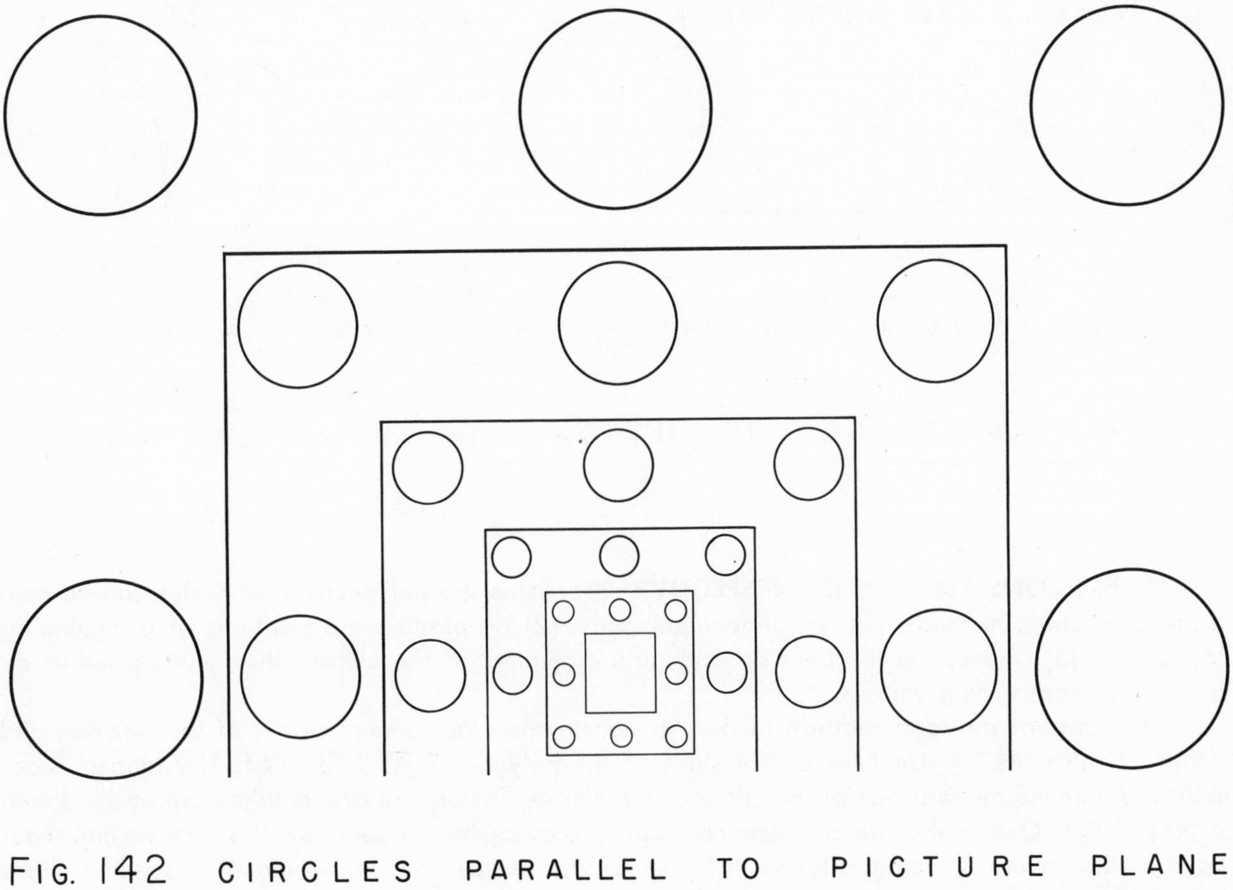

FIG. 142 CIRCLES PARALLEL TO PICTURE PLANE

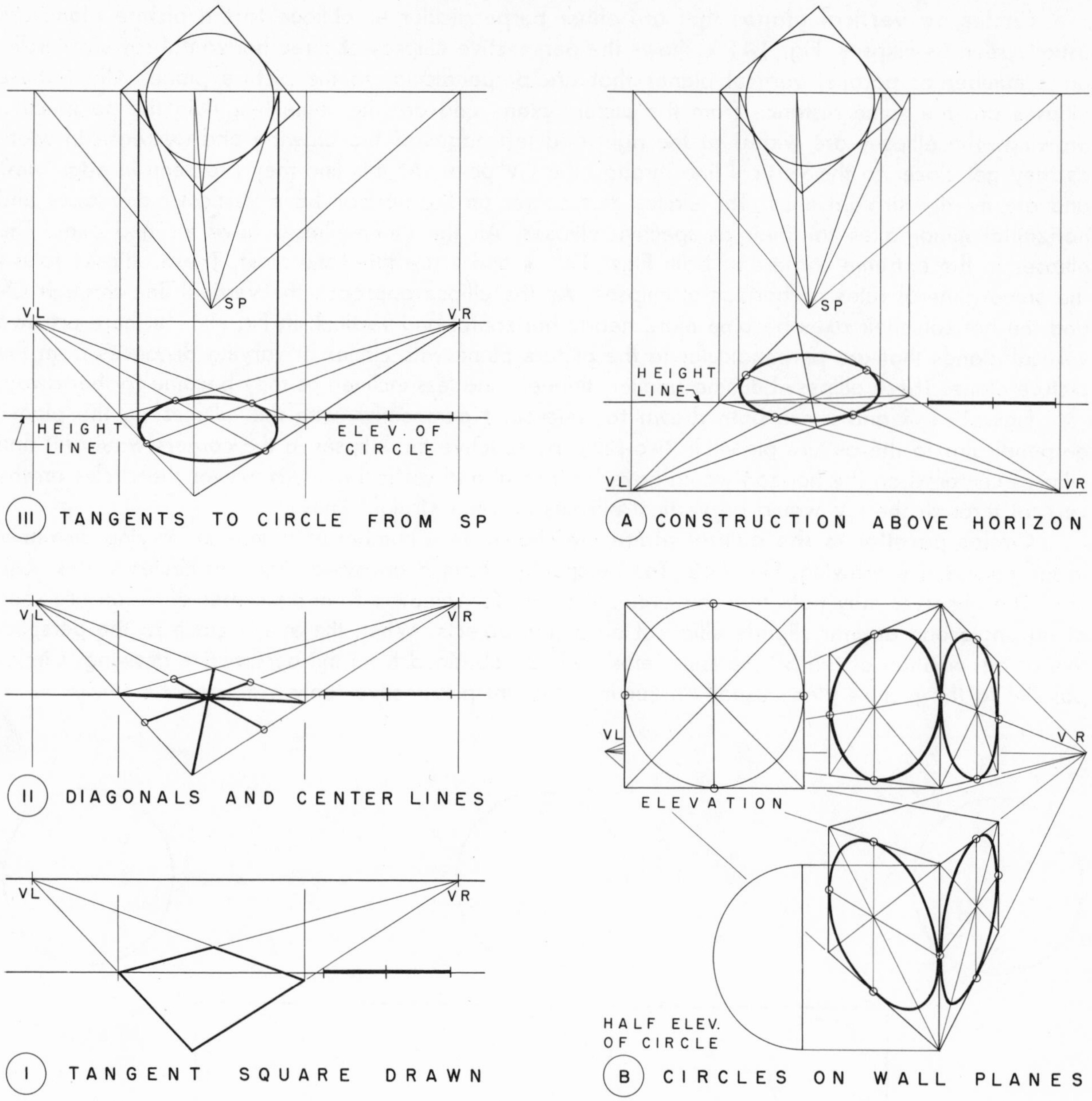

FIG. 143 TANGENT SQUARE METHOD–CIRCLES IN PERSPECTIVE

ELLIPSE CONSTRUCTION IN PERSPECTIVE. Ellipses as the perspectives of circles can be constructed by three methods: (1) by tangent polygons, (2) by plotting the positions of a number of points, and (3) by locating the axes or conjugate diameters of the ellipse, then plotting points by methods of constructing ellipses.

The tangent polygon method locates as construction the tangent points of the polygon and circle and also the tangent lines of the sides of the polygon, Figs. 143, 144. The tangent sides help to determine the direction of the curve of the ellipse. The square and octagon are easily drawn in perspective. One of the two is commonly used to provide the tangents for this construction. Four sides of the square or octagon follow the lines of the perspective. In two-point perspective these four sides vanish to the two vanishing points. In one-point perspective one pair of these parallel

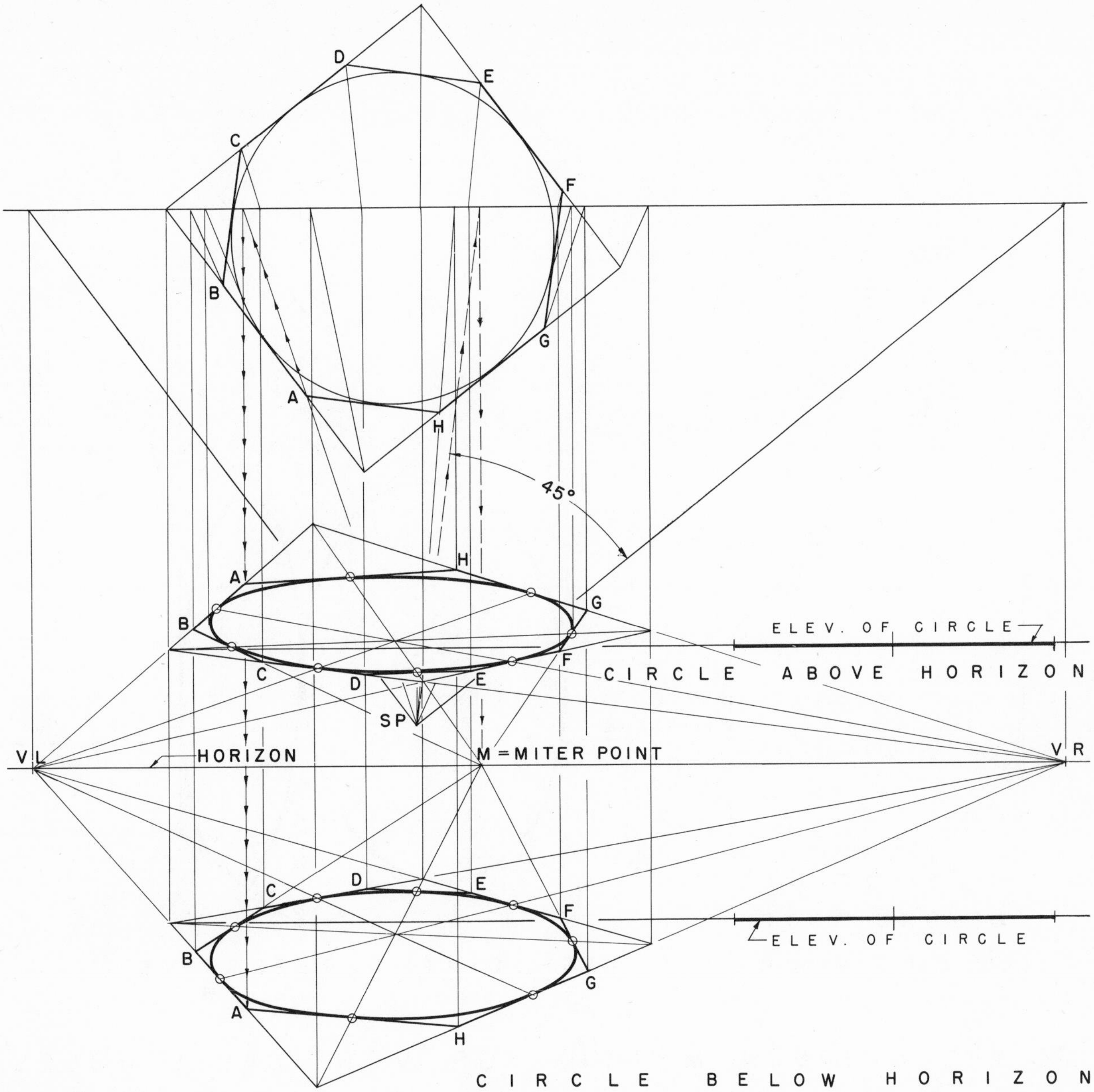

FIG. 144 OCTAGON METHOD OF CIRCLES IN PERSPECTIVE

sides is drawn to V and the other pair is horizontal. The remaining four sides of the octagon parallel the diagonals of the square. They are miter 45° lines and vanish to miter points. Both the miter points are usually within reach in one-point perspective. In two-point perspective one is usually very far away. These M points are helpful as shown in Fig. 144 but are not needed for the construction because it is easy to plot both ends of lines B–C and F–G, which vanish in M. The tangent square is adequate for small circles, as shown in Fig. 143. The octagon with its greater number of tangent guiding lines and points of tangency is more accurate and better for larger circles, Fig. 144.

With the tangent square construction it is necessary to draw the lines toward SP from the edges of the circle in plan to intersect the picture plane and determine the exact length of the ellipse as shown in Fig. 143 III. It is also advisable to locate these points for the octagon construction.

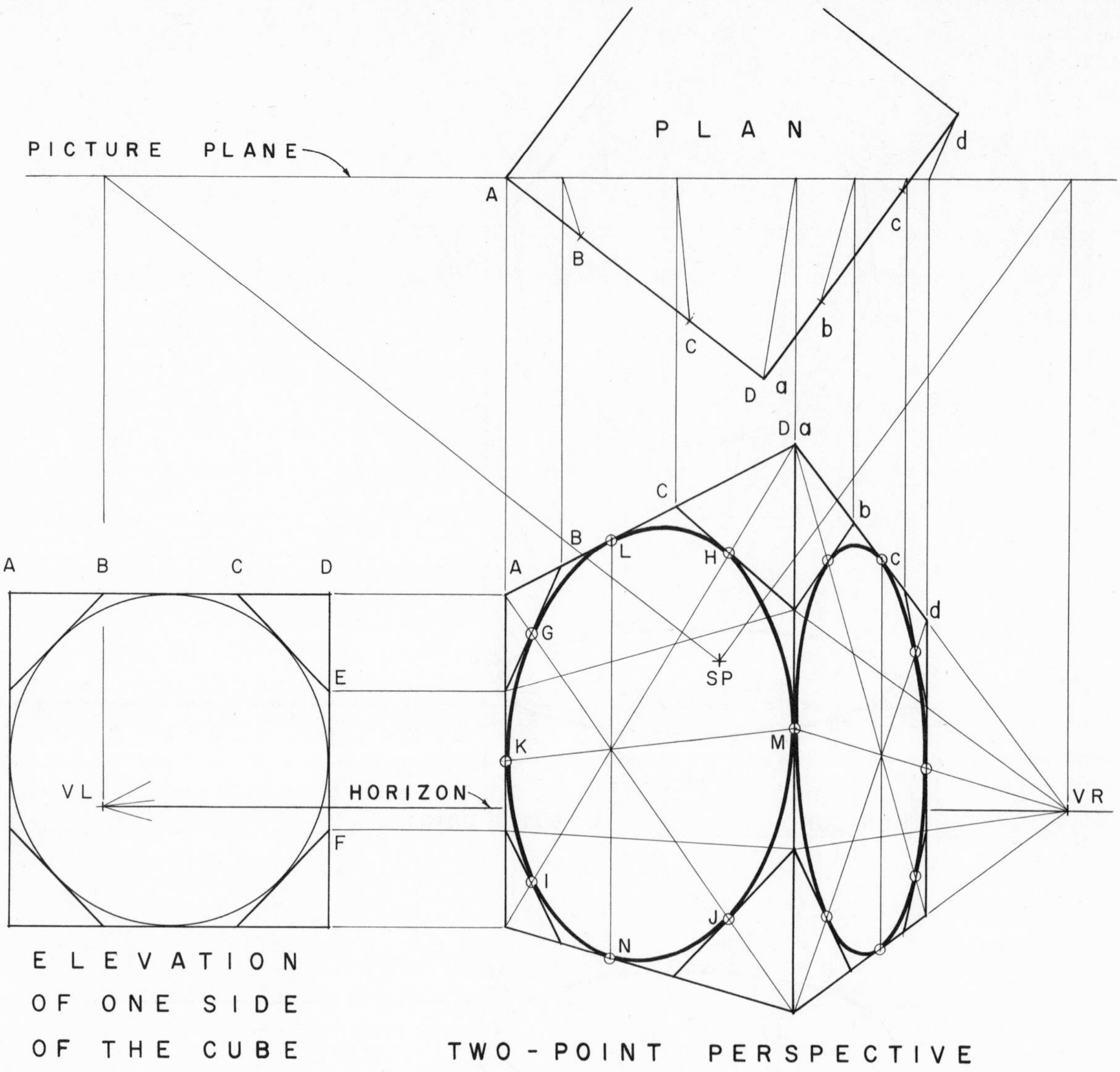

FIG. 145 OCTAGON METHOD FOR VERTICAL CIRCLES

The use of the octagon method for vertical circles on two-point perspective wall surfaces is shown in Fig. 145. Because the object represented is a cube and all its sides are the same size, the one elevation of the circle represents any side of the cube for the perspective construction of the ellipses. A tangent circle is drawn inside the square to make the elevation view. The four sides of the octagon that are not also sides of the square are then drawn tangent to the circle with the 45° triangle and two of them provide the spacing A, B, C, D in elevation. This spacing is transferred to both sides of the plan, which will be visible in the perspective. From the plan positions of these points projectors are drawn to the picture plane and then vertically to their correct positions on the perspective of the cube. Lines are carried over from points E and F to provide the other four corners for each octagon. The diagonals of each perspective of a square intersect the four octagon sides in points of tangency, G, H, I, J. Through the intersection of the two diagonals the perspectives of the vertical and horizontal center lines of the square are drawn to locate the other four points of tangency, K, L, M, N. The ellipses are then drawn inside of the perspectives of the octagons and through the eight points of tangency of each circle and octagon.

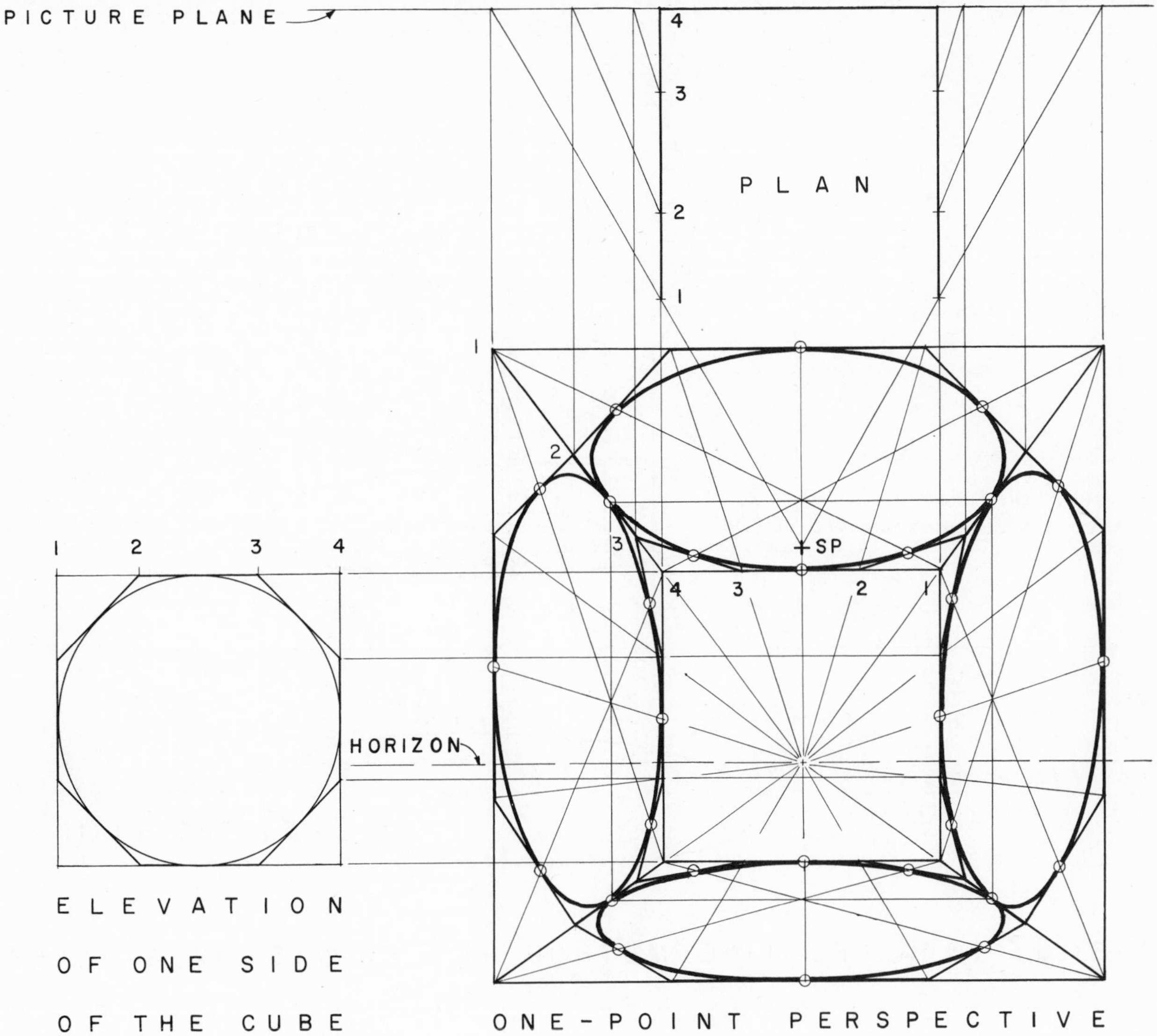

FIG. 146 TANGENT OCTAGON METHOD FOR CIRCLES

Fig. 146 represents a hollow cubical box with one open side through which the ceiling, floor, two side walls, and the rear wall of the interior of the cube are seen. The elevation of the one side of the cube and its inscribed circle will then represent each face of the interior of the cube. It will provide measurements for side walls, floor, and ceiling in constructing the ellipse on each of these four surfaces. The circle on the rear wall is a circle in the perspective and an exact duplicate of the elevation, because the rear wall is in the picture plane. It is not shown on the perspective. The one set of measurements 1, 2, 3, 4 is transferred from the elevation to both sides of the plan. They are in this case transferred directly to each edge of the scale size end wall in the perspective from which lines are traced away from V for the construction. If the end wall were not in the picture plane these measurements would be located on the plan of the end wall and enlarged or reduced as required for the perspective with projectors from SP.

Note that a true shape view of the circle must always be given in one of the auxiliary drawings for construction. The draftsman should also observe that the vertical and horizontal center lines of the circles of Fig. 146 are not the major axes of the ellipses.

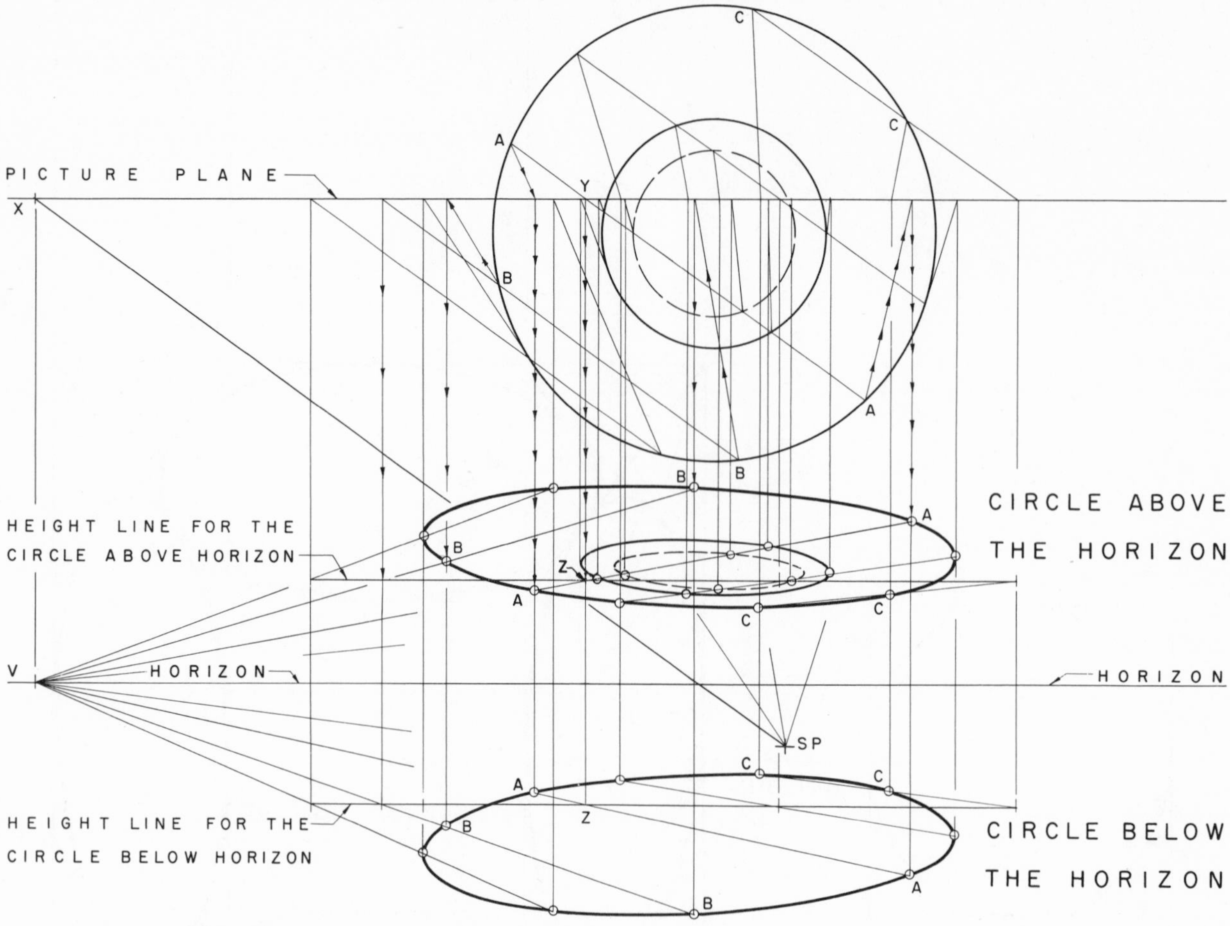

FIG. 147 PARALLEL LINE METHOD FOR POINTS ON CIRCLES

The point method can be used to locate any number of points on ellipses of any size. However it is most useful for large ellipses for which the eight points of the octagon method seem inadequate for accuracy. The points can be plotted by any procedure for locating a point in perspective. Either a plan or elevation that shows the true shape of the circle is required for the construction as shown in Figs. 147 and 148. The point method can be used for irregular curves or other forms as well as for circles.

The parallel line method is a simple one for locating points on horizontal circles, Fig. 147. Any line A–A can be drawn in plan parallel to SP–X and intersecting the circle. Line A–A crosses the picture plane at Y in plan, and in perspective it will cross the height line of the circle at its intersection Z with the vertical through Y. Line A–A and all lines parallel to it will be drawn to vanishing point V, which is located where the vertical from X meets the horizon. The same line in plan can be used to locate points on any number of circles it intersects. When the circles are all in the same horizontal plane the points for all of them are found on the same line in perspective, as shown on line A–A for the concentric circles above the horizon in Fig. 147. When the circles are not in the same horizontal plane a separate line A–A must be drawn for each different height as shown for the circle above the horizon and the one below the horizon in Fig. 147. The parallel lines in the direction A–A in plan must always be drawn parallel to SP–X so that they will be lines to the vanishing point V for this construction. This is a very good method for concentric or other multiple circles.

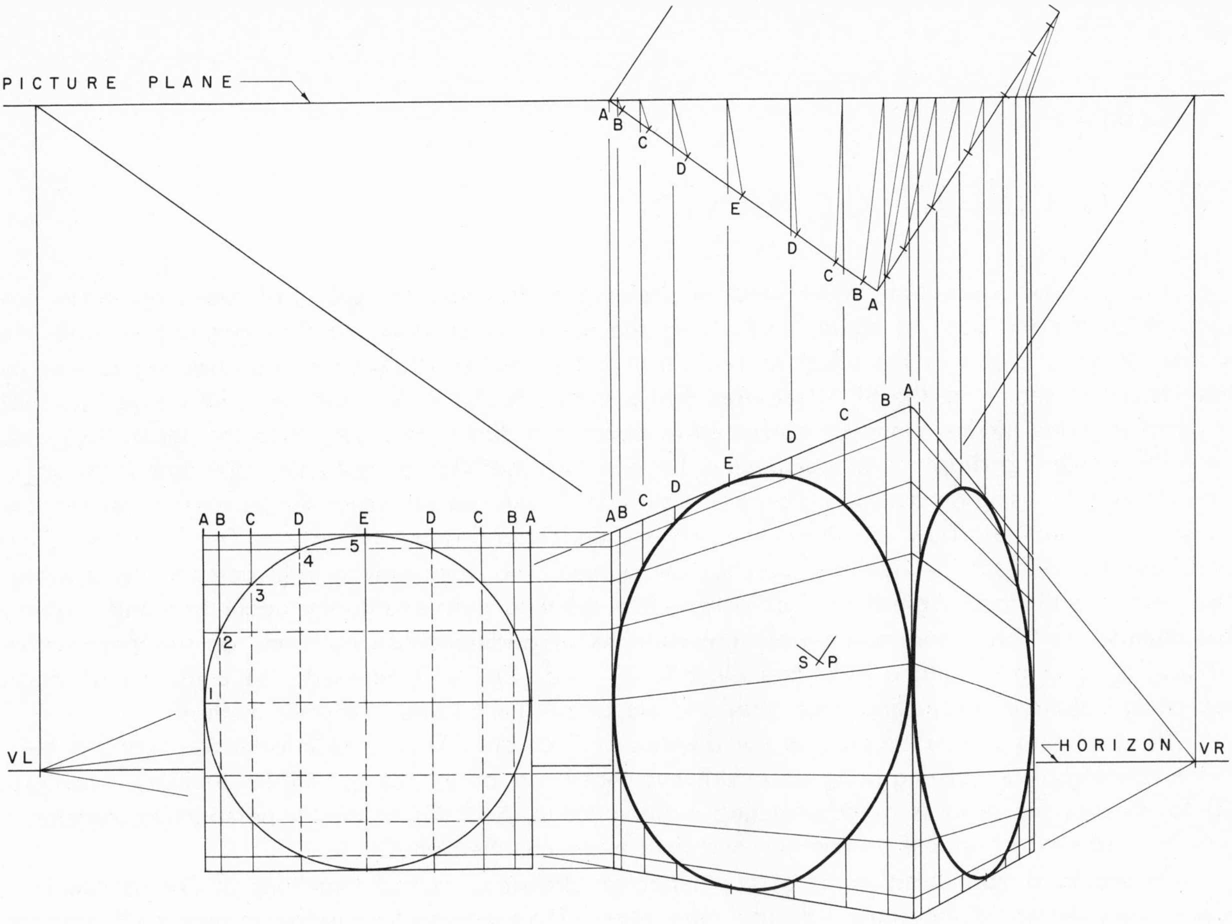

FIG. 148 OFFSET METHOD FOR POINTS ON CIRCLES

The offset method of locating points on ellipses has been used for the vertical circle of Fig. 148. A good procedure in using this method is to make approximately equal divisions around one fourth of the circle as at points, 1, 2, 3, 4, 5 and then transfer these points by drawing parallel to the edges of the tangent square as shown by the dotted lines in Fig. 148 to make symmetrical divisions in the other three fourths of the circle. The offset lines are then drawn on the circle and plotted for the ellipse. This method can be used for either horizontal or vertical circles.

PART CIRCLES IN PERSPECTIVE. It is rather rare to have a parabola or hyperbola as the perspective of a circular form. However it does occur occasionally and it usually disturbs the draftsman if he is not aware of the conditions causing the shape. When the SP is on a vertical line through the edge of the horizontal circle the perspective of the visible arc will be a parabola. When the SP is within the area of the circle in plan the visible arc will be a hyperbola in perspective. The perspectives of these shapes can be located by the point method that has been described for ellipses on this page, using offsets, or by the parallel line method described on the preceding page.

The drawing of ellipses or other irregular curves requires either skill at freehand drawing or infinite patience and care with irregular curves. Ellipses are of unlimited variety of sizes, proportions, and directions of axes. If the same shape and size repeat, it is sometimes helpful to make a pattern of transparent plastic or other material. This requires considerable time and work and is seldom practical for a single ellipse. When only a part of the ellipse is visible, some or all of the hidden part should be drawn in order to secure greater accuracy in the shape of the visible part.

CHAPTER 24

THE DIVISION OF LINES

The principal operation in perspective drawing is the foreshortening of measurements. This process causes the sizes of equal divisions on the object to decrease as they get farther from the station point. It produces the effect of realism in a perspective drawing by representing spaces as they would appear from the SP. It requires that equal measurements made on a measuring line that is parallel to the picture plane be corrected to become a diminishing sequence for perspective use.

The preceding chapters on perspective have shown methods of obtaining divisions in perspective drawing by using an auxiliary plan and elevation. These are the usual simple routine perspective construction methods. They are in general easy to understand and easy to use. They are the safest and best methods for the beginner and for the person who does only a little perspective drawing. The person who does a great deal of perspective drawing may eventually begin to wonder about two things: (1) "Isn't there some way that changes or additions can be made on this perspective without starting over with a plan and elevation?" and (2) "Is it necessary to construct all these repeating details by projecting from plan and elevation? Isn't there a shorter method?"

The purposes of this chapter on the division of lines are (A) to give information that will help in the revising of an existing perspective drawing that is no longer set up with its auxiliary drawings, (B) to shorten the process of constructing a perspective, and (C) to aid in perspective sketching.

First some very simple procedures and then more complex ones.

To locate a vanishing point of a perspective drawing, extend two lines of the perspective, which were drawn to the same VP, until they meet. Their intersection is the required VP. Choose long lines that are as far apart as possible in order to obtain maximum accuracy, Fig. 149 A.

Vertical spacing can be laid out for the vertical space between any two lines to a VP on any convenient vertical line between the two given lines or their extensions. The scale is kept in a vertical position and moved along horizontally until the required spacing fits between the two converging lines. This method can be used for equal or unequal spaces. Any convenient divisions on the scale that fit the space can be used for this purpose, as shown in Fig. 149 B. In this example scale II is the most convenient one to use because it fits between the lines of the drawing. Scale I requires extension of the two lines of the drawing to the left and scale III to the right.

The center of the perspective of rectangle A–B–C–D, Fig. 149 C, is found by drawing its diagonals A–C and D–B. This procedure can be repeated to divide the halves and fourths of the original rectangle. Divisions are limited to two, four, eight, etc., divisions of the given rectangle. A given rectangle E–F–G–H of Fig. 149 D can be assumed to be a half rectangle and its half diagonal E–X extended to add an equal rectangle F–I–J–G to it. This process can be repeated indefinitely.

The method of triangles is one of the most useful of the methods of division of lines. The flexibility of this method is shown in the sequence of illustrations of Figs. 149 E, F, G, and H. It is used to convert scale measurements that have been laid out on a vertical measuring line to correct perspective measurements and transfer them to a line to a VP or use them for vertical divisions on the object. Line K–Y to VR is the given line which is to be divided in Figs. 149 E and F. Lay out on the vertical from K the required divisions at any convenient scale. From the last measurement N draw a line to Y. Lines from the measurements toward VR intersect the diagonal N–Y at the required distances. Verticals from these points locate the divisions on line K–Y or make vertical divisions on the object. The order of divisions can be reversed by either of the methods in Figs. 149 G and H.

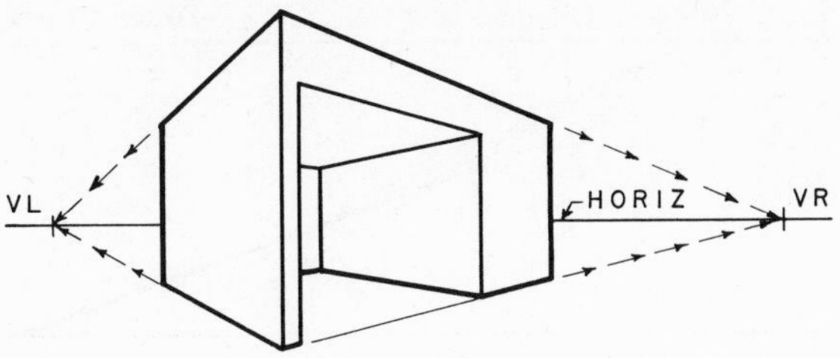

(A) LOCATING VANISHING POINTS BY EXTENDING LINES TO MEET

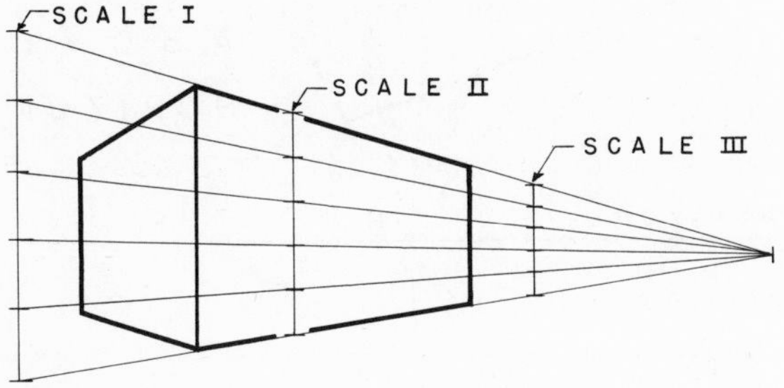

(B) VERTICAL DIVISIONS USED WHEREVER A SCALE FITS

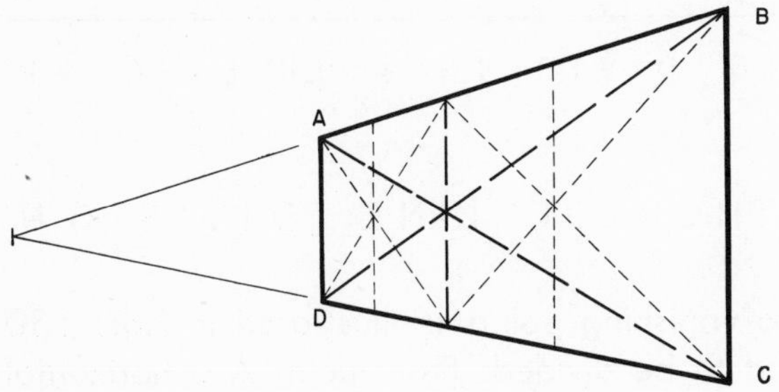

(C) EQUAL DIVISIONS WITH DIAGONALS OF RECTANGLES

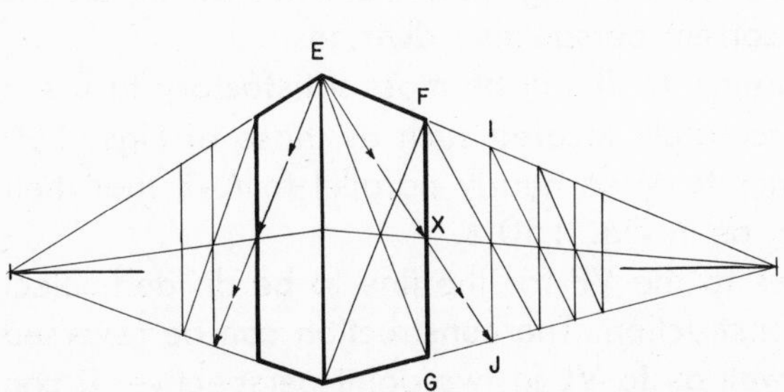

(D) EQUAL ADDITION BY USING DIAGONAL OF HALF RECTANGLE

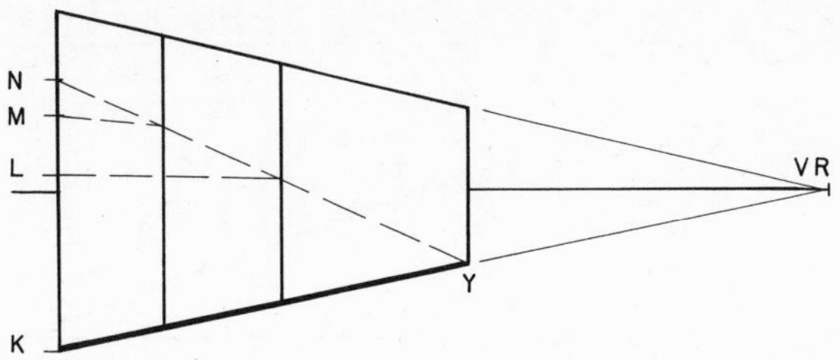

(E) SMALL SCALE ON VERTICAL DIVIDES GIVEN LINE TO VP

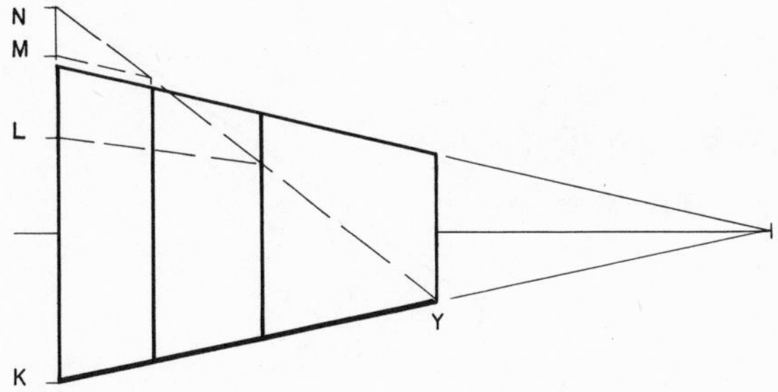

(F) LARGER SCALE ON VERTICAL GIVES SAME DIVISIONS AS E

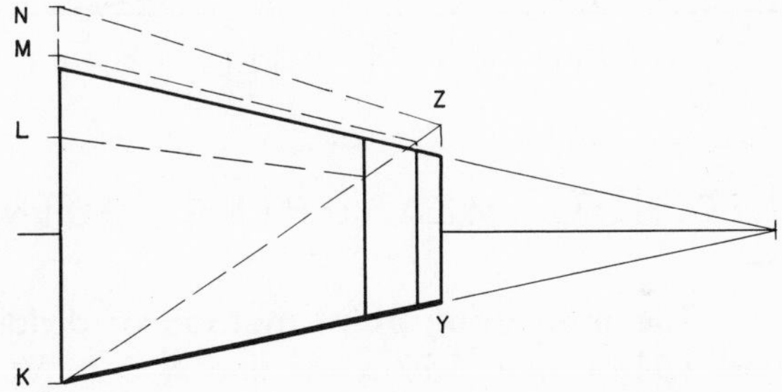

(G) USE OF OTHER DIAGONAL REVERSES ORDER OF DIVISIONS

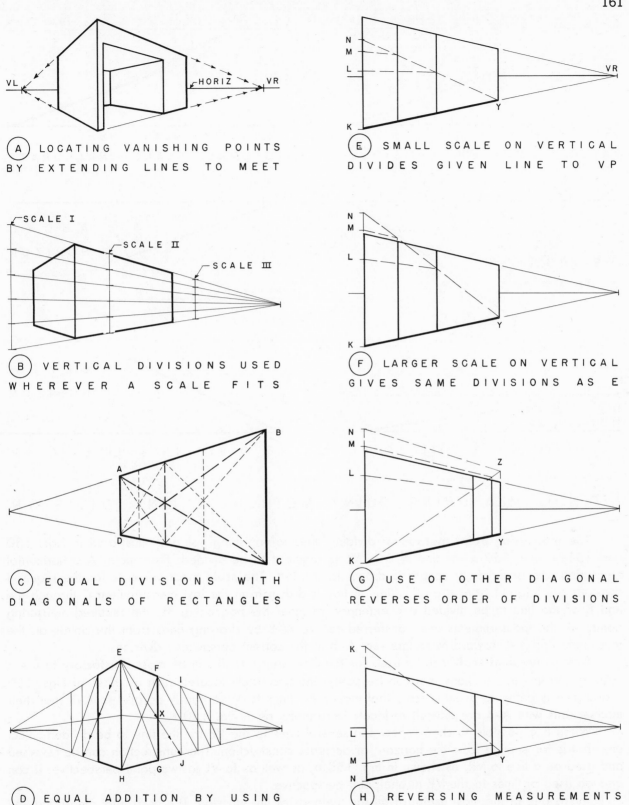

(H) REVERSING MEASUREMENTS ALSO REVERSES THE ORDER

FIG. 149 SIMPLE PERSPECTIVE LINE DIVISION METHODS

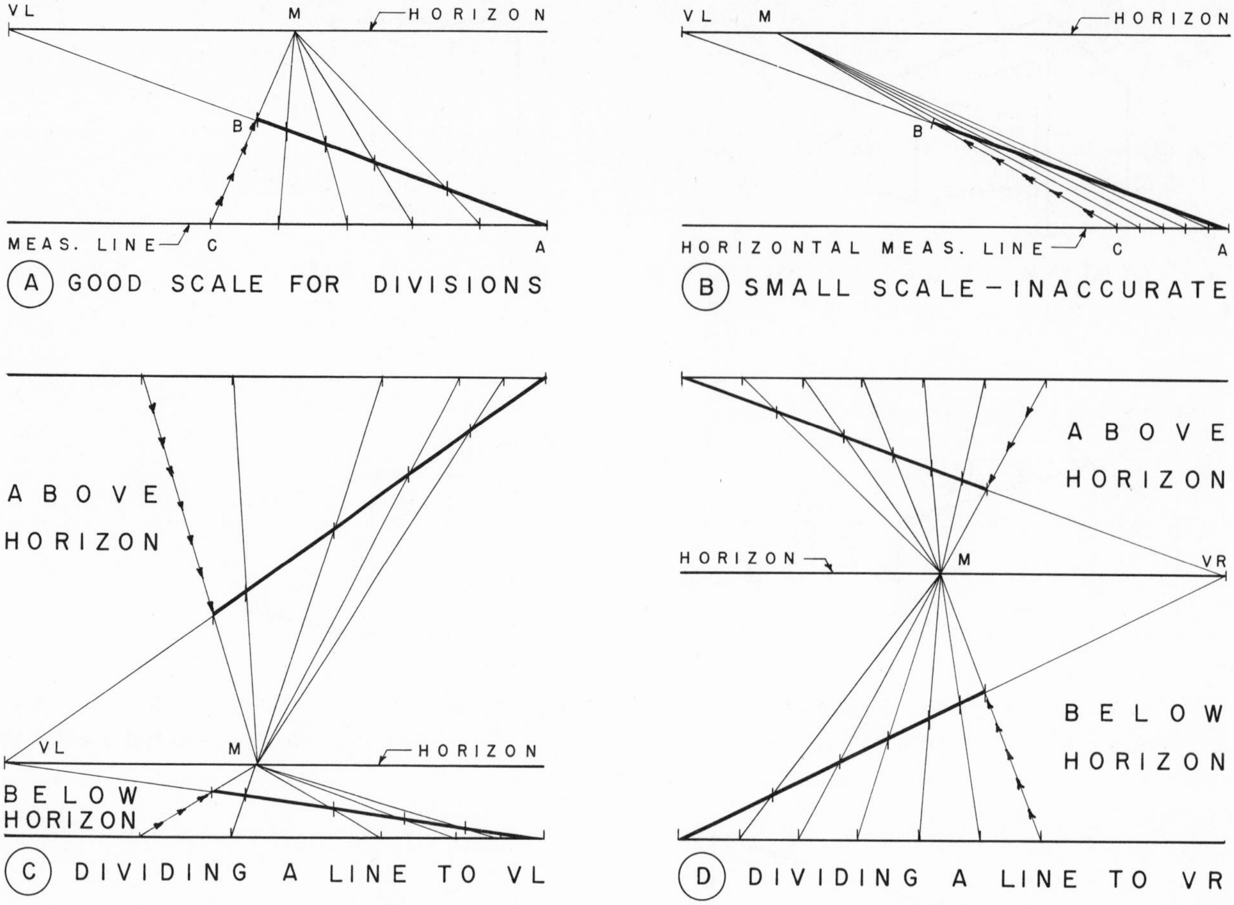

FIG. 150 MEASURING POINT METHOD OF LINE DIVISION

The measuring point method of dividing lines to vanishing points is illustrated in Figs. 150 and 151. In Fig. 150 A the line A–B to VL is required to be divided. From point A a horizontal measuring line of indefinite length is drawn to the left. The scale measurements for the required divisions are laid out from A on this line. A line is drawn from the last measurement C through the end B of the line to be divided and extended to meet the horizon at M, the required measuring point. All the measurements are transferred to line A–B by drawing lines from the points on the measuring line A–C toward M to intersect A–B in the correct perspective divisions.

Any convenient scale can be used for the measurements. It will be most satisfactory to use a scale giving line intersections that can be easily and accurately located such as those of Figs. 150 A and D. It is better to avoid a scale that makes the lines to M so nearly parallel to A–B that their intersections with A–B are difficult to locate accurately, as in Fig. 150 B.

When it is possible to choose between several lines to the VP for the line to be divided select one that is far enough from the horizon for accurate construction. The construction can be reversed and used on a line to VR, as shown in Fig. 150 D, as well as to VL in two-point perspective. It can also be used on lines to the VP in one-point perspective.

This is one of the most useful of all the methods of line division. The horizontal measuring line is assumed to be parallel to the picture plane and therefore is at the same scale throughout its length. The lines from A–C to M are the perspectives of parallel lines in a horizontal plane. They convert the scale measurements on A–C to the correct perspective sizes on line A–B. Different scales can be used on different constructions for the same perspective.

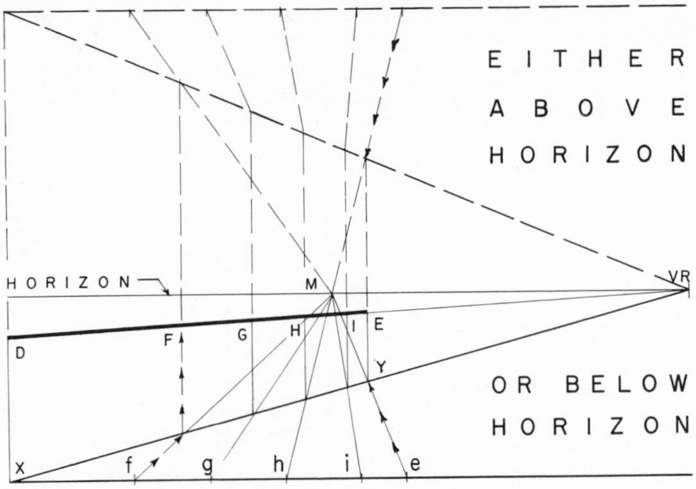

(I) USING A SUBSTITUTE LINE TO VP WHEN LINE IS TOO CLOSE TO HORIZON

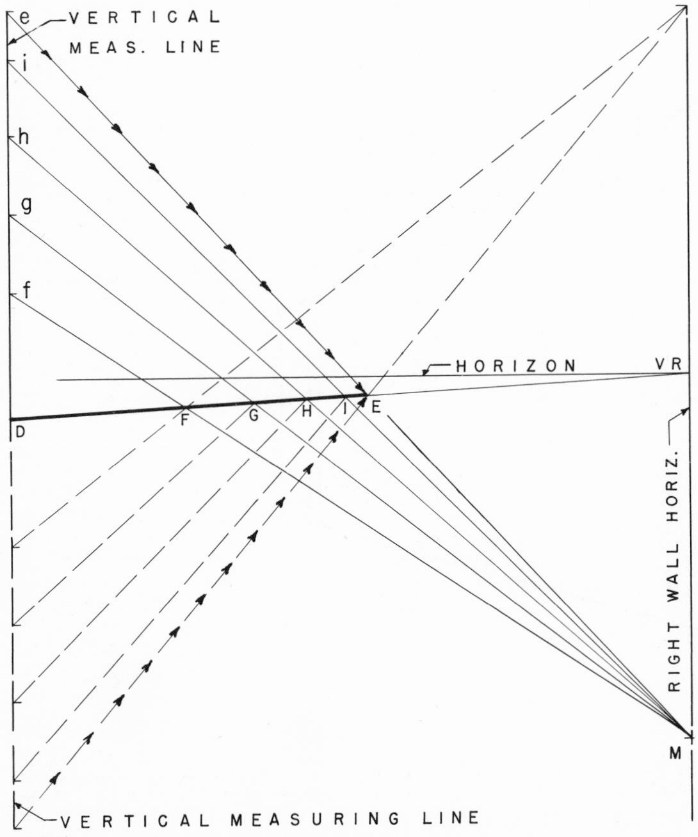

(II) VERTICAL MEASURING LINE USED TO DIVIDE A LINE TO VP

FIG. 151 VARIATIONS IN THE MEASURING POINT METHOD

When the line to be divided is too close to the horizon for accurate construction, either of two procedures can be followed:

I. A substitute line to the same VP as the line to be divided and either vertically below or above it can be used for the construction. The measurements are transferred with vertical lines from the substitute line to the line to be divided as shown in Fig. 151 I. In this example D–E is the given line to be divided and X–Y the substitute line on which the divisions are first worked out and then transferred vertically to required positions on D–E. The dotted lines show the same construction from above.

II. The second method uses a vertical measuring line D–e from D and a measuring point on the right wall horizon. The right wall horizon is the vertical line drawn through the vanishing point VR of line D–E, Fig. 151 II. After the measurements are laid out on the vertical measuring line D–e, a line is drawn from e through E to locate M, the required measuring point. The construction lines are then drawn from the measurements on D–e toward M to locate the required points on D–E. Choose a scale that will give reasonable construction. A large scale will cause M to be far from VR and a small scale will give a flat angle of lines to M with inaccurate intersections. The measuring line can be either above or below D with identical results, Fig. 151 II. The construction is used to either VR or VL as required by the line to be divided.

This method may be more convenient to use in some instances even though the line to be divided permits the use of the horizontal measuring line and M on the horizon. In this method the construction is assumed to be in a right wall plane of which the triangle D–e–E is a part. D–e is a vertical line and is the same scale throughout its length because vertical lines are parallel to the picture plane.

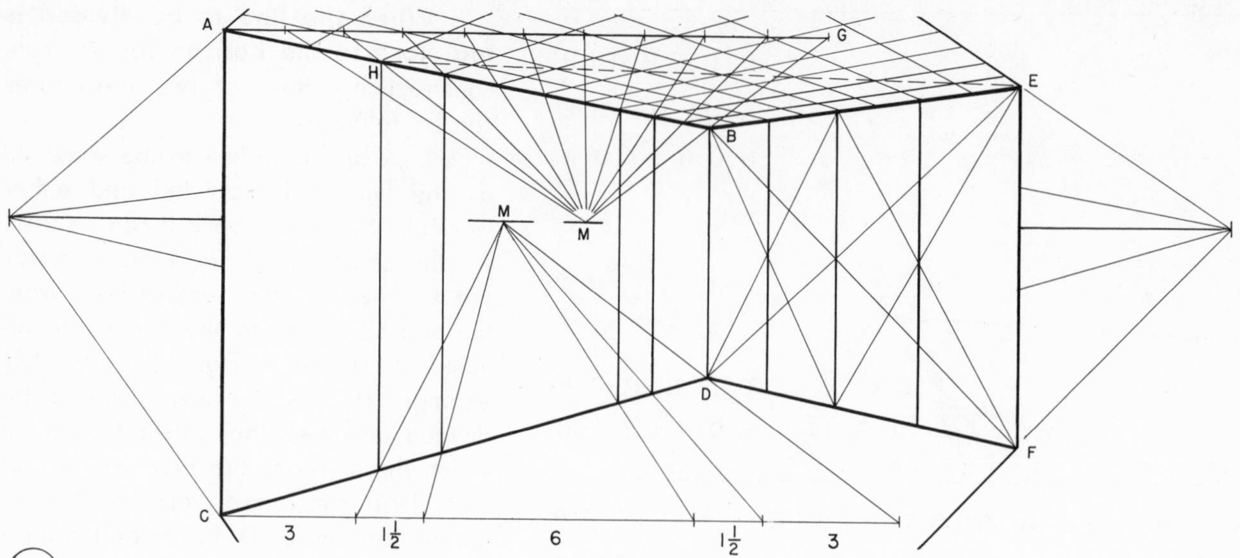

(A) DIVISIONS ON INTERIOR WALLS AND CEILING

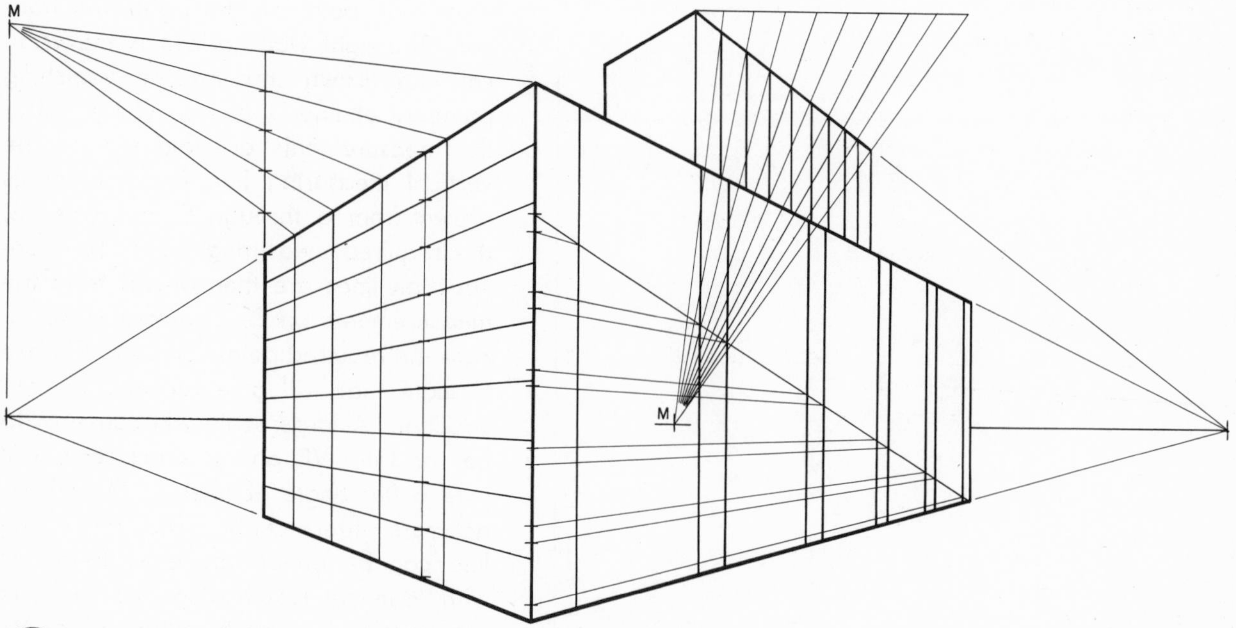

(B) DIVISIONS ON EXTERIOR OF BLOCK SHAPES

FIG. 152 LINE DIVISION IN TWO-POINT PERSPECTIVE

Line division methods are useful for supplying details on the block shapes of a perspective that is being constructed and for adding to or changing an existing completed perspective. In either of these cases the basic dimensions of the object must be known and the details fitted to conform to the known sizes. In the example of Fig. 152 A the distances A–B = 15 feet, B–E = 12 feet, and B–D = 8 feet are given. The wall B–E–D–F is divided by diagonals to represent four equal vertical wall panels each 3 feet wide. The 15-foot wall C–D is divided to represent 3-foot wall panels at each end. The center 9 feet is divided with $1\frac{1}{2}$ feet at each edge and 6 feet in the center. The ceiling has been divided for $1\frac{1}{2}$-foot squares. The measurements for these divisions are laid out on

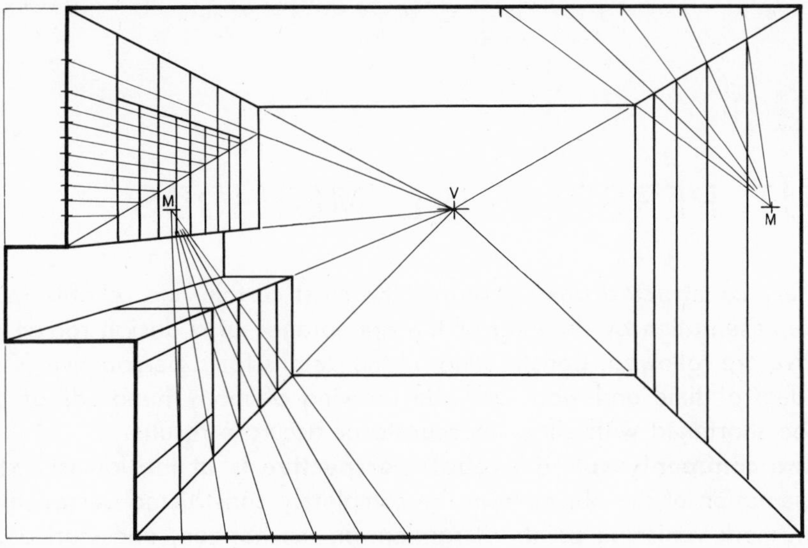

(I) DIVISIONS ON INTERIOR OF A ROOM

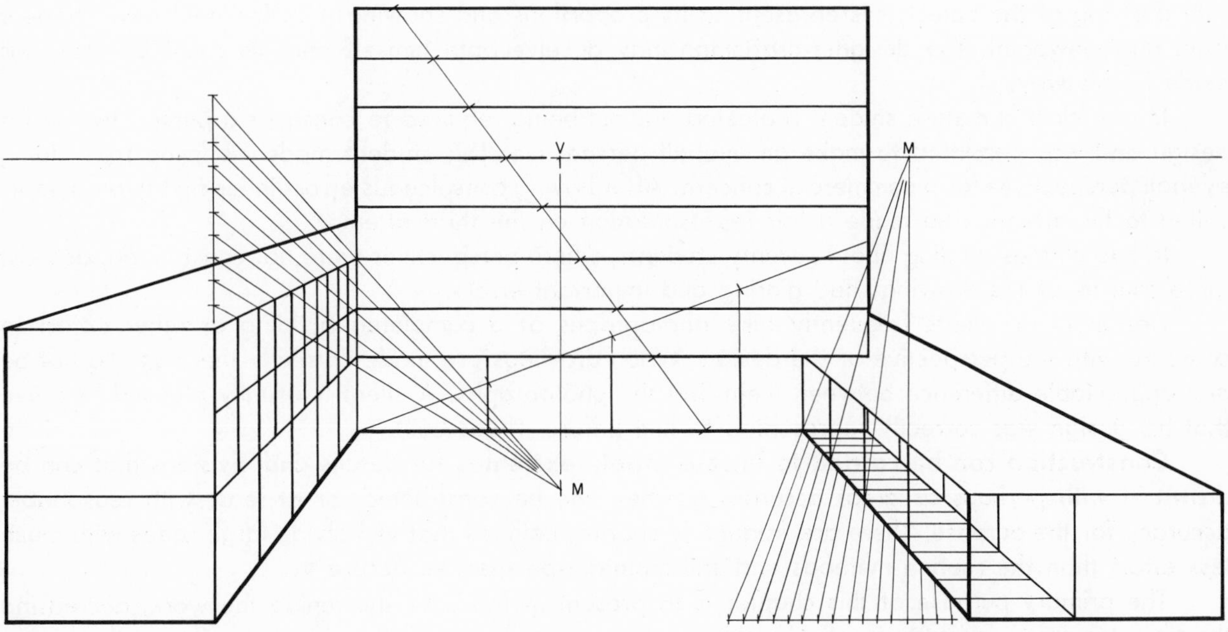

(II) DIVISIONS ON EXTERIOR OF BLOCK SHAPES

FIG. 153 LINE DIVISION IN ONE-POINT PERSPECTIVE

line A–G and transferred to A–B. The dotted diagonal line E–H is at 45° because points E and H are the same number of feet from B. It intersects the ceiling lines from A–B to give the second set of ceiling lines. This second set of ceiling lines is drawn from the right vanishing point of the perspective through the intersections of the dotted line E–H and the first set of ceiling lines.

Line division in perspective must be made to conform to the dimensions and design of the object represented. However the objective is to make proportionate divisions that are correct for the perspective. Any convenient scale can be used for each construction. Several different scales may then be used for measurements for different line division constructions on the same drawing.

CHAPTER 25

SHORT-CUT PERSPECTIVE METHODS

The completely constructed perspective is the most certain and reliable way of producing a true and correct representation by drawing of the appearance of a design for an object when rules for good perspective are followed. Constructing all the details for a perspective of a complex design requires a great deal of time and work and the drawing of many hundreds of construction lines. This process can be shortened with either inaccurate or accurate results.

The procedure commonly called eyeball perspective is at the lowest extreme in accurate and truthful representation of the object from the completely constructed perspective. This method is to draw a horizon, mark vanishing points at random on the horizon, and start drawing perspective lines and masses by guess to represent the object according to the imagination of the draftsman. The person with much experience in drawing perspectives may make a fair representation of the object. The person with a little or even a moderate amount of experience may make a very inaccurate drawing of the object, misrepresenting its proportions and showing it as it would never appear from any viewpoint. The designer-draftsman may deceive both himself and his client by drawings made in this way.

In one class a mature student protested against being required to construct a perspective of his design and was permitted to make an eyeball perspective. This student made his living from doing eyeball perspectives for a commercial concern. After having conspicuous errors in his first two attempts called to his attention he made a fair representation on the third attempt.

In two classes totaling about seventy students, where perspectives were not constructed, as least three fourths of the drawings had glaring and important errors.

Designers or clients frequently take photographs of a completed building or other object to compare with the perspective of the design. When drawings are made correctly there should not be any appreciable difference between them and the photographs. A client is usually pleased to prove that his design was correctly represented to him before it was built.

Construction can be carried to unreasonable extremes for details and divisions that can be drawn in with perhaps as great accuracy as they can be constructed, or at least with reasonable accuracy for the purpose. There are frequently shorter methods that will divide large areas with much less effort than the routine methods and still maintain perspective accuracy.

The primary purpose of this chapter is to present methods of shortening the work, decreasing the time required, and reducing the working area in making perspective drawings. The methods presented should enable the designer-draftsman to work in a freer way, in less space, and to produce drawings that have the accuracy required for good perspective representations.

Main perspective shapes are constructed at the size required for the perspective drawing in Fig. 154. This skeleton drawing assures that the principal masses and areas are correctly represented. It enables the draftsman to check the general appearance of the perspective after a minimum amount of work. He can then make another study in the same way with changes of one or more of the variables if he is not satisfied with his first effort.

After constructing a satisfactory block perspective at the required size, the plan and SP are no longer needed. Details of the design can be added by methods of line division to complete the perspective. If accuracy of details is not essential, some of the minor divisions can be drawn in by a good draftsman without constructing them. Some good draftsmen know instinctively when an incorrect line appears on a perspective drawing and are able to locate and correct errors.

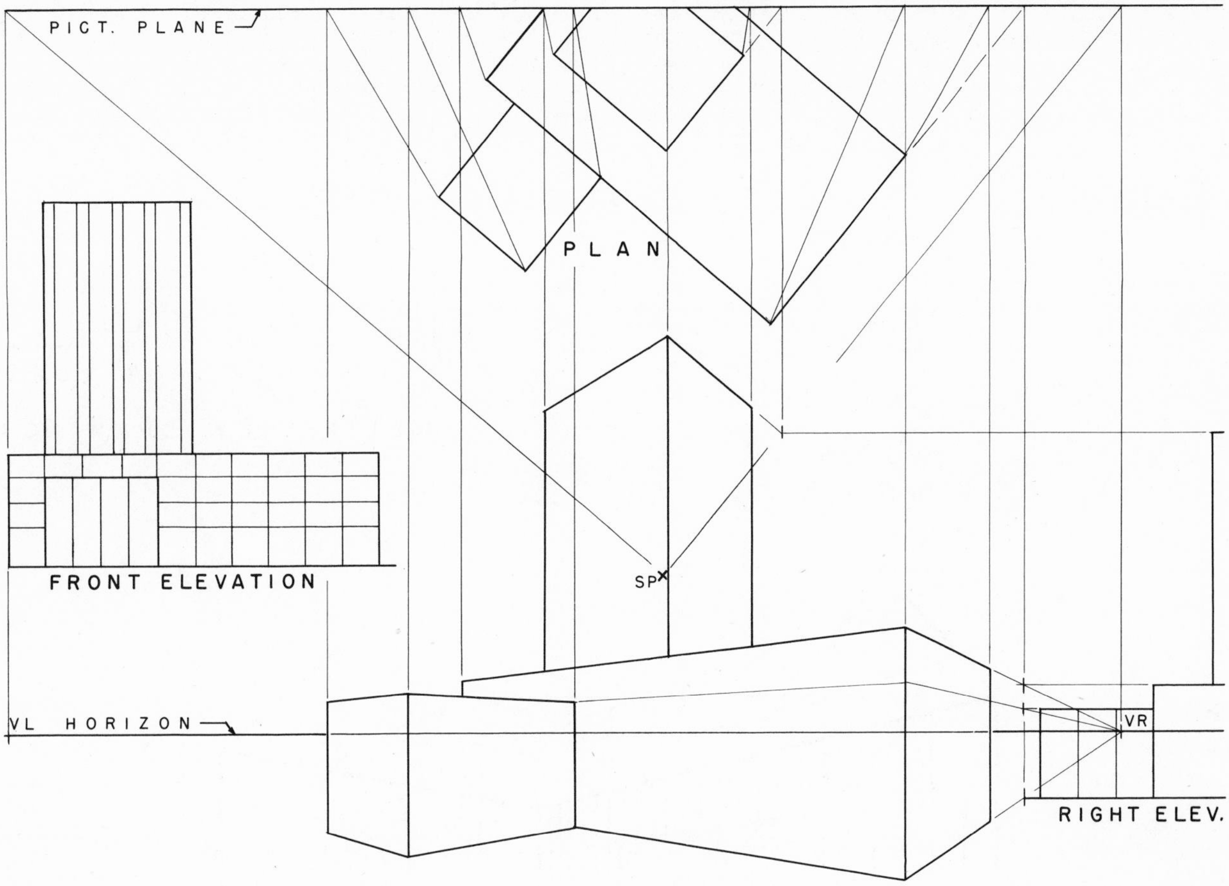

BLOCK PERSPECTIVE SHAPES CONSTRUCTED

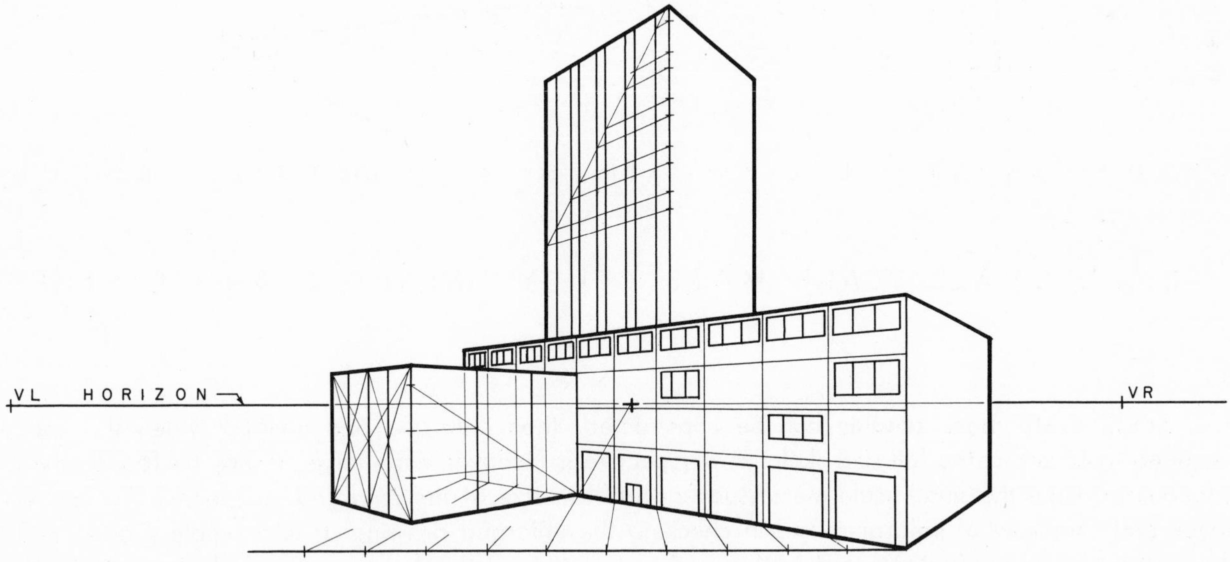

BLOCK SHAPES COPIED ON FINAL PAPER AND DIVIDED

FIG. 154 MASSES CONSTRUCTED-DIVISIONS CONSTRUCTED OR DRAWN

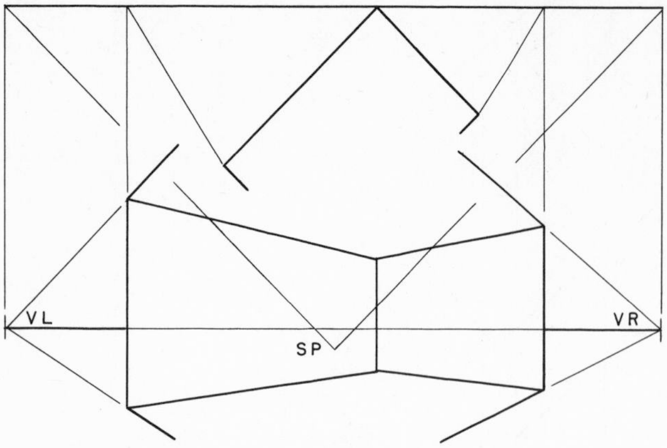

S M A L L S C A L E M A S S
S T U D Y C O N S T R U C T E D

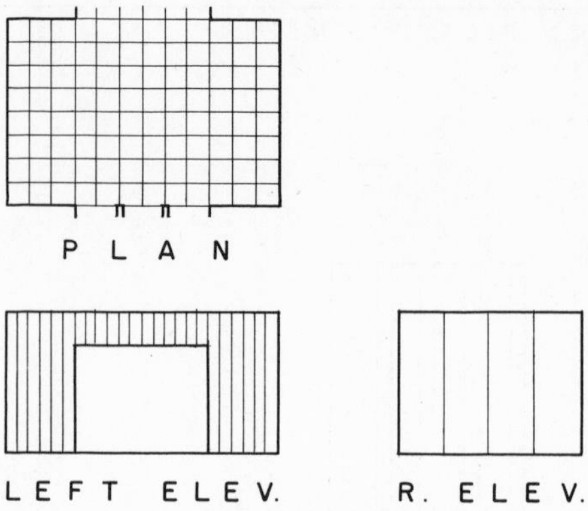

M U L T I - V I E W D R A W I N G S

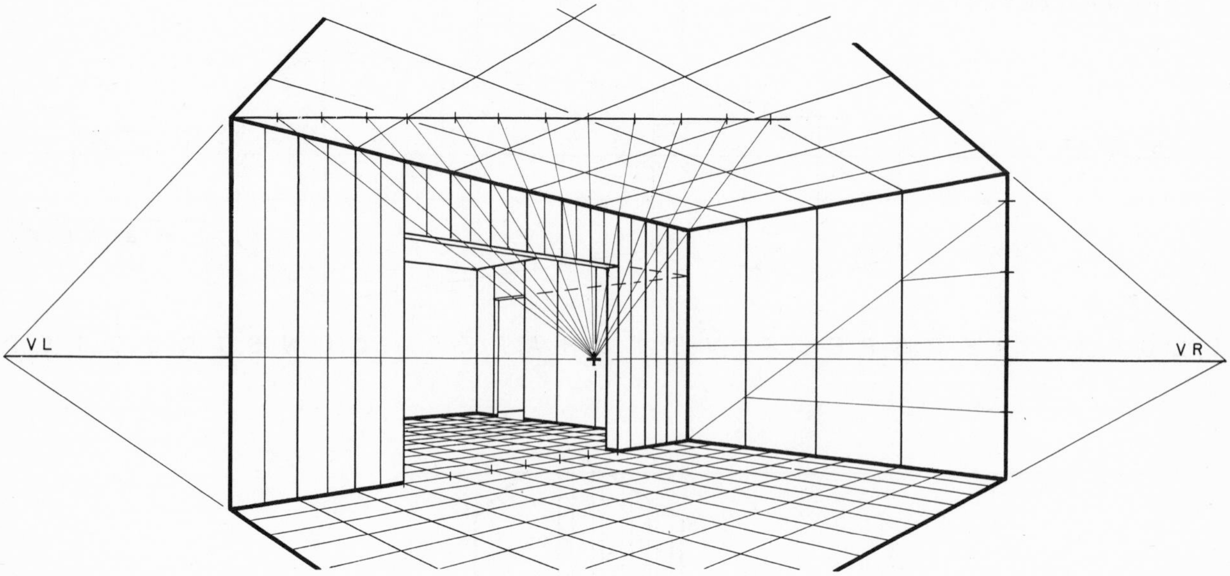

S T U D Y E N L A R G E D T W O T I M E S A N D D E T A I L S A D D E D

FIG. 155 SMALL SCALE MASS STUDY ENLARGED AND DIVIDED

Small scale mass studies can be constructed, then enlarged and divided, when the space required to construct the full size skeleton perspective is inconveniently large. It may be found advantageous to make the small scale mass study at half the size of the enlarged perspective for convenience and simplicity of enlarging and in checking the enlarged drawing. It is a simple procedure to move the picture plane backward or forward to get the width of the constructed block study one half or any other fractional proportion of the width of the enlarged perspective. However, other fractional sizes can be used for the small studies.

The small study can be made at any convenient size, then enlarged to any desired size by the method of radiating and parallel lines that is described on page 123. This method of enlarging has no limit on the variation in size between the small and large block perspectives. It should be remembered that extreme enlargements magnify inaccuracies and should be avoided.

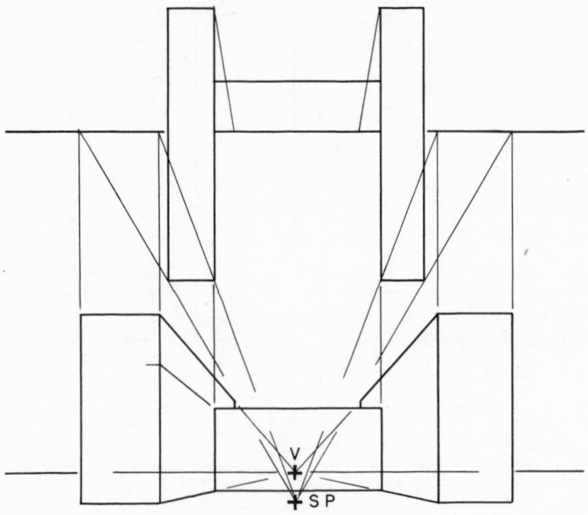

CONSTRUCTED MASS STUDY

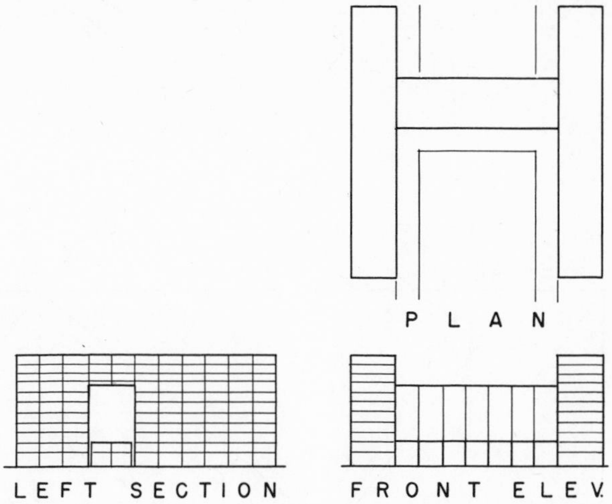

MULTI-VIEW DRAWINGS

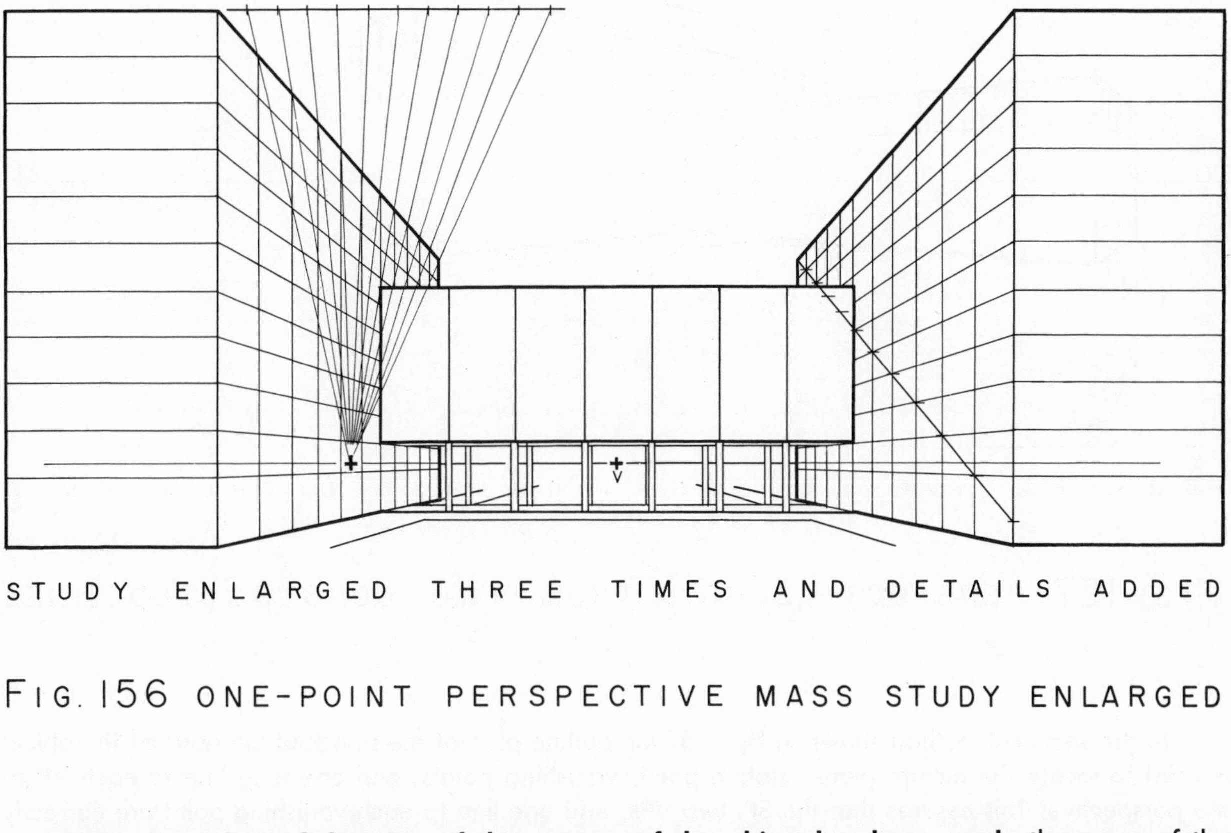

STUDY ENLARGED THREE TIMES AND DETAILS ADDED

FIG. 156 ONE-POINT PERSPECTIVE MASS STUDY ENLARGED

After the enlarged drawing of the masses of the object has been made the areas of the perspective can be divided by methods of line division with a great many of the minor spaces drawn in when they can be drawn directly with reasonable accuracy.

Drawing in of details without any construction can be either reasonable and accurate or unreasonable and erroneous depending on the knowledge, experience, and sensitivity to correct representation of the individual making the perspective drawing. The term *faking* of perspective forms is commonly used for any drawing in without constructing each line. There are however two different classifications of drawing in. If the draftsman understands the appearance of the shapes he draws and is sure that he has made a correct representation of them on the perspective this is not faking. When the draftsman puts in lines of a perspective without knowing positively that they are right he is drawing from ignorance and is really faking the representation of forms he cannot visualize.

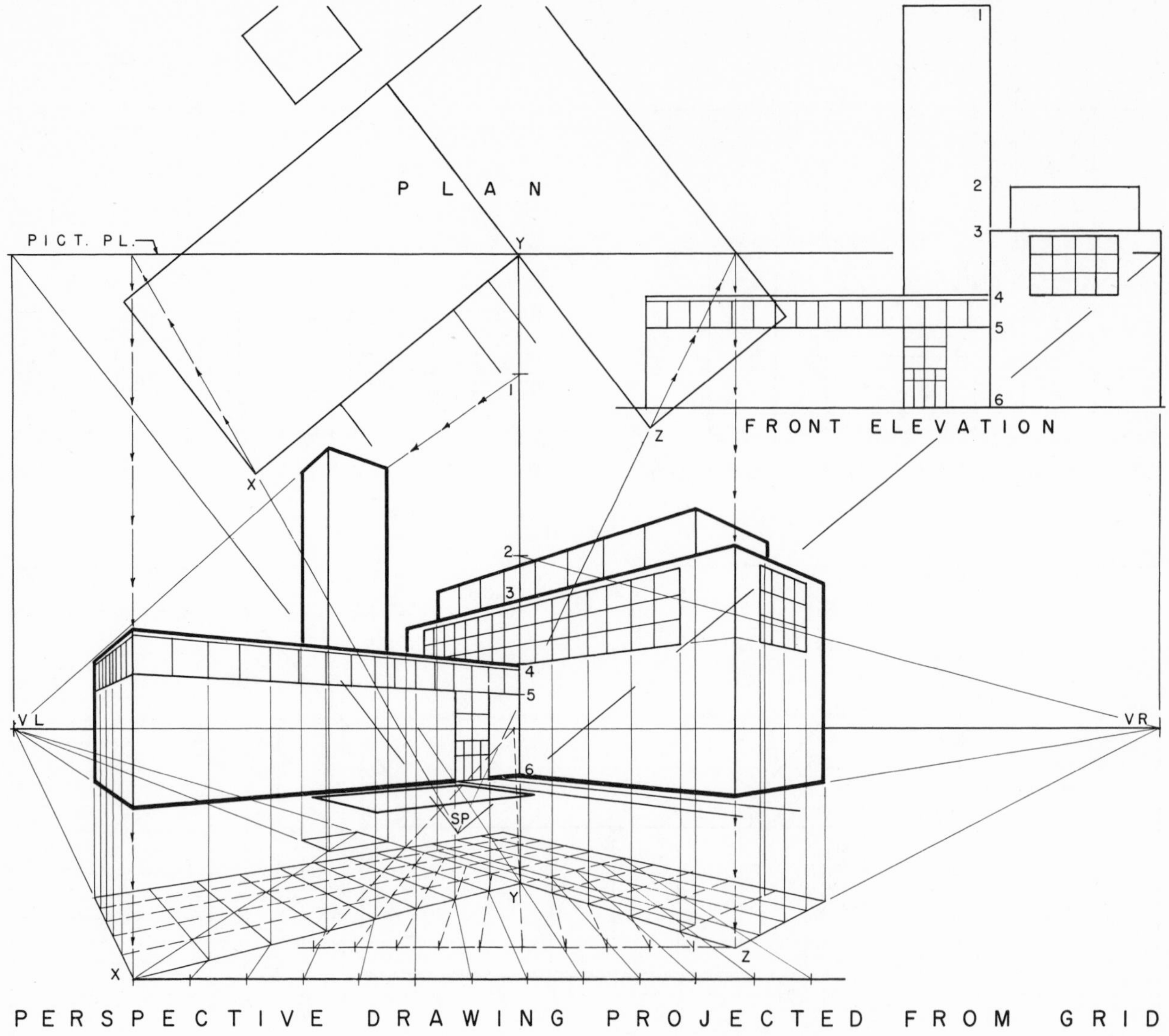

FIG. 157 PERSPECTIVE GRID FROM TWO CONSTRUCTED LINES

In the short-cut method shown in Fig. 157 an outline plan of the principal divisions of the object is used to locate the picture plane, station point, vanishing points, and one long line to each VP of the perspective. This assures that the SP, two VPs, and one line to each vanishing point are correctly located for good perspective. It also provides the location for a scale height line 1–6. This plan can be drawn on scrap paper and discarded after the required information is provided on the perspective. A perspective plan grid can then be constructed on a plan below, above, or at some horizontal plane of the object. The size for the spaces of the grid should be selected to be most useful for the object. For a piece of furniture or appliance the grid spaces could represent one or more inches, a grid representing 1 foot could be used for a very small building, and grids representing a number of feet for larger buildings.

The principal masses of the object can be drawn to fit the grid with interpolation where necessary. The heights can be carried to correct perspective position from the scale height line. Details can be drawn in by eye if the draftsman's judgment of size is good. This method assures a perspective that is essentially correct with speedy results and minimum space required.

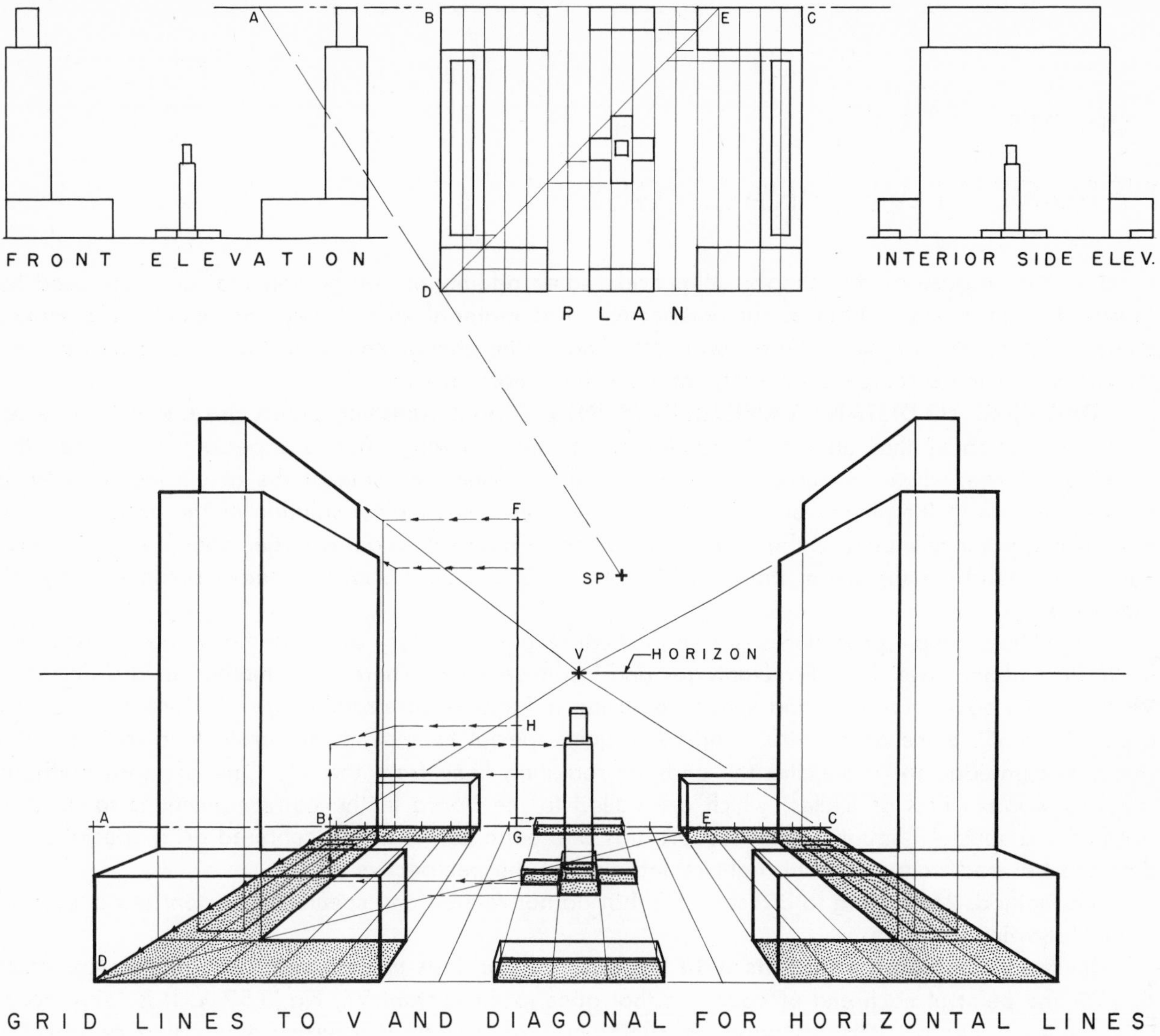

FIG. 158 ONE-POINT PERSPECTIVE DRAWN FROM GRID LINES

In the one-point perspective of Fig. 158 a plan at smaller scale was used to select a station point and obtain the left wall width A–B at the picture plane. The widths B–C of the plan and A–B of the left wall are laid out at correct scale on the perspective. A height is chosen for the horizon, and vanishing point V is located to agree with the horizontal position of SP. On this example grid lines to V are intersected by diagonal D–E to locate positions of the essential horizontal lines of the grid. Heights are traced from height line F–G as shown by the lines with arrows.

When the base plane of the object gives sufficient area vertically the perspective plan and grid can coincide with the bottom of the object as demonstrated here. In Fig. 158 this plan has been drawn with heavy lines and shaded and part of the concealed lines of the perspective drawn so the perspective grid lines and plan can be better understood. The perspective grid and plan can be on the perspective of any horizontal plane either above or below the horizon.

When an element of the object is vertically on line with V or very nearly on line its height will be inaccurate from the usual construction. The height can be determined with more accuracy by tracing it to one side of the perspective and then to its position as shown for height H.

CHAPTER 26

PERSPECTIVE PRACTICES

It is the purpose of this chapter to provide some additional information that is rarely used by those who learn only a little about perspective. This material should help the person who makes many perspectives to have a clearer understanding of the phenomena of perspective so that he can do better and more complete drawings and do them more quickly.

DRAWING TO DISTANT VANISHING POINTS. Distant vanishing points are one of the necessary inconveniences that go with two-point perspective drawing. This is especially true when the drawing is large, when the angle of vision is small, or when one side of the object makes a much smaller angle with the picture plane than the other side. The simplest solution of the difficulty when a vanishing point falls beyond the area of the drawing board is to get a larger board. Another solution is to extend the surface of the board by attaching a second board or heavy cardboard to it to reach the VP.

When these simple procedures are impractical or unsatisfactory other methods can be used. All of these methods have their disadvantages and inconveniences. There is no method of drawing to a VP that is as easy, accurate, and speedy as using a T-square or straightedge with one end against a pin at the VP. Some of the other methods require special equipment that provides a track to control a straightedge for producing the ends of radiating lines from the VP. One of these methods requires wooden arcs of circles, which are nailed to the board in the correct positions to provide tracks for a special T-square. This T-square has one edge of the blade centered on a special head that can be used from either the right or left side of the perspective.

Two methods of drawing to a distant VP that do not require any special equipment are described in the following paragraphs.

The method of plotting points with the near VP for lines to the distant VP requires construction for the point at each end of each line that goes to the distant VP, Fig. 159 A. It is fairly accurate for long lines but it is not good for short ones, as a small inaccuracy may cause an obvious error in direction. However a short line can be extended in plan to provide a long line, which makes a more accurate construction for the required short line. It may be practical and reasonable to draw short lines that are inaccurate to follow the general directions of the long lines near them.

The scale method of drawing to a distant vanishing point uses the horizon line as the zero point for two vertical scales, which extend as far above and below the horizon as necessary for the lines of the perspective. When the lines of the object do not go exactly through the marked divisions on the scales, it is necessary to estimate by eye the same relative positions on the two scales used. Choose scales that will give many small divisions for greater accuracy.

Locating the scales to the distant vanishing point is a rather simple procedure as illustrated in Fig. 159 B when the plan of the object, picture plane, and SP are given. A line parallel to the lines of the plan that go to the distant VP in the perspective drawing is drawn through SP in Fig. 159 B. Any two scales that give equal vertical measurements between this line and the picture plane line will locate the positions of the vertical lines for those two scales in the perspective.

One line to the distant VP and the horizon of the perspective can be used to locate two scales for drawings to a distant VP on any perspective drawing, Fig. 159 C. The line to the distant VP should be far from the horizon for greater accuracy. Find any two scales that give the same measurement vertically between the two lines and are in good positions for their use. Lay out the two scales from the zero points at the horizon on the vertical lines located for them on the perspective drawing.

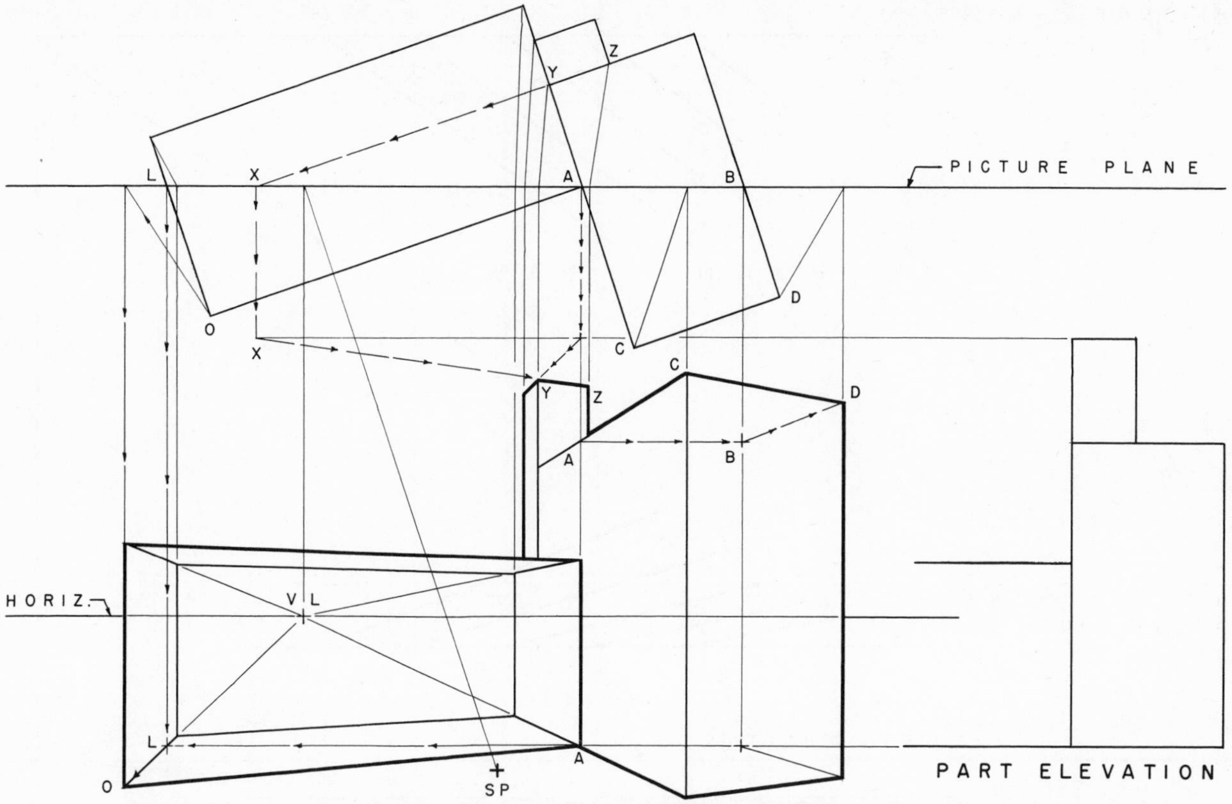

(A) LINES TO DISTANT VP PLOTTED FROM NEAR VP

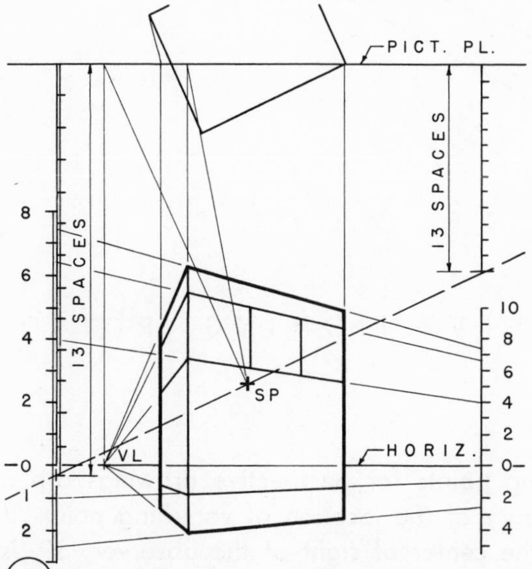

(B) PLAN USED TO LOCATE SCALES

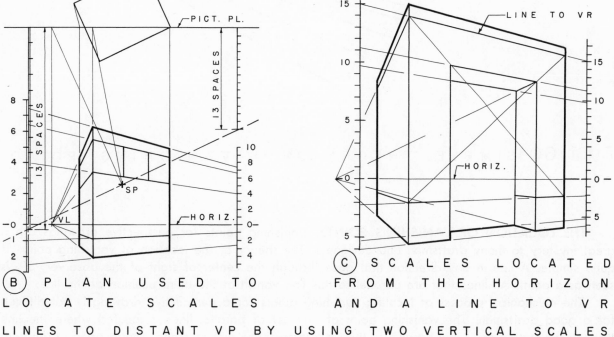

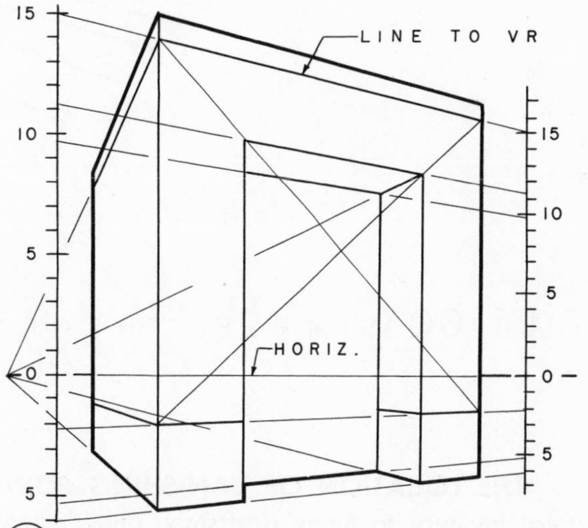

(C) SCALES LOCATED FROM THE HORIZON AND A LINE TO VR

LINES TO DISTANT VP BY USING TWO VERTICAL SCALES

FIG. 159 DRAWING TO DISTANT VANISHING POINTS

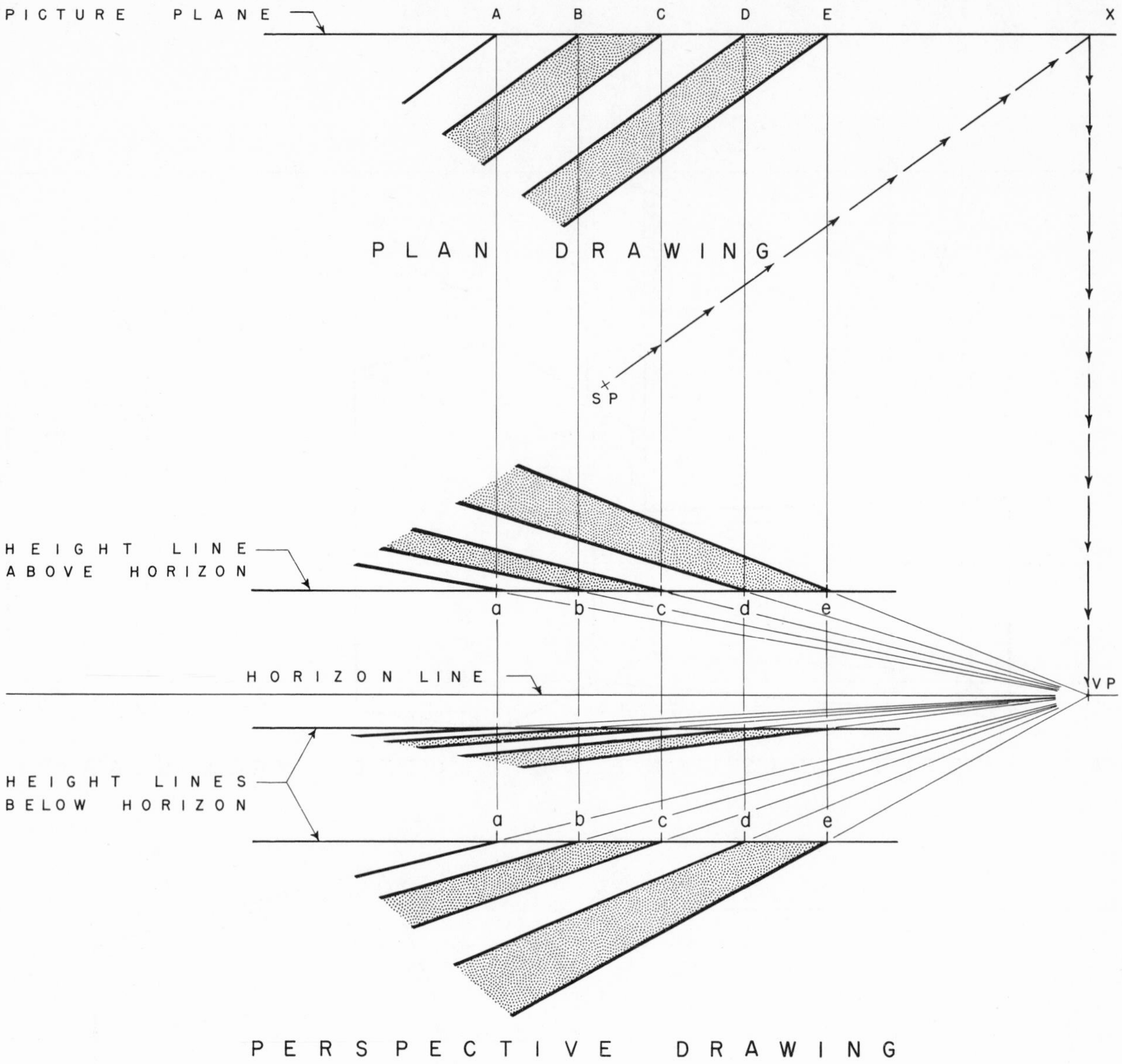

FIG. 160 SIMPLE THEORY OF A VANISHING POINT

THE LOCATION OF VANISHING POINTS. Vanishing points for perspective drawings are a great mystery to many draftsmen and designers. The theory of the location of vanishing points is quite simple. A line in any direction that goes through the center of sight of the observer, SP, is seen as a point. All lines that are parallel to this line vanish at the point position of the line.

The mechanical process of locating vanishing points for a perspective drawing is not difficult for a good draftsman. The vanishing point of any set of parallel lines is located where the line through the station point and parallel to the set intersects the picture plane. *The location of the vanishing point of any line in a perspective drawing is the drafting problem of locating the intersection with the picture plane of a line through the station point and parallel to the given line.*

Horizontal lines always have their vanishing points on the horizon. The following procedure is used to locate the vanishing point of any given set of horizontal lines, Fig. 160. In plan draw a line

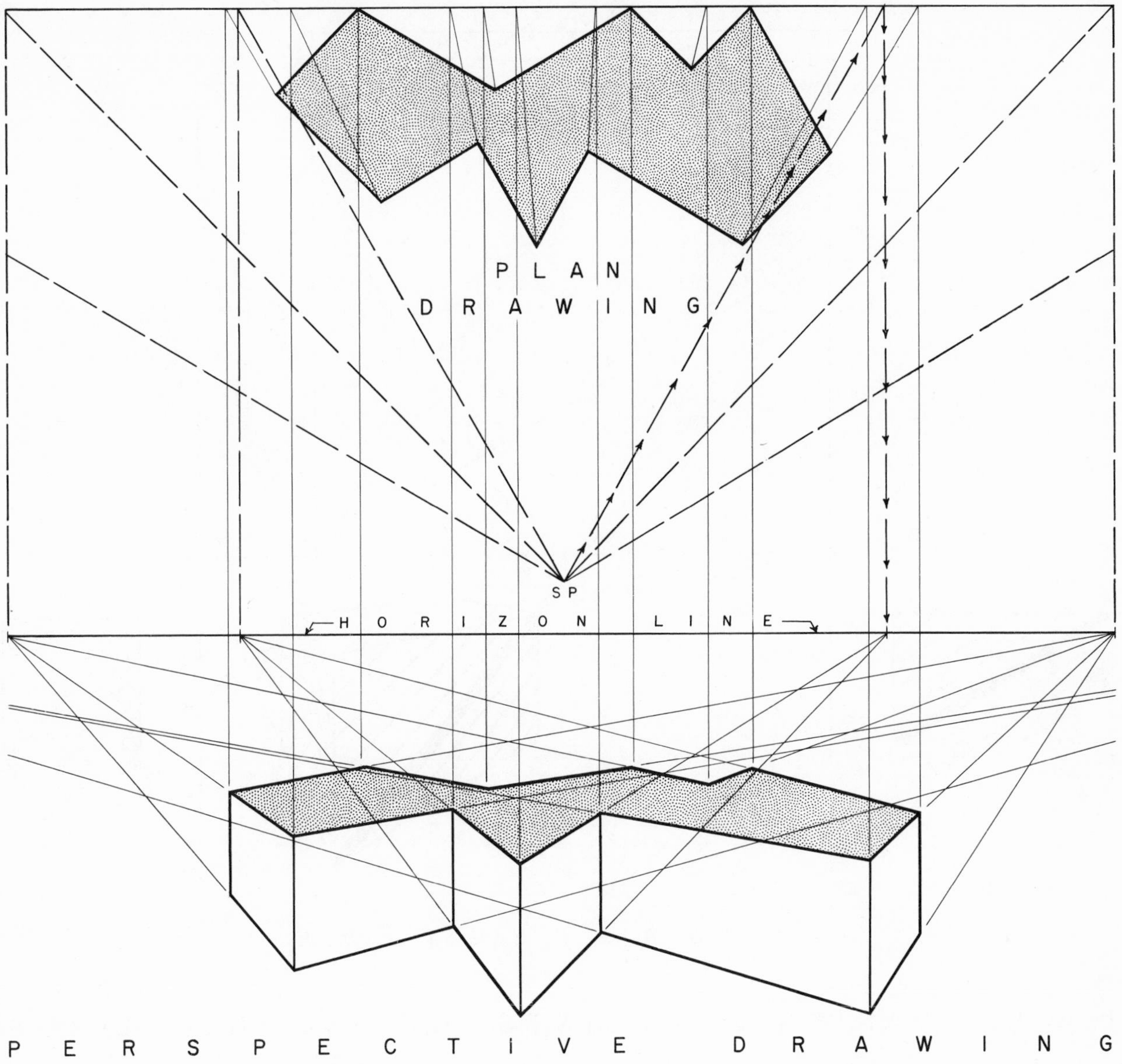

FIG. 161 VANISHING POINTS OF HORIZONTAL LINES

parallel to the set and through SP to meet the picture plane at X, the plan position of the required VP. A vertical line from X intersects the horizon in the location of the perspective position of the required VP. This method has been used to locate the standard vanishing points of two-point and one-point perspectives in preceding pages. It is used to find the vanishing points of all horizontal lines which are not parallel to the picture plane.

In Fig. 161 there are horizontal lines in several directions. Each horizontal line has its vanishing point on the horizon. Some of these vanishing points are beyond the limits of the drawing whereas others are conveniently near. It is often helpful to use vanishing points other than the standard one for one-point perspective and the standard two for two-point perspective.

"To which VP does this line of the object go?" is a common puzzle in perspective drawing. It goes to the VP that was located by drawing parallel to it through the SP in plan.

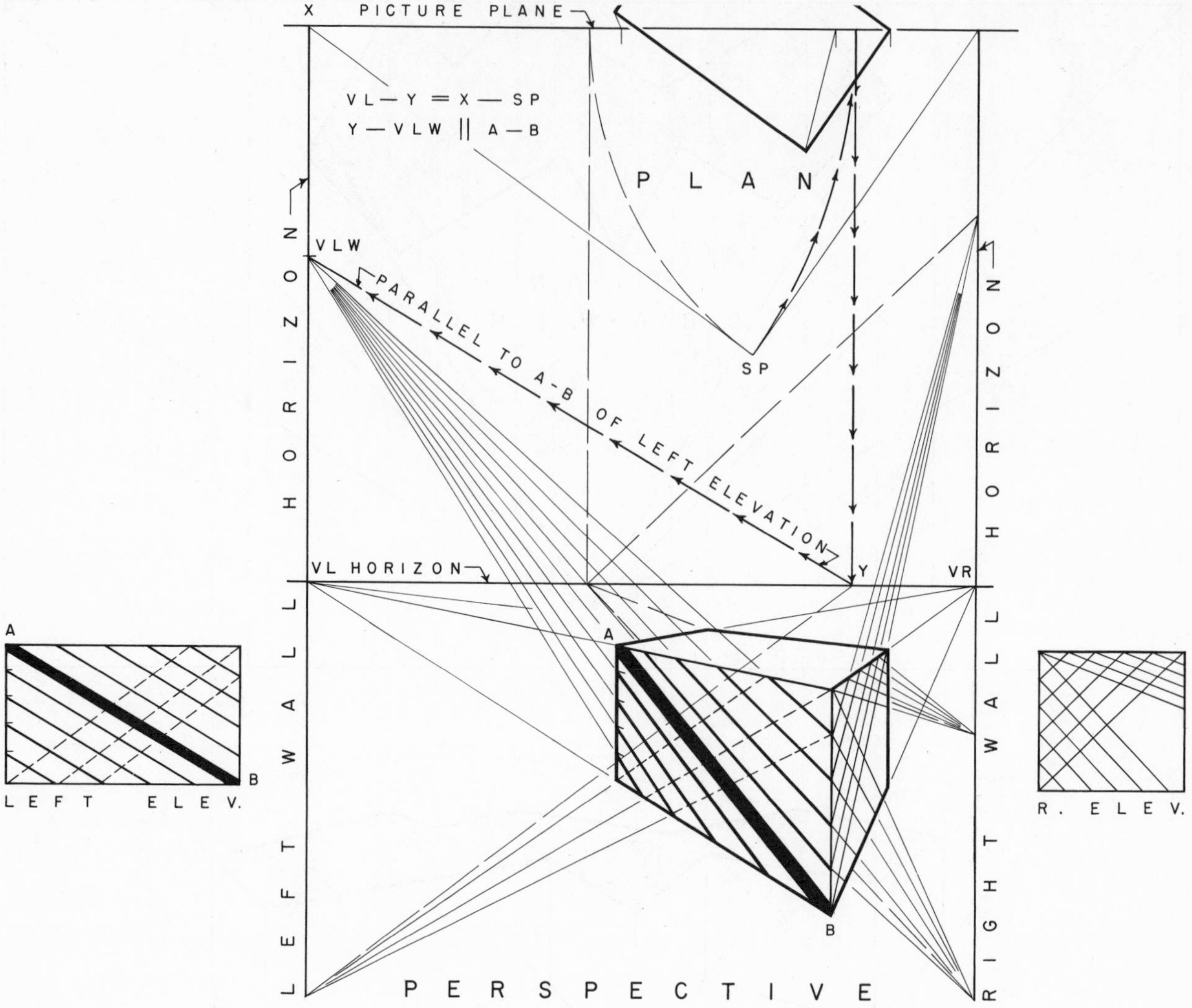

FIG. 162 VANISHING POINTS OF INCLINED LINES

Inclined lines in or parallel to wall planes have their vanishing points either above or below the horizon on the vertical line through the vanishing point of horizontal lines in the same planes. Thus in Fig. 162 all inclined lines in or parallel to the left wall plane will have their vanishing points on the vertical through VL. All inclined lines in the right wall plane direction will have their vanishing points on the vertical line through VR. This line through VR is called the right wall horizon and the vertical through VL is called the left wall horizon. These two wall horizon lines are the vanishing lines of all wall planes in these two directions and the loci of vanishing points of lines in all possible directions oblique to the picture plane in the wall planes. They compare with the horizon, which is the vanishing line of all horizontal planes, and the locus of vanishing points of horizontal lines oblique to the picture plane in all possible directions.

In order to locate the vanishing point of line A–B of Fig. 162 and all lines parallel to A–B the following construction is used. The distance X–SP is laid out to the right of VL on the horizon to locate point Y. A line drawn from Y parallel to the left elevation of A–B intersects the left wall horizon at VLW the perspective vanishing point of A–B and of all lines parallel to A–B.

The above construction is a partial left elevation of the perspective setup. The left wall horizon,

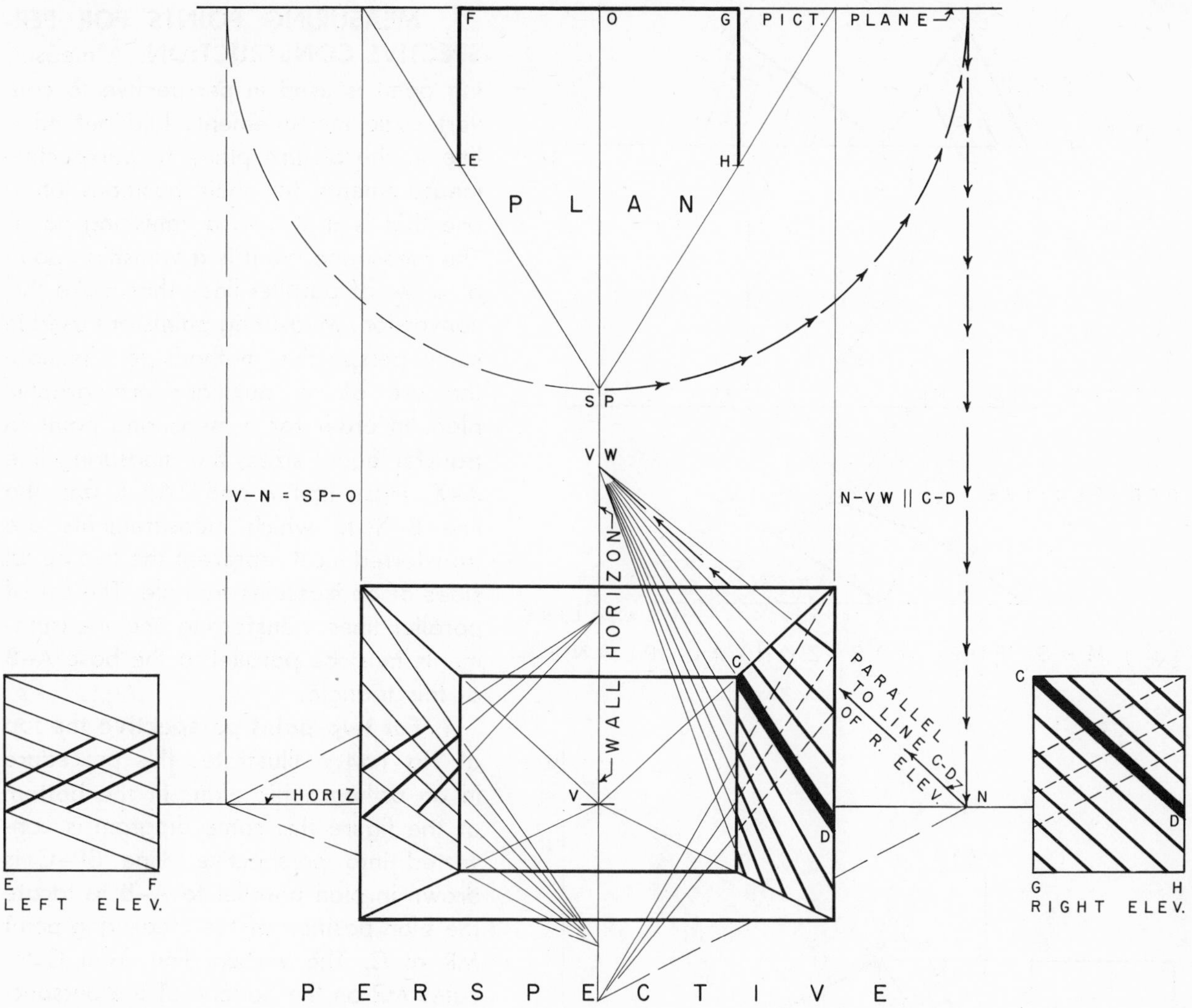

FIG. 163 VANISHING POINTS OF INCLINED LINES

the horizon, the Y–VLW are parts of this elevation. VL–Y of the part elevation is the same line as X–SP in plan. The plan line X–SP also represents the plan of VLW–Y. The lighter lines on the right side of the object show the location and use of a number of vanishing points of inclined lines in right wall planes.

Inclined lines in wall planes of one-point perspective are shown in Fig. 163. The construction locating vanishing point VW of line C–D and all lines parallel to C–D is shown with heavy lines and arrows. The distance SP–O from plan is laid out to the right of V on the horizon to locate point N. A line from N parallel to the right elevation of C–D intersects the vertical through V in VW the perspective vanishing point of C–D and all lines parallel to C–D. It should be observed that parallel inclined lines on the left and right elevations would go to the same vanishing point. This vanishing point could be located with construction from either side of V.

Inclined lines not in or parallel to the wall planes of the object have their vanishing points located by using auxiliary wall planes through these lines in plan. For each new plan direction a new VP on the horizon and a new wall horizon is established. The construction is identical in other respects with that of Fig. 162 in locating the required VP of the inclined lines.

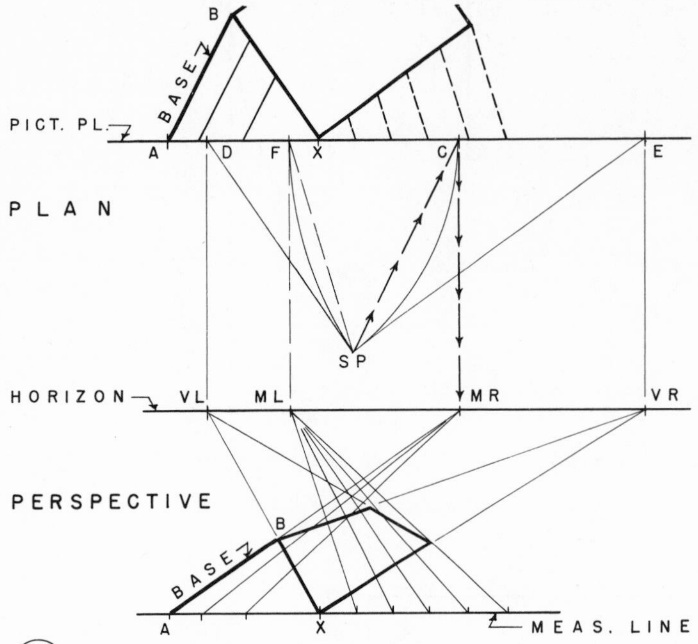

(A) MPS FOR HORIZONTAL PLANES

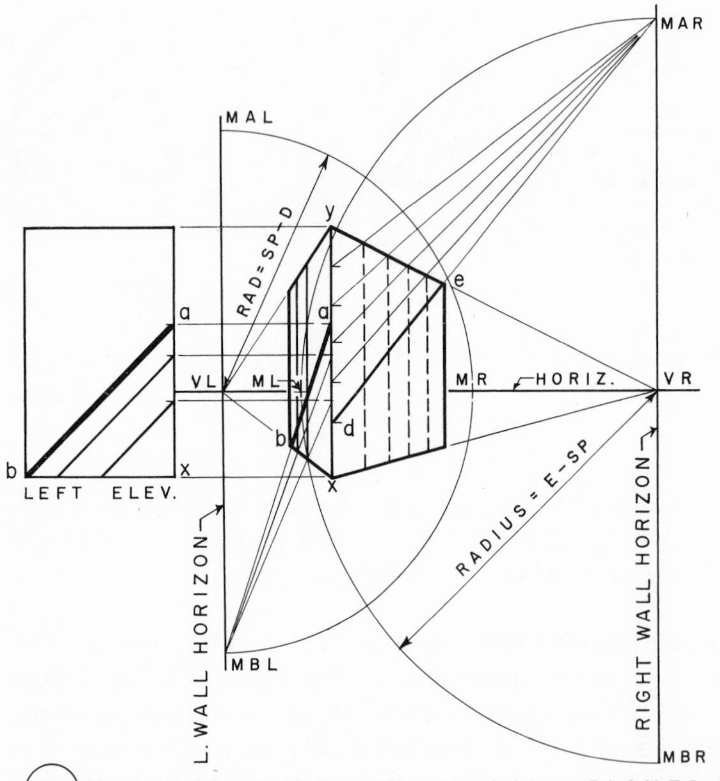

(B) MEASURING POINTS IN WALL PLANES

FIG. 164 MEASURING POINTS FOR TWO-POINT PERSPECTIVE

MEASURING POINTS FOR PERSPECTIVE CONSTRUCTION. A measuring point is used in perspective to convert scale measurements laid out on a line in the picture plane to perspective measurements for their positions on a line that is drawn to a vanishing point. The measuring point is a vanishing point of a set of parallel lines that make this conversion. Measuring points are used in some perspective methods to eliminate the use of an auxiliary orthographic plan. In order for a measuring point to transfer equal sizes, the measuring line A–X, Figs. 164 A and 165 I, and the line B–X to which measurements are transferred must represent the two equal sides of an isosceles triangle. The set of parallel lines transferring the measurements must be parallel to the base A–B of this triangle.

For two-point perspective the top of Fig 164 A illustrates this procedure in an orthographic plan. In the bottom of the figure this same diagram is converted into perspective. Line SP–C is drawn in plan parallel to A–B to locate the plan position of the measuring point MR at C. The vertical line from C locates MR on the horizon of the perspective. MR is the vanishing point of line A–B and all lines parallel to A–B in the perspective drawing.

Because triangles A–B–X and D–C–SP have all three of their sides parallel they are similar triangles. Therefore D–C and D–SP are equal distances because they parallel the two equal sides A–X and B–X of the triangle A–B–X. A variation of the method of locating MR is to lay out a distance D–SP from D on the picture plane line of the plan to locate C and draw vertically to the horizon to find MR. To locate ML lay out distance E–SP horizontally to left of E to obtain point F from which a vertical to the horizon locates ML. These distances D–SP and E–SP can be laid out directly on the horizon from VL and VR respectively to locate MR and ML.

In one-point perspective, Fig. 165 I, the line from SP parallel to A–B locates the point O from which a vertical is drawn to the horizon to locate ML. Measuring point ML transfers dimensions from X–A to X–B of the perspective. This construction can be worked out on the ceiling or any other horizontal plane of the one-point perspective. The distance V–ML is equal to SP–P, the perpendicular distance from SP to the picture plane. This distance SP–P can be laid out on the horizon to the left of V to locate ML and to the right of V to locate MR in one-point perspective.

Either ML or MR can be used to work out the depth construction in a one-point perspective. Sometimes it may be more convenient to use one than the other because of the available room on the drafting board. When the construction lines become numerous it may be convenient to use both ML and MR.

Measuring points for wall planes are located on the verticals through the vanishing points of the perspective. These verticals are the wall horizons, Figs. 164 B and 165 II. An inclined line in the direction of a wall plane in plan and at 45° to a horizontal plane passes through SP and locates a wall measuring point where it intersects the picture plane. Because this duplicates vertically the distance SP–D, Fig. 164 A, this distance can be laid out vertically above and below VL to locate the two measuring points MAL and MBL on this wall horizon of Fig. 164 B. The distance E–SP can be laid out above and below VR to locate the two measuring points MAR and MBR on the right wall horizon. Since these distances equal VR–ML, a radius E–SP can be used with a center at VR to locate with an arc ML and the measuring points MAR above and MBR below VR on the right wall horizon. The radius SP–P can be used in one-point perspective, Fig. 165 II, with a center at V to locate four measuring points. Two on the horizon, two on wall horizon.

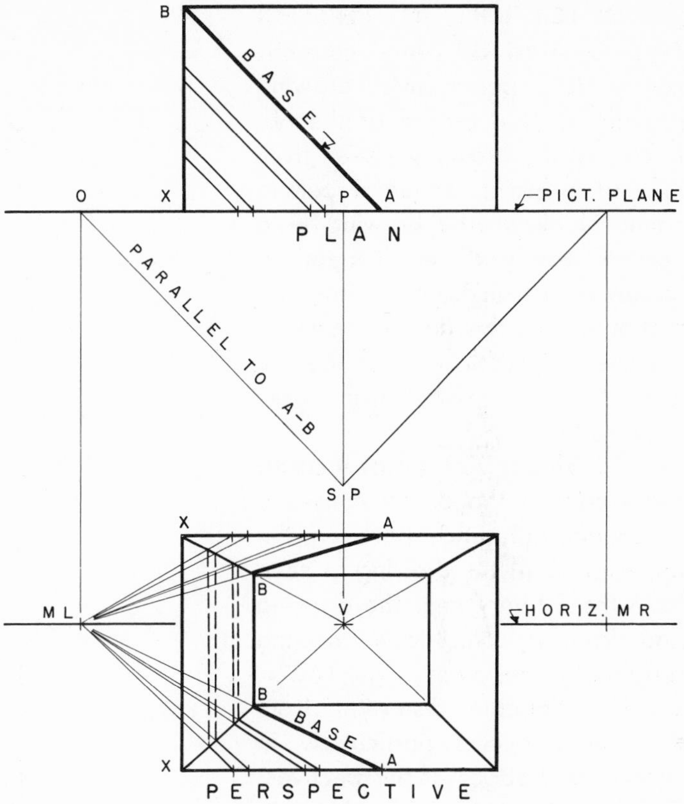

I MPS FOR HORIZONTAL PLANES

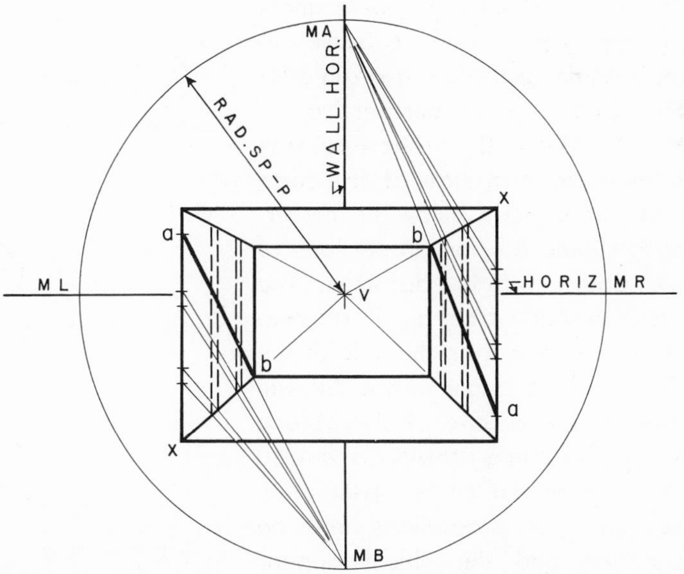

II MEASURING POINTS IN WALL PLANES

FIG. 165 MEASURING POINTS FOR ONE-POINT PERSPECTIVE

DISTORTION IN PERSPECTIVE DRAWINGS. Any correctly constructed perspective drawing provides a true picture of the object when the drawing is seen from its station point. When a person cannot look at the drawing in a normal way and see it approximately as it would appear from the station point, the drawing gives a distorted representation of the object. There are two general causes of distortion.

1. The station point located too close to the object causes a disturbing difference between the appearance of the drawing as seen from the SP very near the drawing and from a comfortable viewing distance farther away, Figs. 166 A, B. Objectionable distortion from this cause occurs particularly in corners and edges of perspectives. Circular objects and furniture in these positions are likely to be most distorted. Interiors frequently have important shapes in corners and at the edges. Therefore a wide angle of view is more likely to cause objectionable distortion in an interior than in an exterior perspective.

2. When the station point is located to one side of the plan and not directly below its center, as it should be, the proportions of the object will be distorted. The drawing made from an SP off center when seen from the side at the distance and angle of the SP will give a true picture of the object. When this same drawing is viewed from the natural center observation position the proportions will be changed and the object appear distorted. The proportions seen in plan will not be repeated in the perspective. Fig. 167 I shows how a square shape in plan may appear to be a long rectangle in perspective and a rectangle look square.

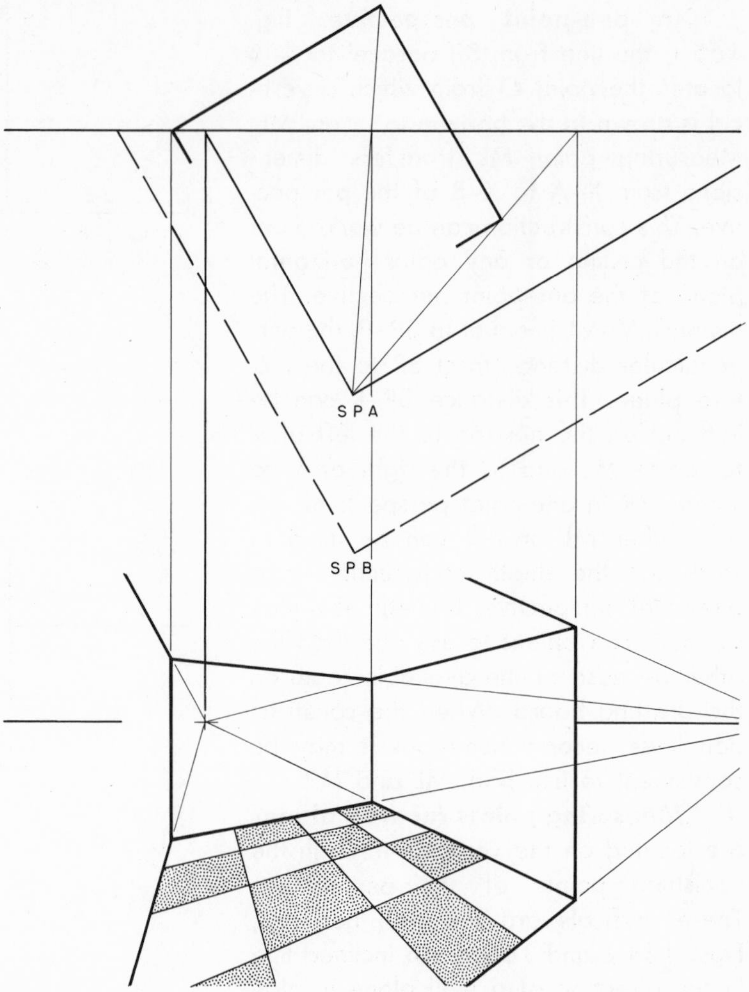

(A) SPA TOO CLOSE TO OBJECT PROPORTIONS ARE DISTORTED

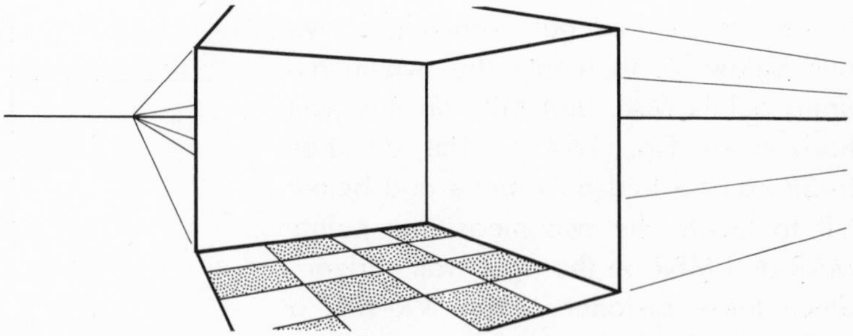

(B) SPB IS FARTHER AWAY AND GIVES MORE NORMAL PERSPECTIVE WITH MORE PLEASING SHAPES

FIG. 166 DISTORTION FROM SP TOO CLOSE

Some very correct perspectives seem distorted while some distorted perspectives are accepted as correct. There seems to be a mental block to the acceptance of correct but extreme three-point perspectives. They give the observer a decided shock with the feeling of being unreal. Most of us just do not consciously observe and accept such phenomena in our daily lives. It seems we feel that the objects "just are not like that," and that they should not be shown from such extreme and unnatural points of view. Few of us ever get above a tall building and looking down on it realize the forms which are visible. Even furniture seen daily from above seems wrong in pictures.

There is a mental acceptance of vertical lines on aerial and "worm's eye" views. Perhaps this is because the height of the observer is obvious from the drawings. Furthermore we know that the vertical lines are vertical and we like to see them drawn that way. A horizontal displacement of the SP is not indicated by anything in a two-point perspective. In one-point perspective the vanishing point explains the way the object is seen and a position moderately to one side of center is accepted by eye and mind. We often see things that way when walking down one side of a street or corridor. When the SP is obviously off center, the mind and eye adjust to its position in the perspective drawing. There may be nothing to mark positively the exact position of the SP of a one-point perspective drawing. However the converging lines and areas of the perspective point to it and suggest its position even though the conscious mind of the observer may not be aware of its location for the perspective.

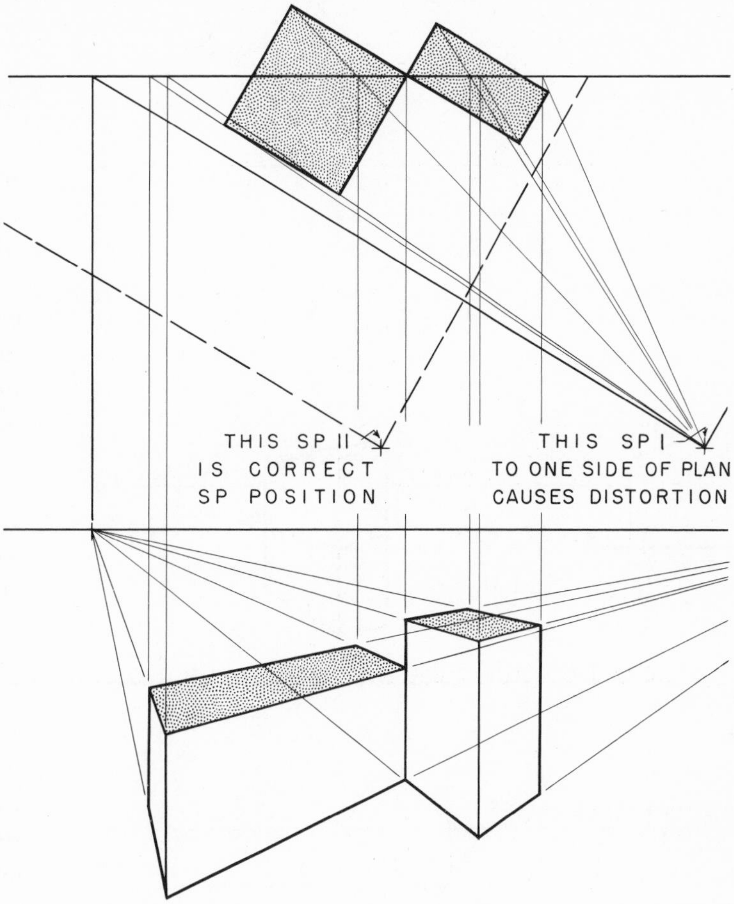

(I) SP I GIVES DISTORTED SHAPES
COMPARE TOP AREAS WITH PLAN

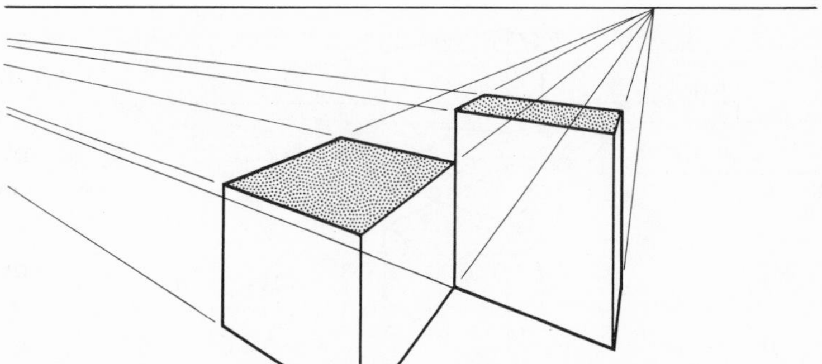

(II) SP II CENTERED BELOW THE PLAN
GIVES CORRECT PROPORTIONS
COMPARE TOP AREAS WITH PLAN

FIG. 167 DISTORTION FROM SP TO SIDE

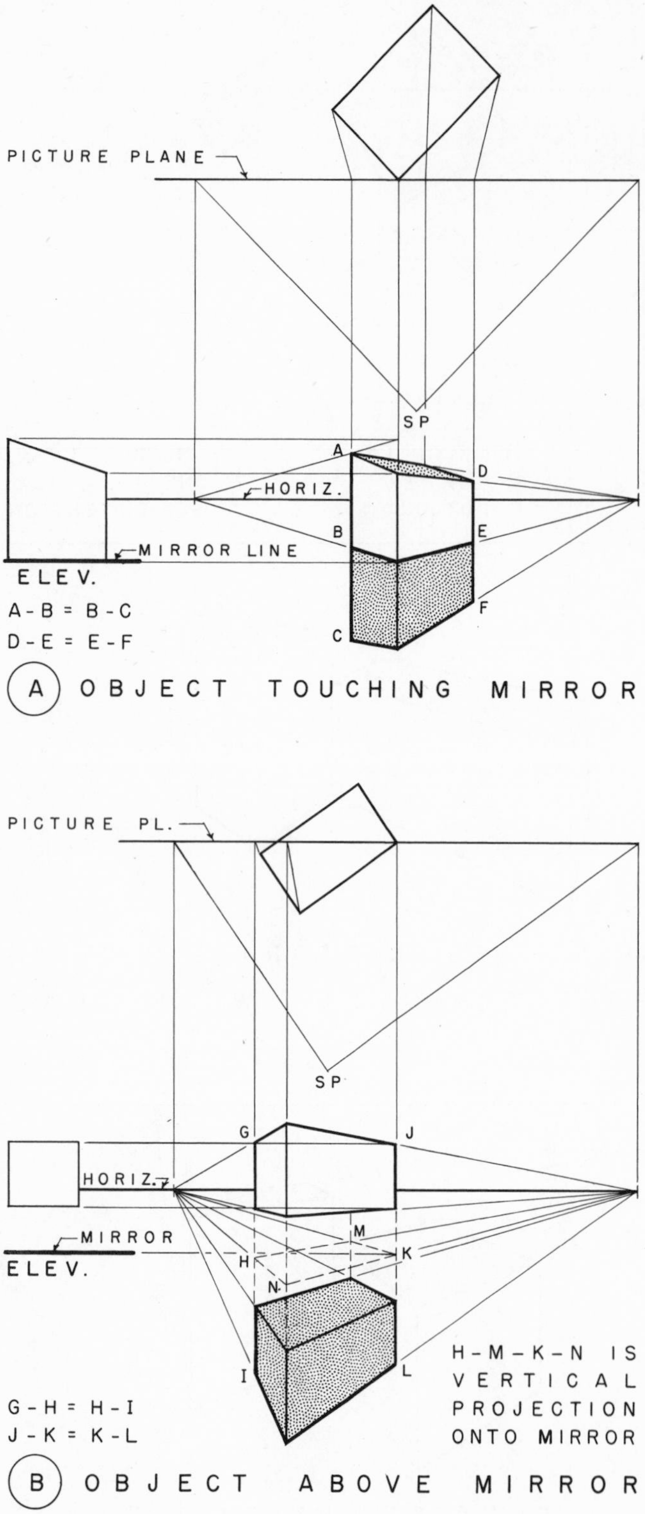

FIG. 168 EQUAL HEIGHTS USED FOR REFLECTIONS ON HORIZONTAL MIRRORS

REFLECTIONS IN PERSPECTIVE. Reflections are an important part of the design and presentation of three-dimensional objects. We usually think of reflections as belonging to mirrors or still bodies of water. Any shiny surface such as a table top, floor, wet pavement, display window, piece of polished metal, or painted area can provide reflections of lights, shapes, and colors from other objects. The sharpness and clarity of a reflection depends on the perfection of the reflecting surface and lighting conditions. Mirrors, smooth water, and polished metal often give reflections that are very nearly perfect. Some surfaces such as table tops or shiny paint may give only a suggestion of the reflected object. The reflection is never an exact duplicate of the object because it is never seen from the same angle as the object. The reflection is most nearly like the object when the observer views the two from almost the same angle. This condition occurs when the line of sight is almost parallel to the reflecting surface. When the reflection is seen from a much higher, lower, or otherwise greatly varying angle of view than the object, the two differ decidedly. Reflections may add to the effect of a presentation by showing details of the opposite side of the object. The bottom of a spoon may be reflected on a polished horizontal surface. The back of a vase or other object may be seen in a vertical mirror. Thus a reflection may make one drawing give two views of the same object in a perspective. Reflections can be undesirable or even disturbing. The reflection from the polished surface behind a bar or counter may reveal stored material that is not attractive. Reflections of horizontal walks and vertical forms on slanting glass or other inclined wall surfaces will be tilted, Fig. 171 II. They may be disturbing and dangerous to pedestrians. The designer-draftsman should be able to represent reflections correctly and accurately. They are a part of his designs and a part of their accurate presentation in order to give correct visual effects in the illustrations of his designs.

Horizontal mirror surfaces occur often in design, and produce reflections which can be constructed easily for simple shapes. In Fig. 168 A the simple block shape with a slanting top rests on a horizontal mirror surface. The perspective of the object is drawn first. The vertical lines of the object are continued in the reflection. Their lengths in the reflection are the same as in the object. This reflection can then be laid out by the drawing of equal verticals and connecting lines.

This method of vertical measurements is most easily used when the object rests on the mirror. The vertical lines of the object touch the reflecting surface where the reflection begins. When the object does not touch the mirror it is necessary to draw its projection on the plane of the mirror. The verticals must be measured to the plane of the mirror. In Fig. 168 B the object is suspended above the mirror. The verticals include the extension to the mirror in measuring for this reflection. When the visible mirror does not extend under the vertical plane of the object, the projection onto the plane of the mirror can be drawn to establish the vertical distances from the object to the mirror. These distances can then be duplicated below for the reflection.

Because the reflection is an inverted duplicate of the object, the inverted elevation can be used in constructing the reflection, Figs. 169 I and II. The heights of the reflection are constructed from this inverted elevation in the same way that the heights of the object are constructed from the standard elevation. Some parts of an object may be partly or completely concealed in the reflection. This is more often true when the mirror does not extend under the object, Fig. 169 II. However it may be caused by the shapes of the object as in Figs. 168 A and 169 I where the top surface is concealed in the reflection by the reflected block shape above it. Fig. 169 II shows how more distant objects may show only a little in the reflection or even be entirely hidden.

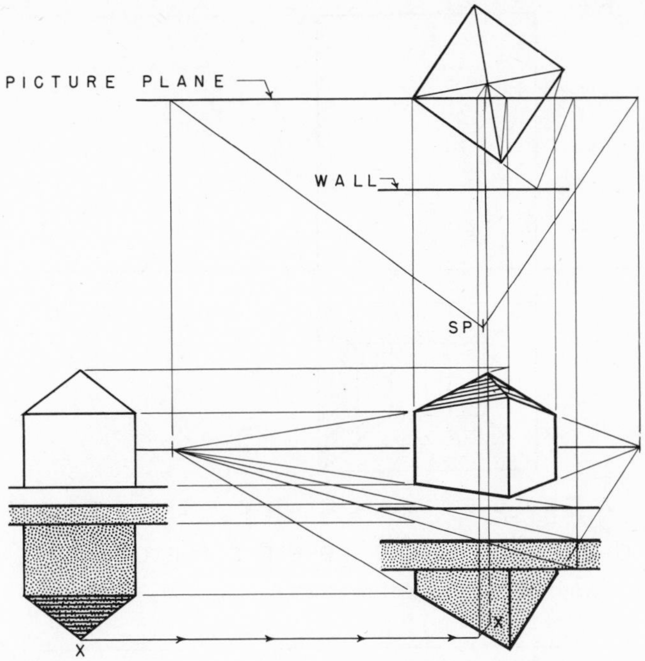

I MIRROR IN FRONT OF OBJECT

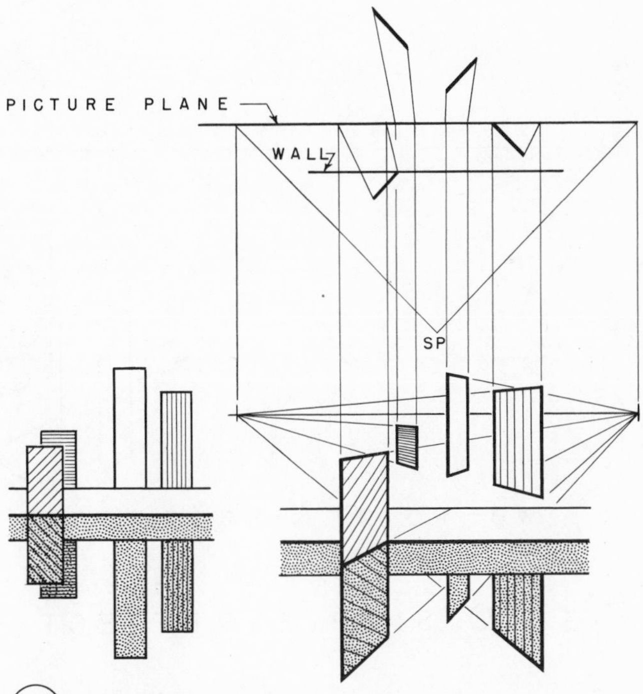

II AMOUNT REFLECTED VARIES

FIG. 169 INVERTED ELEVATIONS USED FOR REFLECTIONS ON HORIZONTAL MIRRORS

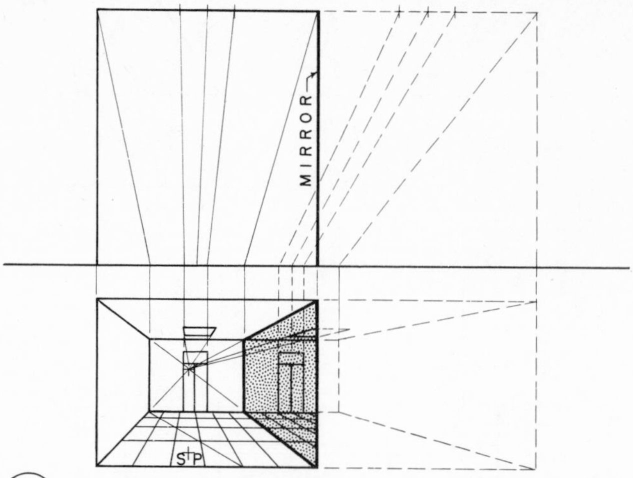

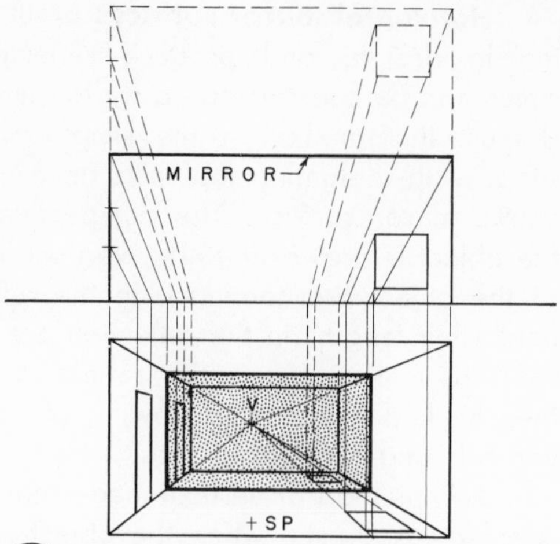

Ⓐ SIDE WALL REFLECTION　　Ⓑ END WALL REFLECTION

ONE POINT PERSPECTIVES OF WALL REFLECTIONS

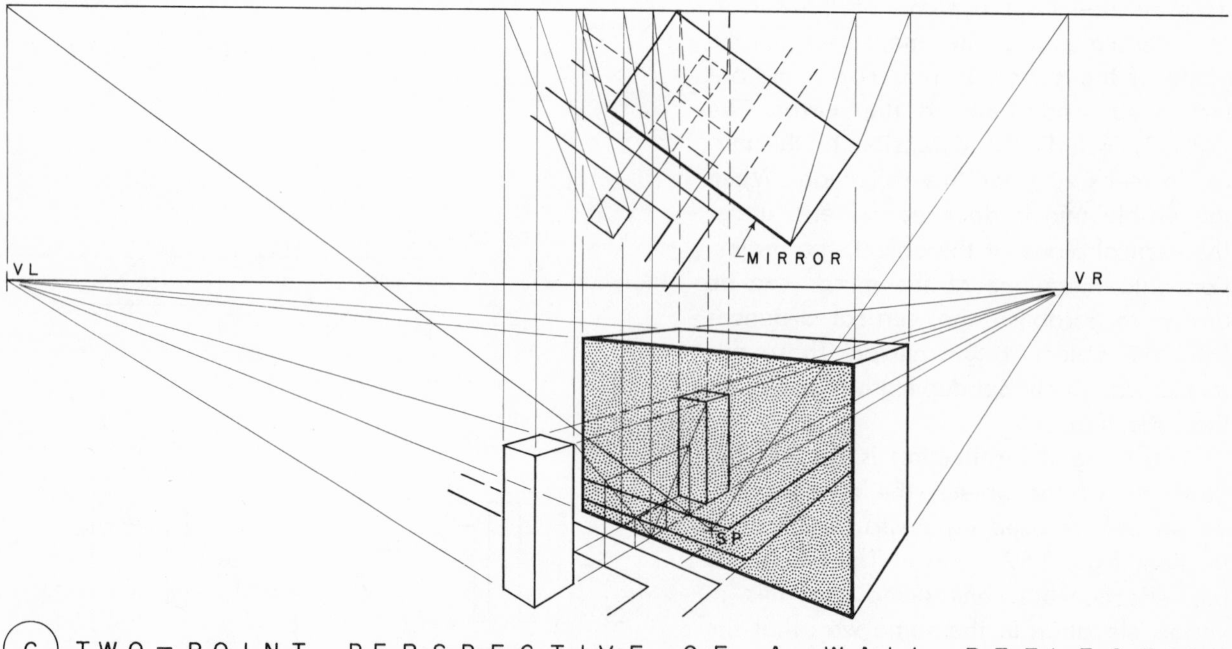

Ⓒ TWO-POINT PERSPECTIVE OF A WALL REFLECTION

FIG. 170 SIMPLE REFLECTIONS ON WALL SURFACES

Vertical mirrors on planes perpendicular to the picture plane provide duplicate horizontal measurements that are reversed from left to right. This is illustrated in the one-point perspective of Fig. 170 A. This reflection can be constructed by duplicating the plan of the object in the reversed position beyond the mirror as shown. In the one-point perspective of Fig. 170 B the mirror is on the end wall and parallel to the picture plane. The reflection is farther away and is smaller than the object. When the mirror is on a side wall as in Fig. 170 A the proportions are changed but the size remains the same in object and reflection.

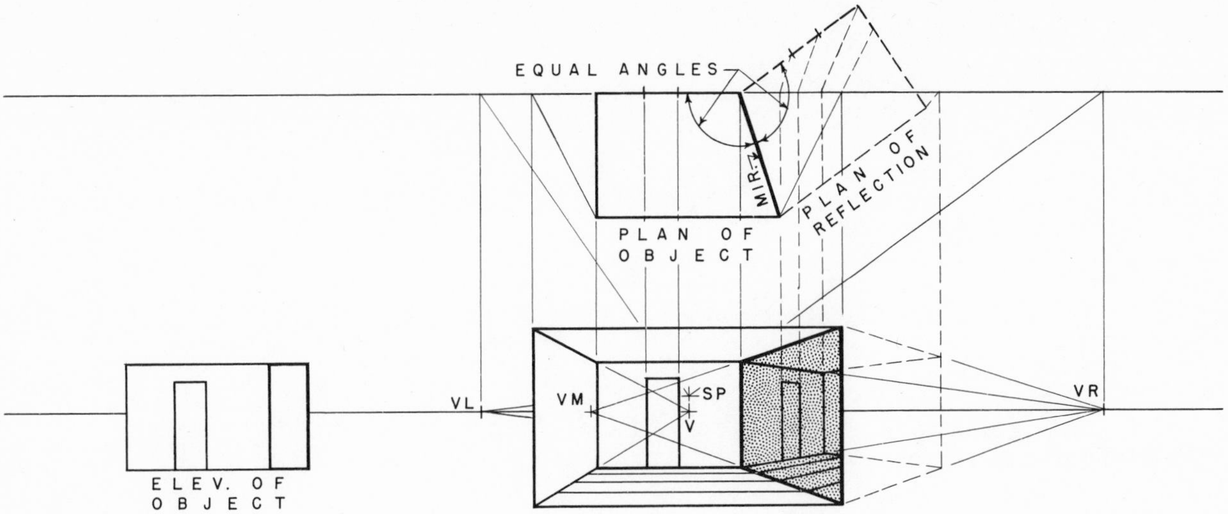

(I) VERTICAL REFLECTING WALL AT OBLIQUE ANGLE

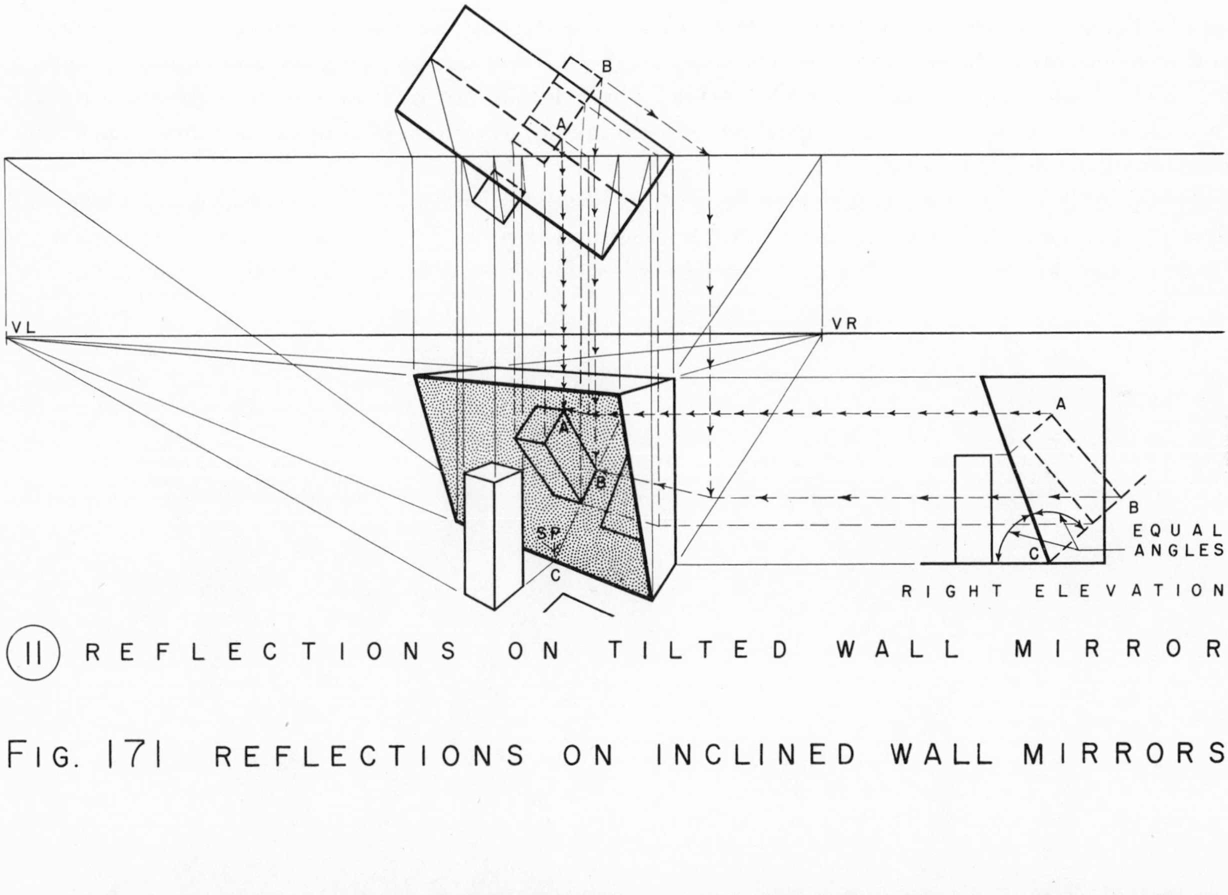

(II) REFLECTIONS ON TILTED WALL MIRROR

FIG. 171 REFLECTIONS ON INCLINED WALL MIRRORS

Vertical mirrors in two-point perspective are illustrated in Fig. 170 c. The plans of parts reflected are duplicated in reverse beyond the mirror for the construction of the reflection.

Inclined mirror planes duplicate the object beyond the plane of the mirror as is the case with all reflecting planes. However the lines of the object are neither parallel nor perpendicular to the mirror. Their directions are therefore changed in the reflection and it is necessary to establish new vanishing points for them, Figs. 171 I and II, or locate points on the reflection and connect them without use of special vanishing points.

PART FIVE

Shadows on Drawings

CHAPTER **27**

SHADOWS IN DESIGN

Shadows are an inevitable part of our every day lives. Wherever we go, either indoors or outside, if there is directional light there are shadows. These shadows provide tones, masses, contrasts, and explanation of forms. They are an integral part of any design. Objects and drawings without shadows usually appear flat and uninteresting. Their details are obscured so that they are difficult to understand. Shadows are an important part of seeing. They reveal shapes, distances, and directions of elements, Figs. 172, 173.

Fig. 172 A shows an object with no distinct shadows. In Fig. 172 B a strong light from one direction produces a shadow on object and background. Fig. 173 compares the effect of small weak shadows and larger strong ones on three examples. Shadows are important design elements.

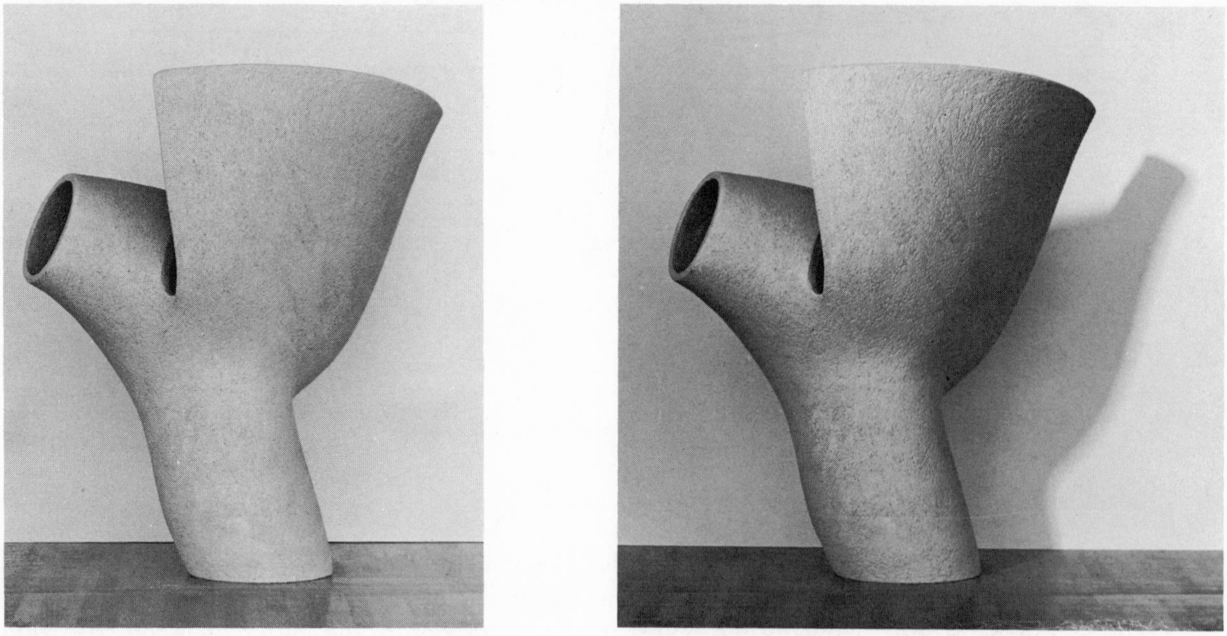

A CERAMIC DESIGN BY HAROLD S. NASH

(A) WITH SLIGHT SHADING (B) WITH DEFINITE SHADOWS

FIG. 172 SHADOWS ADD TO AN OBJECT OR DRAWING

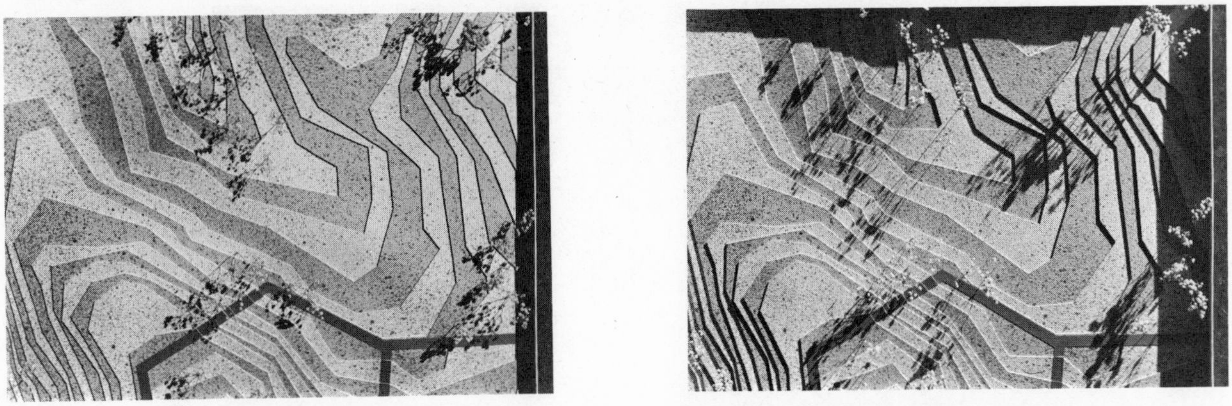

(I) CONTOUR MODEL BY STUDENT DON MC CARTY

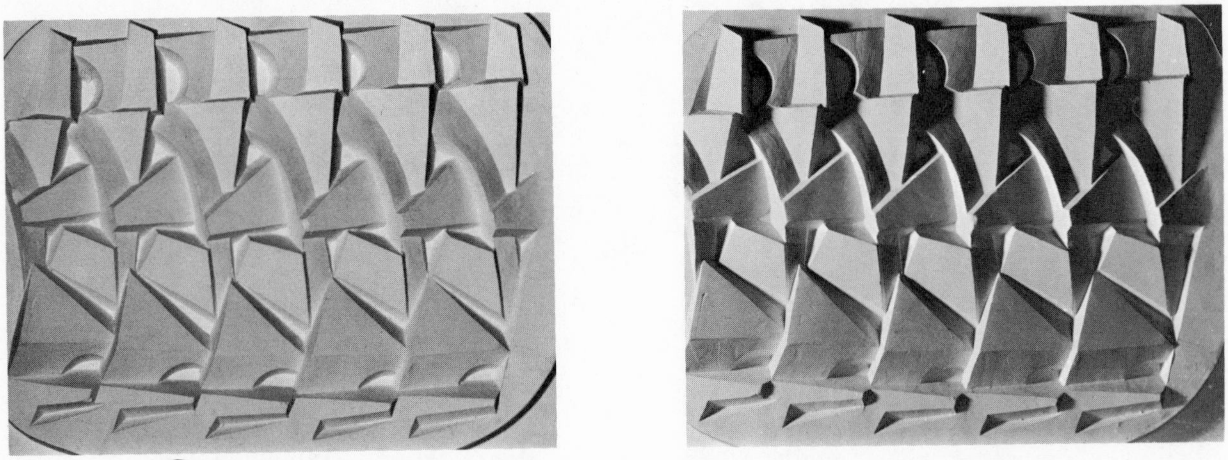

(II) CAST OF A DESIGN BY HAROLD S. NASH

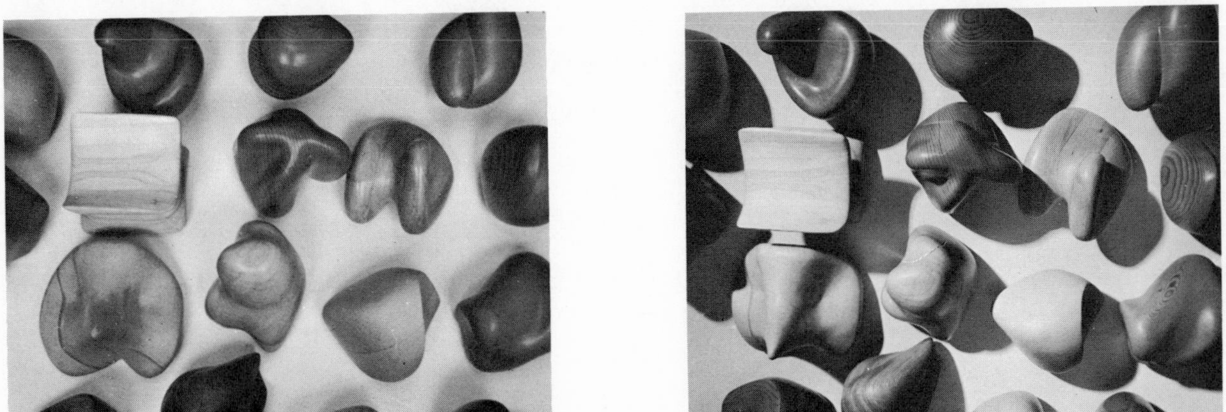

(III) WOOD CARVINGS BY FRESHMAN STUDENTS

MINIMUM SHADOWS — LARGER SHADOWS

FIG. 173 SHADOWS EXPLAIN THE OBJECTS

MOBILE BY STUDENT GARY L. HERFEL

REPEATING VARIATIONS IN OBJECT AND SHADOW

FIG. 174 SHADOWS PROVIDE DESIGN ELEMENTS

Shadows can produce an atmosphere of clarity, brilliance, excitement, mystery, etc., Fig. 175. They are powerful elements in the presentation of objects and of drawings of designs. The shadows on the object itself help to explain the object. The shadow of the object may add an interesting design form on another plane, Fig. 174. When the object moves, the shadow provides an interesting repeating variation of the shapes and movements of the object.

As a part of a study of shadows on drawings the student should observe the shadows of objects in different types of light. Small objects and scale or improvised models can be used either in sunlight or with artificial lighting in addition to the observation of actual large full size objects.

WOOD CARVINGS BY FRESHMAN STUDENTS

EXCITEMENT FROM CURVING AND DIAGONAL SHADOWS

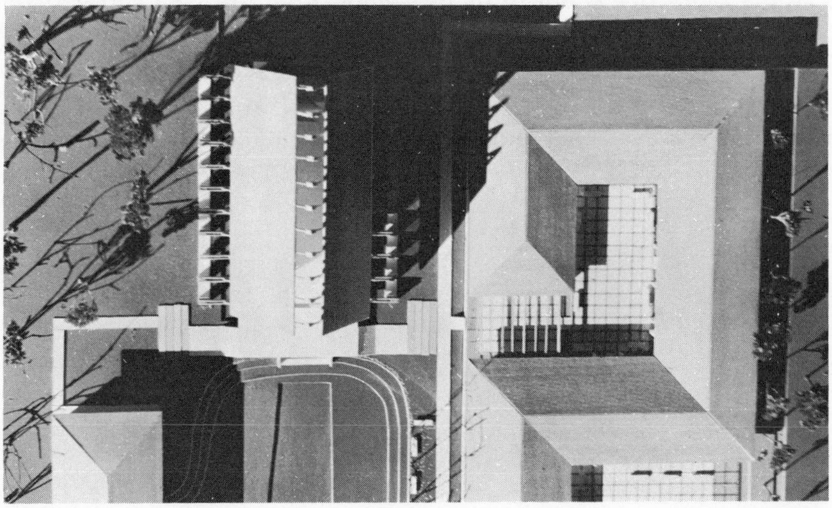

MODEL BY STUDENT GEORGE J. KELSO JR.

RESTFUL EFFECT FROM LARGE SHADOW SHAPES

FIG. 175 SHADOWS HELP PRODUCE ATMOSPHERE

In shadow casting and rendering, the distinction between shade and shadow is more of a technicality than a reality. Both terms refer to the exclusion of light from an area or areas. Because both result in the absence of direct light on surfaces, the effects are often identical. There is no consistent variation of darkness or other optical difference between shades and shadows.

In shadow casting, a shade is caused by the exclusion of light from a surface by the shape of the object itself. A shadow goes through the air from one object to another or from one part of an object to another part of the same object. Because an attempt to distinguish between these two terms is often more confusing than helpful, both will usually be called shadows in this text.

CHAPTER **28**

MULTI-VIEW SHADOWS

SHADOW CONSTRUCTION. The subject of shadow construction deals with only the sizes and shapes of the areas in shadow. Rendering is concerned also with the variations of intensity of light and shadow that add life and expression of form and distance to the representation of an object.

The conventional direction of light is almost always used for shadows on multi-view drawings. Light is assumed to be from the sun or some source that provides parallel rays. The conventional direction of light is the diagonal of a cube from the top, left, front corner to the lower, right, rear corner, Fig. 176 A. In each of the six standard views the direction of light will appear to be the diagonal of a square, Fig. 176 B, and it can be traced on any of these views with a 45° triangle.

The advantages of the conventional direction of light are, (1) simplicity of shadow construction, and (2) precise information from the shadows. In Fig. 177 I the wall plane and surface of the block projecting from it are parallel to the front view plane. The shadow widths from the vertical and horizontal edges of the block are equal to its projection from the wall surface. This is true because light travels back, down, and to the right equally, telling exactly how far the block projects.

The true angle of light with a horizontal plane can be determined by drawing an auxiliary view of a cube on a diagonal vertical plane that is parallel to the top view direction of light, Fig. 176 C. This angle is used in some shadow constructions on circular objects. It is of minor importance.

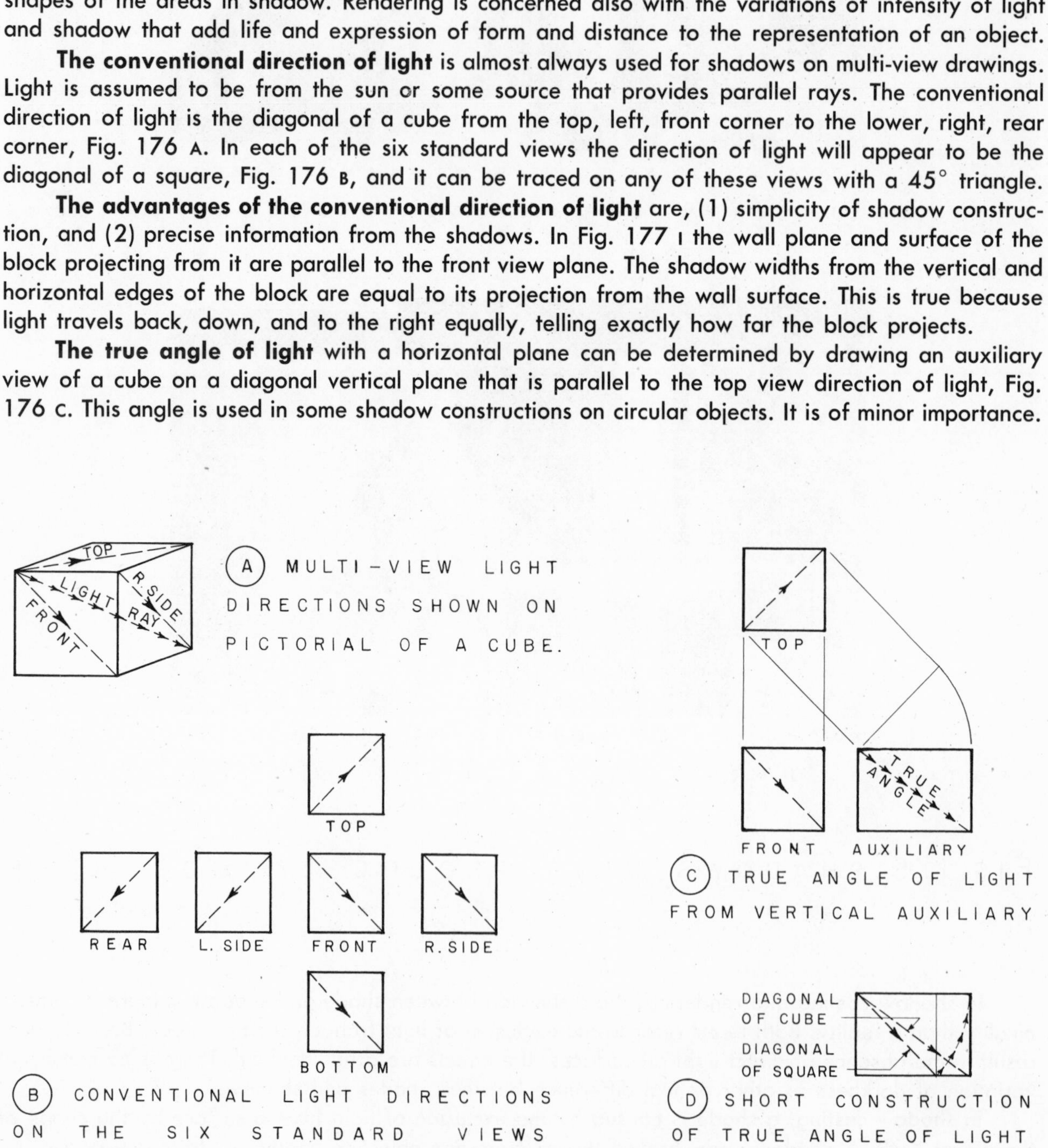

FIG. 176 THE CONVENTIONAL DIRECTION OF LIGHT

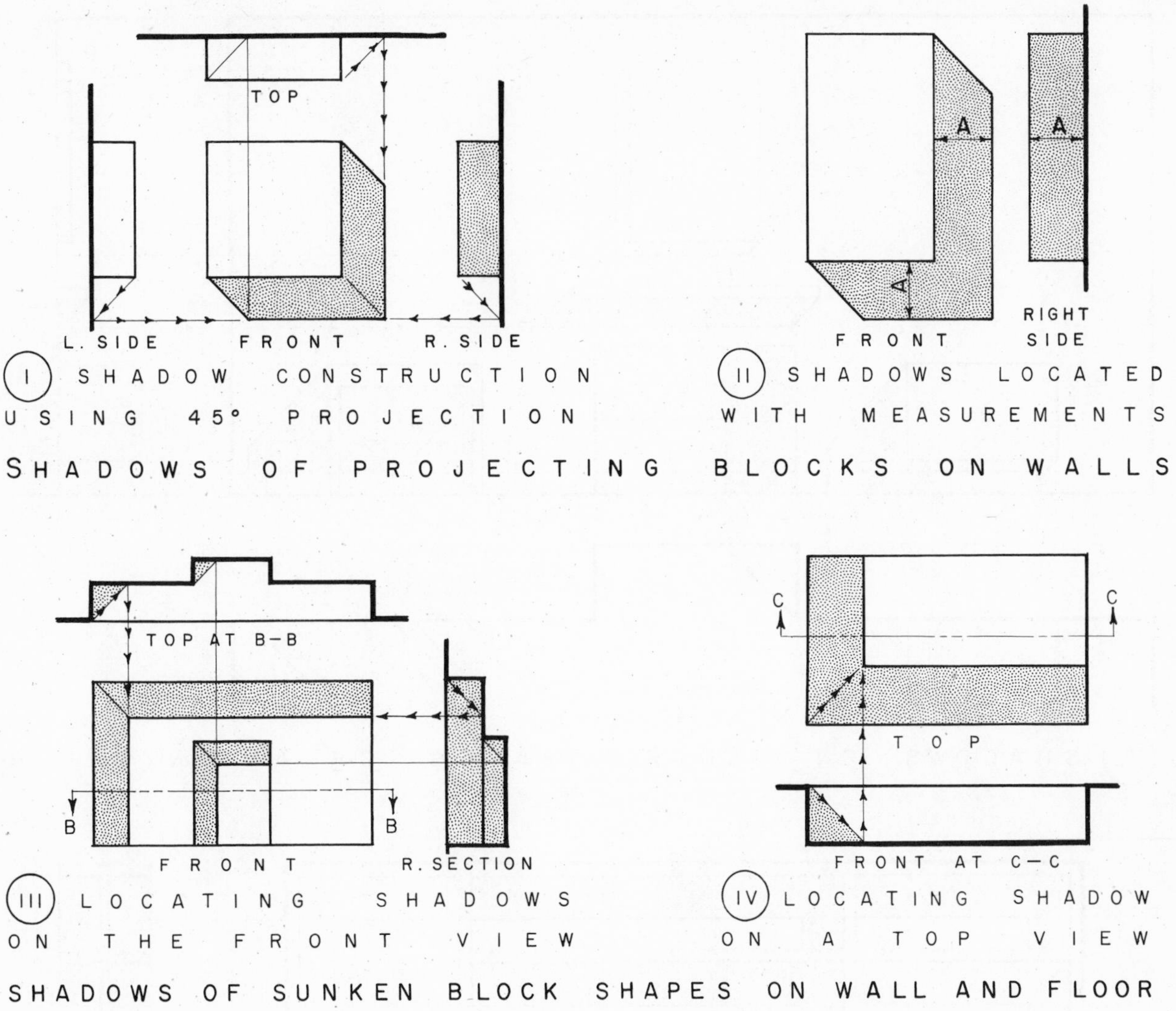

FIG. 177 SHADOWS OF SIMPLE BLOCK SHAPES

BLOCK FORMS ON WALL SURFACES. Some of the simple shadows occur very frequently on drawings. Block forms turned in different directions, and of different shapes are used in the following paragraphs to illustrate and explain some of these shadows.

Simple block shapes with horizontal and vertical edges cast shadows that are equal in width to the projection of the block from the vertical wall. The shadow widths can be worked out from top view or from either side view by 45° projection as shown in Fig. 177 I. They can also be worked out directly on the front view from measurements when the projection A is known, Fig. 177 II. The slanting shadow lines at the top right and bottom left corners of the projection are parallel to the front view direction of light. These corner points represent the front views of the lines perpendicular to the wall plane. Because one point represents each line in front view, every part of each line casts its shadow at 45° from that point making a 45° shadow.

Areas that sink into the wall surface have the horizontal shadow at the top and the vertical shadow at the left, Fig. 177 III. This is the reverse of the shadow positions of the projecting block.

In a top view the shadows of these same simple forms are similar to those in an elevation. Although the direction of light is different, the shadows on the horizontal plan plane are constructed by the same procedure and have similar characteristics to those in elevation, Fig. 177 IV.

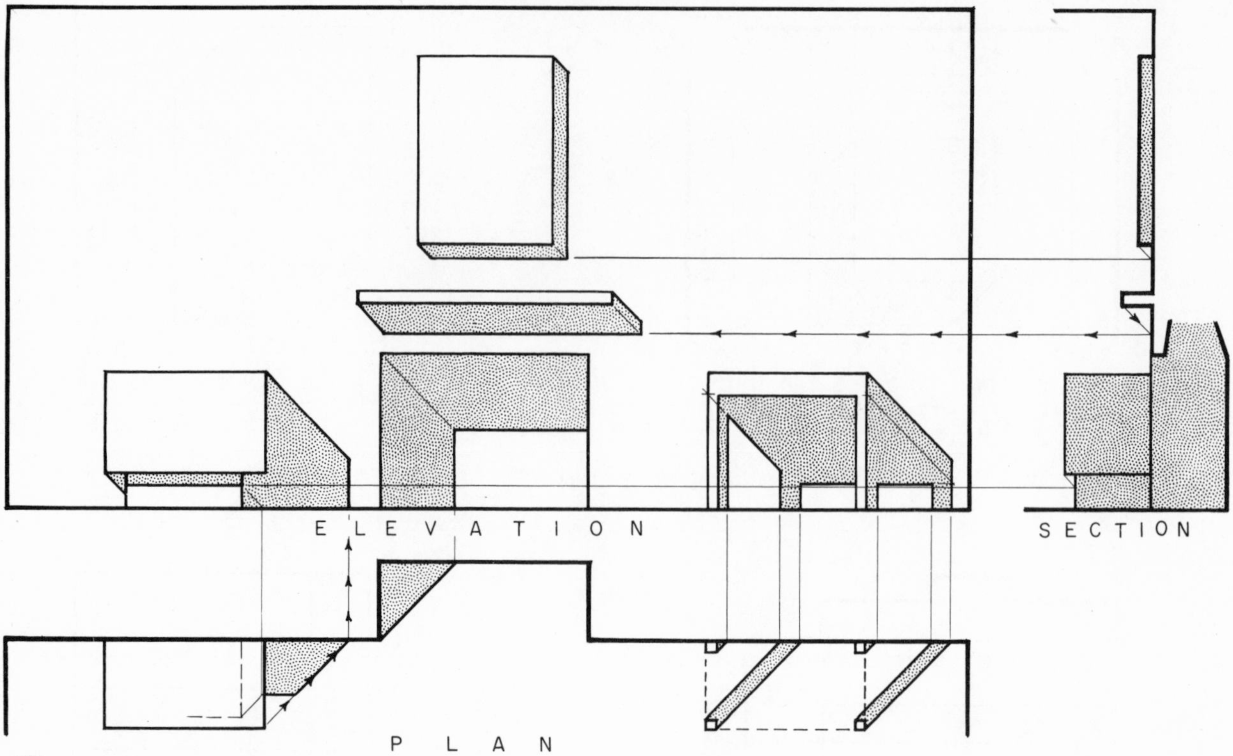

(A) SHADOWS ON BLOCK SHAPES OF AN INTERIOR

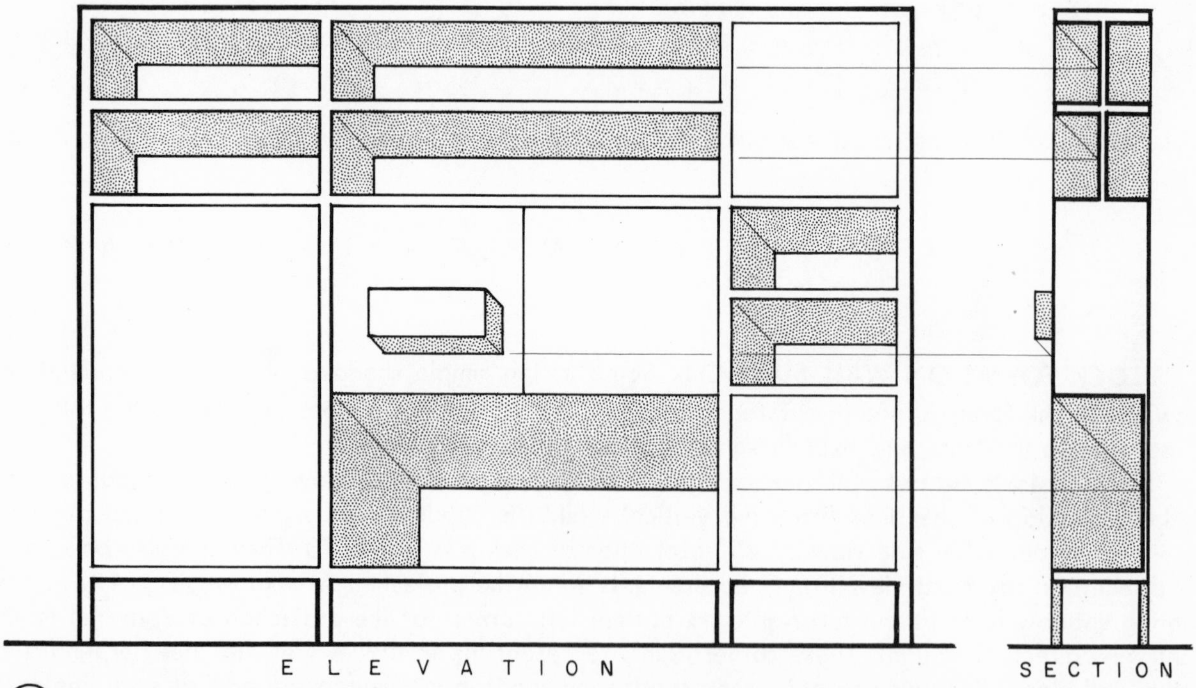

(B) SHADOWS ON A SPACE DIVIDER CABINET

FIG. 178 EXAMPLES OF SIMPLE SHADOWS

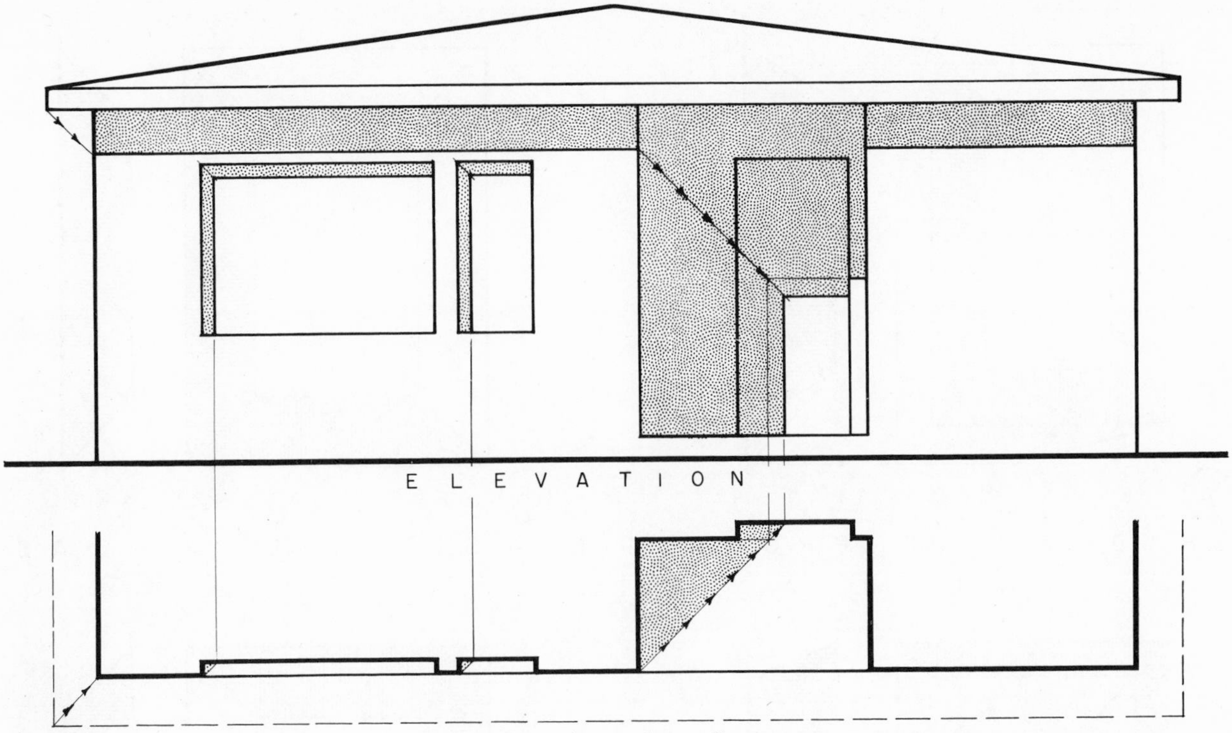

(I) PRINCIPAL SHADOWS ON A SMALL BUILDING

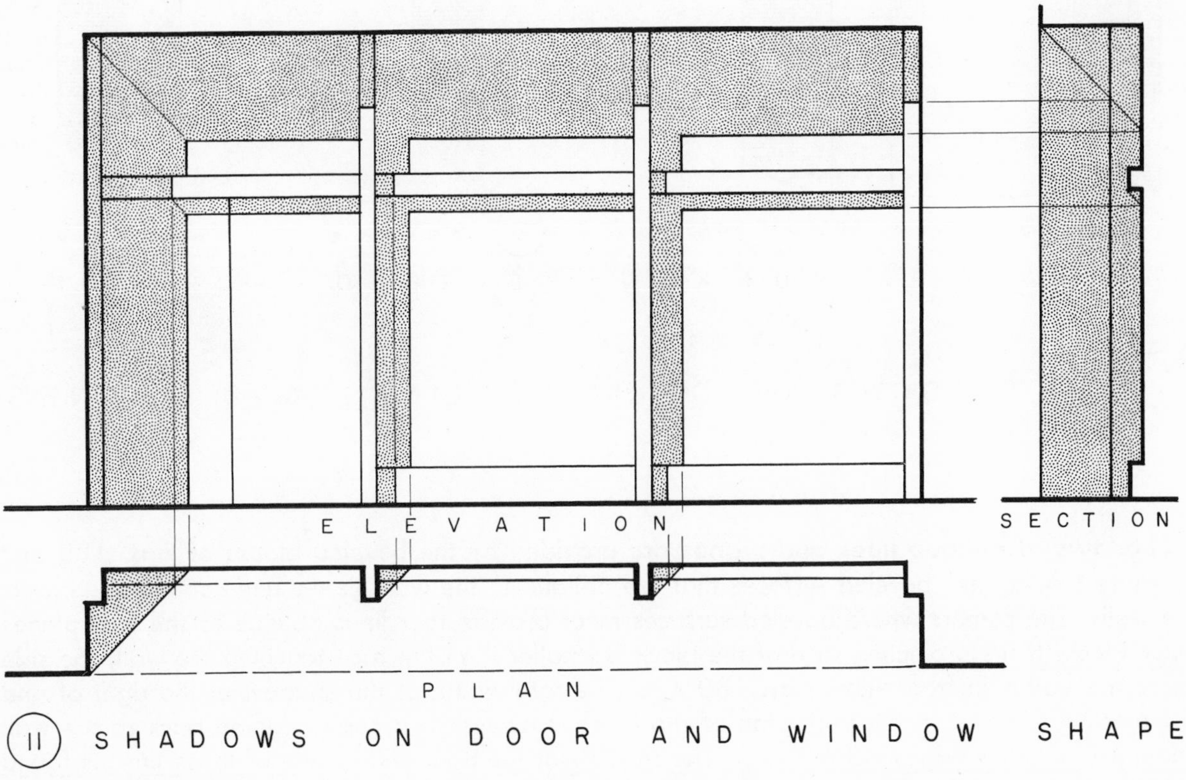

(II) SHADOWS ON DOOR AND WINDOW SHAPES

FIG. 179 EXAMPLES OF SIMPLE SHADOWS

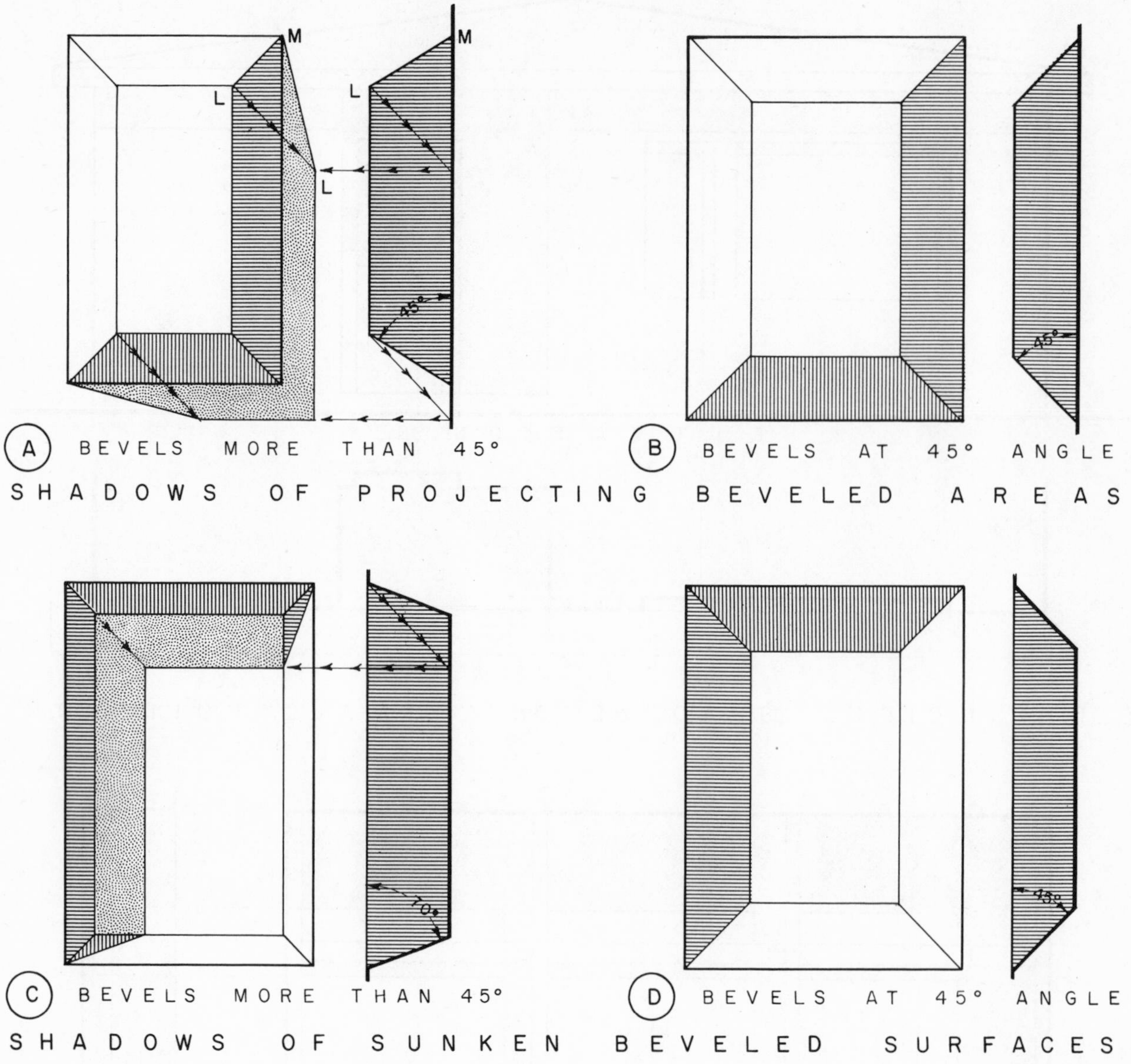

FIG. 180 SHADOWS OF OBLIQUE LINES AND PLANES

Shadows of oblique lines and planes are provided by the beveled blocks of Figs. 180 and 181. These blocks have beveled surfaces that are oblique to the wall planes and connect the blocks to the walls. The corners where beveled surfaces meet provide four lines oblique to the wall planes on each block. If the projecting face of the block is smaller than the face touching the wall, the side surfaces are visible in front view, Figs. 180 A, B. The total width of the shadow at the right of and below block A is equal to the projection of the block. However two corners going back to the wall are now 45° shadow edges in front view. The shadow of the near end of one of these lines is found by 45° projection as shown for point L of Fig. 180 A. The other end of the line touches the wall at point M. The shadow of line L–M is the line connecting the front view of M to the shadow of L. The shadow at the top corner is more nearly vertical and the one at the lower left corner more nearly horizontal than a 45° line. When the side surfaces are at more than 45° to the wall as shown in side view (or plan) the shadow will have the characteristics shown in Fig. 180 A. When the side sur-

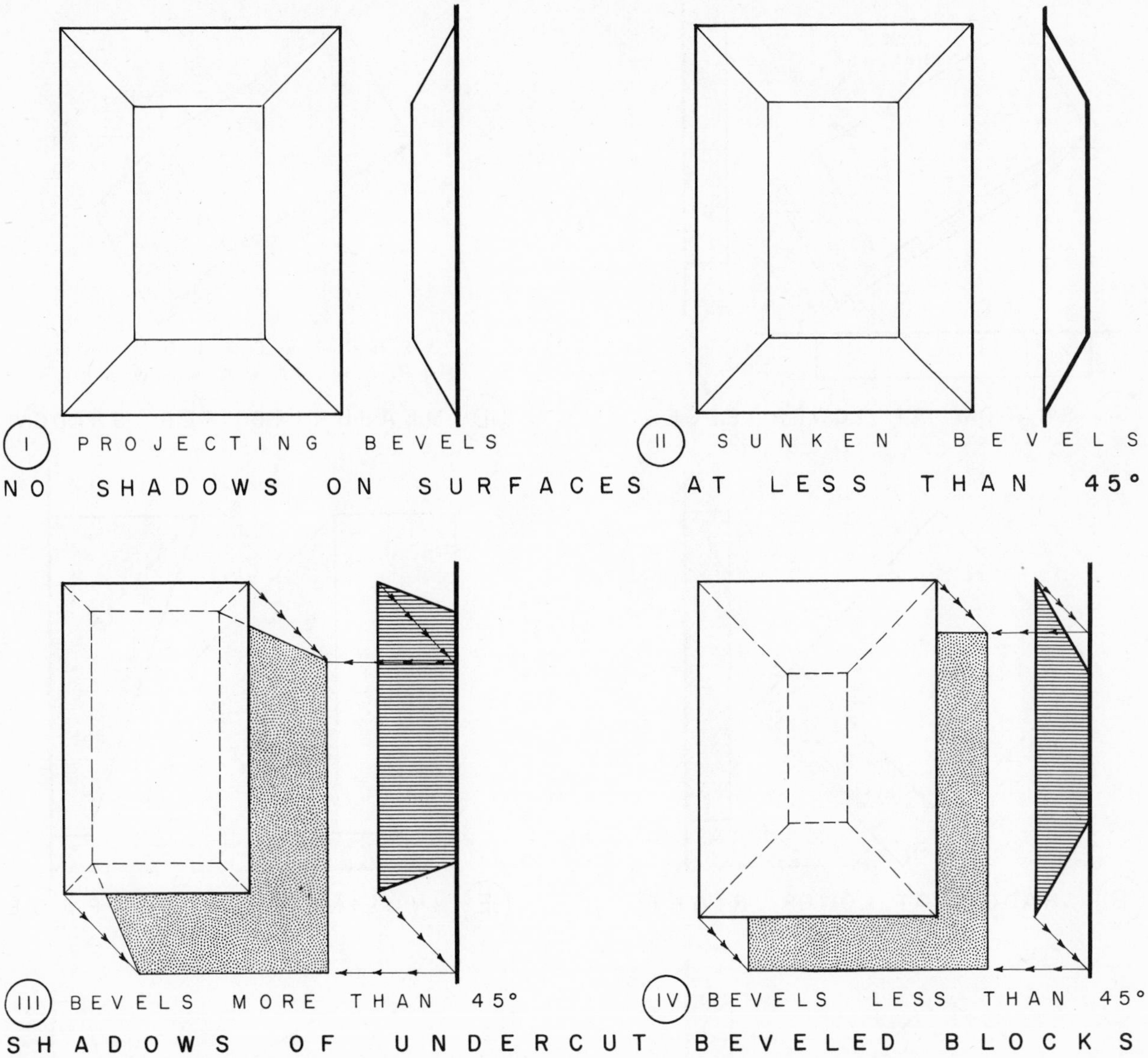

FIG. 181 SHADOWS OF OBLIQUE LINES AND PLANES

faces are at 45° they will be in shadow but there will be no shadow bands below and to the right of them, Fig. 180 B. When the angle between the side surfaces and wall is less than 45° there will be no shadow on or from the block, Fig. 181 I. There will, however, be variations of intensity of light on the planes seen at different angles. These variations are a part of rendering and not of shadow casting. When the bevels sink back into the wall plane the same general rules apply. When the bevel is at more than 45° with the wall plane it will be in shadow at the top and left and its near edges will cast a shadow onto the sunken wall on these two sides, Fig. 180 C. When the bevel is at 45° there will be shadow on the top and left slanting surfaces but no shadow on the wall plane, Fig. 180 D. When the bevel is less than 45° there will be no shadow areas. Fig. 181 II.

When the projecting surface of the block is larger than the surface touching the wall the corner lines make shadows when the angle between side surfaces and wall is greater than 45°, Fig. 181 III. The shadow is entirely from the face of the block when this angle is 45° or less, Fig. 181 IV.

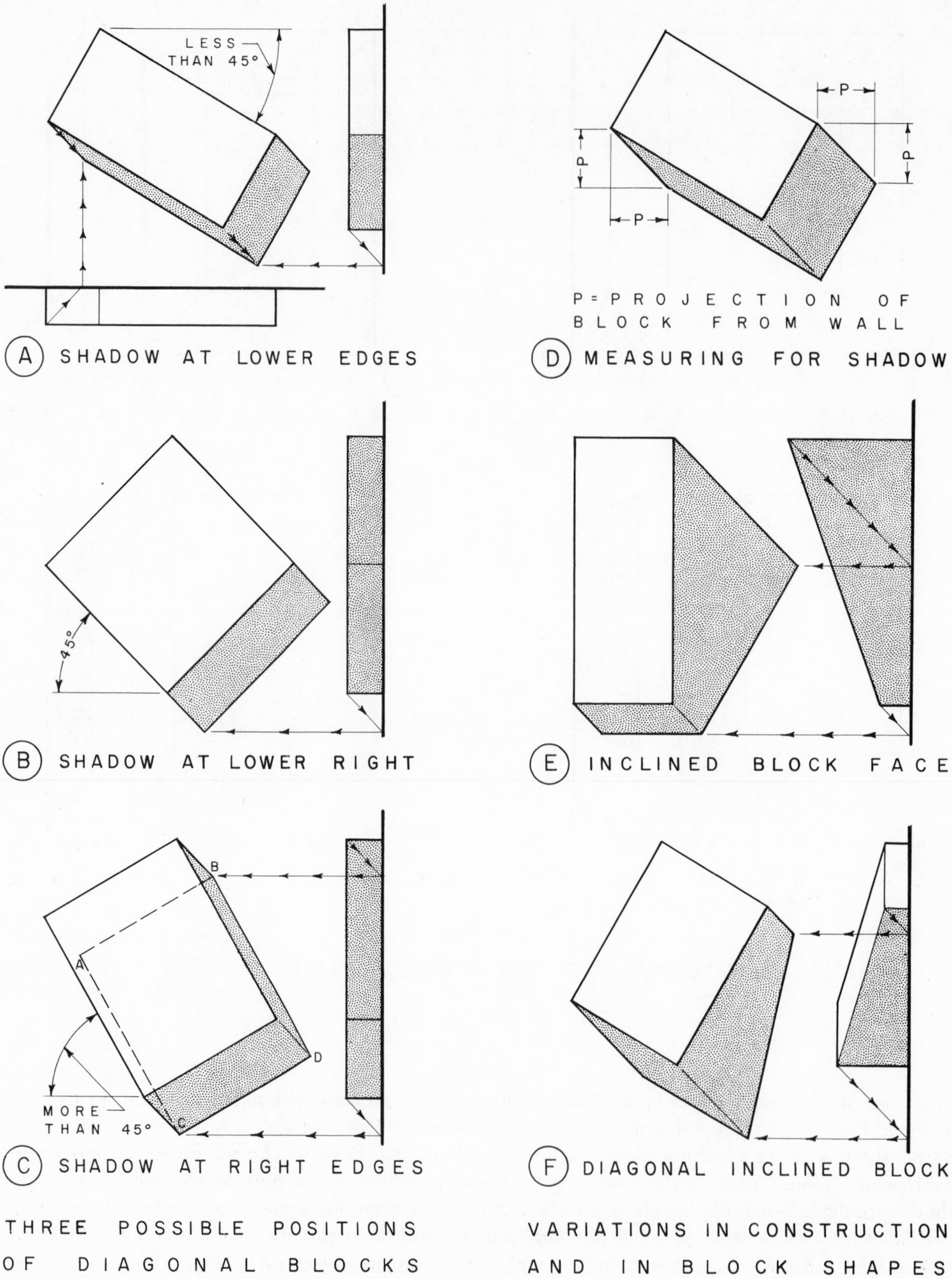

FIG. 182 SHADOWS OF DIAGONAL LINES AND PLANES

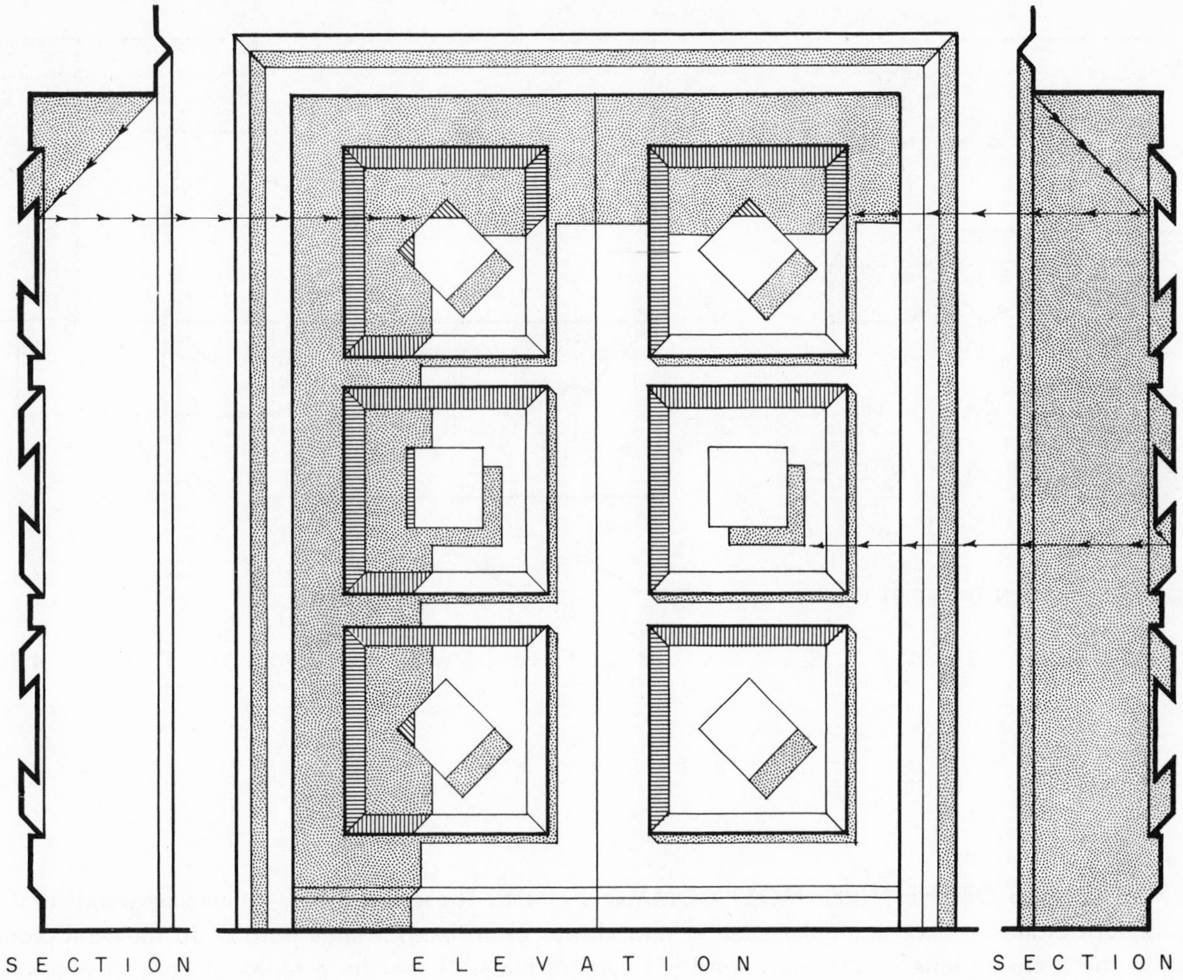

FIG. 183 BEVEL AND BLOCK SHADOW EXAMPLES

Diagonal projecting blocks cause various shadow effects that depend on the angles at which the blocks are turned. When the block is not at 45° the shadows of the two shade line corners can be located by 45° projection from side view (or plan), Fig. 182 A. The shadow lines can then be drawn parallel to the front view of the lines casting the shadow. One shadow band will be greater than the projection of the block from the wall and the other less than the projection. The shadow of a corner can also be located by measuring the amount of the projection vertically and horizontally in an L shape, Fig. 182 D. The remainder of the shadow can then be located by using 45° projection lines and parallels. It should be observed that lines perpendicular to the wall always make 45° shadow lines. When the block is turned at 45° there will be only one shadow band. It is located at the lower right of the projecting block, Fig. 182 B.

When the surface of the block is not parallel to the wall the shadow of each corner of the block is located. The shadows of the corners are then connected, Figs. 182 E, F.

SHADOWS OF PLANE FIGURES. Any plane figure parallel to the plane on which the shadow falls has a shadow duplicating the figure as shown by a rectangle A–B–C–D of Fig. 182 C. One point on the shadow can be determined by 45° projection or measuring and the shadow drawn in the simplest manner possible. This rule applies to any shape of plane figure. Plane figure sections cut through a solid object are often useful in locating shadows of critical points or a sequence of areas around which the shadow can be drawn.

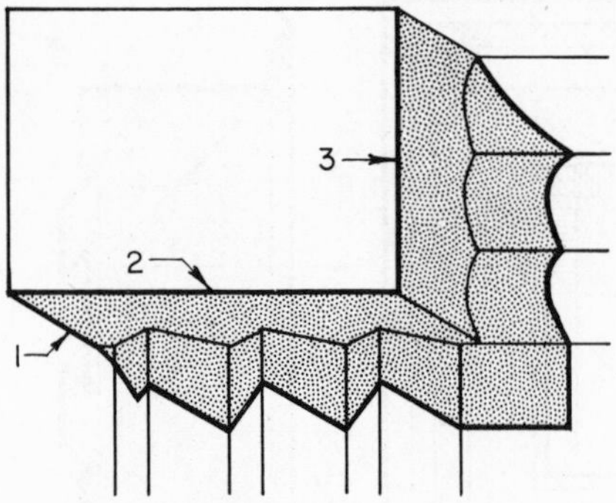

PICTORIAL VIEW OF THE THREE MOST COMMON LINES AND THEIR SHADOW SHAPES

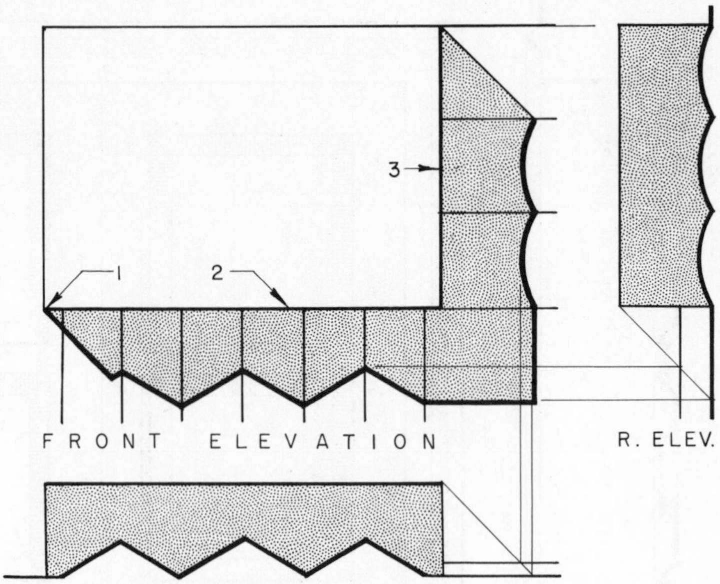

MULTI-VIEW SHADOWS OF THE LINES

FIG. 184 THE THREE MOST COMMON LINES

SHADOWS OF THE THREE MOST COMMON LINES. These lines are (1) lines perpendicular to the picture plane and consequently seen in end view, (2) horizontal lines parallel to the wall planes and to the picture plane of the view, and (3) vertical lines. These three types of lines cast a large proportion of all multi-view shadows. They are the three line directions of any simple box shape and are the most common lines of multi-view drawings. The student should understand the construction and shapes of their shadows so he can locate them quickly and accurately. In Fig. 184 the three common line types and their shadows are shown on a single object. They are explained in detail in the following pages. Each of these line types has definite shadow characteristics. The last two have shadow outline forms that are similar in shapes and distances to the forms shown in other multi-view drawings of the object as shown in Fig. 184. Although the shadows of all three can be plotted over irregular surfaces it is much quicker and more satisfactory to know the shapes produced in the shadows and draw them in the most efficient and easiest way.

1. Lines seen in end view make shadows that appear to be straight lines in any type of drawing and over any surface. This is true whether the surface be flat, curved, warped, or made of several different forms. In many cases the shadow is not actually straight. However it always appears to be straight as it is seen in the drawing because the observer is looking at the end of the line making the shadow, Figs. 185 and 188 A front elevations and plans. Any straight line that is not parallel to the rays of light casts a plane of shadow. When a person looks at the end of such a line he looks parallel to its shadow plane, which is seen as a straight line. Then any line form in the plane appears to be a straight line.

Only lines seen in end view have the characteristics explained here. When a line is inclined parallel to the direction of a flight of steps and is seen as a vertical line in front view, its shadow on the steps will be made of a series of inclined shadow lines, as shown in Fig. 185 B. The shadow can be located on the elevation of one step by locating a point at the top edge and one at the bottom edge of a riser (vertical surface). All the remaining shadows on the steps from this line will be vertically in line with and parallel to the one constructed and they can be drawn in as shown.

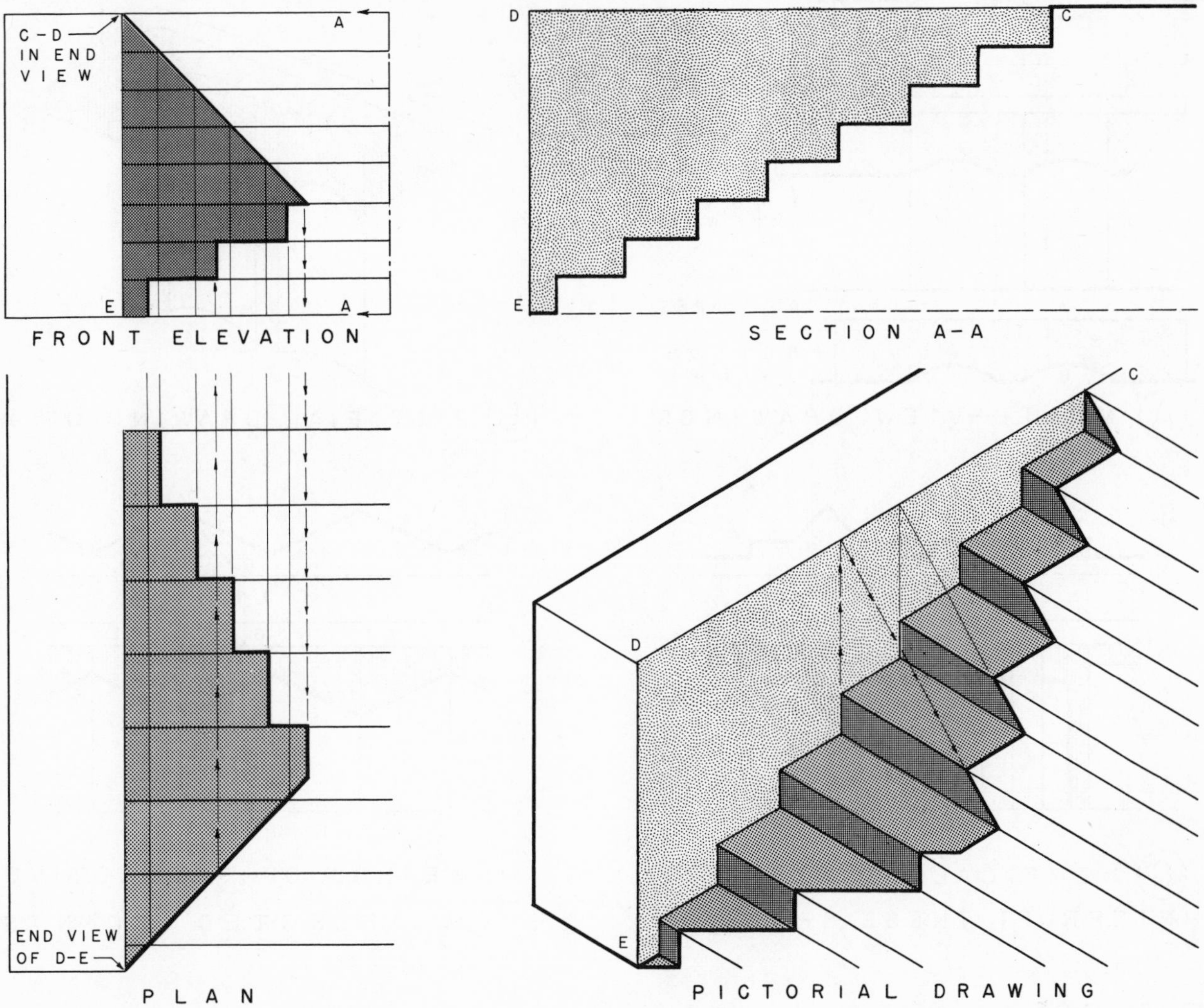

(A) SHADOWS OF LINES SEEN IN END VIEW

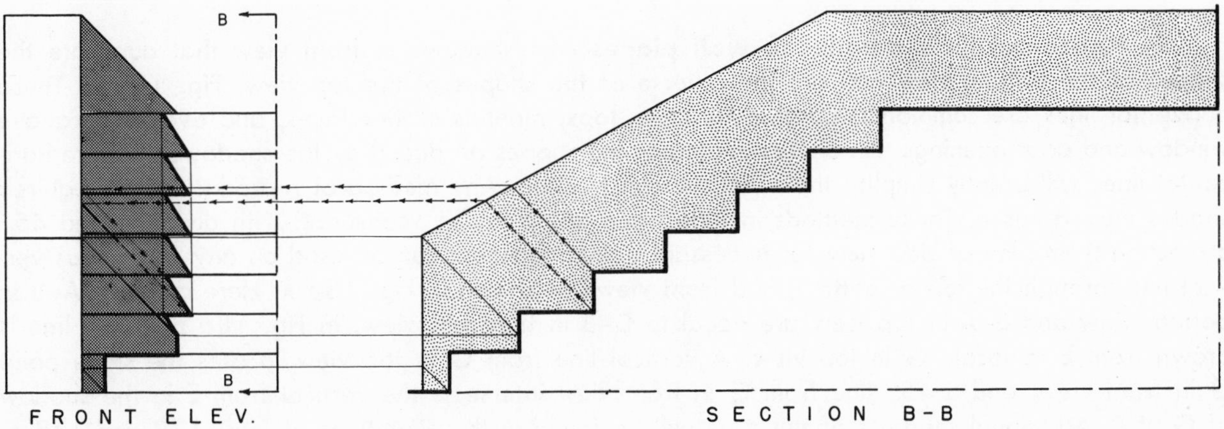

(B) SHADOW OF AN INCLINED LINE OVER STEPS

FIG. 185 COMMON SHADOWS OVER BROKEN SURFACES

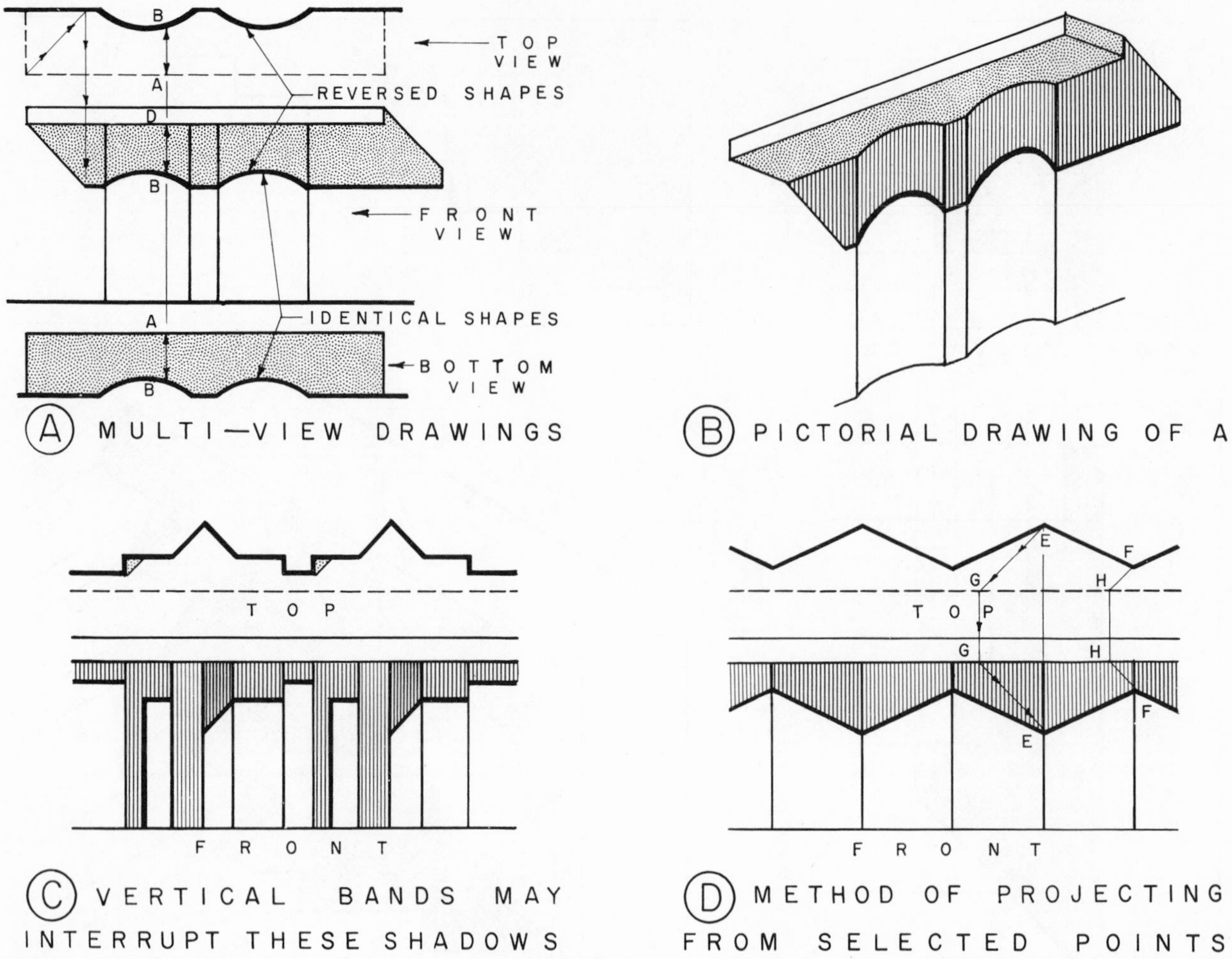

FIG. 186 SHADOWS OF HORIZONTAL LINES PARALLEL TO WALL

2. Horizontal lines parallel to wall planes cast shadows in front view that duplicate the shapes of the bottom view and are the reverse of the shapes of the top view, Fig. 186 A. These horizontal lines are commonly found in furniture tops, mantels or fireplaces, and overhangs above window and door openings. An understanding of the shapes produced by the shadows of these horizontal lines will greatly simplify their shadow construction. Any method of reproducing the required shapes may be used. These methods include trace and transfer, measuring with dividers, and 45° projection from plan or side view for necessary points. Dividers can be used on any continuous vertical line through the top or bottom, and front views as shown in Fig. 186 A. Here distance A–B in bottom view and B–A in top view are equal to D–B in the front view. In Fig. 186 D a 45° line is drawn from E to locate G in top view. A vertical line from G in top view locates the same point G in front view, and a 45° line from G in front view intersects the vertical from E in the shadow of G at E. Additional shadows of this type will be found in the elevations of Figs. 179 and 188 A.

3. Vertical lines in front views cast shadows on plane surfaces and horizontal bands that duplicate the distances from these vertical lines in side views, Fig. 187 I distance R–S. The shapes of the shadow edges are identical with those of the right side views and the reverse from left to right of those shown in left side views, Fig. 187 I. These vertical lines cast 45° planes of shadow back, down, and to the right. These planes of shadow go back and to the right equally. The dis-

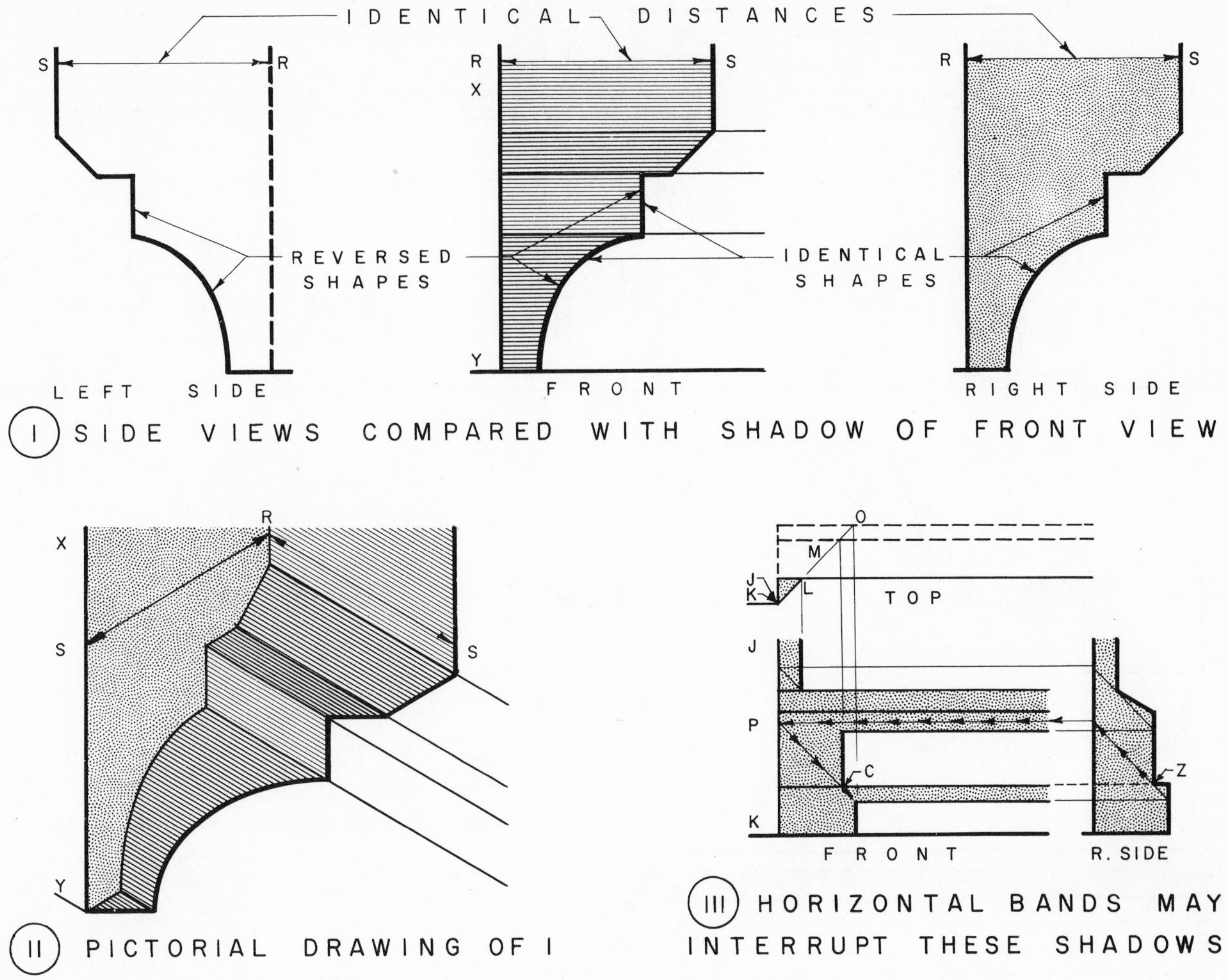

FIG. 187 SHADOWS OF VERTICAL LINES IN FRONT VIEW

tances to the right can be constructed from either the plan or the side view, both of which show the distances back from the line, Fig. 187 III.

In the top view of Fig. 187 III a 45° construction line is drawn from the point representing line J–K. This 45° line intersects the lines representing the vertical planes at points, L, M, and O. From these points of intersection vertical lines are drawn to the corresponding areas of the front view to locate the shadow outline. In the same figure the construction for one point is also made from the right side view. From any point Z on the side view a ray of light is traced back to locate point P on line J–K. A 45° construction line is drawn from P to locate its shadow C on the horizontal line from Z. As many points as necessary are located by this system to complete the shadow.

The distance to the right from the shadow-casting vertical line on the left in the right side view must be equal to the distance from the front view of the same line. It is possible to transfer these equal distances with dividers or in any other convenient way to obtain the shadow outline. The shape can be traced and transferred. The easiest method should be used to construct any shadow.

When the shadow made by the vertical line is interrupted by horizontal bands of shadow from projections, the parts of the shadow of the vertical line in front view will be identical with the right side profile, Fig. 187 III. It should be observed that circular, irregular, curved, and slanting shapes repeat in the shadow of front view the identical forms and angles of the right side view.

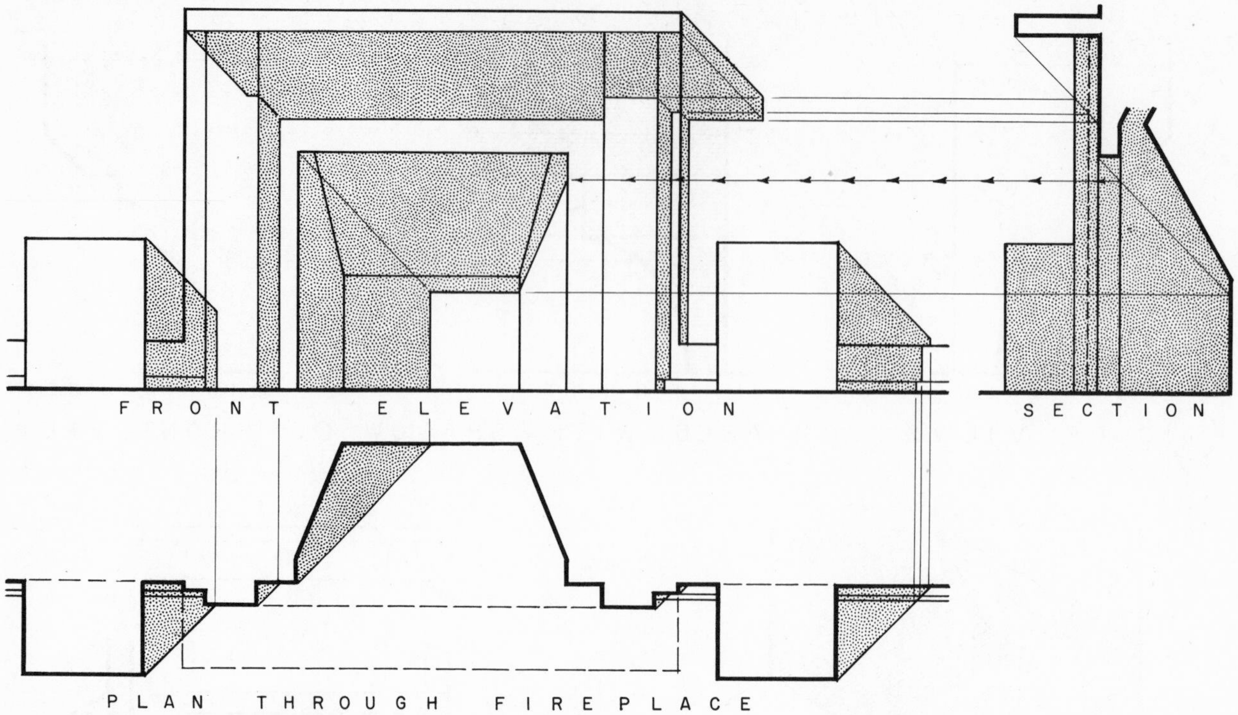

Ⓐ SHADOWS AROUND A FIREPLACE

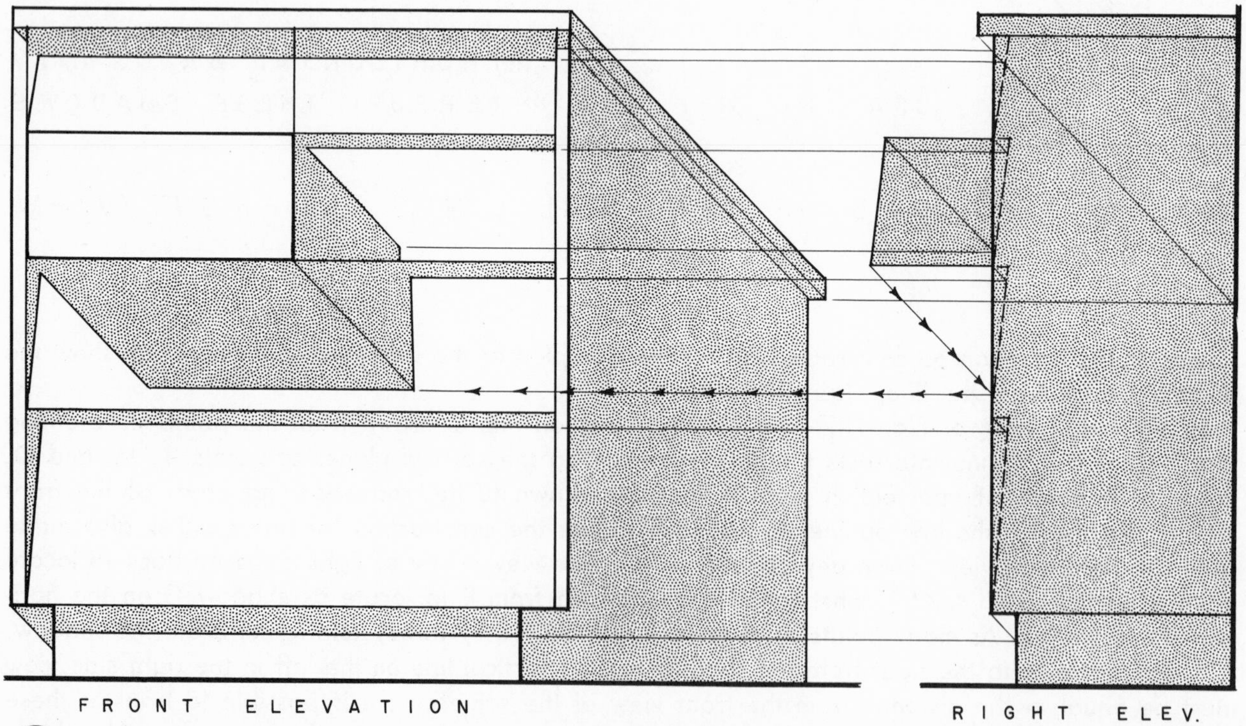

Ⓑ SHADOWS OF A CHEST OF DRAWERS

FIG. 188 EXAMPLES OF SHADOW CONSTRUCTION

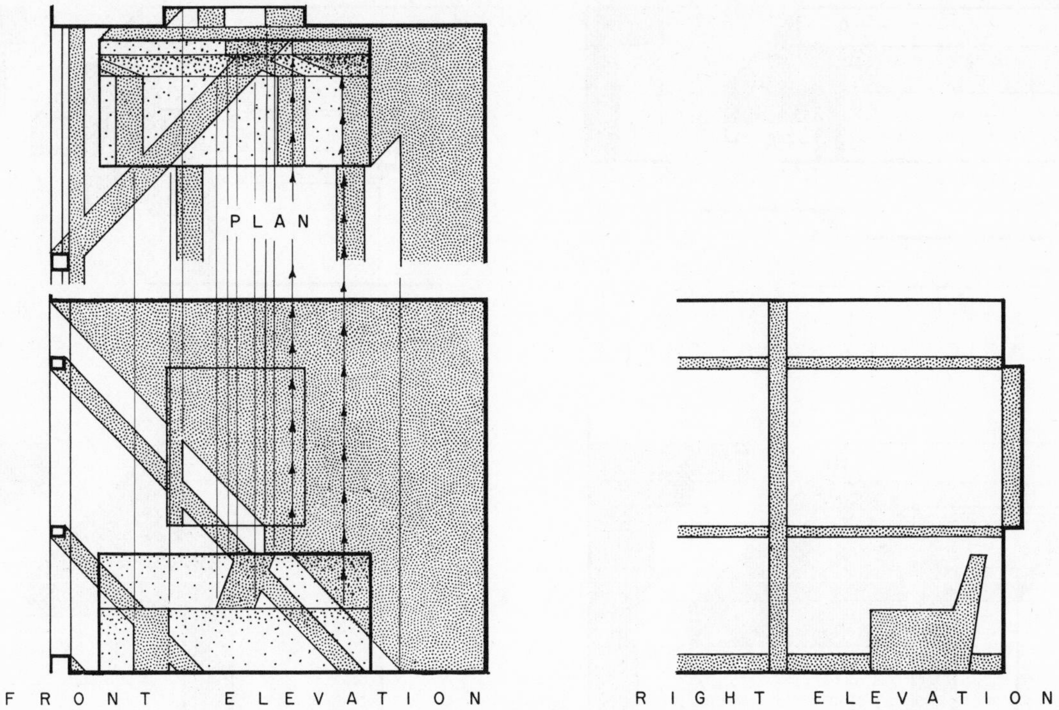

(C) SHADOWS INTO A ROOM INTERIOR

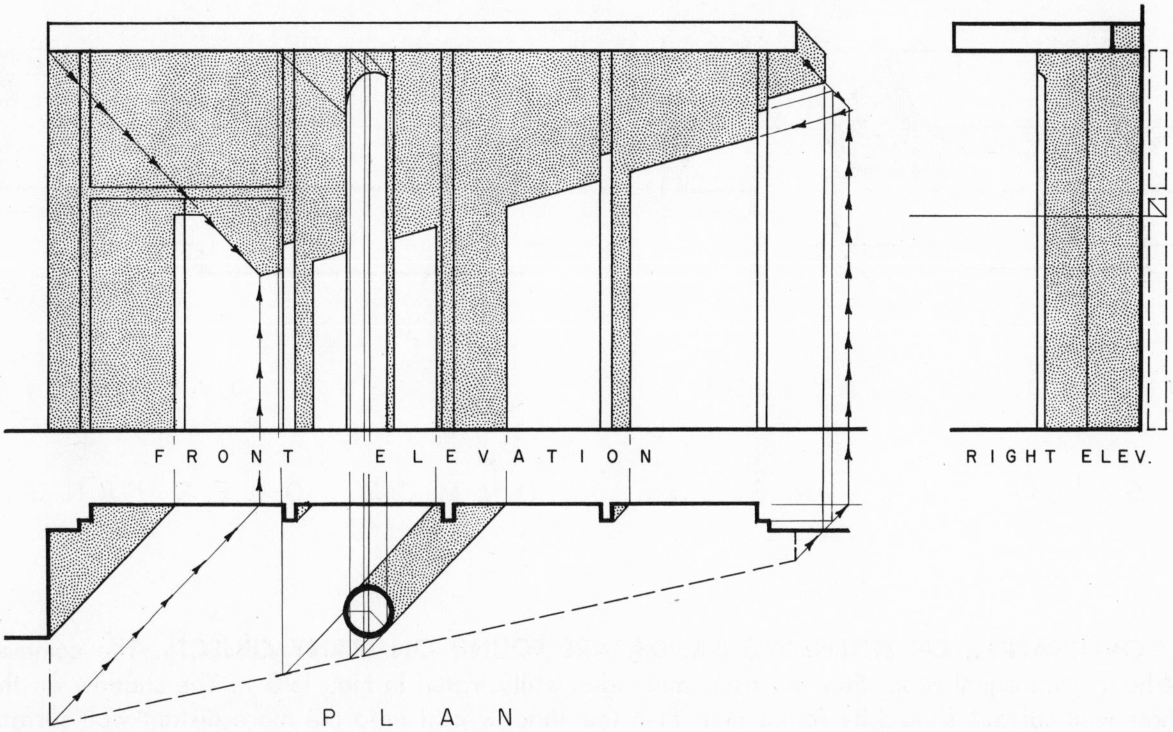

(D) SHADOWS ON AN ENTRANCE TO A BUILDING

FIG. 189 EXAMPLES OF SHADOW CONSTRUCTION

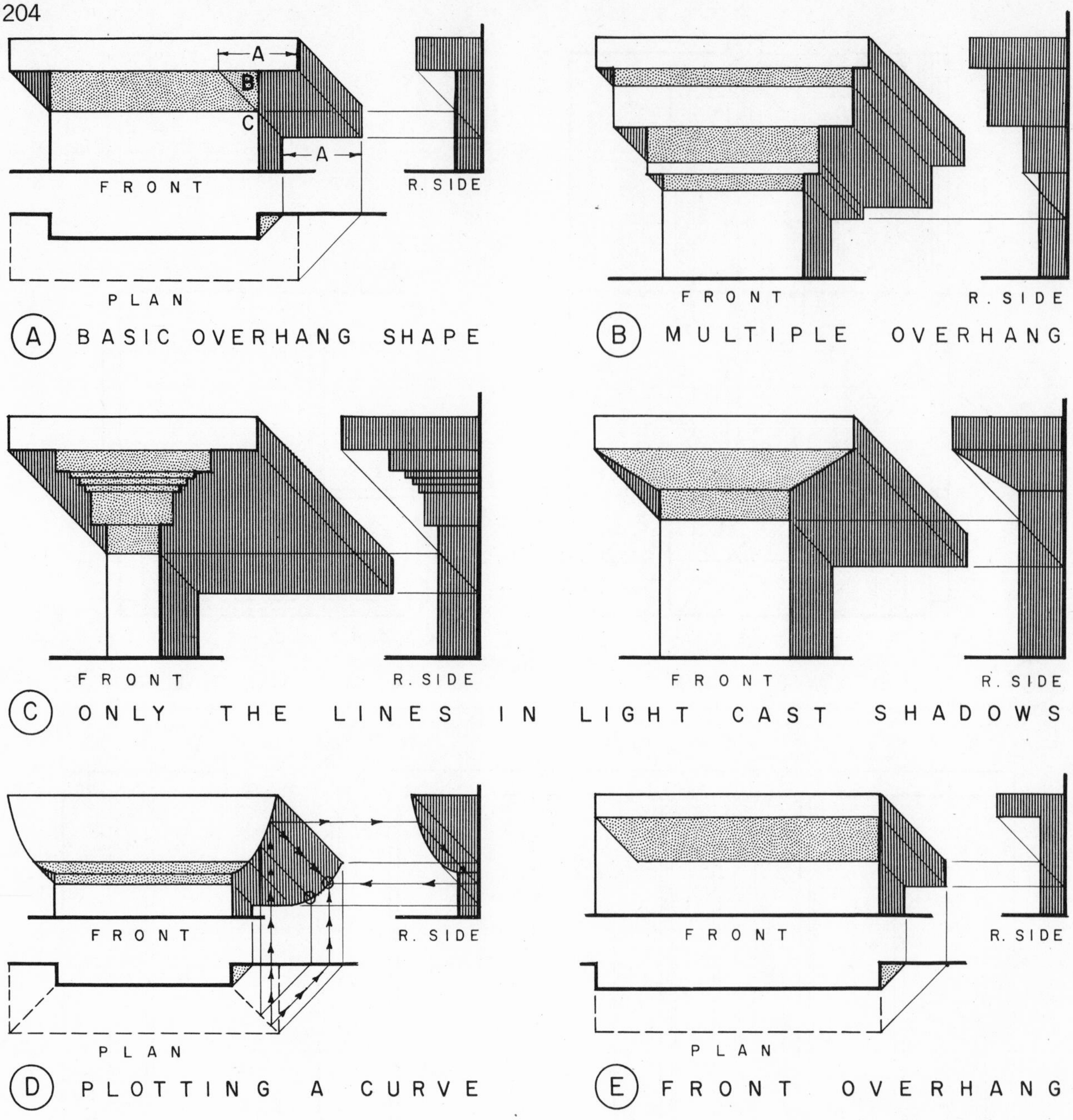

FIG. 190 SHADOWS OF COMMON OVERHANGS

OVERHANGS, OR EXTENDING BANDS, ARE FOUND ON MANY OBJECTS. The common overhang with equal projections on front and sides is illustrated in Fig. 190 A. The shadow on the nearer wall surface should be found first, then the shadow cast onto the more distant wall surface around the projecting parts. This procedure helps prevent construction from lines in shadow that cannot cast shadows. The shadow can be constructed on the front view from either the plan or side view. The horizontal projection A of the shadow is greater than the overhang at the right side because of the equal extention in front. Its horizontal distance is the sum of the side and front projections. It should be observed that the part B–C of the right vertical edge is in shadow and consequently cannot make a shadow on the wall or anything else. Fig. 190 B shows a multiple overhang with each element partially in light. Each part in light makes a shadow on the wall at the side of the over-

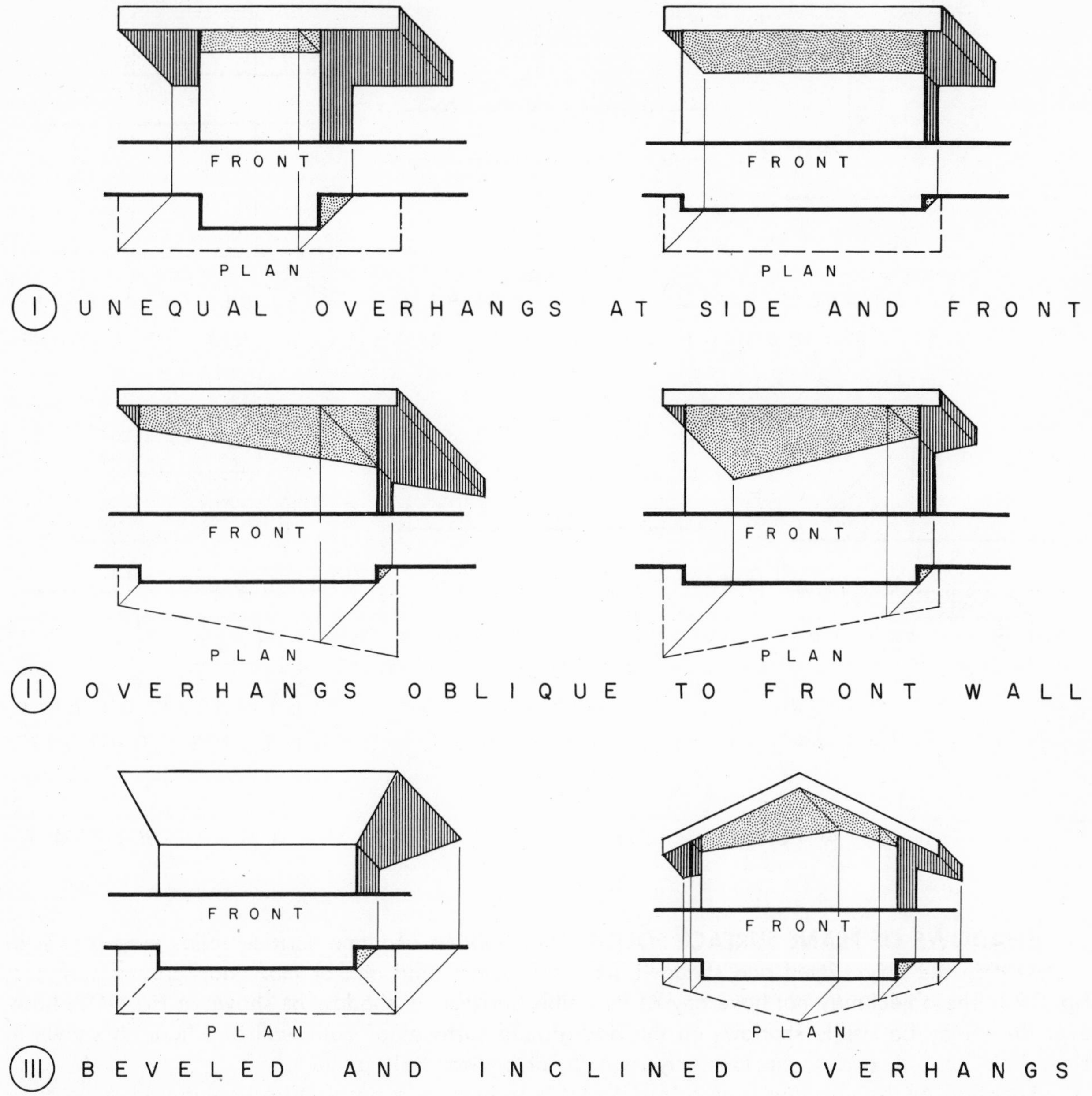

FIG. 191 SHADOWS OF IRREGULAR OVERHANGS

hangs. A similar treatment in Fig. 190 C has greater projections and all elements except the top one are completely in shadow. The general shadow shape on the wall is similar to that on Fig. 190 A. The parts in shadow have no effect on the shadow outline. In Fig. 190 D the molding shape is in light. Shadow points can be plotted from the elevation and either the plan or side elevation of the molding. Be sure to use the points that are on the same vertical line in plan and elevation or on the same horizontal line in elevation and side elevation in tracing construction to find a shadow point. These points represent the same point on the object and must be used together.

Unequal overhangs are illustrated in Fig. 191 I and oblique ones in Figs. 191 II and III. The two segments of the slanting shadows are parallel in each illustration of Fig. 191 II because they are shadows of the same line on parallel surfaces.

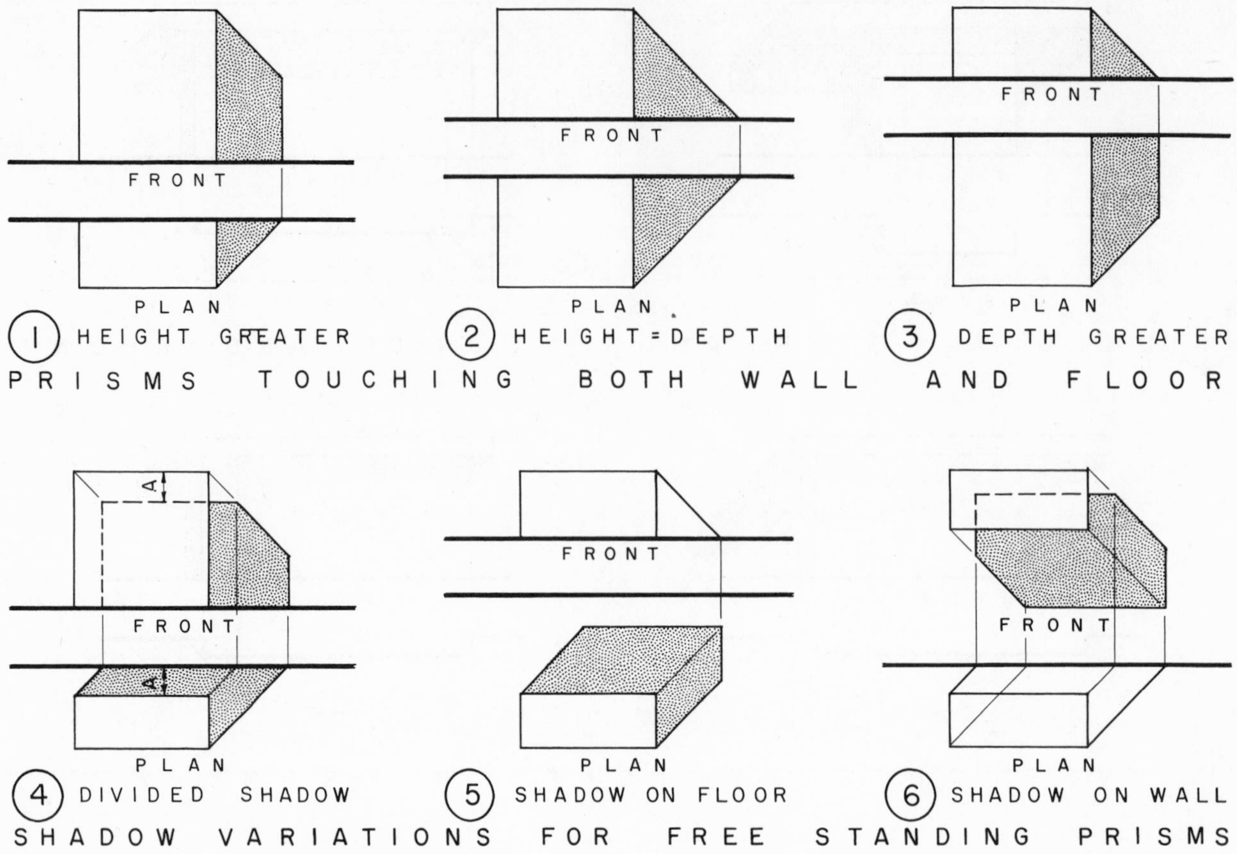

FIG. 192 SHADOWS OF RECTANGULAR PRISMS

SHADOWS OF PLANE SURFACE SOLIDS. The shadows of plane surface solids may consist of shadows on the object itself and shadows from the object onto one or more background surfaces, Fig. 193. The object may not have any of its visible surfaces in shadow as shown in Fig. 192; however there may be visible shadows on the background surfaces of both wall and floor as shown in Figs. 192 1, 2, 3, and 4, on floor only as in 5, or on wall only as in 6.

Location of the shadow from a free object is sometimes a puzzle to a beginner in the casting of shadows. It may require study to learn to visualize the object and its shadow positions from multi-view drawings. The sequence of illustrations of rectangular blocks in Fig. 192 shows the effect on the shadow of different distances from the wall and floor planes. The following paragraphs are numbered to coincide with the numbers of the illustrations.

1. The box touches both wall and floor planes as though it were attached to them. This form is a projection from the two planes with its height greater than its depth in the first illustration. This gives a triangular shadow in plan and a vertical shadow with a 45° top in elevation.

2. In the second illustration the box has equal height and depth. The shadows are triangles.

3. When the box extends farther from the wall than from the floor as shown in the third illustration the wall shadow is a triangle and the floor shadow a rectangular area with a 45° point.

4. The box has been moved out from the wall. It still rests on the floor and is close to the wall. The shadow of the top of the box drops down at its top edge the distance A.

5. When the distance from the wall as shown in plan exceeds the height of the object above the floor the entire shadow falls on the floor.

6. When the object is suspended above the floor at a height greater than the distance back to the wall shown in plan the entire shadow falls on the wall.

The vertical prisms of Fig. 193 A illustrate the varied shadows of commonly used prism shapes on wall planes. When the entire shadow falls on the wall the complete shadows of the parallel top and bottom of a vertical prism will be identical as shown for the triangular prism of Fig. 193 A. Because only a part of top and bottom casts a shadow and each part is from an opposite side of the prism, the part shadows are never alike. The shadow of the complete end of the prism on the floor will always be identical with its plan view shape since the ends are parallel to the floor as shown in the illustration of the octagon.

The shadows of a simple pyramid are shown in Fig. 193 B. The first example shows the complete shadow falling on the floor and the second the complete shadow on the wall. The last two examples illustrate how the complete shadow can be outlined in plan or elevation to find the part shadows on the two drawings.

The shadow on and from a pyramid will vary with its shape. The illustrations are of pyramids having a sufficiently steep slope so that two sides are in shadow. When the slope is 45° there is no shadow in plan or elevation from the sides of the pyramid, although two sides are still in shadow (shade). When the slope is less than 45° there is no shadow on the sides of the pyramid. When the slope is 45° or less any shadow in either plan or elevation is from the base only.

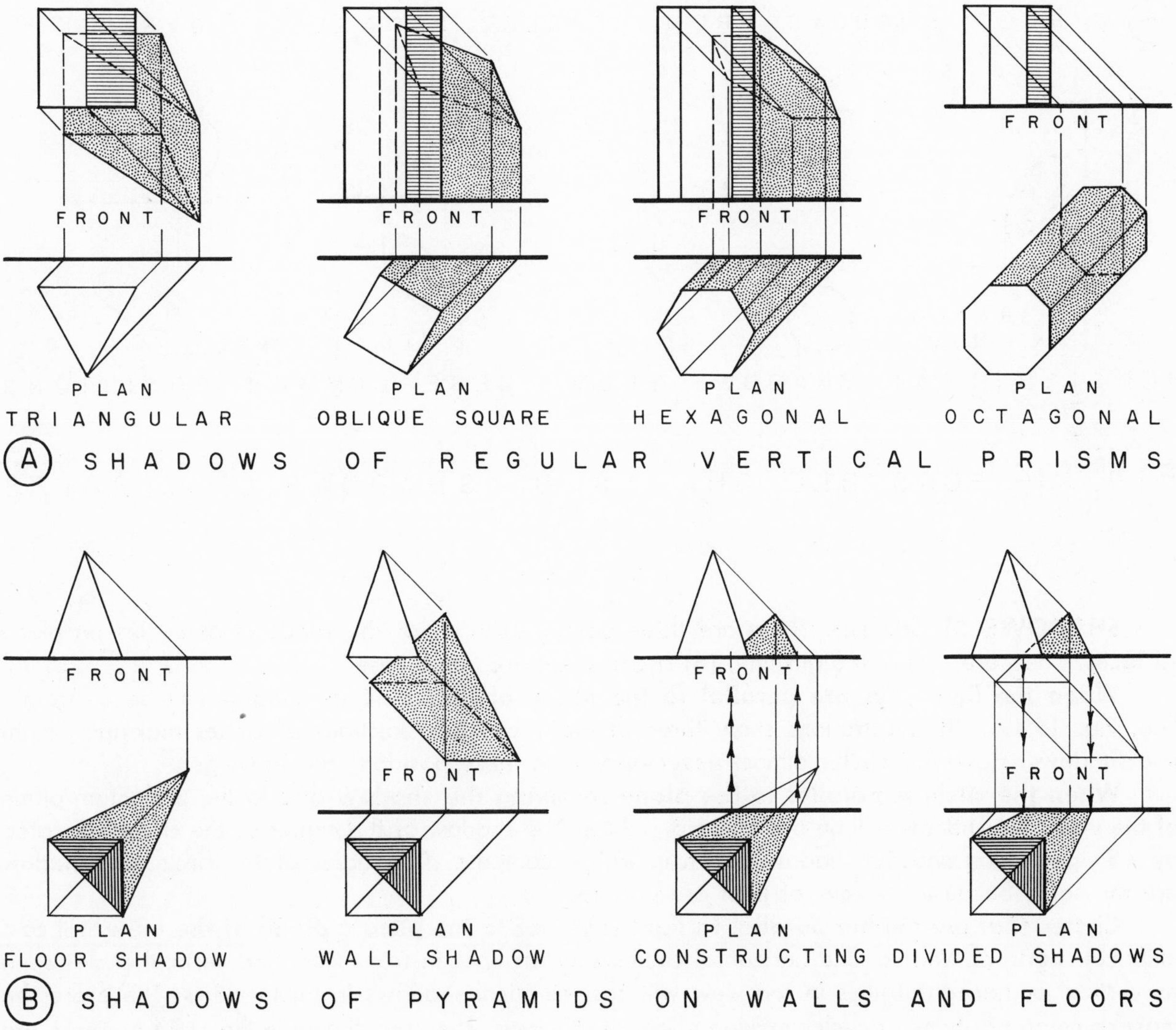

FIG. 193 SHADOWS OF PRISMS AND PYRAMIDS

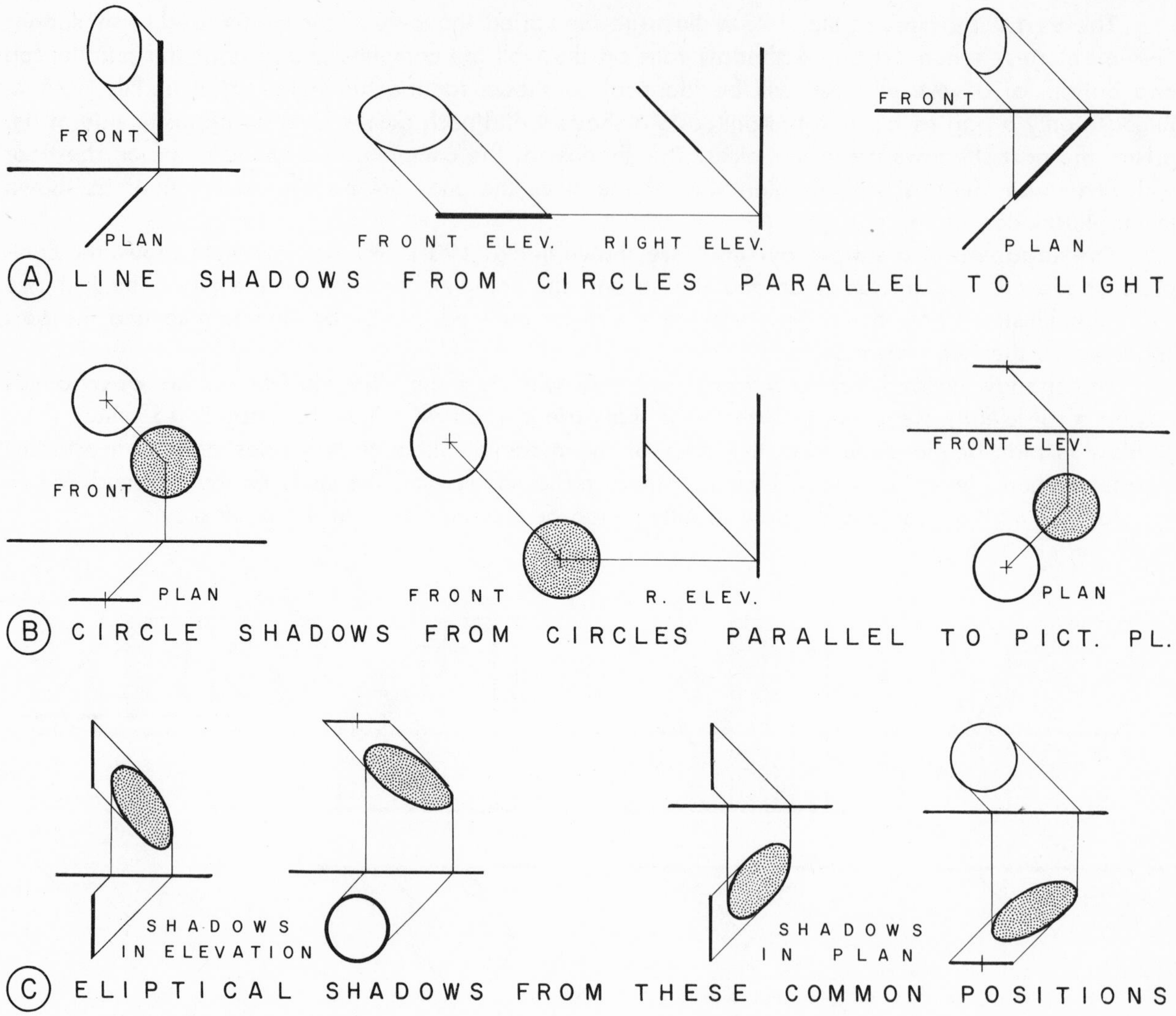

FIG. 194 POSSIBLE SHAPES OF SHADOWS OF CIRCLES

SHADOWS OF CIRCLES. There are three possible shapes of the shadows of circles on plane surfaces. They are, (A) a straight line, (B) a circle, and (C) an ellipse.

When the light rays are parallel to the plane of the circle its shadow will be a straight line, Fig. 194 A. The illustrations show three of many possible positions of circles making straight line shadows. However, circles almost never appear in these positions on drawings.

When the circle is parallel to the plane receiving the shadow and to the projection plane of the view, the shadow will be a circle, Fig. 194 B. The shadow of the center of the circle is located by 45° projection and the shadow drawn in with a compass. The radius of the circle and shadow are the same because the rays of light are parallel.

Circles that are neither parallel to light rays nor to the picture plane of the view will cast elliptical shadows. Vertical and horizontal circles seen as lines in front view and vertical circles seen as vertical or horizontal lines in top view will cast elliptical shadows in those views. These are the most common positions of circles making elliptical shadows. They are shown in Fig. 194 C. There are two common methods of constructing the ellipses that are the shadows of circles. They are (1) the method of tangent polygons, (2) the point method.

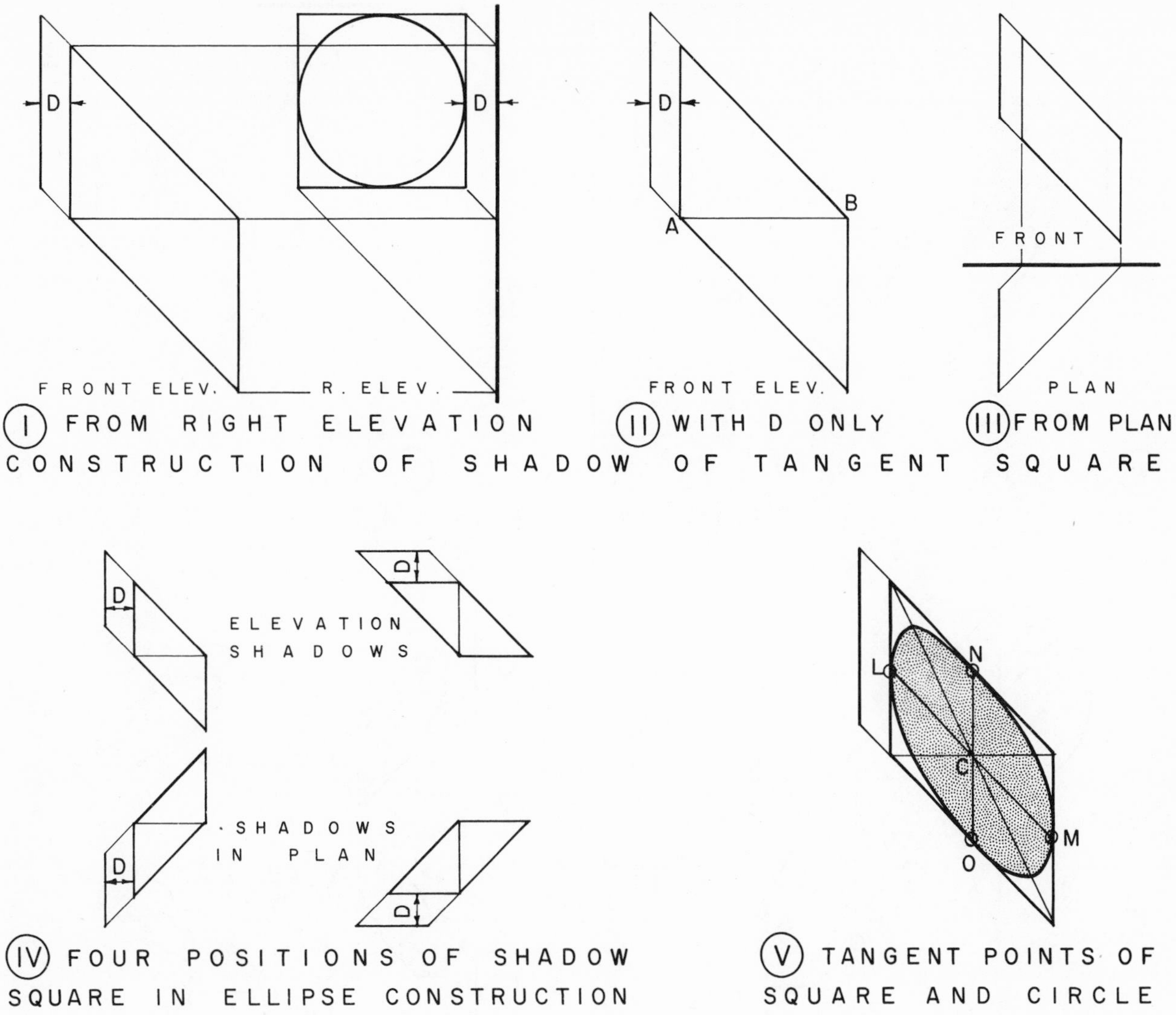

FIG. 195 TANGENT SQUARES FOR SHADOWS OF CIRCLES

The tangent polygon is turned in the most convenient direction for easy construction. In Fig. 195 a tangent square is used. As shown in the right elevation view of Fig. 195 I two sides of the square are parallel and two are perpendicular to the wall on which the shadow falls. The two sides that are parallel to the wall cast shadows that remain parallel to the front elevation of the circle. The two sides perpendicular to the wall cast 45° shadow lines. An inspection of the shadow of the square in Fig. 195 II shows that two corners appear on the same construction line A–B, which is horizontal for this position of the circle. Because the distance D is the same in front and side view the construction can be made without the side view or the plan when D, the distance from the circle to the wall receiving the shadow, is known. This construction for the tangent square is shown in the four commonly used positions in Fig. 195 IV. The points of tangency of the four sides of the square with the circle can be located easily, Fig. 195 V. First draw the diagonals of the shadow of the square to locate its center C. Then through C draw lines L–M and N–O parallel to the sides of the shadow of the square. The intersections with the shadow of the square at L, M, N, and O are the required points of tangency of the square and circle. The ellipse can be drawn through these four points—It is difficult to draw a good ellipse with only four points and four tangents.

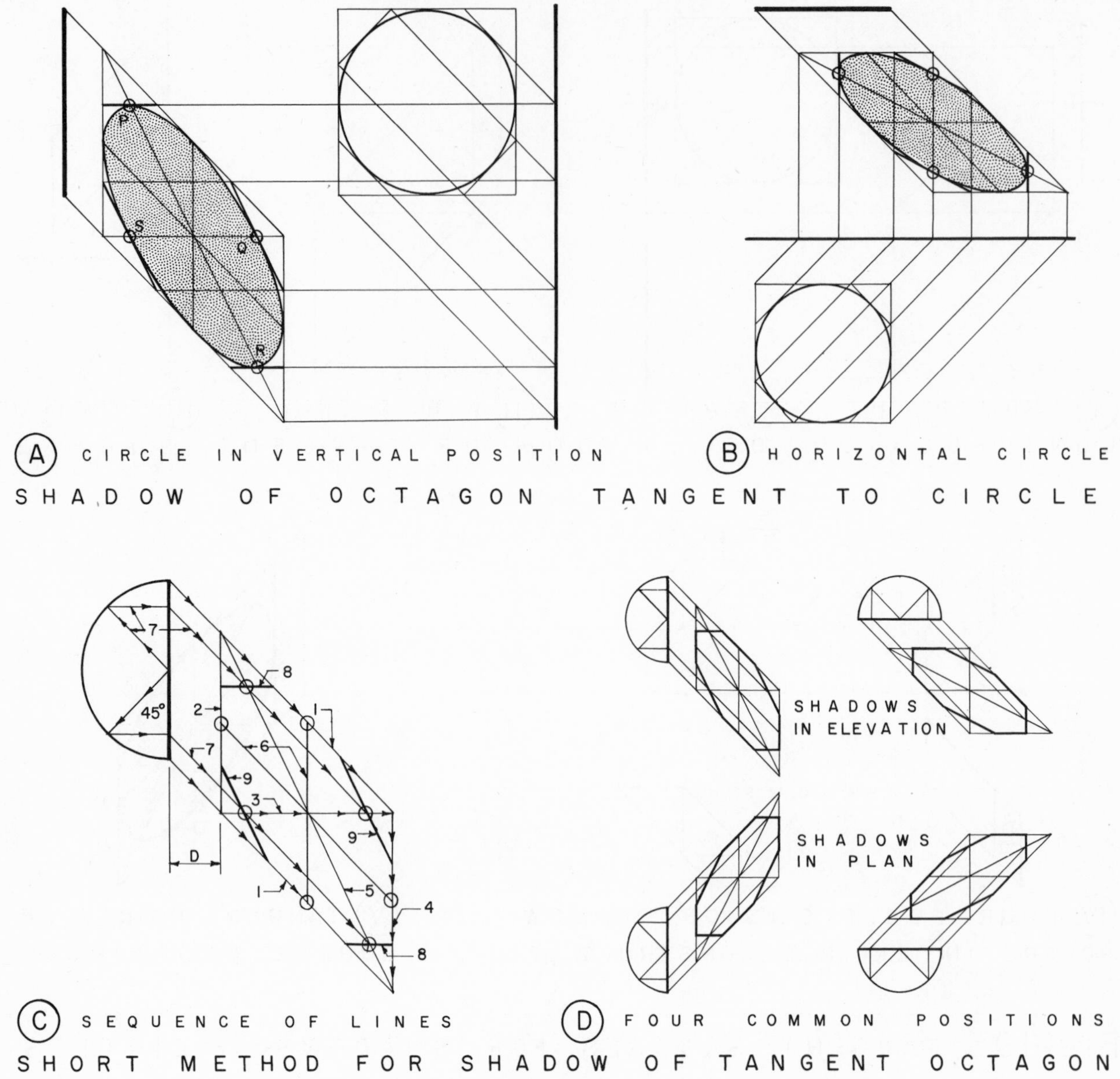

FIG. 196 OCTAGON METHOD FOR SHADOWS OF CIRCLES

The tangent octagon can be used to provide four additional tangent lines and points when the tangent square does not give sufficient construction for the accuracy required. The octagon is drawn around the circle in the side view of Fig. 196 A and projected onto the shadow construction in the front view as shown. The shadows of the four added octagon sides cross the diagonals of the shadow of the square in the required points of tangency P, Q, R, S. Fig. 196 C shows a short cut in locating the octagon points of tangency and sides of the octagon when distance D is given. Two sides of the shadow of the octagon are parallel to each shadow of a diagonal of the square. The numbers give the order of drawing the lines and the arrows the directions they are drawn.

The point method of constructing the shadow of a circle locates the shadows of points only. It does not provide lines tangent to the curving shape of the shadow. It requires two views of the circle for the shadow construction. In Fig. 197 I the plan view of the circle is true shape. Points G

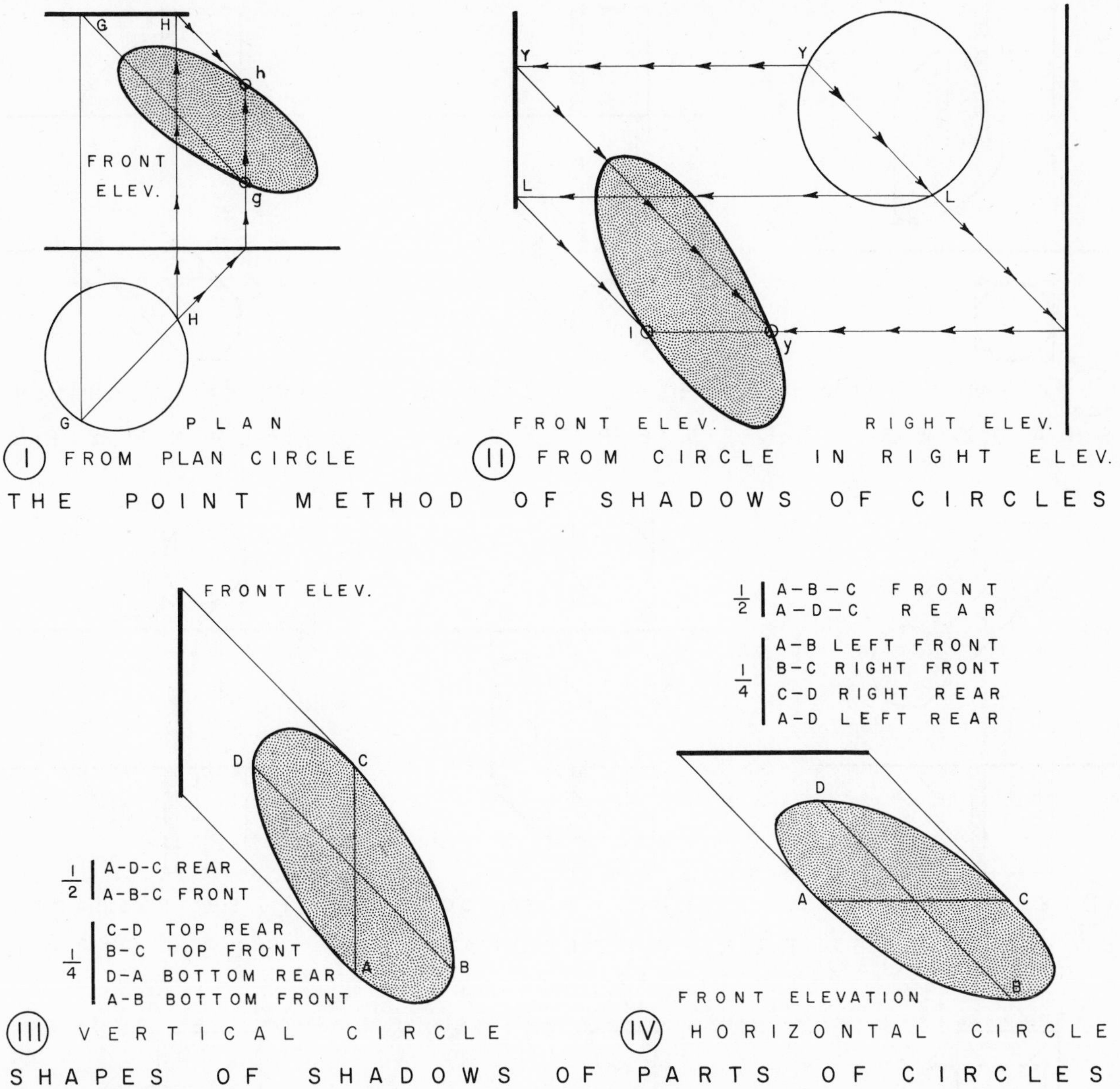

FIG. 197 CONSTRUCTION OF SHADOWS OF CIRCLES

and H are located on both views and their shadows *g* and *h* are located by 45° projection. When sufficient points have been located in this manner for the accuracy required, the curve is drawn through them.

When both given views of the circle are straight lines it is necessary to draw an additional view which will give the true shape of the circle for construction.

Shadows of parts of circles can be constructed by either the point or polygon method. It is more accurate to construct a greater amount of the circle than the small part required in order to get the ends of the curves precisely. A careful observation of the characteristics of shadows of half and quarter circles as shown in Figs. 197 III and IV will help in drawing these shapes correctly. Note particularly that the end directions of shadows of quarter and half circles are 45°, vertical, or horizontal for the shadows of circles in common positions.

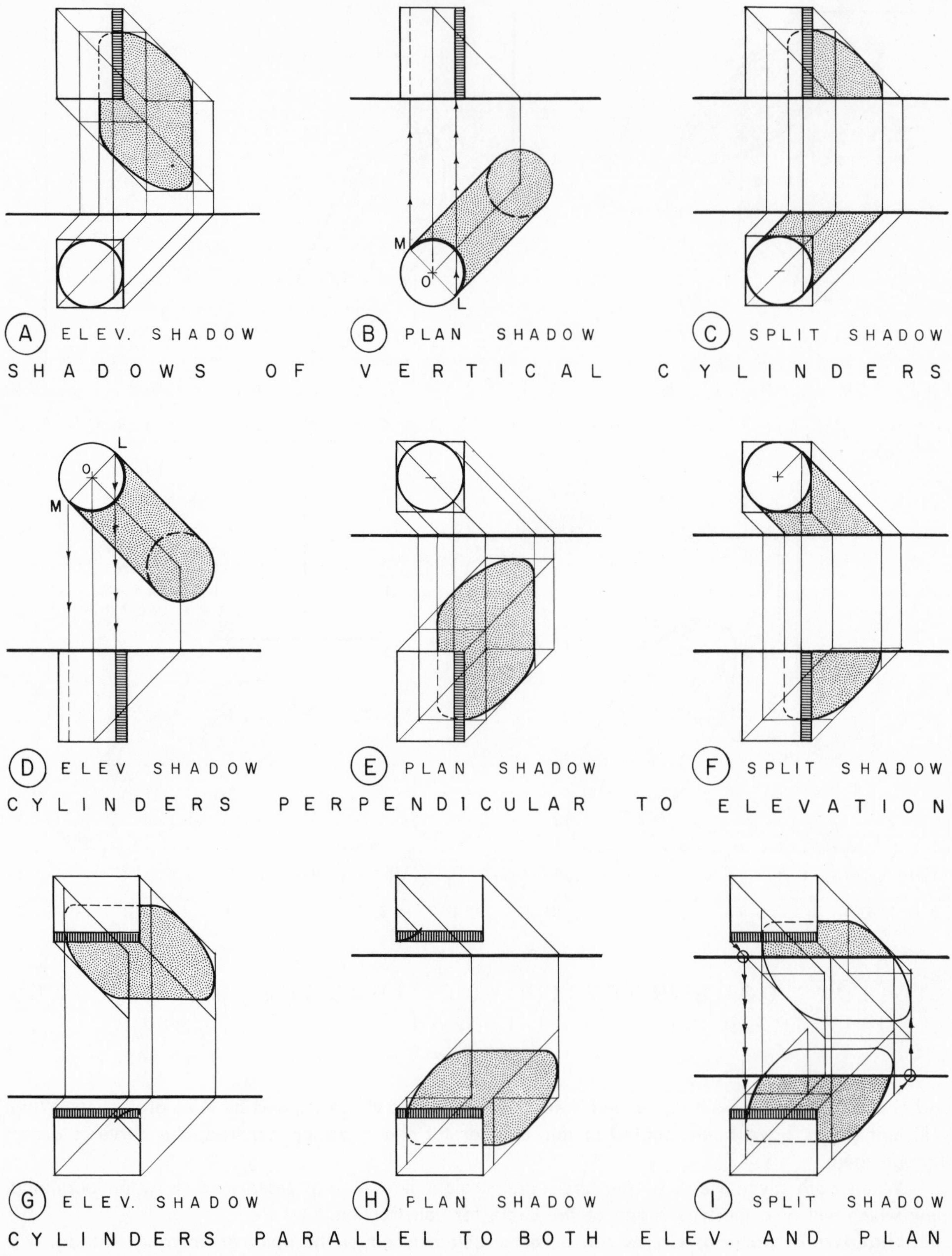

FIG. 198 SHADOWS AND SHADE LINES OF CYLINDERS

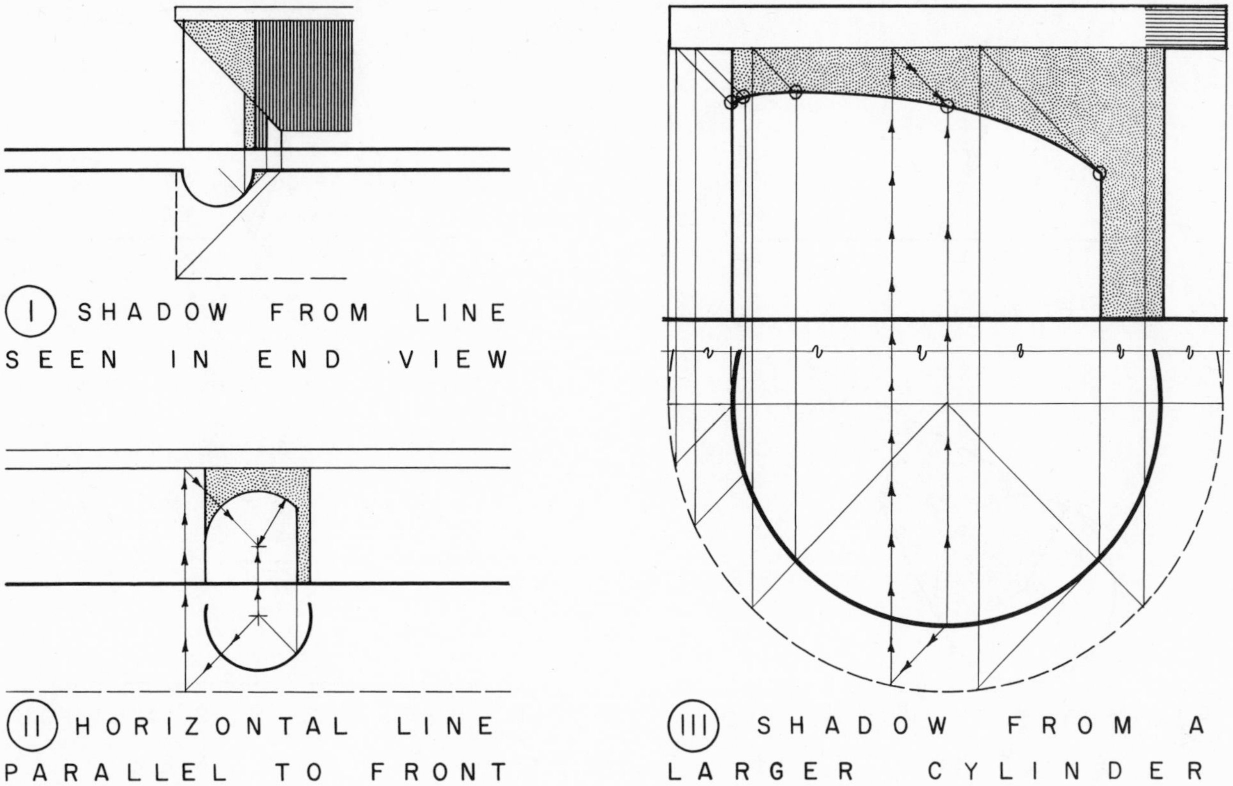

FIG. 199 COMMON SHADOWS ON CYLINDERS

SHADOWS OF CIRCULAR SOLIDS. The simple geometric forms of cylinder, sphere, and cone are the simplest circular solids. Other less common circular geometric solids are the ellipsoid and the torus. Bowls, plates, urns, door knobs, and many other forms shaped by revolving on an axis are also circular solids. Most of these forms produce interesting shadows.

The shade line on a cylinder is located by finding the tangent point of light in the view where it is seen as a circle, Figs. 198 B and D. The point of tangency L is located accurately by drawing from the center O of the circle the line O–L perpendicular to the tangent. The shadow area on the surface of the cylinder extends from the visible shadow starting at L to a hidden shade line at M.

The shadow of a cylinder consists of the shadow of its bases and the straight line shadows made by its shade lines, Fig. 198 A. When the circular base is parallel to the floor or wall on which its shadow falls the shadow is a circle, Figs. 198 B, D. When the base is perpendicular to the wall or floor on which its shadow falls the shadow is an ellipse, Figs. 198 A, E, G, H.

Shadows on cylinders from overhangs above them fall into three common classifications:

1. When the straight line making the shadow is seen in end view, the shadow is a 45° straight line, Fig. 199 I.

II. When a line perpendicular to the axis of a vertical or horizontal cylinder and parallel to the plane of the view casts a shadow on the cylinder, the shadow will be an arc of a circle in the view where the length of the cylinder is seen, Fig. 199 II. The radius of the arc will be the same as that of the cylinder. Sometimes a part of the shadow is type I and part type II.

III. When the shadow is from a larger circular form concentric with the cylinder the shadow will be elliptical in shape. It can be plotted by finding the shadows of a number of points. Be sure to use the same point in each view when plotting a shadow point, Fig. 199 III.

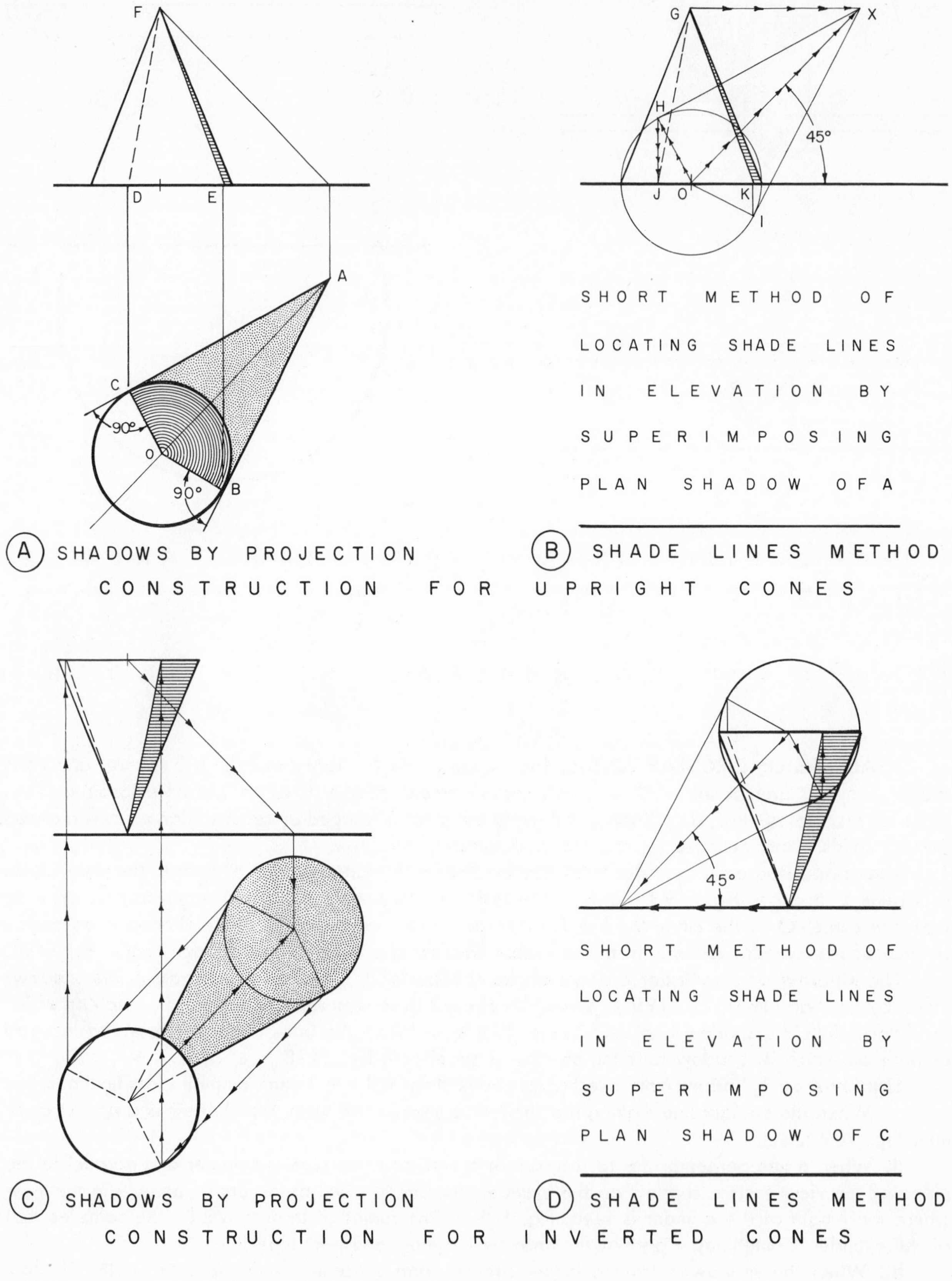

FIG. 200 SHADES AND PLAN SHADOWS OF CONES

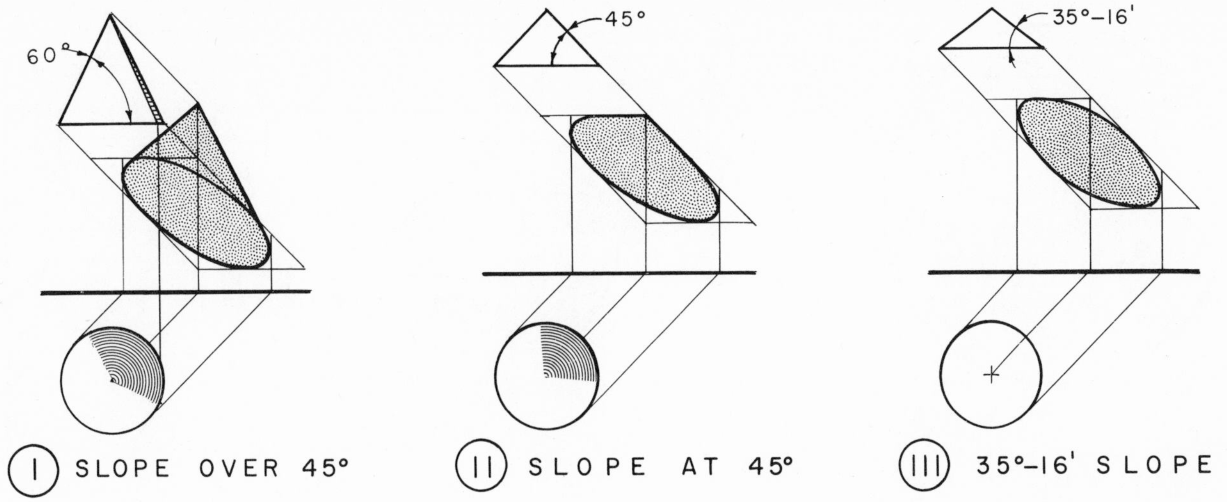

FIG. 201 ELEVATION SHADOWS OF UPRIGHT CONES

The shade lines on a cone are located in an indirect manner. These shade lines cannot be located by tangent 45° lines as in the case of cylinders because the curving surface of the cone slopes instead of being perpendicular to the base of the cone. The shadow of a cone is outlined by the shadows of its base and two shade lines. The shade lines on the cone can be located from their shadows. In Fig. 200 A the shadow of the cone is constructed in plan view. The shadow A of the apex is located by 45° projection. It is connected to the shadow of the base by tangent lines A–B and A–C to complete the shadow outline. Because the base rests on the horizontal plane the shadow of the base coincides with the plan view of the base. O–B and O–C, which are drawn from O perpendicular to the tangents A–B and A–C, locate the points of tangency B and C. O–B and O–C are the shade lines of the cone. They are located in elevation by drawing vertical lines from their plan positions on the base of the cone to locate points D and E from which the shade lines are drawn to the elevation of the apex F. The entire construction can be duplicated more directly on the elevation, Fig. 200 B. From the apex G of the cone draw a horizontal line to the right. From the center O of the base draw a 45° line up to the right to meet the horizontal at X. Draw the circle plan of the base with O as a center. Draw tangents from X to the circle. Locate points of tangency H and I and then the ends of the shade lines on the base of the cone at J and K with verticals from H and I.

The inverted cone of Fig. 200 C touches the floor plane at its apex. Its shadow is located in plan in this figure. The shade point can be traced back to the plan from the shadow and then from the plan to elevation. The entire construction for locating the shade lines can be duplicated on the

The amount of shadow on a cone varies with the proportions and position of the cone. The shadow on an upright cone increases in width as the cone approaches the shape of a cylinder. Its maximum limit is the width of the shadow on a cylinder. When the slope of the cone is 45° there is no visible shadow in front view, Fig. 201 II. At the angle of light 35°–16′ or less there is no visible or hidden shadow on the conical surface, Fig. 201 III.

The shadow on an inverted cone approaches the shadow width of a cylinder as its minimum. At 45° three fourths of the cone is in shadow and at 35°–16′ it is in complete shadow.

It should be observed that the hidden and visible shade lines are not at equal distances from the edges of a cone. The hidden shade line is farther from the edge on an upright cone, line F–D, Fig. 200 A. The visible shade line is farther on an inverted cone, Fig. 200 C. The shadow covers less than half the conical surface of an upright cone, more than half of an inverted cone surface.

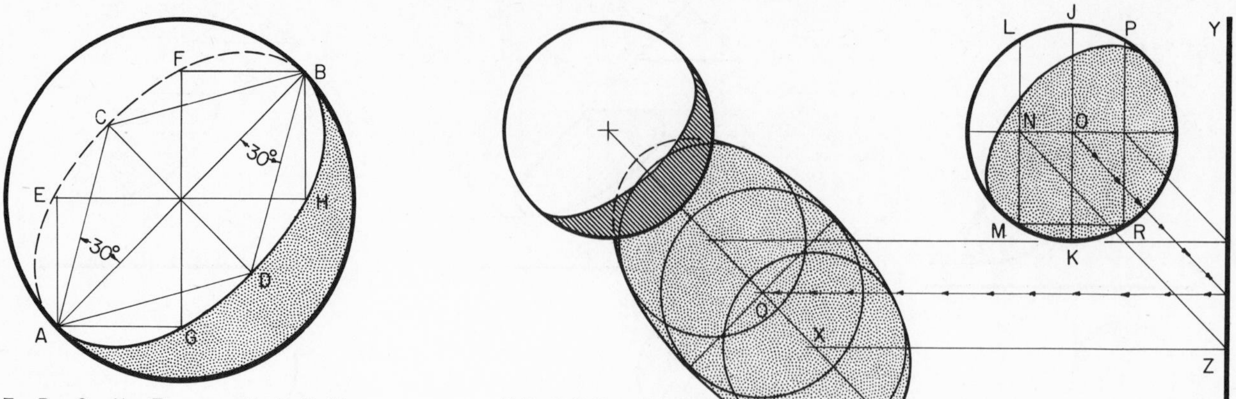

FRONT VIEW OF A SPHERE
(I) SHADE LINE

FRONT VIEW OF SPHERE
RIGHT SIDE VIEW OF SPHERE
(II) SHADOW ONTO A WALL

FIG. 202 SHADE LINE AND SHADOW OF A SPHERE

The shade line on a sphere is an ellipse as seen in any of the standard multi-view drawings. It is actually a great circle of the sphere that is seen obliquely in all multi-view drawings where it appears as an ellipse. In front view the visible shadow is a crescent shape at the lower right of the sphere. The hidden shadow extends from the edge of the visible shadow to an outline at the top left, which exactly duplicates the visible shadow in reverse, Fig. 202 I. The entire shade line is a complete ellipse. Its major axis A–B is a 45° line extending from the lower left to the top right edges of the sphere and passing through its center. This line locates points A and B the tangent points of light at the lower left and upper right edges of the sphere. The minor axis is the 45° line C–D through the center of the sphere and perpendicular to the major axis. From point A or B lines at 30° to the A–B axis locate points C and D. A horizontal and vertical line are drawn from A and from B to meet the vertical and horizontal center lines of the sphere. These intersections E, F, G, and H give four additional points on the shade line. Points A and G are equidistant from the vertical 45° light plane through the center of the sphere. They are therefore on the same horizontal line. The ellipse of the complete shade line can be drawn through the eight points which have been located. These are a sufficient number of points for accuracy if the draftsman will remember to round out the small ends of the ellipse so that they are tangent to the sphere.

The shadow of a sphere is an ellipse with both axes at 45°. In front view the major axis is down and to the right. The simplest method of locating the shadow is to find the shadows of a number of parallel circles in the sphere. The shadow of the sphere is the outline around the shadows of the circles. The circles are cut through the sphere parallel to the surface on which the shadow falls. The shadows of these circles are circles of the same size and can be drawn easily.

In the right side view of Fig. 202 II line J–K represents an edge view of a circle cut through the sphere. This circle is parallel to the wall Y–Z on which the shadow falls. J–K is the diameter of the circle and J–O and K–O its radii. The shadow of the center O of this circle is found by 45° projection. With a center at O and a radius J–O, the shadow of the circle is drawn in front view. Line L–M is the side view of a second circle. The shadow of its center is found at X. Its radius N–L is then used to draw its shadow with X as a center. By drawing horizontally across from L and M in side view a second circle P–R with same diameter is located. These two equal circles have shadows of the same radius. They are equidistant from circle A–B, which passes through the center of the sphere. Find as many circle shadows as necessary to provide the required accuracy in the outline of the shadow of the sphere. The circles can be located at any desired positions in side view. The use of equal pairs of circles provides symmetry and order in the construction.

IRREGULAR CIRCULAR FORMS. The most common irregular circular form has a vertical axis and horizontal circular elements. Such a shape is shown in Fig. 203. Four types of shade or shadow points can be located on these forms.

1. Points can be located on the edges by 45° tangents. Point A1 is the shadow point at the top left located by the tangent to the overhanging edge above. Point A2 is the shade point on the convex surface on the left. Point A3 is the shade point on the right edge at the top.

2. Because of the symmetry of the object and the direction of light there will be a shade or shadow point on the vertical center line of the object at the intersection of the horizontal from each A point. These points are lettered B1, B2, B3. Point B3 is on the hidden shade line.

3. Where the profile of the curving shape is vertical the shade point C will be the same distance in from the edge as on the vertical cylinder of the same diameter. This distance is slightly less than $\frac{1}{3}$ the radius of the horizontal circle at that point. It is usually sufficiently accurate to estimate these distances. They can be worked out precisely on circles of required diameters when necessary.

4. The smallest width of shade or shadow occurs on the left of the object at the 45° points L. The height of these points can be located on the profile by using the true angle of light (35°–16′, which is the diagonal of a cube instead of 45°) as shown by the dotted lines on the left edge of Fig. 203. Points L are located at slightly less than one third the radius from the points of tangency of the 35°–16′ lines.

The above four types of points are all that can be located on this type of form by 45° projection.

The vertical light plane method can be used to determine shade and shadow points on irregular circular solids. The light planes are at 45° in plan. Their intersections with the object lie in vertical light planes. Any point on an intersection line of a plane and the object will cast its shadow on the intersection line. Therefore 45° projection lines can be used on each profile cut through the object to determine shade and shadow points. The method is long and tedious. There are few projects that justify its use.

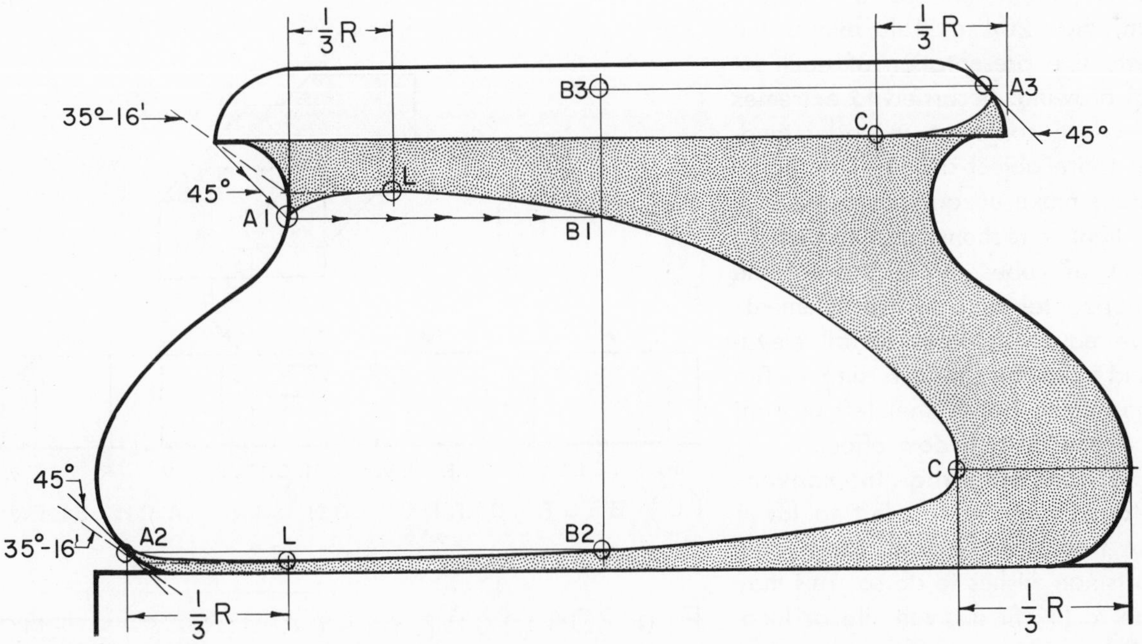

METHOD OF EASILY LOCATED POINTS

FIG. 203 SHADE LINES ON CIRCULAR SOLIDS

The direction of light on different views of the same object is often a matter of concern to the draftsman. There are three solutions. Each may be used under conditions where it seems to be the best answer.

A. The direction is chosen for the object as a unit and each view made to conform to that direction. This method is particularly logical if the object will be placed with a constant direction of light on it. However this system leaves two of the elevations in complete shadow, Fig. 204 A. These shadowed drawings will not explain the object as clearly as those which have both light and shadow areas.

B. The same direction of light can be used on each elevation as though they are all turned the same way and are in the same plane. In this system the front direction of light may be used on all the elevations. The plan views should conform to the same light direction as the front view when shadows are shown on the plans. This arrangement is usually quite satisfactory and is commonly used on a set of multi-view drawings, Fig. 204 B.

C. A direction of light can be chosen for each view as a separate problem, Fig. 204 C. This allows the most effective presentation of each individual drawing. If carried to extremes it may cause confusion in understanding the entire object because the equal projections make unequal shadows.

If light directions are limited to diagonals of cubes, projections of the same horizontal and vertical elements will give equal shadows on all elevations and keep the shadows simple. The light may come from either left or right to secure the best shadow effect.

Directions other than the conventional one from the top left to lower right on front view can be used when the draftsman wishes to do so. This may be done to (1) fit a given site or location, (2) avoid unsatisfactory shadow forms, (3) produce a different effect, or

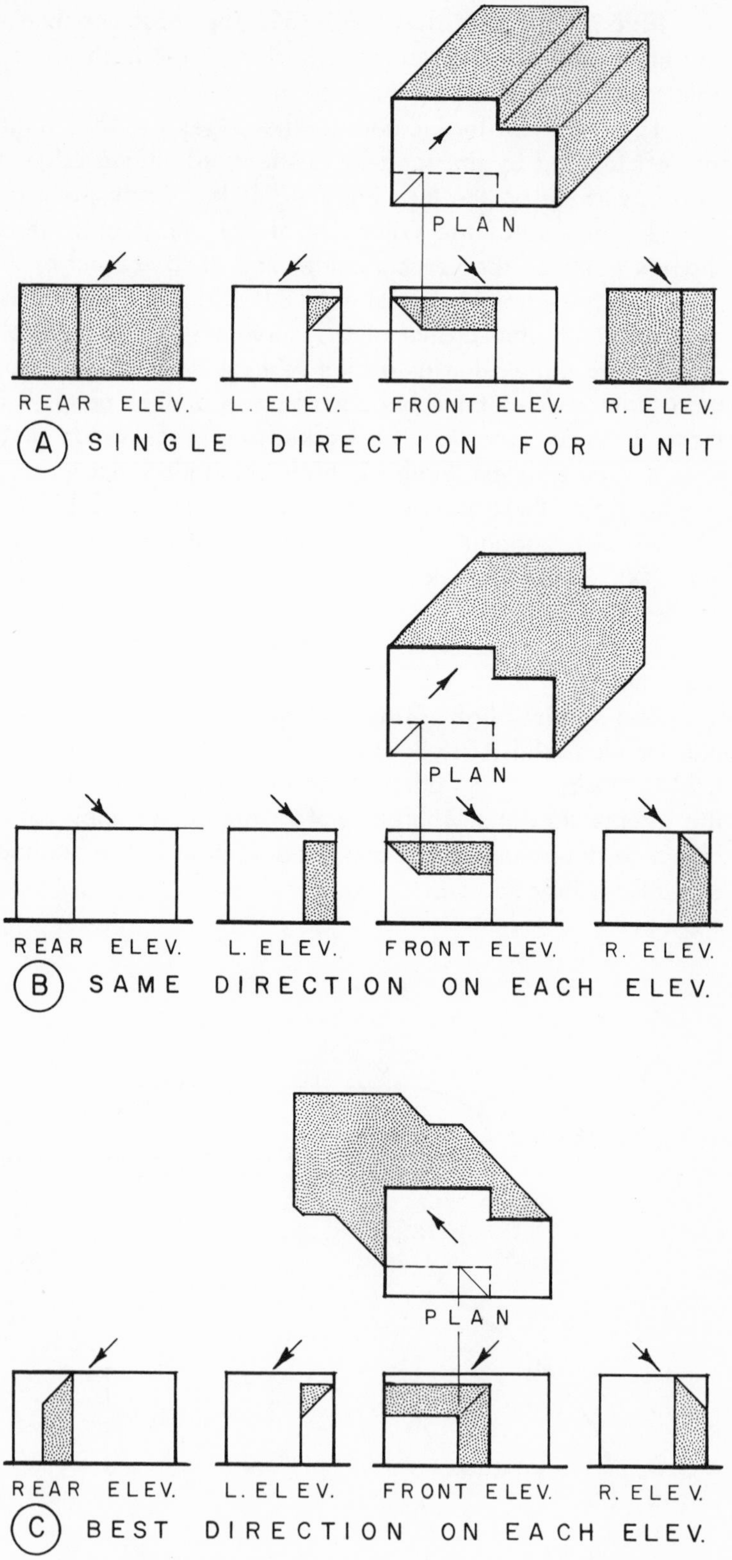

FIG. 204 LIGHT DIRECTION SYSTEMS FOR SHADOWS ON SEVERAL VIEWS

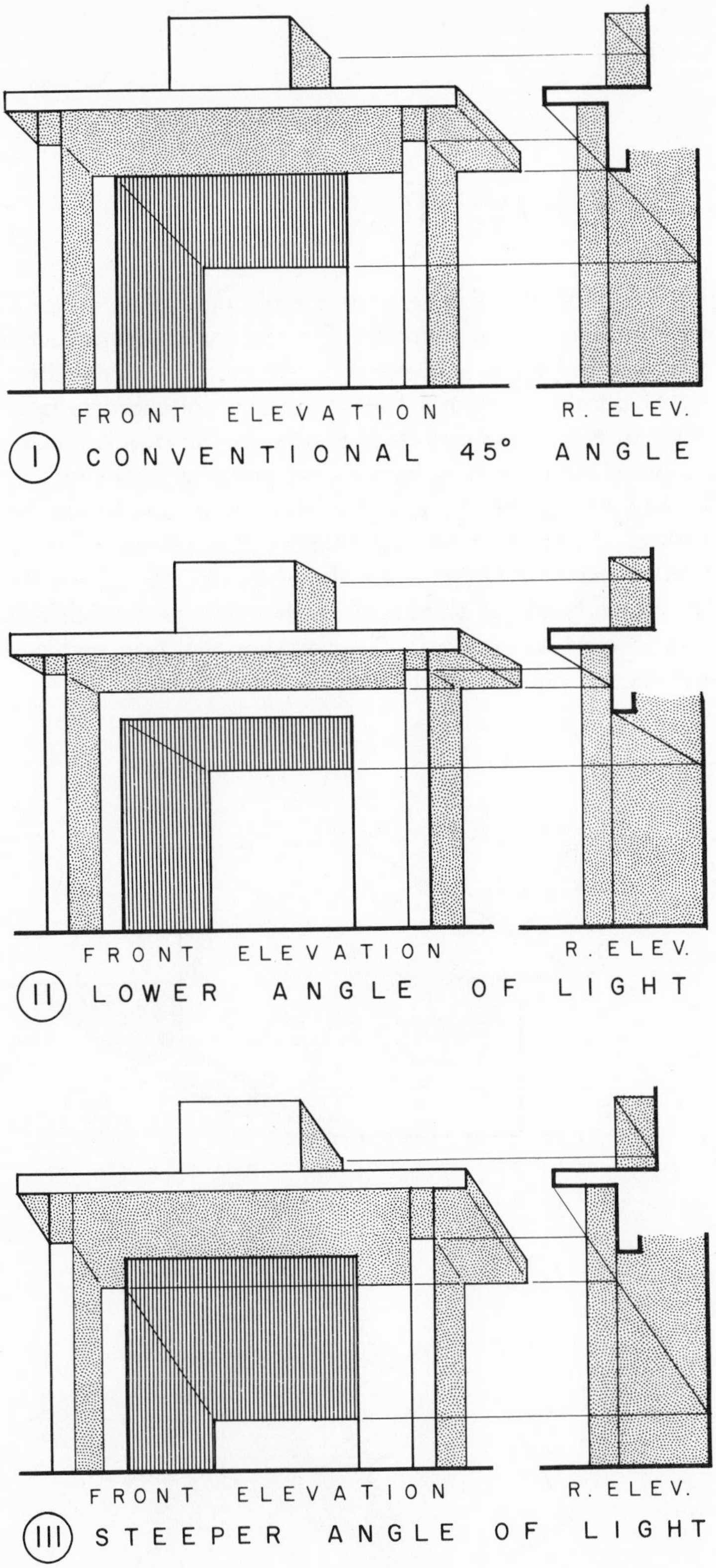

FIG. 205 SIMPLE VARIATIONS IN ELEVATION ANGLE OF LIGHT

for other reasons. The location of the object either inside or out of doors may give a constant direction of light or a limited variation of light direction, which leaves one or more sides of the object in shadow. The designer may wish to recognize this fact in his renderings and present the object as he expects it to be seen.

Shadow forms are sometimes unsatisfactory with the conventional direction of light. The shadow of an overhang may fall at a bad height. This may give a tiny shadow, one that is too large, one that coincides with the edge of another form or shadow, Fig. 205 I, or is unsatisfactory in some other way. The simplest change that can be made from the conventional direction is to use a larger (60° or 75° perhaps) or smaller (30° or 15°) angle of light than 45° on elevations, Figs. 205 II, III. If the plan angle of light remains at 45° all elevation views will have the same angle of light. This angle can be one of those suggested above which are obtained with standard triangles or any other angle desired. A constant light direction for the entire object must be assumed in working out the shadows on a single view. If the elevation direction of light is 30° and the plan direction 45° then all other elevations must have a 30° angle of light when used to construct front view shadows. When the plan angle of light is not 45° each two opposite elevations have the same light angle. Adjacent elevations have different angles of light.

A lower angle of light, one more nearly perpendicular to the walls in plan, or a combination of the two can be used to decrease shadow areas on the object. A steeper angle of light, one more nearly tangent to walls in plan, or a combination of the two variations from the conventional direction can be used to produce larger elevation shadows. These variations will help change the mood of a presentation.

CHAPTER **29**

SHADOWS ON PARALINE DRAWINGS

In addition to their value in design, paraline shadows also serve a useful purpose as an intermediate step between the study of multi-view and perspective shadows. The more easily constructed paraline drawing shadows serve as an introduction and aid to understanding three-dimensional shadows on perspective drawings. Characteristics of paraline shadows follow the general characteristics of the type of drawing used. Any parallel lines of the object and its shadows remain parallel in the drawing. The following three rules explain a great many of the shadows on paraline drawings.

1. When a line is parallel to a plane receiving the shadow, the shadow is parallel to the line. In Fig. 206 A the vertical lines cast vertical shadows on the wall planes. The horizontal overhangs make shadows parallel to the direction of the overhangs in the drawings. In Fig. 206 B the horizontal overhang edge A–B is parallel to the parts of the shadow from this line on wall at a–x and floor at x–b. The right top edge B–C and rear top edge C–D have shadows b–c and c–d parallel to them on the floor because these lines are parallel to the floor surface.

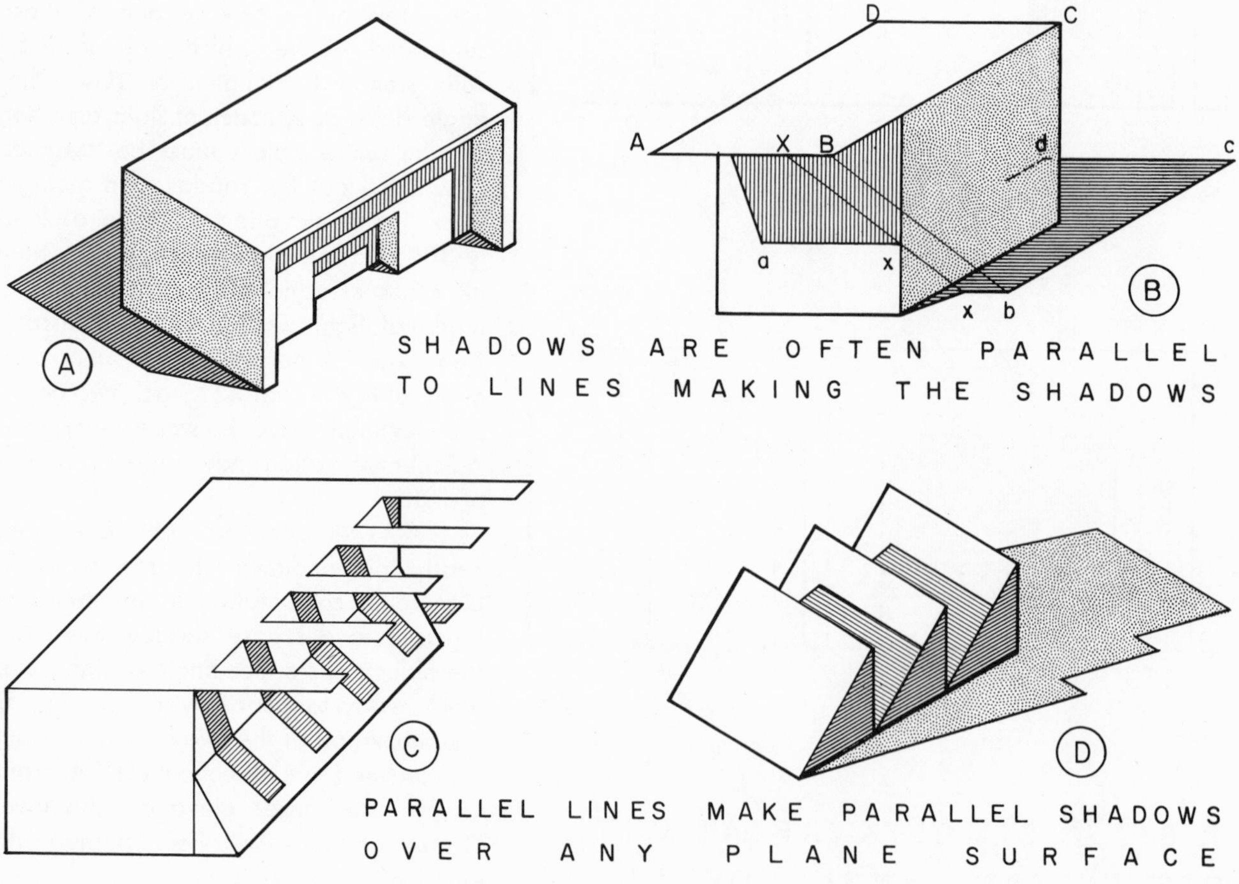

FIG. 206 SHADOWS ON PARALINE DRAWINGS

(I) SHADOWS OF PLANE FIGURES ON PARALLEL PLANES

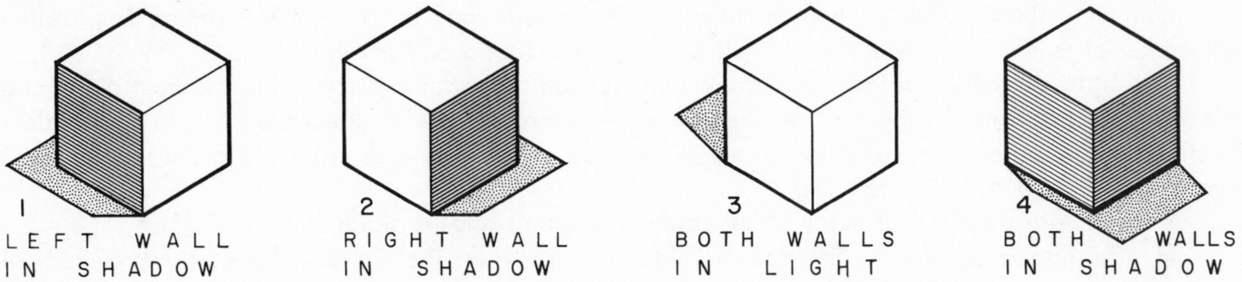

(II) FOUR BASIC PARALINE SHADOW SCHEMES

FIG. 207 SHADOWS ON PARALINE DRAWINGS

2. Parallel lines make parallel shadows on the same plane or on parallel planes. In Fig. 206 C the parallel lines projecting from the right wall plane make parallel shadows on that plane. The continuation of their shadows on the slanting surface and on the floor are also parallel to each other. The top edges of the triangular horizontal prisms cast parallel shadows on the adjoining prisms and on the floor, Fig. 206 D. The slanting right edges also make parallel shadows on the floor.

3. When a plane figure casts a shadow on a plane parallel to the figure, the drawings of the figure and its shadow are identical, Fig. 207 I. This fact is useful not only for shadows of plane figures but for shapes cut by planes parallel to the surface receiving the shadow as a method of shadow construction as shown in Fig. 207 I, right illustration.

The basic shadow schemes for paraline drawings are designated by the light and shadow conditions of the two visible wall planes and one horizontal plane of the outside of a box shape. When a wall is in light it may have shadow areas over a part of its surface from projections or from sunken areas. When a wall plane is in shadow its surface and all surfaces parallel to it are completely in shadow. These are the basic shadow schemes for paraline drawings, Fig. 207 II.

1. Left wall in shadow with the right wall and top in light.
2. Right wall in shadow with the left wall and top in light.
3. Both walls in light with the top in light also. The direction of light may give larger shadows from projections on one wall than on the other.
4. Both walls in shadow. The light may strike the top and make shadows of projections there. The shadow of the object will extend onto the floor plane in front of the object and be a prominent part of the composition.

The direction of light for paraline shadows can be chosen to give the best effect on the drawing. The simple and obvious procedure would be to use the conventional direction of light that is used on multi-view drawings. This direction is never satisfactory on isometric drawings. With both walls in light there are no visible shadows from projections and no visible shadows on the floor. All shadows are completely concealed by the object. When one wall is in shadow the horizontal tops of projections conceal their shadows on the wall which is in light. The conventional direction of light is satisfactory for some other paraline drawings.

The most satisfactory procedure is to choose a suitable direction of light for each paraline drawing. The direction should be chosen to give the best effect on that drawing. This can usually be done by choosing a direction which will give a good effect in some one main shadow area.

PARALINE SHADOW METHODS. Shadow construction on paraline drawings can be done by two methods. The shadows can first be worked out on the three multi-view drawings, which show the areas of the paraline drawing. They can then be transferred to the paraline drawing. Because the conventional direction may not give satisfactory results this may be more complicated than standard multi-view shadow construction. Furthermore the results may be difficult to predict. Duplication of work makes the theoretically easy task become rather long and involved.

The light direction method of shadow construction on paraline drawings is the most direct and most satisfactory one. In this method there are four standard useful directions of light for shadow casting on any paraline drawing. An example of each of these four directions is given on the large block of Fig. 208 C. They are

L The true direction of light, which connects a point and its shadow.

H The horizontal or plan direction of light, which provides the direction for shadows of vertical lines on areas representing horizontal surfaces of the paraline drawing.

RW The right wall direction of light, which gives the direction for shadows of perpendiculars on right wall planes of the paraline drawing.

LW The left wall direction of light, which gives the direction of shadows of perpendiculars on left wall planes of the paraline drawing.

When any two of these directions are given or assumed, the remaining two can be determined. In Fig. 208 A the true direction of light L and the plan direction of light H have been assumed for the object. Direction H is made the diagonal of a plan rectangle that has its sides parallel to the horizontal lines of the paraline drawing of the object, Fig. 208 A step I. From one of the two corners of the rectangle, which are on the diagonal H, a light direction line L is drawn to meet a vertical from the other corner, which is located on the diagonal, Fig. 208 A step II. This point establishes the height of the light direction prism, which is now completed by drawing parallels to the lines already drawn as shown in Fig. 208 A step III. The LW and RW directions are then drawn on the completed prism as shown in Fig. 208 A step IV, which gives all four of the useful light directions for this paraline drawing. The H, RW, and LW directions are the projections of the ray of light A–B (which is the diagonal of the light prism) onto the bottom, right side, and left side respectively of the light prism. These are the paraline representations of the directions that light rays appear to take in each of these views. Any two of the four light directions L, H, RW, and LW determine the proportions of the light prism and the other two directions. The actual size of the prism does not have any effect on the direction of light. When one face of the prism is drawn around the diagonal for that face the size of the prism is established. Because the face of the prism that is drawn first can be made any size, the prism can be made any size but will keep the same proportions regardless of its size. The light prism must be in the same type of paraline drawing as the object, its lines parallel to the axes of the object. This method of shadow construction works on any type of paraline drawing.

In Fig. 208 B the plan direction of light H and the right wall direction of light RW as assumed for the large block are used to construct this light prism.

In the large block shape of Fig. 208 C, LW is the assumed direction of the shadow of D–E, which is a perpendicular to the left wall plane. RW is the chosen direction of the shadow of F–G, a perpendicular to the right wall plane.

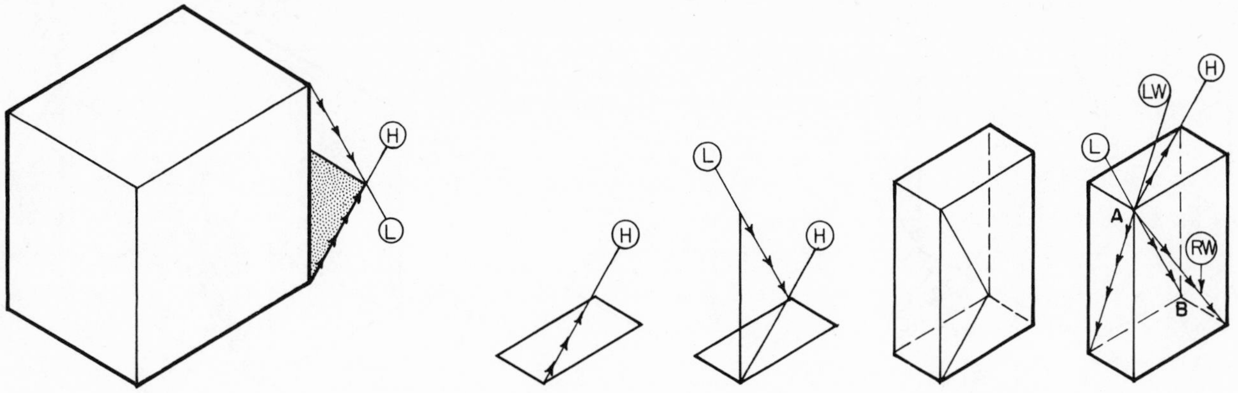

H AND L GIVEN ON OBJECT — STEP I — STEP II — STEP III — STEP IV

(A) PRISM CONSTRUCTED FROM DIRECTION H AND L

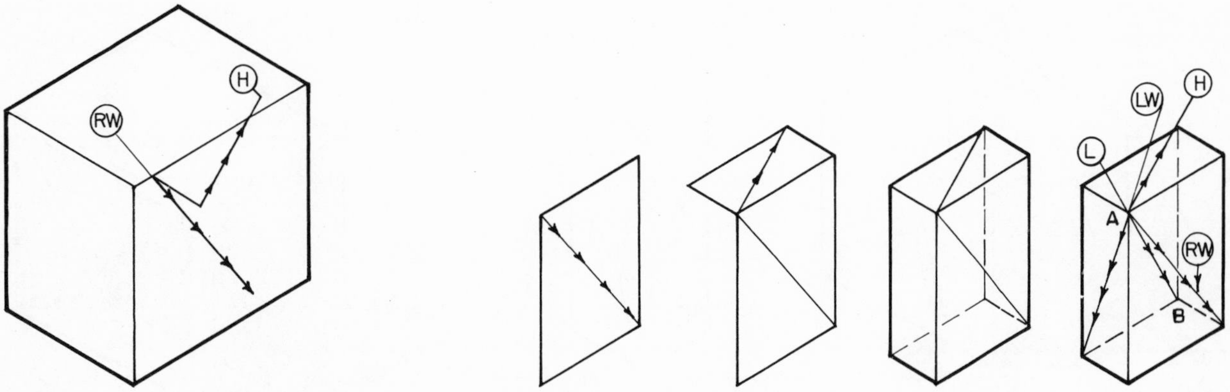

H AND RW GIVEN ON OBJECT — STEP I — STEP II — STEP III — STEP IV

(B) SAME PRISM CONSTRUCTED FROM H AND RW

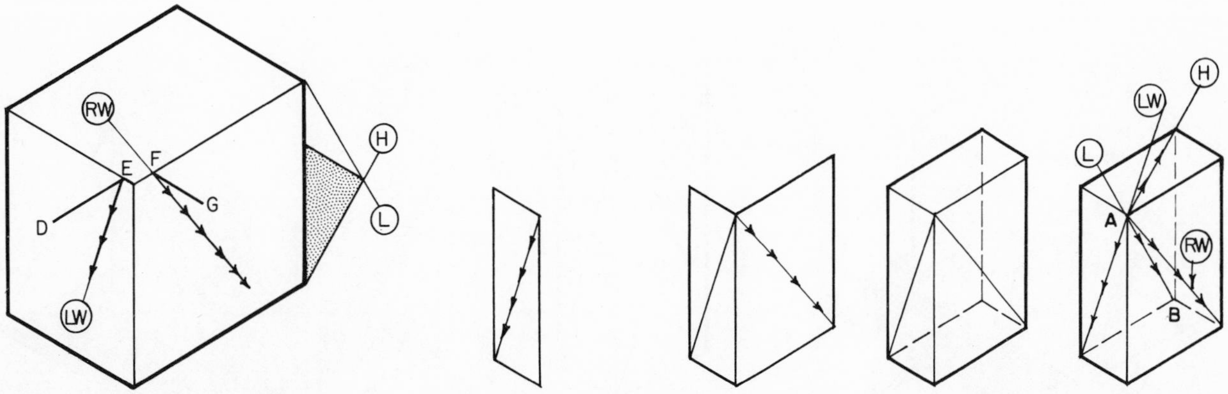

LW AND RW GIVEN ON OBJECT — STEP I — STEP II — STEP III — STEP IV

(C) SAME PRISM CONSTRUCTED FROM LW AND RW

FIG. 208 LIGHT PRISMS FOR PARALINE SHADOWS

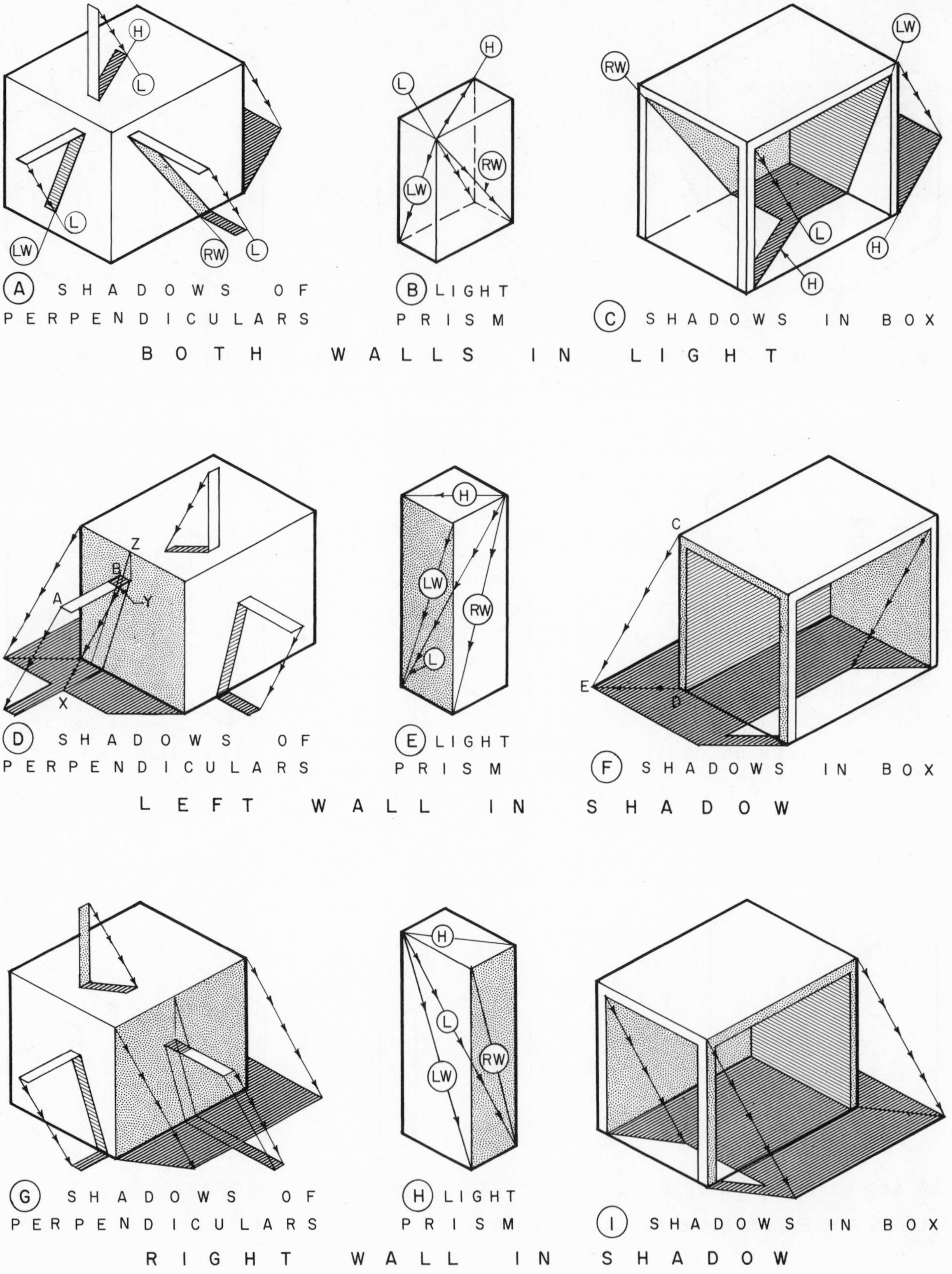

FIG. 209 USES OF THE FOUR LIGHT DIRECTIONS

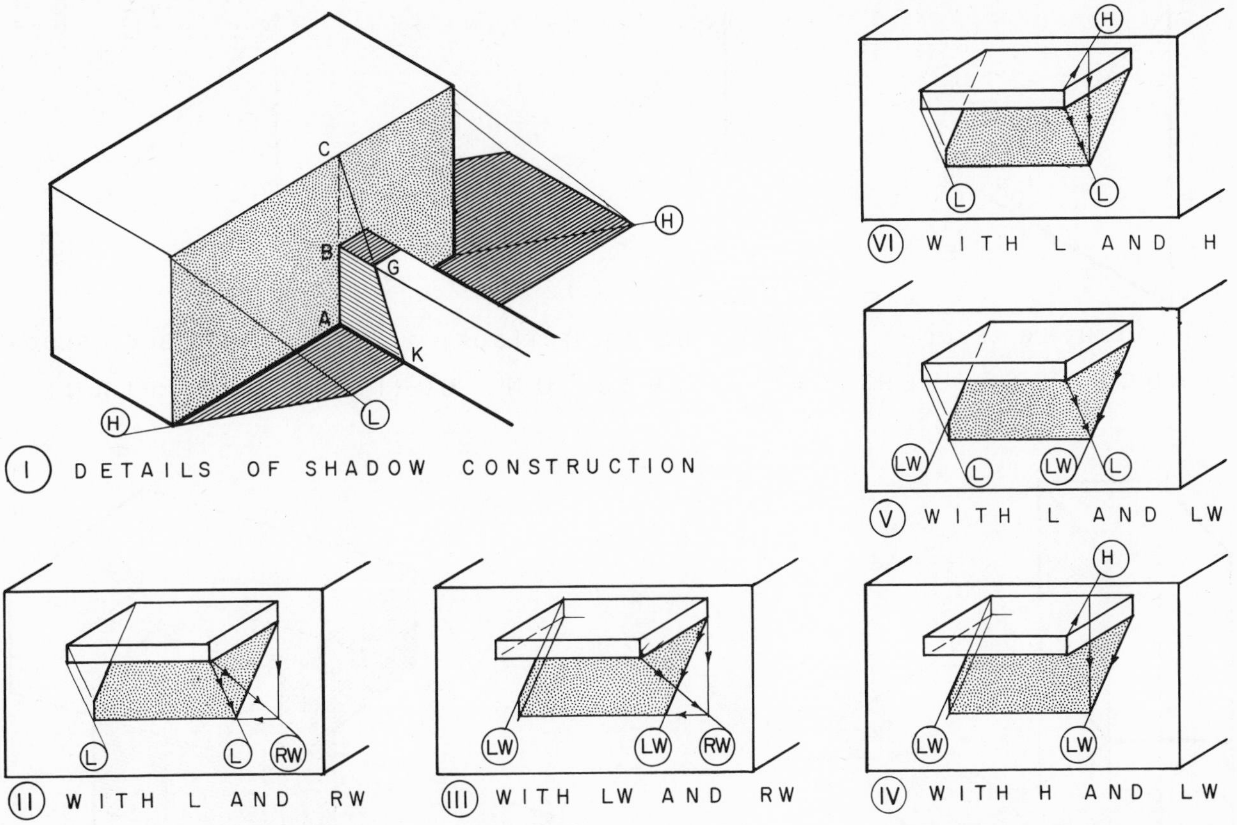

FIVE DIFFERENT CONSTRUCTIONS FOR SAME SHADOW

FIG. 210 CONSTRUCTION OF PARALINE SHADOWS

In Fig. 209 A the shadows of the perpendiculars to the top, right wall, and left wall are located by drawing the construction lines shown parallel to the direction lines of the prism in Fig. 209 B. Shadows are constructed in the hollow box of Fig. 209 C with the same directions. Different shadow effects can be obtained by using different directions for light as shown in Figs. 209 D, E, F, and G, H, I. It is often convenient to use one or more of the light directions to trace lines where there are no actual shadows. The vertical line C–D of Fig. 209 F does not cast a shadow. However its imaginary shadow D–E can be used to locate point E on the shadow outline. The line A–B does not cast a shadow on the left wall of Fig. 209 D. Nevertheless the left wall direction of light can be traced from B to the ground and then along the ground to locate the visible part of the shadow. From point X a ray of light can be traced back to determine point Y where light and shadow meet. The same point Y can be located by drawing a vertical line from the right corner of the A–B area to the top corner of the object at Z, then drawing a direction RW from Z to locate Y. There are often different constructions that will locate the same shadow point and check on accuracy.

Although it is seldom necessary to have all four of the light directions provided by the light prism construction, it is often convenient to use them. In Fig. 210 I the direction of the shadow G–K is located by extending line A–B to point C then drawing the line from K toward point C. This line C–K is the LW direction. Directions H and L are often adequate for all shadow construction for a drawing. The wall directions may provide shorter, more direct, and more accurate results.

In Figs. 210 II, III, IV, V, and VI different constructions have been shown for the same shadow. These figures will demonstrate the possible variations in construction for paraline shadows.

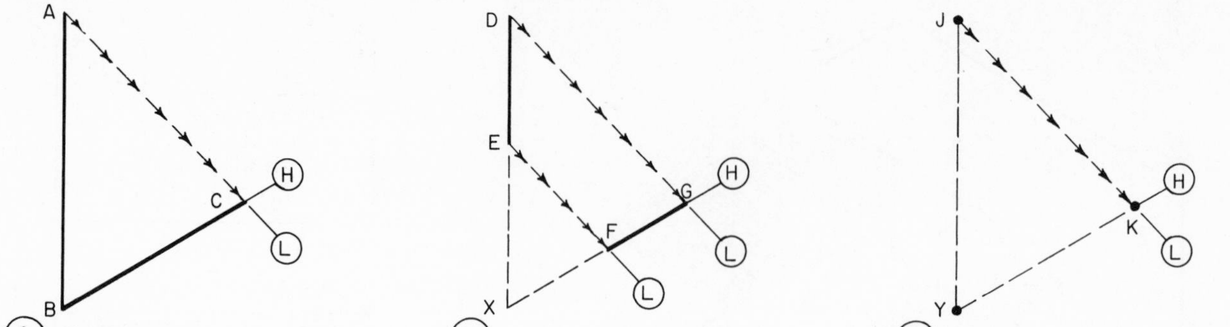

(A) TOUCHING FLOOR (B) LINE ABOVE FLOOR (C) POINT ABOVE FLOOR

SHADOWS OF VERTICAL LINES ON HORIZONTAL PLANES

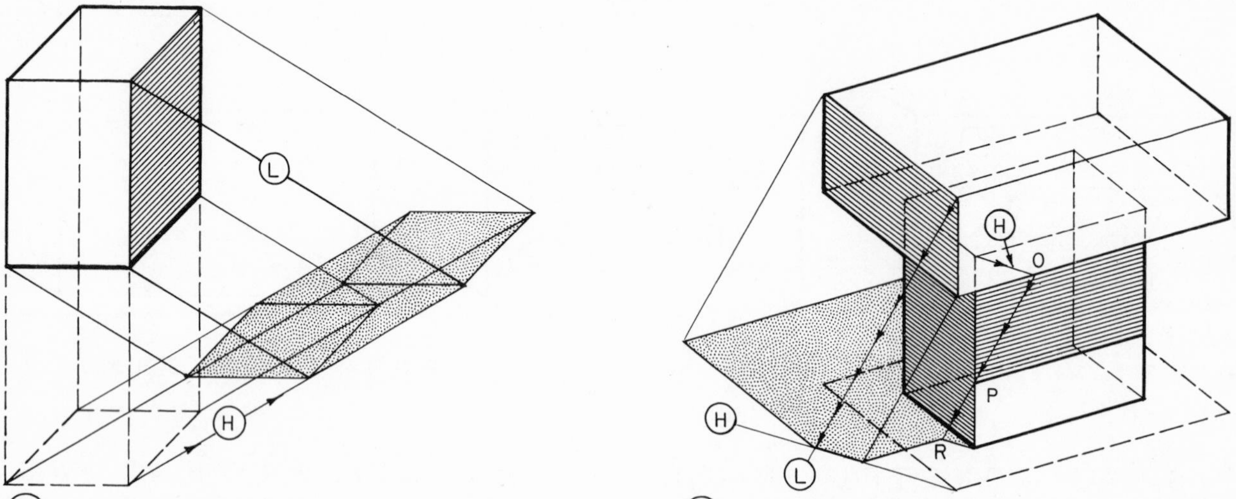

(D) SUSPENDED BLOCK (E) PROJECTING BLOCK

SHADOWS OF BLOCKS ABOVE THE FLOOR PLANE

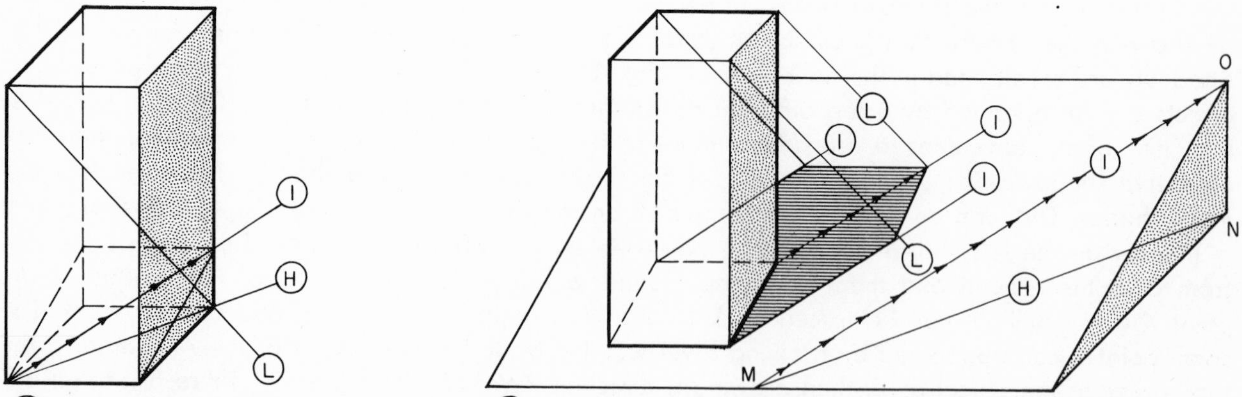

(F) LIGHT PRISM (G) SHADOW ON INCLINED PLANE

SHADOWS OF VERTICAL LINES ON INCLINED PLANE

FIG. 211 CONSTRUCTION OF PARALINE SHADOWS

Shadows of vertical lines on the horizontal planes occur in the shadows of most objects. In Fig. 211 A the shadow of a vertical line A–B extends from the point B where it touches the horizontal plane. The direction of this shadow is the plan or H direction of light. The shadow ends where a light ray L from the top A of the line intersects with the shadow at C. B–C is the shadow of A–B.

When the vertical line D–E is suspended above the horizontal plane on which the shadow falls its extension to point X on this plane must be located, Fig. 211 B. Light ray lines L are then drawn from each end D and E of the line to meet the plan shadow direction line H from X and locate F–G the required shadow.

To find the shadow on a horizontal plane of any point J, a similar construction is used, Fig. 211 C. A vertical line J–Y is drawn from J to meet the horizontal plane at Y. The plan shadow direction line H from Y meets the light ray line L from J at K the required shadow of point J.

This system of locating shadows of vertical lines and points with any chosen plan direction H of light and direction L of light rays can be used to find shadows of areas and solids. In Fig. 211 D a rectangular solid with vertical corners is located above the floor plane on which the shadow falls. Each vertical corner casts a shadow similar to the one of the line in Fig. 211 B. The shadows of the corners are connected to make the shadow area. It should be observed also that the shadows of the top and bottom of the box shape are identical with the shapes of the top and bottom of the object. After one point on each is located these shadows of the top and bottom may be drawn in as directly as possible. These shapes are then connected by tangents to complete the shadow outline. Plane figures parallel to the plane receiving the shadows have shadows identical with the figures.

In Fig. 211 E a large block is supported by a smaller block. The H direction is traced on the concealed surface of the overhang to locate a point O, which casts its shadow at P and also at R.

Shadows of verticals on an inclined plane appear to be difficult. One method of locating these shadows requires the use of an auxiliary inclined plane in the light prism, Fig. 211 F. If this plane exactly parallels the inclined plane of the object the light direction I on the plane in the prism will be the correct direction for the shadows of vertical lines on the inclined plane of the object. The I direction can also be found on the object as shown by triangle M–N–O of Fig. 211 G.

Shadows of circular objects can usually be located by the point method. The H and L light directions are used to locate points on the shadows in the examples of Fig. 212. In number I the top and its shadow on the floor are the same shape.

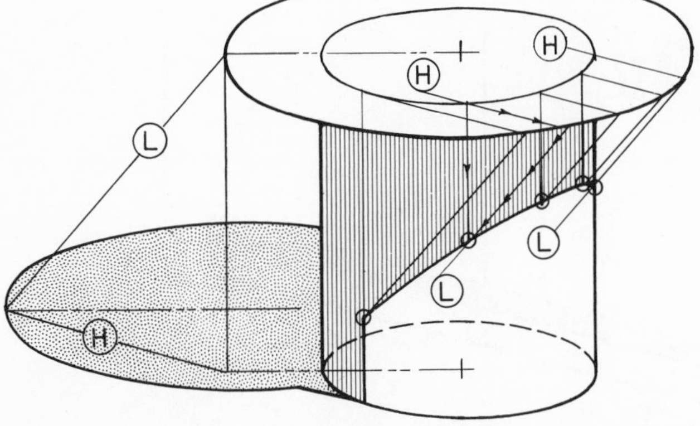

(I) SHADOW FROM CIRCLE ONTO CONCENTRIC CYLINDER

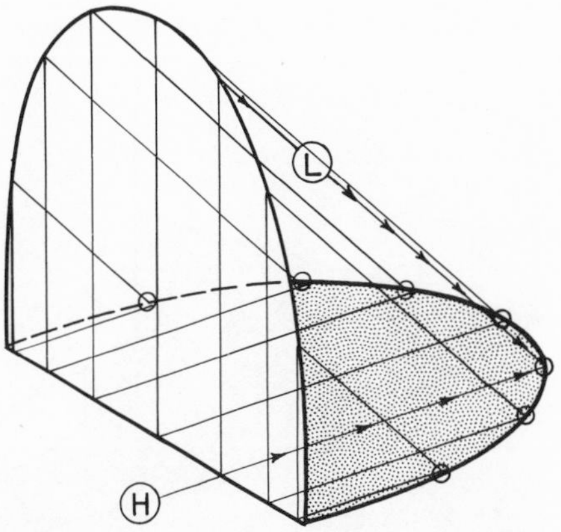

(II) SHADOW ON FLOOR FROM VERTICAL CURVE

FIG. 212 SHADOWS OF CIRCULAR OBJECTS

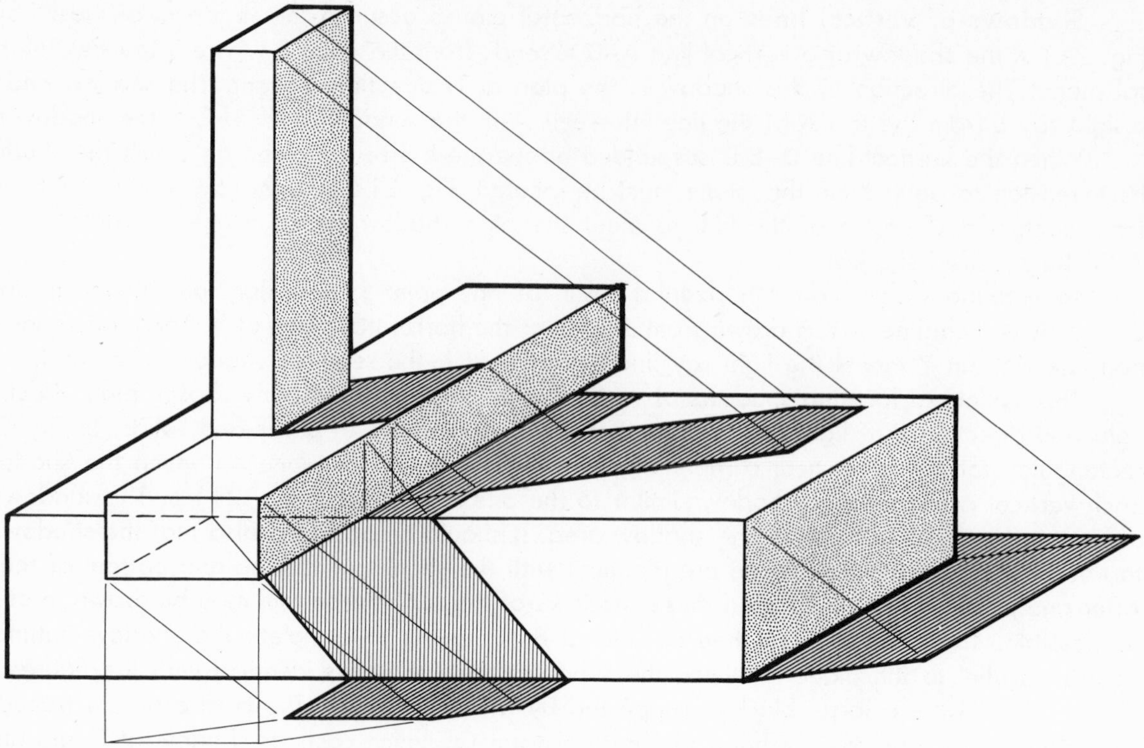

SHADOWS OF BLOCK FORMS

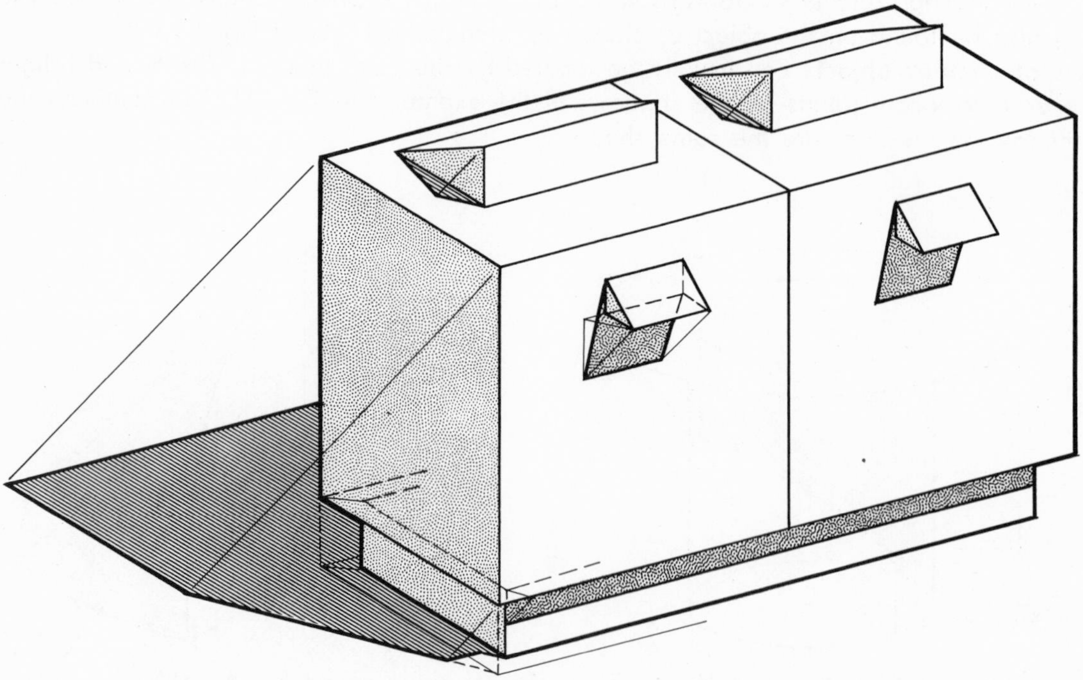

SHADOWS OF AN APPLIANCE

FIG. 213 EXAMPLES OF PARALINE SHADOWS

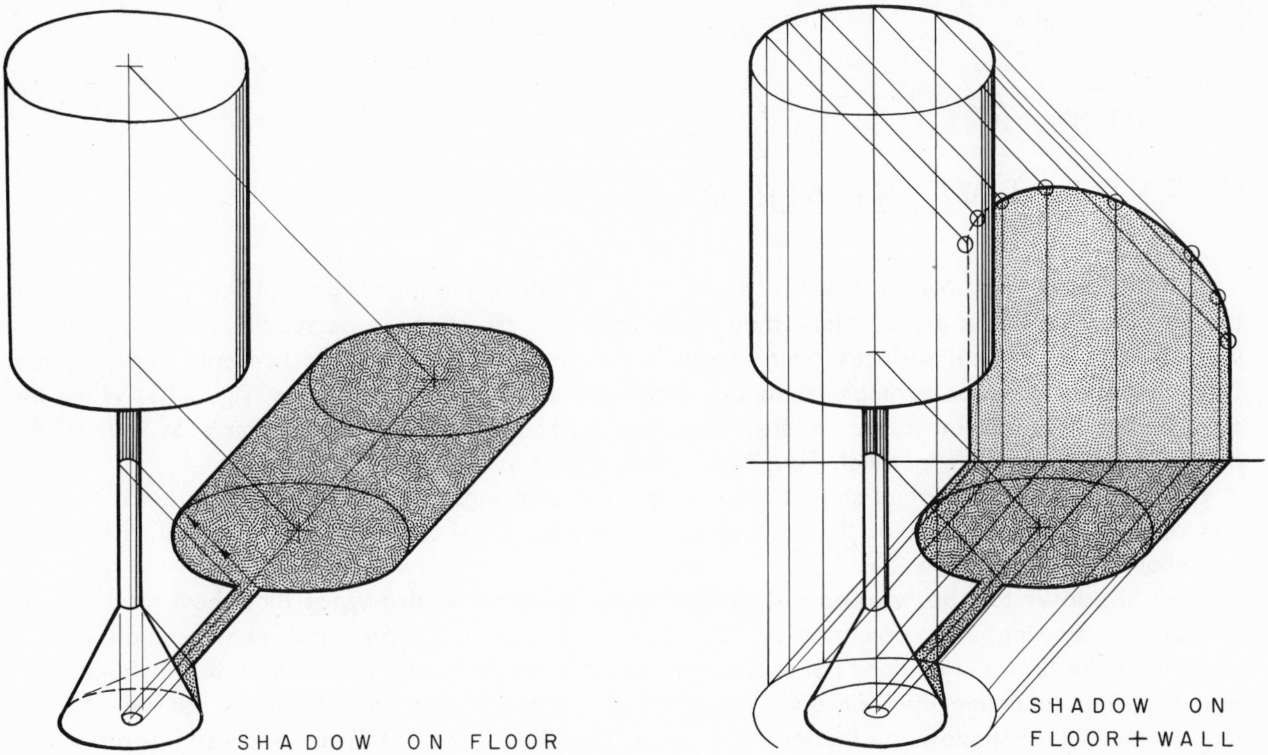

SHADOWS OF A LAMP SHAPE

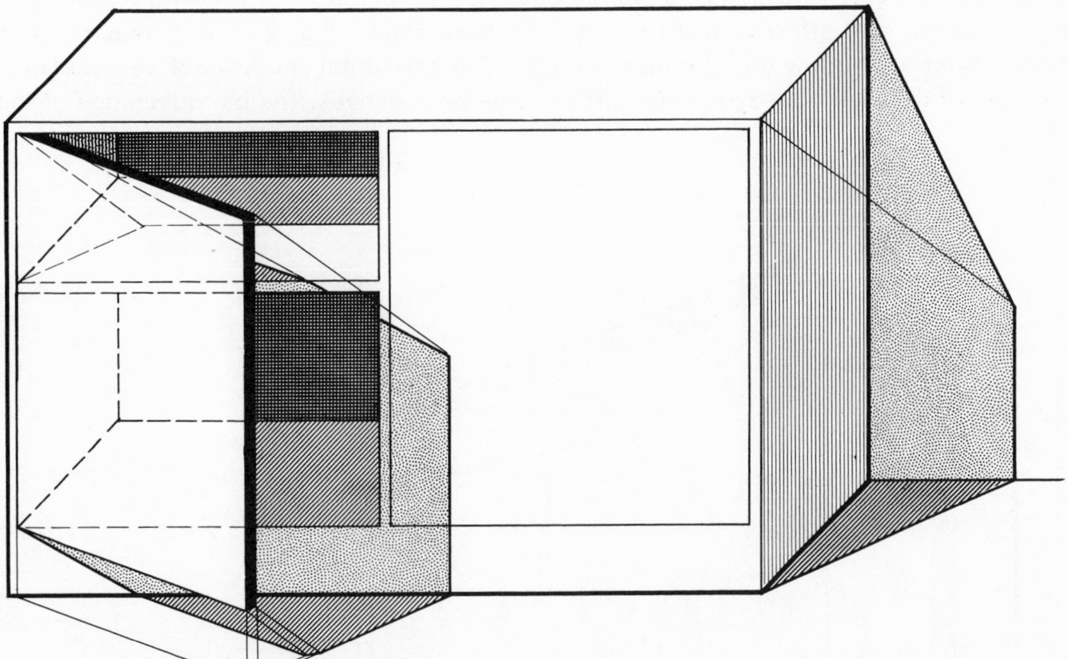

SHADOWS OF A CABINET

FIG. 214 EXAMPLES OF PARALINE SHADOWS

CHAPTER 30

PERSPECTIVE SHADOW METHODS

The shadow lines of a perspective drawing are a part of the line system of the drawing. When they are parallel to the picture plane they retain their true directions in perspective. The shadows of vertical lines on vertical surfaces remain vertical in standard one-point and two-point perspectives. This is the most common example of shadow lines parallel to the picture plane, Fig. 215. When the shadow lines are oblique to the picture plane they go to the same vanishing points as lines of the object to which they are parallel, Fig. 215.

Three methods of casting shadows on perspective drawings are described briefly here. The last two of these are variations of the light direction method. They are explained in detail in the next two chapters.

1. Shadows can be worked out on the three multi-view drawings that show areas of the perspective drawing. They can then be drawn in the perspective from their measurements just as other lines are drawn. This does not require any new theory. It does require shadow construction on four drawings to obtain them on one. When the conventional direction of light is not satisfactory, the construction of shadows on the three multi-view drawings is more difficult. Because this procedure is a repetition of multi-view shadows and perspective that have been described previously, no further explanation is given.

2. The light direction method of perspective shadows with light rays parallel to the picture plane makes the constructing of shadows directly on a perspective drawing relatively easy. This method is a simple and effective one for two-point perspective, Fig. 216 A. It requires that one set of wall planes be in shadow and the other in light. The horizontal shadows of vertical lines that are characteristic of this method may appear stiff on some perspectives. The big advantage of the method

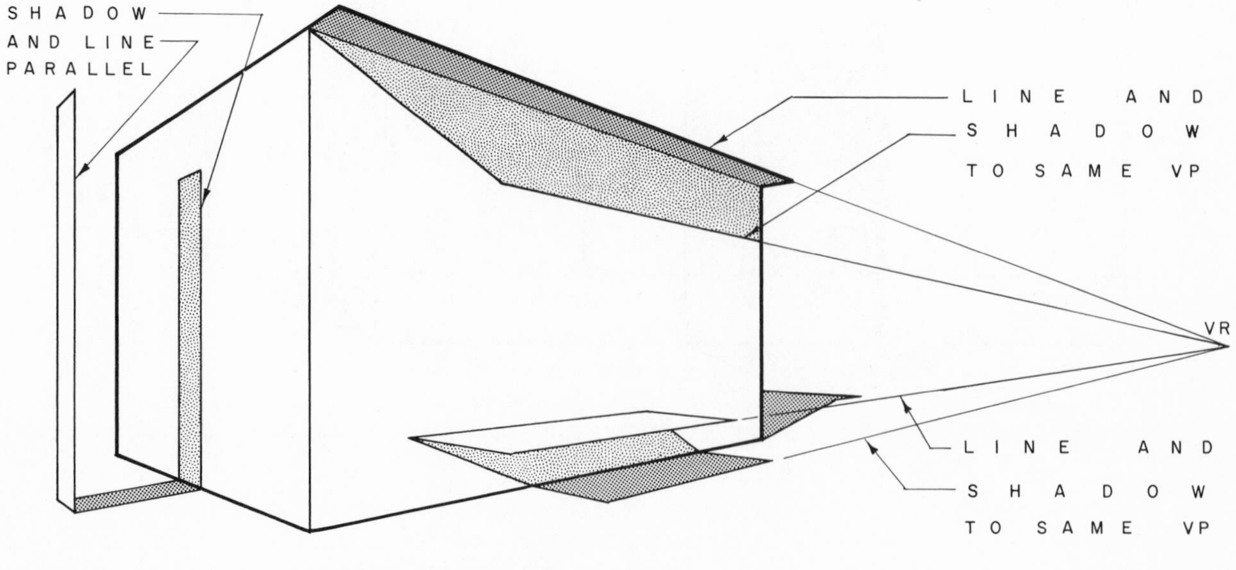

FIG. 215 CHARACTERISTICS OF PERSPECTIVE SHADOWS

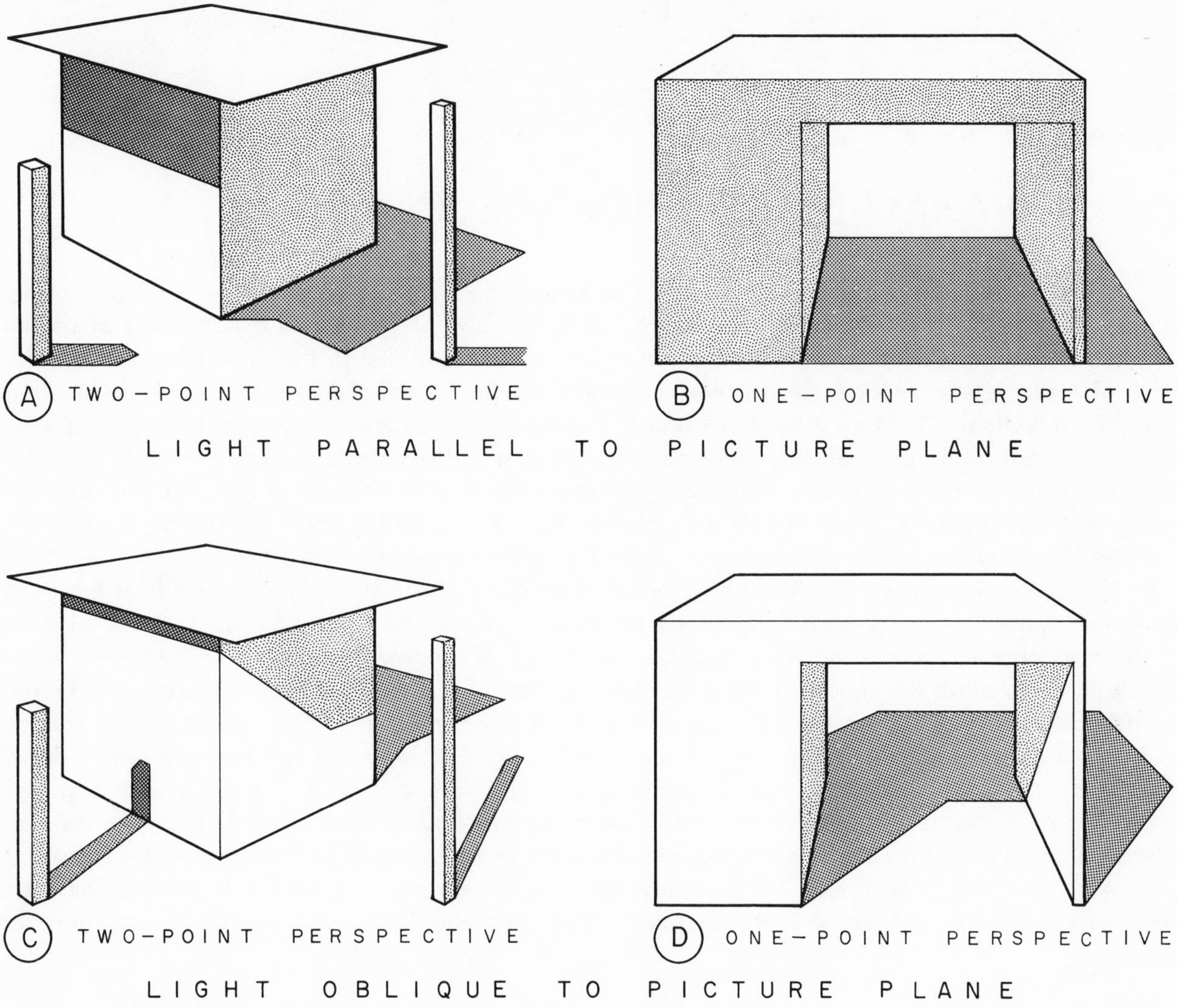

FIG. 216 PERSPECTIVE SHADOW METHODS

is the use of two sets of parallel lines that remain parallel in perspective for construction purposes. The rays of light L are one of these sets of parallel lines and the plan direction of light H the other. They are adequate for all shadow construction. The parallel lines for the other two light directions LW and RW are oblique to the picture plane and will be drawn to their respective vanishing points in perspective. They are sometimes useful for shadow construction.

This method is not satisfactory for one-point perspectives since light parallels one set of wall planes and produces artificial effects with too much shadow area, Fig. 216 B.

3. The light direction method with light rays oblique to picture plane requires a vanishing point for each of the four useful light directions, L, H, LW, and RW that are used for the shadow construction. Points L and H can be located at random with minor restrictions as to their positions. They are usually adequate for shadow construction. Because light in almost any direction can be used for the shadows of a perspective drawing by this method, any lighting condition can be represented. Shadows of verticals can be any direction on horizontal planes thus avoiding the stiff effect of horizontal shadows. This method works equally well on both two-point and one-point perspectives, Figs. 216 C and D. It is a very satisfactory method for good shadow effects.

CHAPTER 31

LIGHT PARALLEL TO PICTURE PLANE

A method using parallel construction lines to locate shadows on two-point perspective drawings is provided by light rays parallel to the picture plane. The rays of light L and the shadows of vertical lines on horizontal planes H (plan direction of light) are both parallel to the picture plane Fig. 217. Both of these sets of shadow construction lines remain actually parallel in the perspective drawing. The plan direction of light must be horizontal in this system. The rays of light can be at any desired angle but must all be parallel. It is convenient to use one of the standard angles given by common triangles when they will provide a satisfactory shadow effect on the object. If 30°, 45°, or 60° will not give suitable results, an adjustable triangle can be set to a better angle for the purpose, or the parallel lines can be drawn at the chosen angle by methods previously explained.

When the two sets of parallel light direction lines L and H are the only ones used for the shadows, this system is one of locating shadows of vertical lines on horizontal surfaces. Some of these H shadow construction lines may be actual boundary lines of shadow areas, others may merely locate points through which the shadow lines are drawn. In Fig. 217 A, vertical line A–B casts an H direction shadow line B–C. Vertical line D–E does not cast a shadow but its H direction imaginary shadow E–F may be used to locate point F on the shadow outline. C–F is drawn to VR and a line is drawn from F to VL to continue the visible shadow outline. The rays of light L connect points and their shadows. An L line is not used for the direction of actual shadow lines. The H lines give the plan direction of light and are the shadows of vertical lines of the perspective on horizontal planes.

A vertical line G–H of Fig. 217 B is suspended above the plane on which its shadow falls. It is necessary to find point I where G–H extended would meet the floor plane in order to construct the

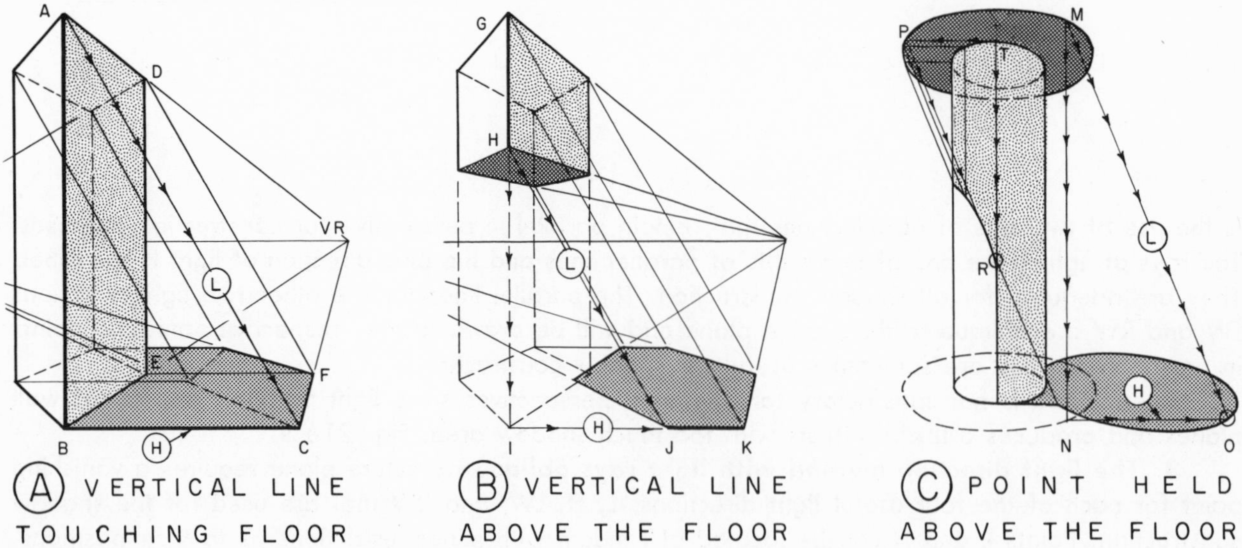

(A) VERTICAL LINE TOUCHING FLOOR

(B) VERTICAL LINE ABOVE THE FLOOR

(C) POINT HELD ABOVE THE FLOOR

FIG. 217 BASIC SHADOW CONSTRUCTION METHOD

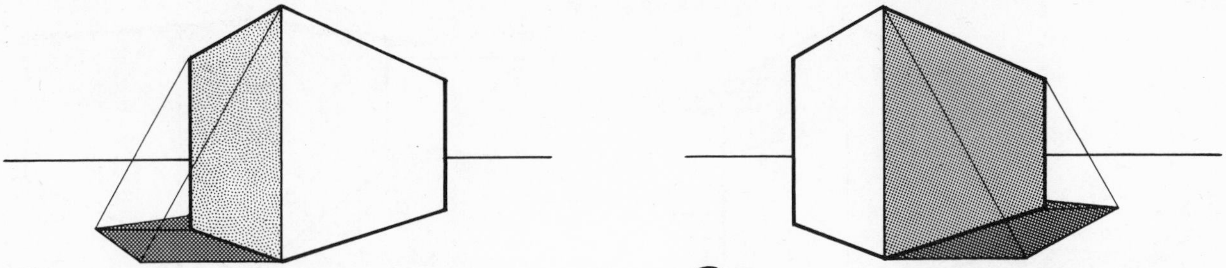

(I) LEFT SIDE IN SHADOW (II) RIGHT SIDE IN SHADOW

ONLY TWO SHADOW SCHEMES ARE POSSIBLE

shadow J–K of this line. The same is true of any form which is above the horizontal plane receiving its shadow. The box shape in Fig. 217 B and the large circle of Fig. 217 C are both projected vertically onto the horizontal or floor plane receiving their shadows. The projection of point M of Fig. 217 C is at N on the floor plane and its shadow is at O.

Line P–T is an example of tracing a plan light direction line that is not a shadow line in order to locate a shadow. The shadow of point P is located on the vertical below T where the L line from P intersects it at R. A series of constructions like P–T–R can be used to locate any number of points on the shadow of the large circle on the vertical cylinder.

Limitations of shadow effects secured with light parallel to the picture plane are a disadvantage of this system. (A) Horizontal shadows of vertical lines may give a stiff and unnatural effect. (B) One set of wall planes must be in shadow and the other in light. They cannot both be in light, Figs. 218 I and II. (C) Change of direction of light rays L has no effect on size of vertical shadows which remain constant. When the shadow areas of overhangs are increased by using a steeper angle of light the shadow of the object on the ground plane becomes shorter. With a lower angle of light the overhang shadows decrease and the shadow of the object lengthens, Figs. 218 III, IV, and V.

Nevertheless this method is often entirely satisfactory. It is the easiest direct method of locating shadows on two-point perspective drawings. A clear understanding of its scope and limitations will help the delineator to use it effectively.

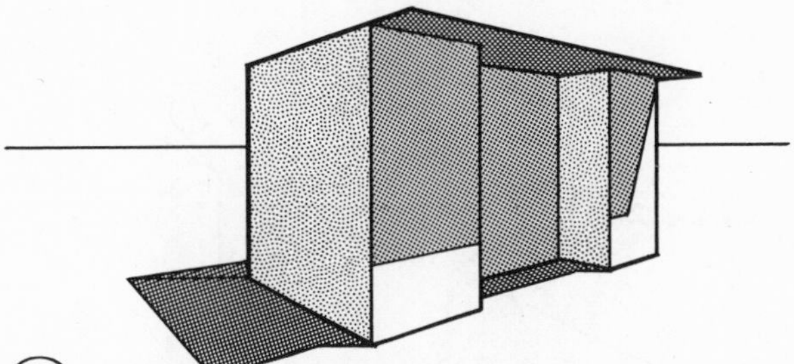

(III) STEEP ANGLE OF LIGHT

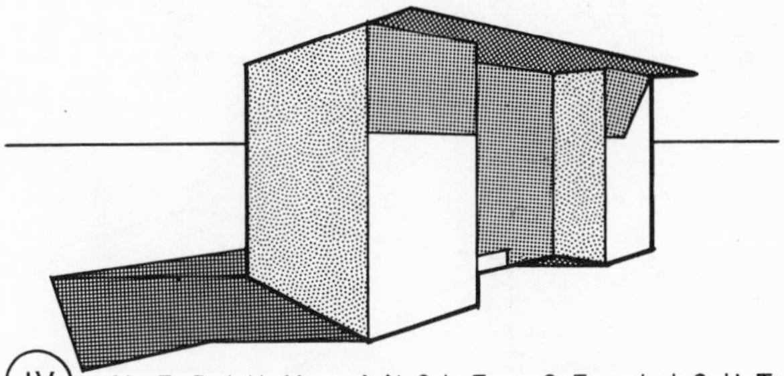

(IV) MEDIUM ANGLE OF LIGHT

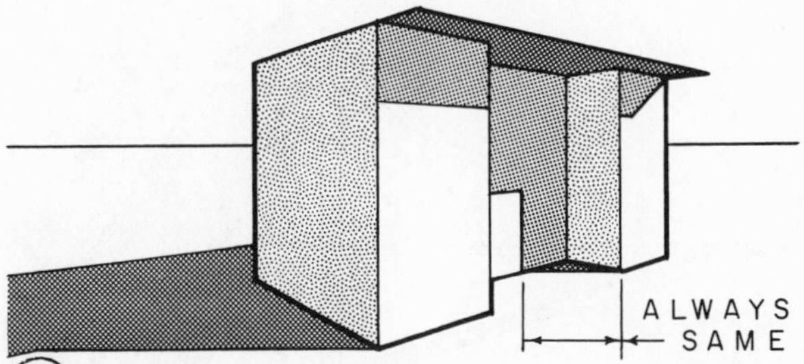

(V) LOW ANGLE OF LIGHT

ANY ANGLE OF LIGHT CAN BE USED TO LEFT OR RIGHT

FIG. 218 SHADOW VARIATIONS LIGHT PARALLEL TO PICT. PL.

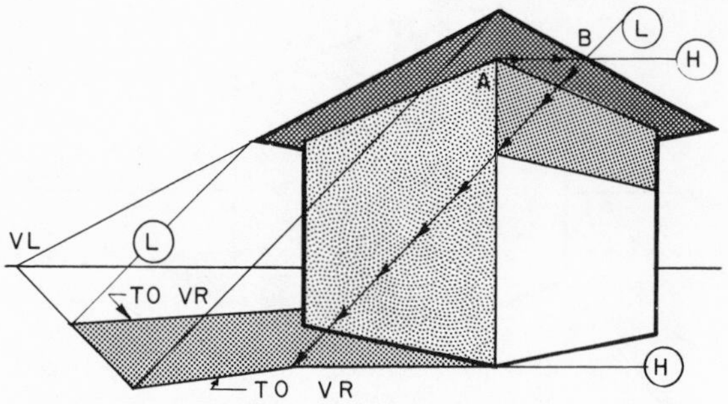

Ⓐ SHADOW CONSTRUCTION ON BOTTOM OF OVERHANG

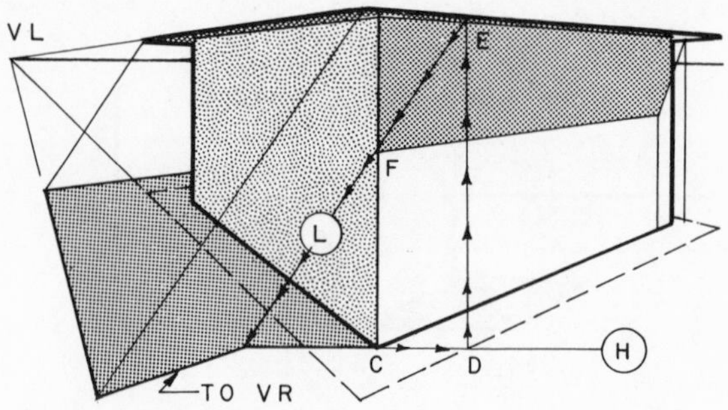

Ⓑ SHADOW CONSTRUCTION PROJECTED TO GROUND

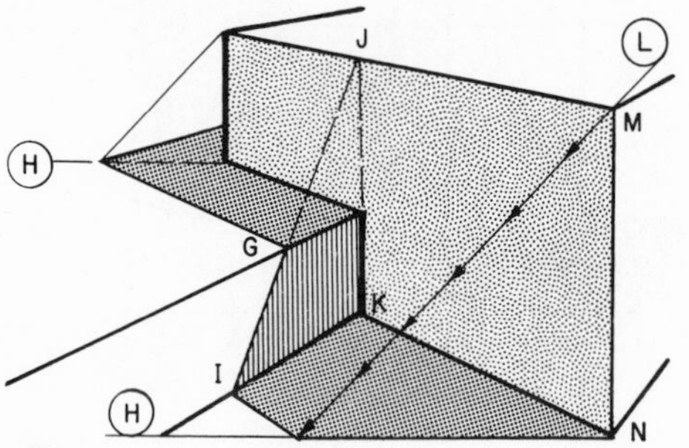

Ⓒ SHADOW OVER A SIMPLE OFFSET

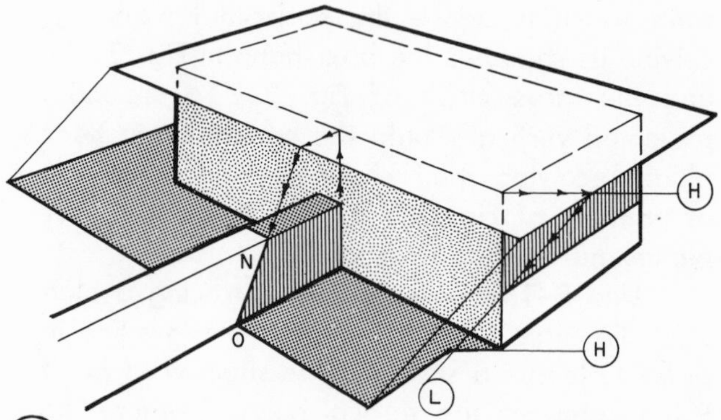

Ⓓ SHADOW CONSTRUCTION ON CONCEALED OVERHANG

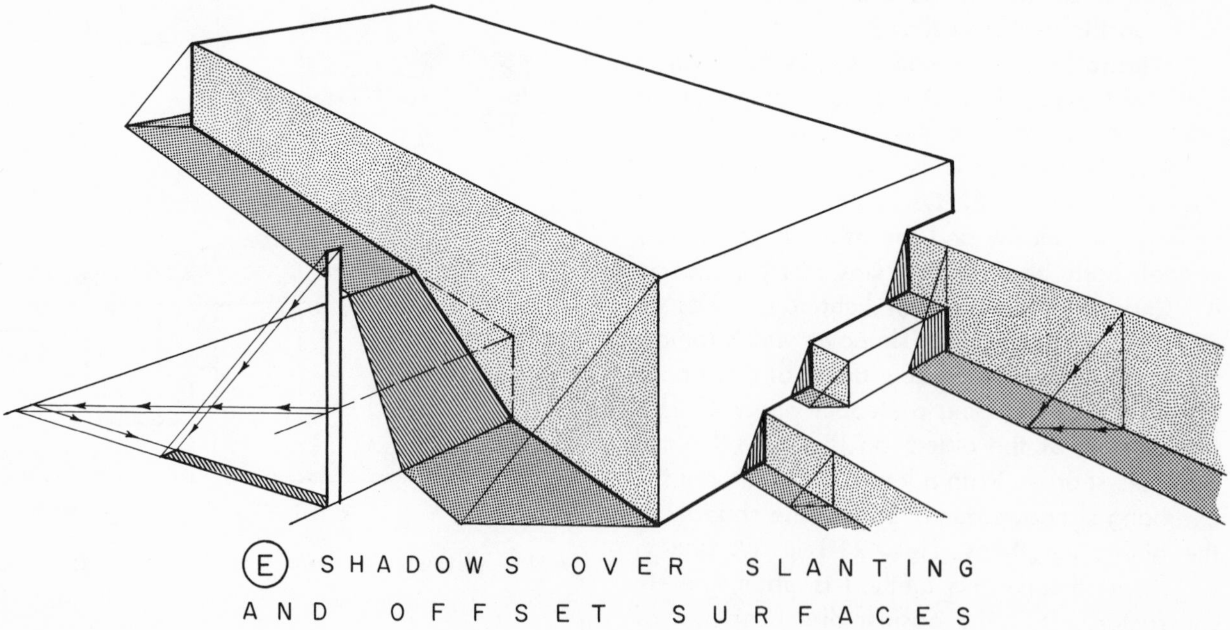

Ⓔ SHADOWS OVER SLANTING AND OFFSET SURFACES

FIG. 219 SHADOW CONSTRUCTION WITH L AND H LIGHT DIRECTIONS

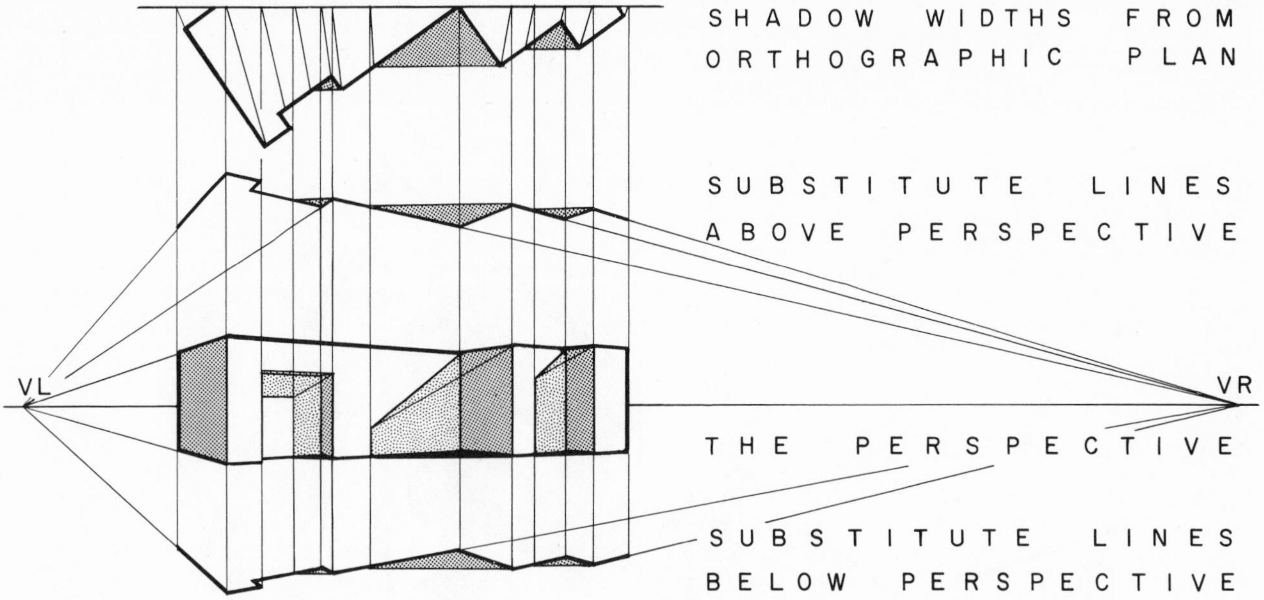

FIG. 220 SUBSTITUTE LINES FOR ACCURACY IN DETERMINING WIDTHS OF SHADOWS

Although shadow construction in two-point perspective is relatively simple with light parallel to the picture plane, it does often require a great deal of ingenuity in working out the shadows. In Figs. 219 A, B, and D the shadow of the overhang has been constructed on different surfaces of the drawings. In Fig. 219 A the bottom surface of the overhang is a visible and adequately large area for this construction with line A–B in the plan direction of light H. In Fig. 219 B the bottom surface of the overhang is too thin and its lines too nearly horizontal for accurate construction with a horizontal line. The projection of the overhang on the ground plane provides an adequate representation of the overhang for construction of the shadow. Line C–D is drawn on this surface and a vertical line from D locates point E. A light ray from E locates the shadow F of point E on the nearest vertical corner of the walls. The shadow of the overhang is drawn from F to VR. In the perspective view from above in Fig. 219 D the concealed surface of the overhang is used for the shadow construction.

Figs. 219 C and E provide examples of constructions of other types of shadows. In Fig. 219 C the shadow line G–I from the top left edge J–M of the large block on the vertical surface of the lower block is constructed in two ways on the example. (1) The shadow of the long vertical corner M–N can be used to locate the shadow on the lower horizontal surface and find point I. The shadow construction from the left vertical corner on the middle horizontal surface locates point G. Then line G–I is drawn. (2) The second method of locating G–I may be more accurate, especially when the vertical surface on which G–I is located is small. After point I is located, the vertical wall above I is assumed to extend to point J. Then the line J–M will cast a shadow J–I of which G–I is a part.

Accuracy in casting shadows directly on a perspective drawing depends on having adequate representations of horizontal lines and areas on which to work out the shadows. When the horizontal lines and areas in a part of a perspective drawing are too horizontal and thin the method of a substitute area on the ground plane used in Fig. 219 B can be extended to areas above or below the perspective. In Fig. 220 neither the tops nor the bottoms of walls provide sufficiently definite forms for shadow construction. When their lines are drawn either above or below the perspective better results are obtained. The orthographic plan can also be used for shadow widths, Fig. 220.

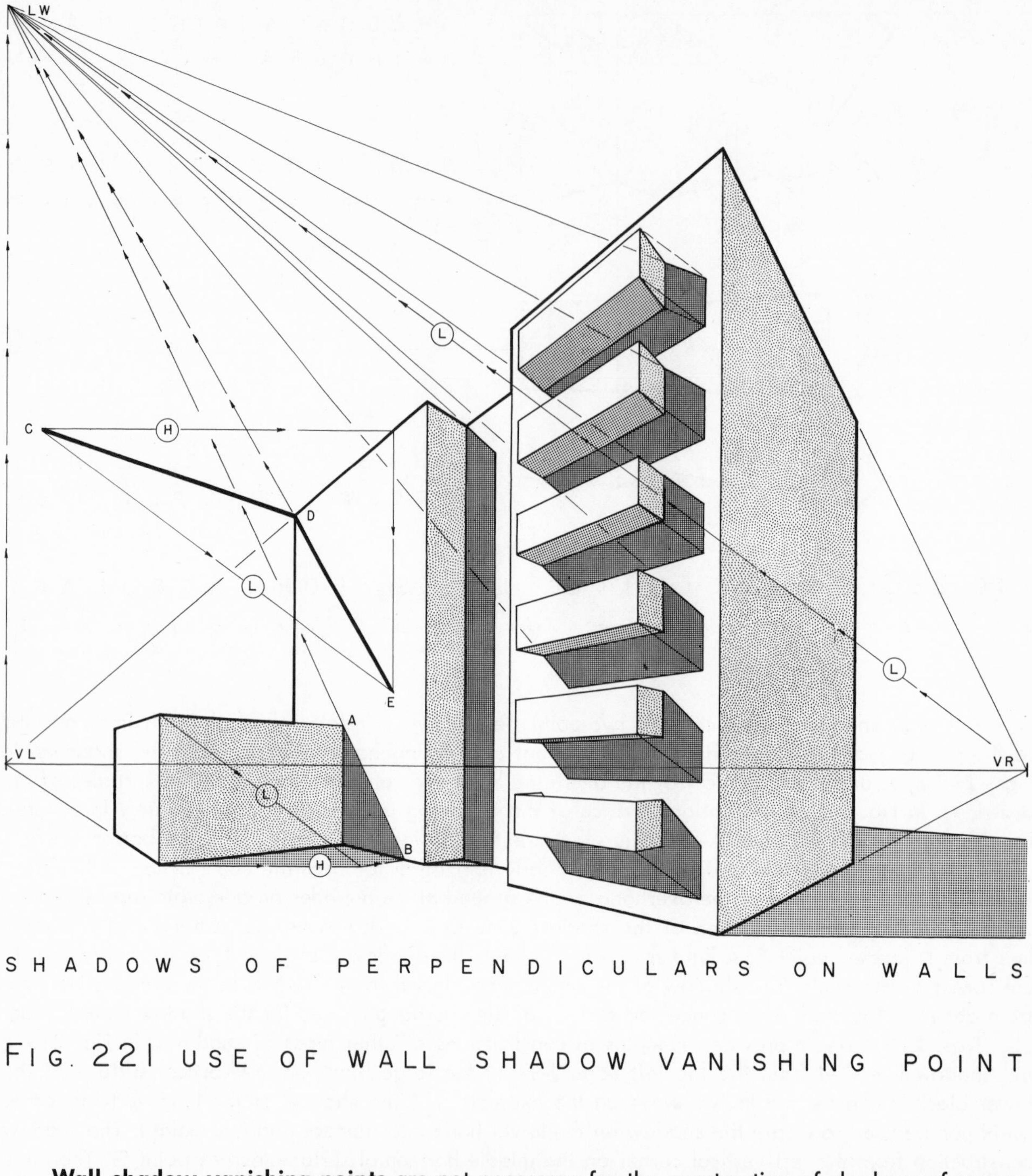

SHADOWS OF PERPENDICULARS ON WALLS

FIG. 221 USE OF WALL SHADOW VANISHING POINT

Wall shadow vanishing points are not necessary for the construction of shadows of perpendiculars to wall planes because these shadows can be worked out rather easily by using the L and H light directions. However the wall shadow vanishing point sometimes provides an easier, faster, more direct, and more accurate construction. This is especially true when there are a large number of perpendiculars casting shadows on wall planes.

The wall shadow vanishing point can be located by finding and extending any long shadow of a perpendicular to the wall in light to meet the vertical above a VP. Fig. 221, line A–B illustrates this construction for point LW. Any long perpendicular C–D can be used for this purpose if the drawing does not provide a satisfactory one. When light is parallel to the picture plane the wall shadow vanishing point can be located more accurately by drawing a light direction line from the VP on the shadow side of the perspective to meet the vertical above the other VP. In Fig. 221 this requires a light direction line from VR to meet the vertical above VL at LW.

CHAPTER **32**

LIGHT OBLIQUE TO PICTURE PLANE

When light is oblique to the picture plane in two-point perspective drawing each group of parallel shadow construction lines goes to a shadow vanishing point in perspective. Two of these shadow vanishing points may be adequate for the shadow construction. They are point L for the true light direction and point H for the plan direction of light.

L is the light rays vanishing point. Lines to point L connect points of the perspective and their shadows. L is never the vanishing point of the actual shadow edges.

H is the horizontal or plan direction of light vanishing point. This point gives the directions of the shadows of vertical lines on horizontal planes of the perspective drawing.

It is especially advantageous to use only these two points for shadow construction because they can be located at random wherever they will give a good shadow effect. The only limitations on their positions are (1) point H must be on the horizon, and (2) point L must be on the vertical through H.

The diagram of Fig. 222 I shows the routine procedure for constructing the shadow B–a of line A–B when point B touches the horizontal or floor plane on which the shadow falls. This procedure is used for constructing shadows of three of the vertical corners of the block below the diagram. The form taken by the lines of the diagram may vary greatly in different positions on a perspective drawing. It may have point H either to the right or left of the line A–B that makes the shadow. In Fig. 222 II the line C–D is extended to meet the floor plane at E in order to locate its shadow d–c on the floor plane. The procedures of pages 234 and 235 are applicable to this method also.

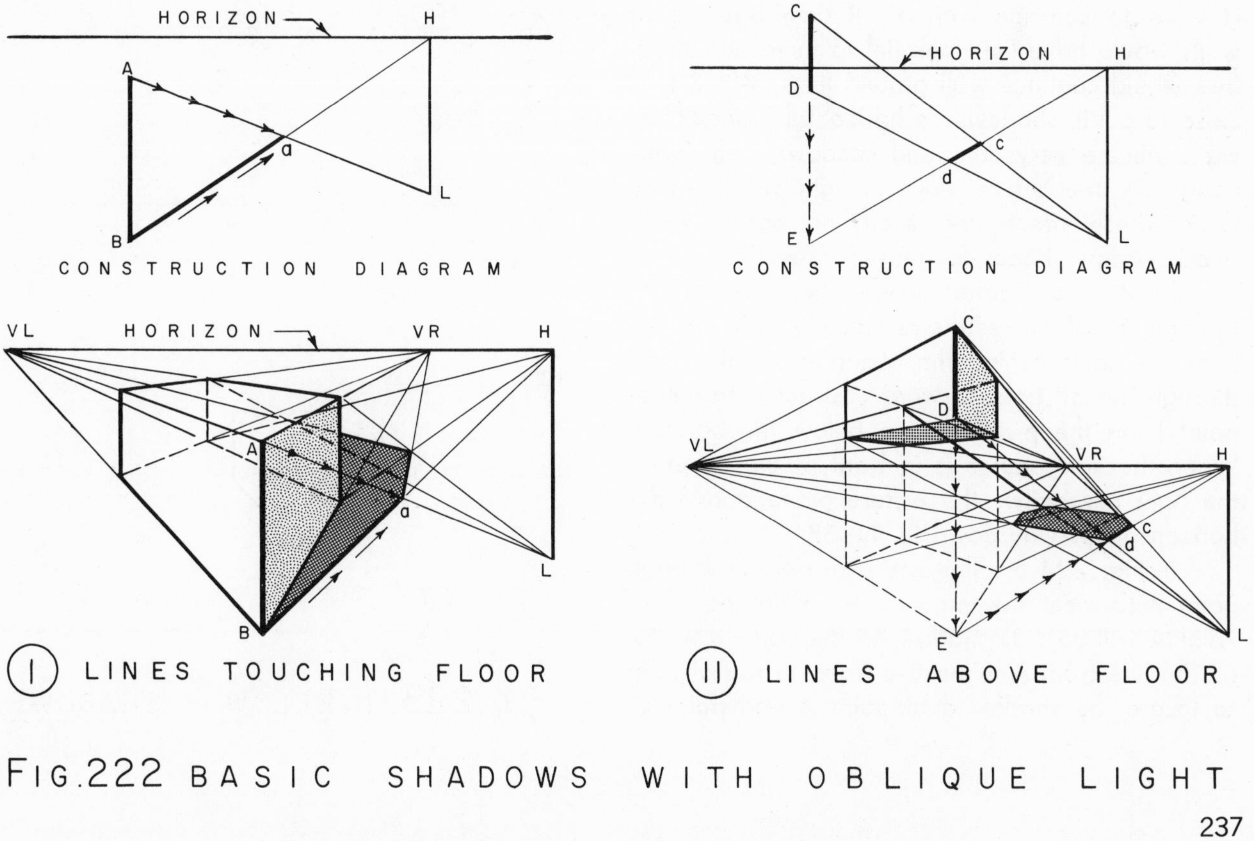

I LINES TOUCHING FLOOR   II LINES ABOVE FLOOR

FIG. 222 BASIC SHADOWS WITH OBLIQUE LIGHT

BASIC SHADOW SCHEMES. With light oblique to the picture plane there are two divisions of basic shadow shcemes. (1) When point L is below the horizon the shadows go away from the observer, Fig. 223. (2) When point L is above the horizon shadows come toward the observer, Fig. 225. Both of these divisions of shadow schemes have advantages. The first one is more widely used but the second is particularly advantageous for some objects.

The location of point H on the horizon determines the plan direction of light on the object. The shadows of all verticals on horizontal planes vanish to this point. Its position determines the direction of the shadows from the object as shown in the three illustrations of Fig. 223.

There are three general positions for point H on the horizon of a perspective drawing. These positions with L below the horizon have the following shadow effects, Figs. 223 A, B, C. (A) With H to the right of right vanishing point VR the right walls are in shadow. (B) With H between the two vanishing points both walls are in light. (C) With H to the left of VL the left walls are in shadow. Any wall in light may have shadows on it from overhangs, projecting walls, or sunken areas as shown in Figs. 224 D, E, F.

Point H should not be close to a VP for the best shadow effects for most perspectives. If H were to coincide with a VP then one set of walls would have light parallel to them and shadows would continue wall ground lines. When H is close to a VP, shadows on horizontal planes from walls will be very thin, and shadows from overhangs on one set of walls in light will be very large. These effects are usually not conducive to good shadow shapes for most perspectives.

Point L is located where the ray of light through the SP strikes the picture plane. When the light source is behind the observer the light ray through the SP goes forward and down to locate point L on the picture plane below the horizon. When the light source is in front of the observer the light ray strikes the picture plane above the horizon on its way down to the SP.

In Fig. 224 D a line is drawn from H through point B to meet the edge of the overhang at A. Point A will cast its shadow on the vertical below B. The line from A to point L traces a ray of light to locate the shadow a of point A and point C.

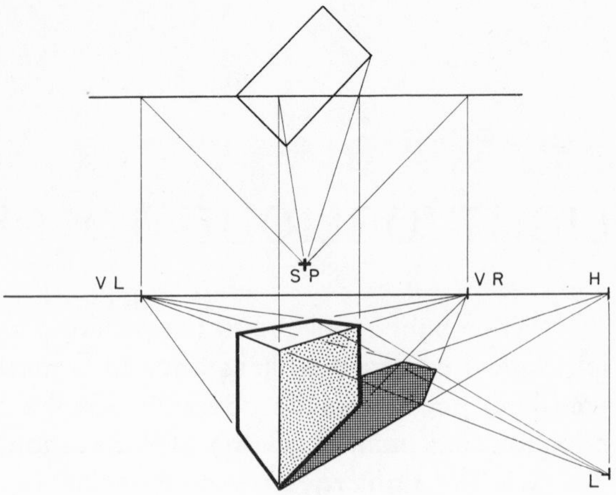

(A) RIGHT WALLS IN SHADOW

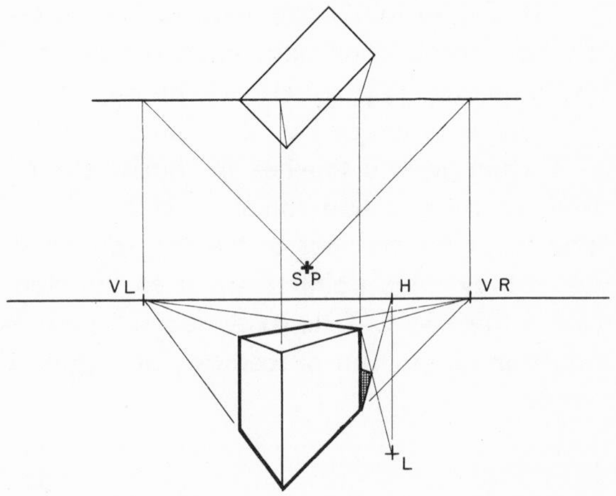

(B) LIGHT ON BOTH WALLS

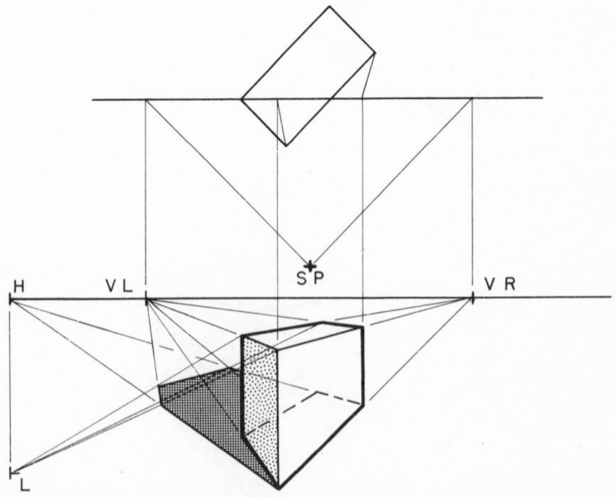

(C) LEFT WALL IN SHADOW

FIG. 223 L BELOW H SHADOWS

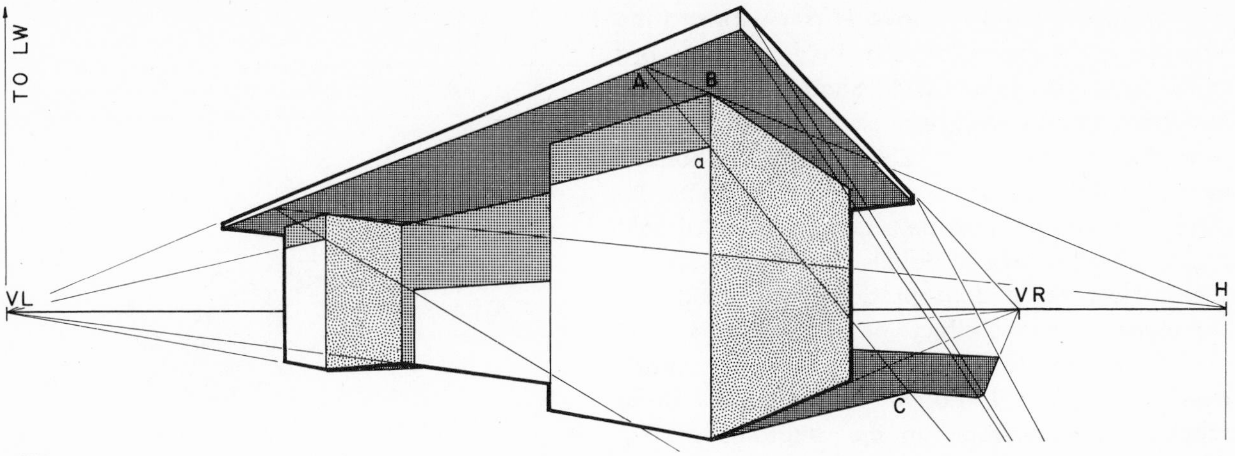

(D) LEFT WALLS IN LIGHT RIGHT WALLS IN SHADOW

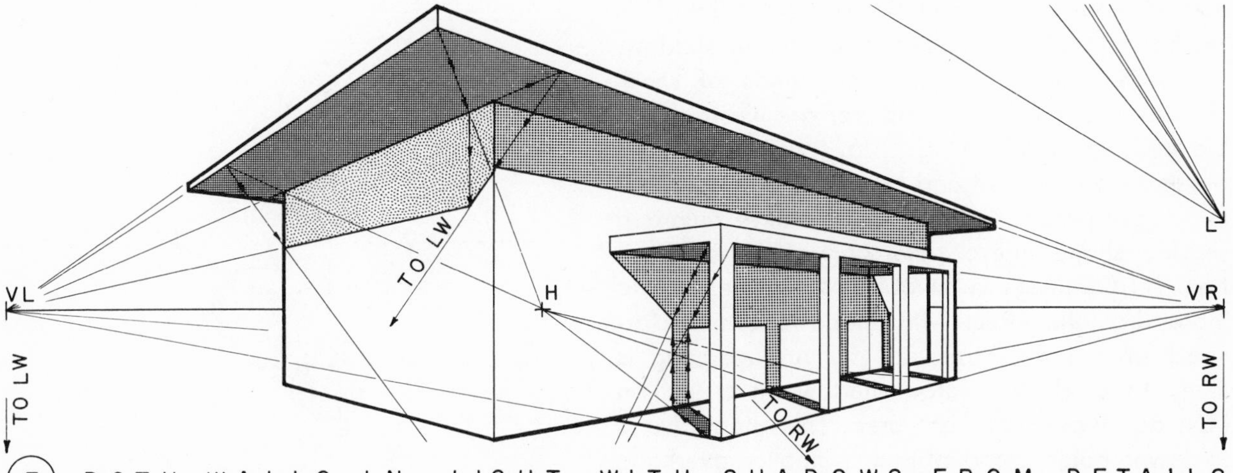

(E) BOTH WALLS IN LIGHT WITH SHADOWS FROM DETAILS

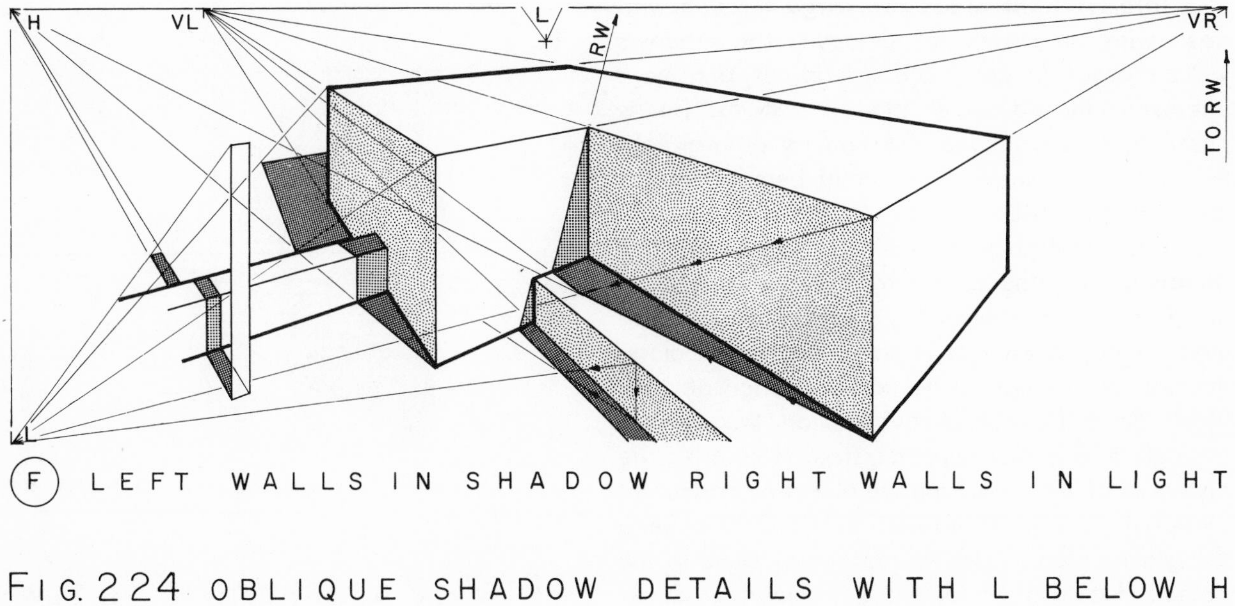

(F) LEFT WALLS IN SHADOW RIGHT WALLS IN LIGHT

FIG. 224 OBLIQUE SHADOW DETAILS WITH L BELOW H

Shadows from L above H come toward the observer and become larger as they come forward in the perspective, Fig. 225. Shadows from L below the horizon decrease in size as they go away from the observer, Fig. 223. L above the horizon may provide too much shadow area for some objects, and may not provide a good relation of light and shadow to explain details clearly on wall surfaces. However it does produce very good and sometimes dramatic effects on some objects.

There are three basic schemes for shadows with point L above the horizon. These schemes are illustrated in the diagrams of Fig. 225 and in the more detailed illustrations of Fig. 226. (I) When H is to the left of VL the right walls are in shadow. (II) When H is between VL and VR both walls are in shadow. (III) When H is to the right of VR the left walls are in shadow.

Advantages and disadvantages of shadows coming toward the observer are illustrated in the three drawings of Fig. 226. (IV) Small objects assume more interest and become more important in a perspective where their entire enlarged shadow shapes are a major part of the composition. (V) Openings in an object sometimes give a more dramatic effect with shadows coming forward toward the observer. (VI) An overhang is likely to produce a large shadow on a wall in light and leave little light area. The alternative is to lower point L and obtain a smaller overhang shadow. However this will produce a larger shadow on the ground.

Interior light areas are large through windows with this system for shadows. The shadows will be larger, longer, more spread out, and more interesting than by other shadow systems. This is possibly the best shadow system for natural light for both one-point and two-point perspectives of interiors, Fig. 228.

The shadow is controlled in position and distance from the object by the positions of H and L. The reader should try to imagine the movement of the shadow as H would be moved along the horizon throughout its possible range of positions. Point L must always be on the vertical through H. The distance of L from H controls the distances of shadows from the object on horizontal planes. L usually has to be far above H to keep the ground plane shadows reasonably close to the object. H near a VP seldom gives good shadows.

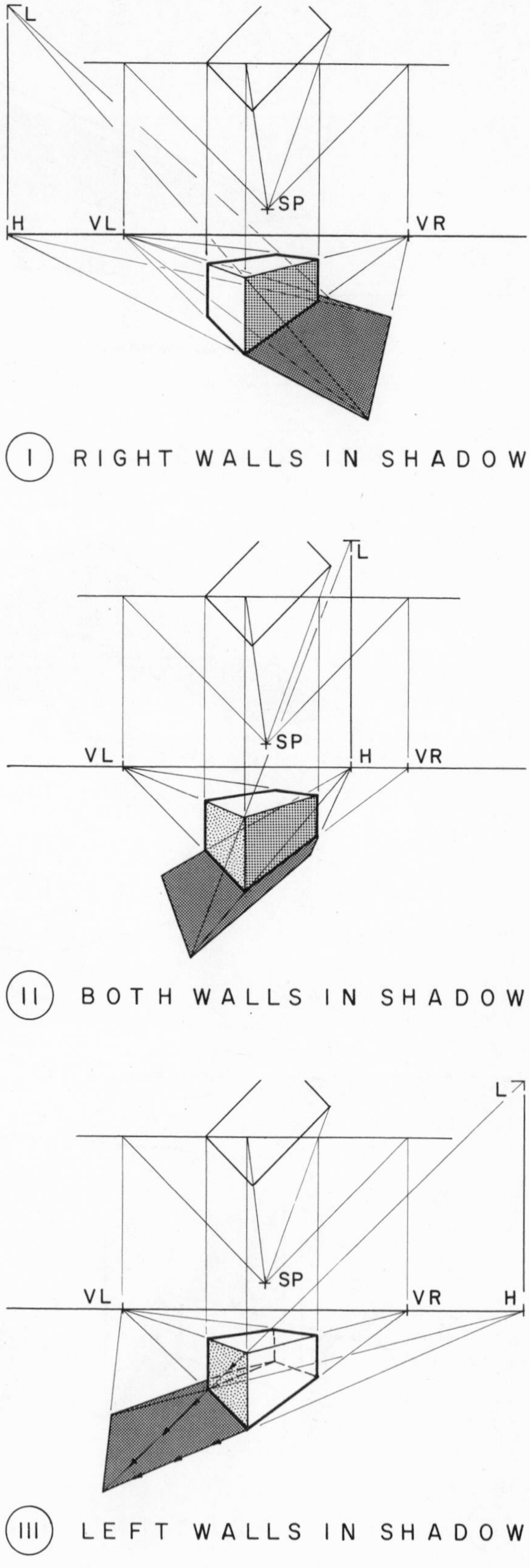

FIG. 225 L ABOVE H SHADOWS

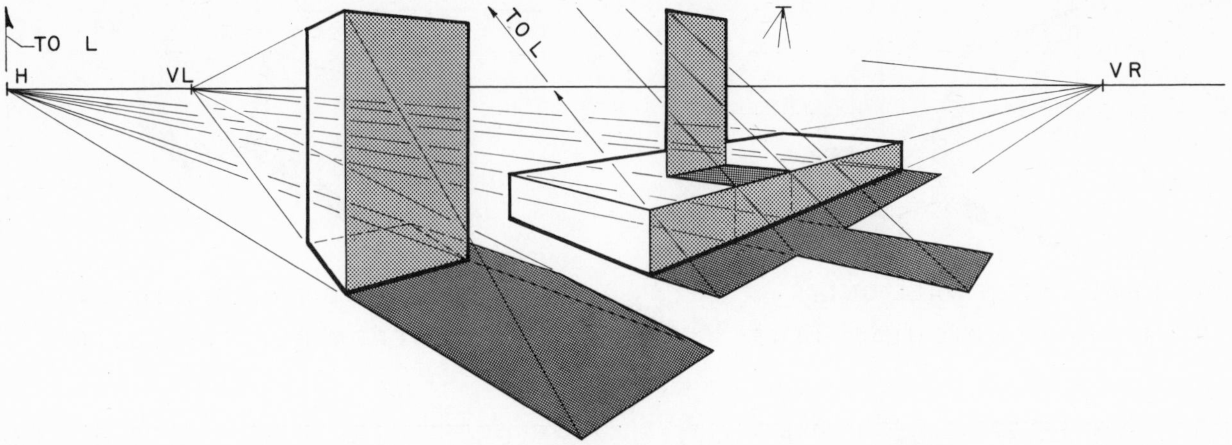

(IV) RIGHT WALLS IN SHADOW LEFT WALLS IN LIGHT

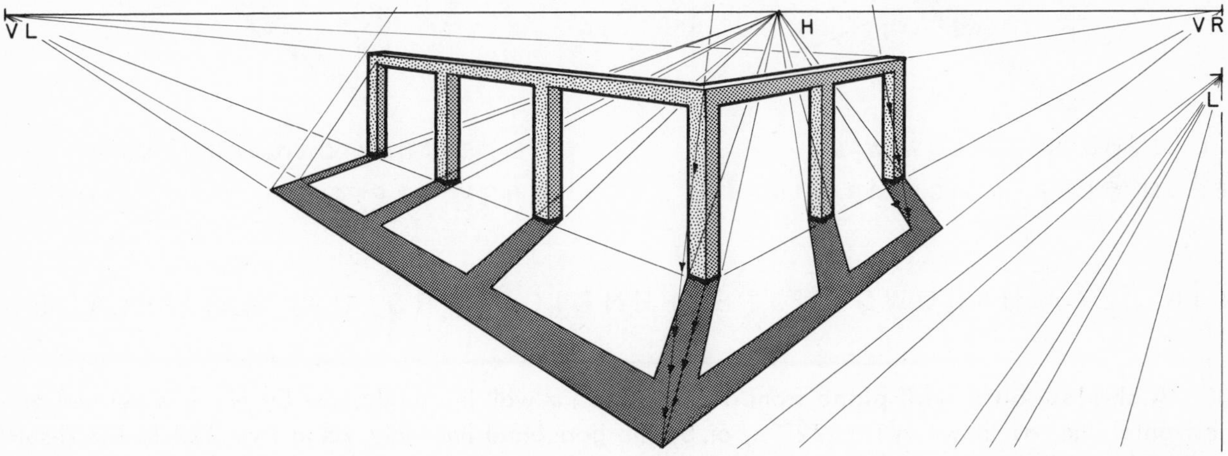

(V) BOTH WALLS IN SHADOW LIGHT ON HORIZONTAL PLANES

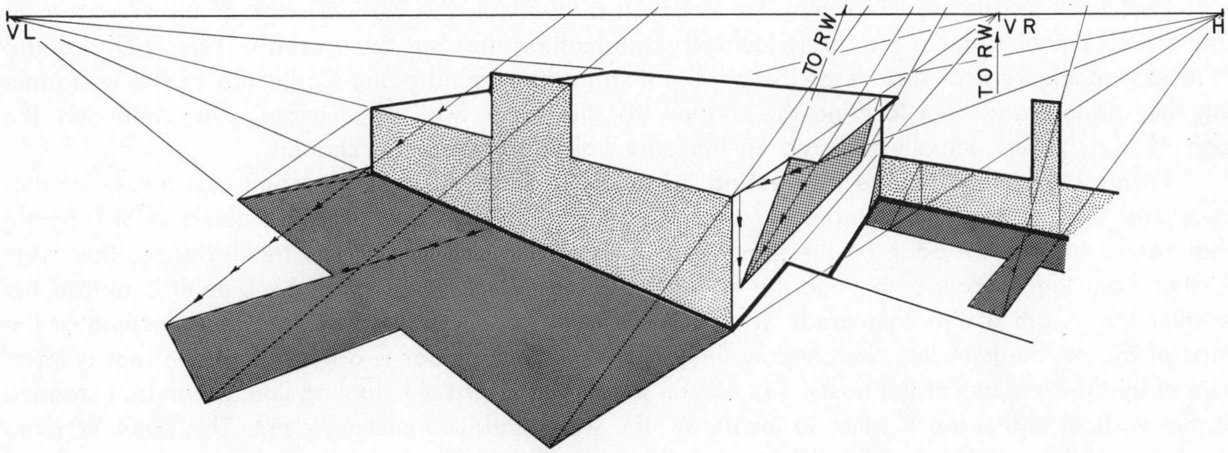

(VI) LEFT WALLS IN SHADOW RIGHT WALLS IN LIGHT

FIG. 226 OBLIQUE SHADOW DETAILS WITH L ABOVE H

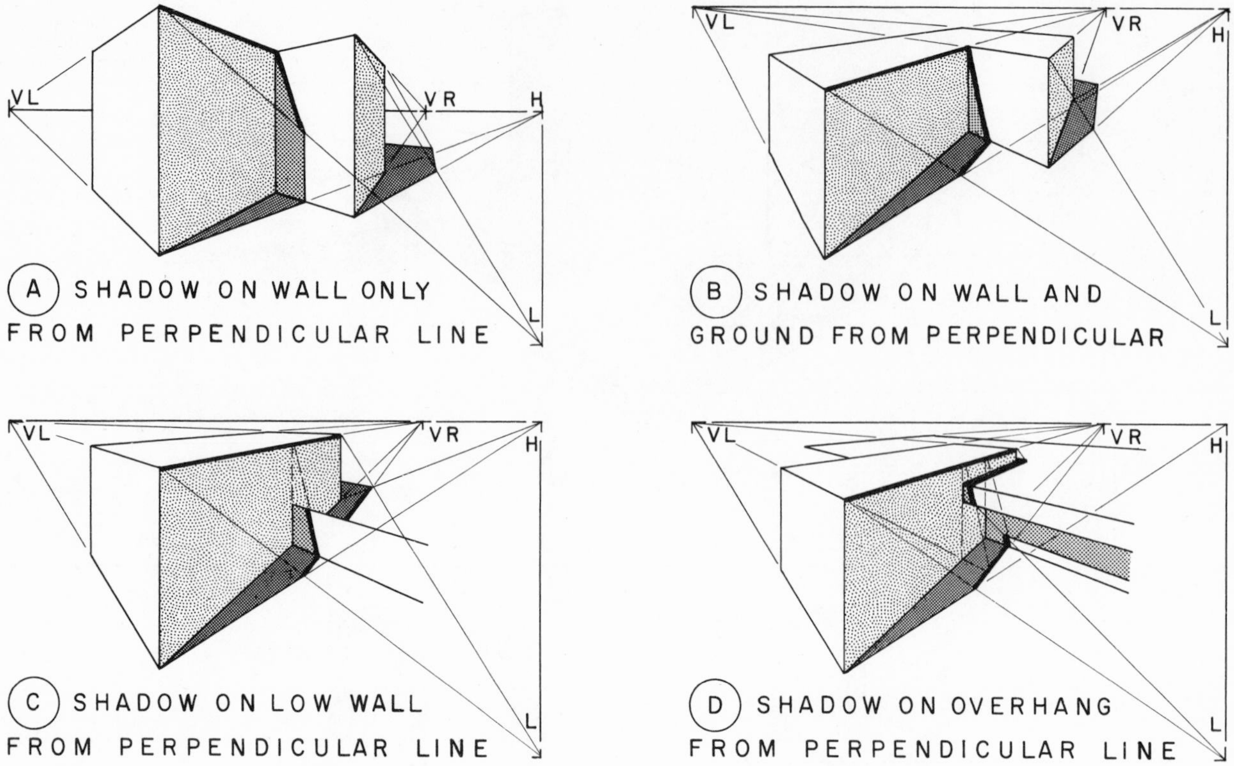

FIG 227 SHADOWS OF PERPENDICULARS ON WALL PLANES

A shadow on a wall plane from a perpendicular wall is usually cast by either a vertical and horizontal line, as shown in Fig. 227 A, or by the horizontal line only, as in Fig. 227 B. The resulting shadow will depend on the relative heights of the two walls and the distance of L from H, which determines the angle of light. With L farther from H the shadow in A could be like that in B. With L about half as far from H the wall shadow in B would assume a shape similar to that shown in A.

Part wall shadows, which may be made on a low wall, the vertical edge of an overhang, or any other vertical surface, are easily located. One method that has been used in Figs. 227 C and D is to extend the vertical surface of the part wall from the ground plane to the top of the wall making the shadow and then locating the shadow for the entire wall as in example B. Then only the part of the shadow actually required on the part wall is retained and shaded.

Points L and H will give interesting interior shadows on both one-point and two-point perspectives. On the one-point interior perspective of Fig. 228 I point L is located above H at a height that keeps the shadow edge on the floor area. A lower position of L would make the shadow edge farther from the window or beyond the floor area of the room. The higher the L point is placed the smaller the length of the light areas. It should be noted that the outside edge of the ceiling at the tops of the openings makes two shadow lines. The one on the floor is a horizontal line that is interrupted by the shadows of the posts. The one on the wall is a straight slanting line. It can be extended to the vertical above the V point to locate W, the wall shadow vanishing point. This point W is on the horizontal line from L where it intersects the vertical through V.

A single straight line always makes a single straight line or point shadow on any plane surface.

The two-point perspective of Fig. 228 II has H located between the vanishing points. In order to have light fall on the visible wall on the left it would be necessary to locate H to the right of VR. The shadow pattern of the posts on the floor can be varied by moving H to left or right.

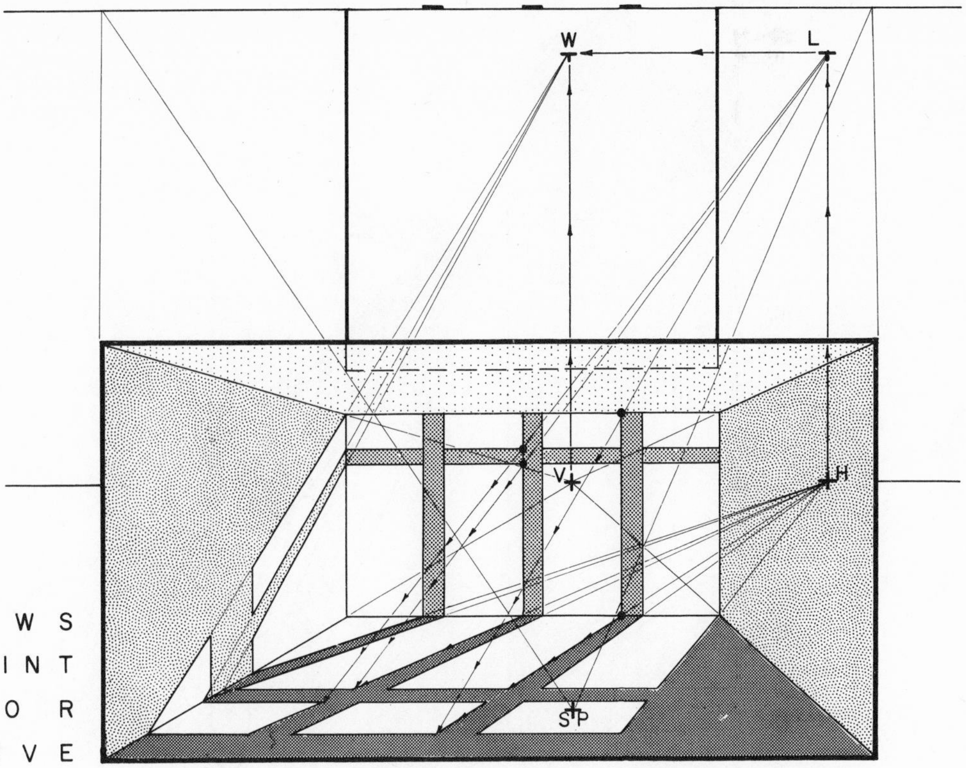

(I) SHADOWS ON ONE-POINT INTERIOR PERSPECTIVE

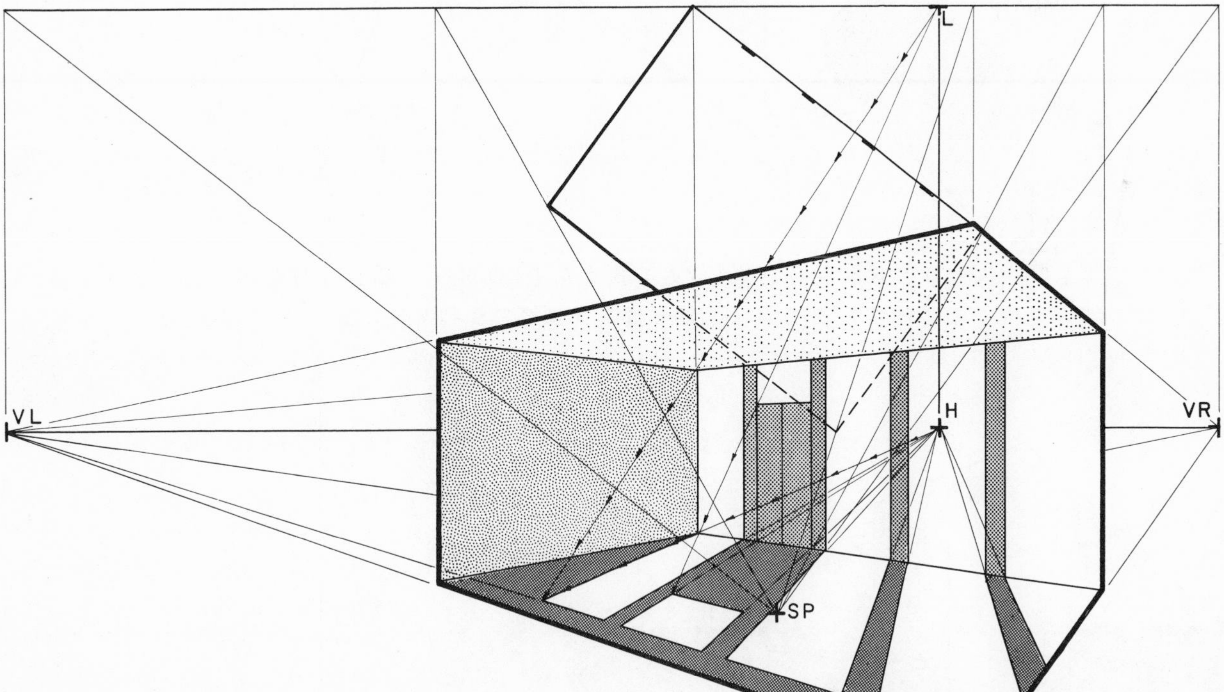

(II) SHADOWS ON TWO-POINT INTERIOR PERSPECTIVE

FIG. 228 USING H AND L FOR INTERIOR SHADOWS

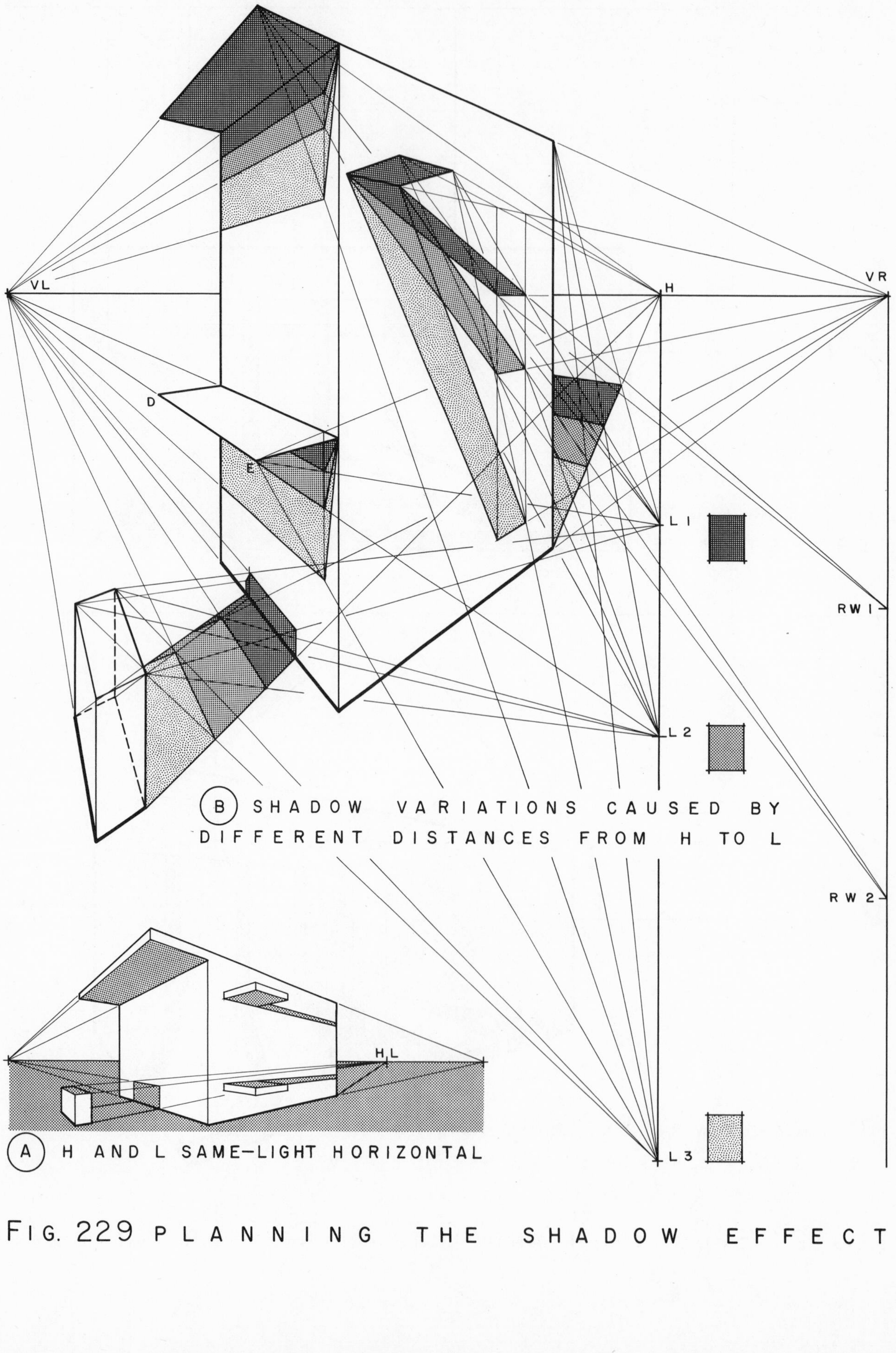

FIG. 229 PLANNING THE SHADOW EFFECT

The distance of point L from H determines the amount of shadows visible under overhangs and on floor planes. When L is at H on the horizon, rays of light are horizontal and there will be no shadows under overhangs. Light is parallel to horizontal surfaces which will be in shadow (shade) on both top and bottom surfaces, Fig. 229 A. This is seldom a satisfactory light direction.

When L is close to H there are small shadows under overhangs and large shadows on ground planes, Fig. 229 B. As L moves farther from H the shadows under overhangs become larger and shadows on ground planes become smaller. This has been shown in Fig. 229 B by using three distances of the L point below H. Point L1 is closest to H and L3 is farthest from H. Shadows have been worked out and shaded in a different way for each of these points L1, L2, and L3.

By varying the position of H on the horizon and the distance of L from H, the shadow areas can be adjusted to give the best effect for an object. When the possible results from all shadow systems are combined any lighting effect can be secured on a perspective drawing.

The method of locating LW and RW by finding the shadow of a long perpendicular to the wall in light and extending it to meet the vertical through the VP of horizontals in that wall can be used for oblique lighting on two-point perspectives. This method is suggested on pages 239 and 241. It is demonstrated also on Figs. 229 B and 230. With one wall in shadow LW or RW may be far away.

A more accurate method is to draw a line through L and one VP to meet the vertical through the other VP, as shown in Fig. 230 where a line from VL through L meets the vertical through VR in RW. The line from VR through L locates LW on the vertical through VL. The explanation of this is that the perpendicular to the wall, the shadow of the perpendicular on the wall, and the light ray from the end of the perpendicular form a triangle. The plane of this triangle meets the picture plane in the locus of the VPs of all three sides of the triangle. This line must go through point L and the VP of the perpendicular. Then the wall VP of the shadow of the perpendicular must be at the intersection of this line and the vertical through the other VP.

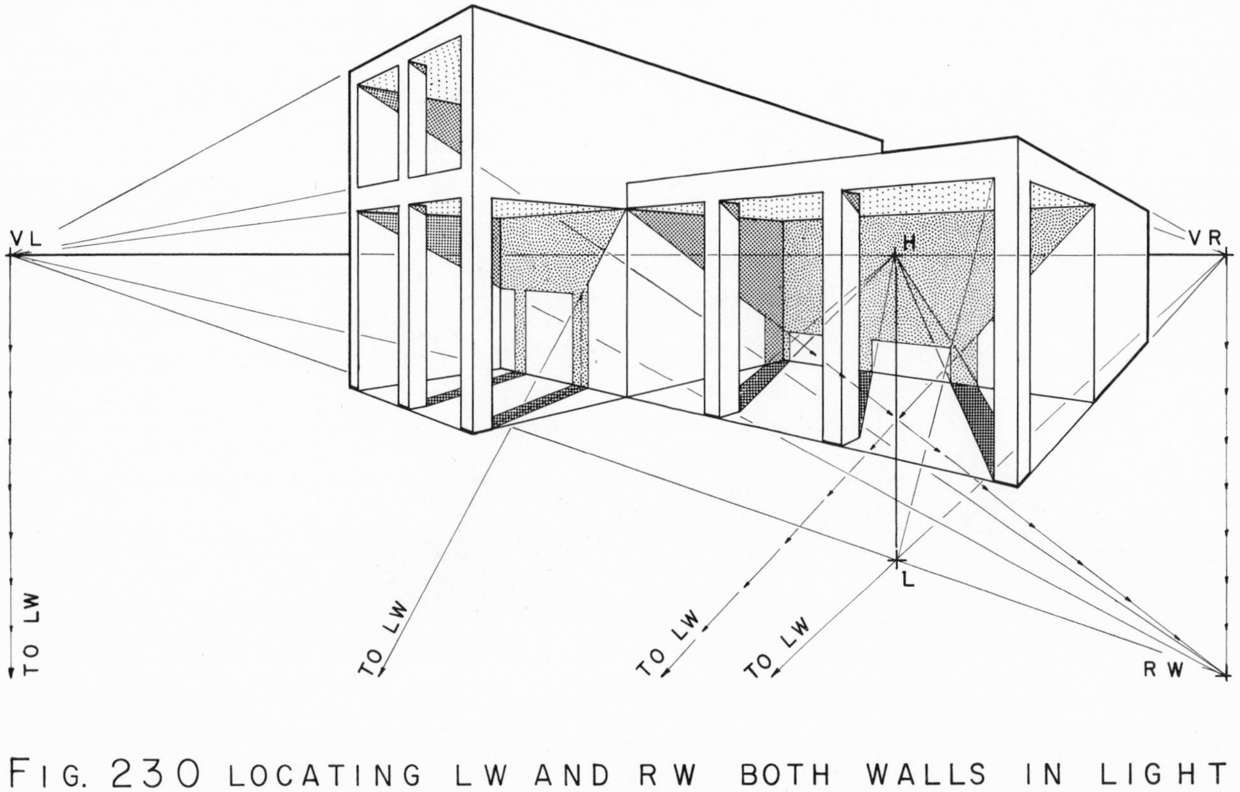

FIG. 230 LOCATING LW AND RW BOTH WALLS IN LIGHT

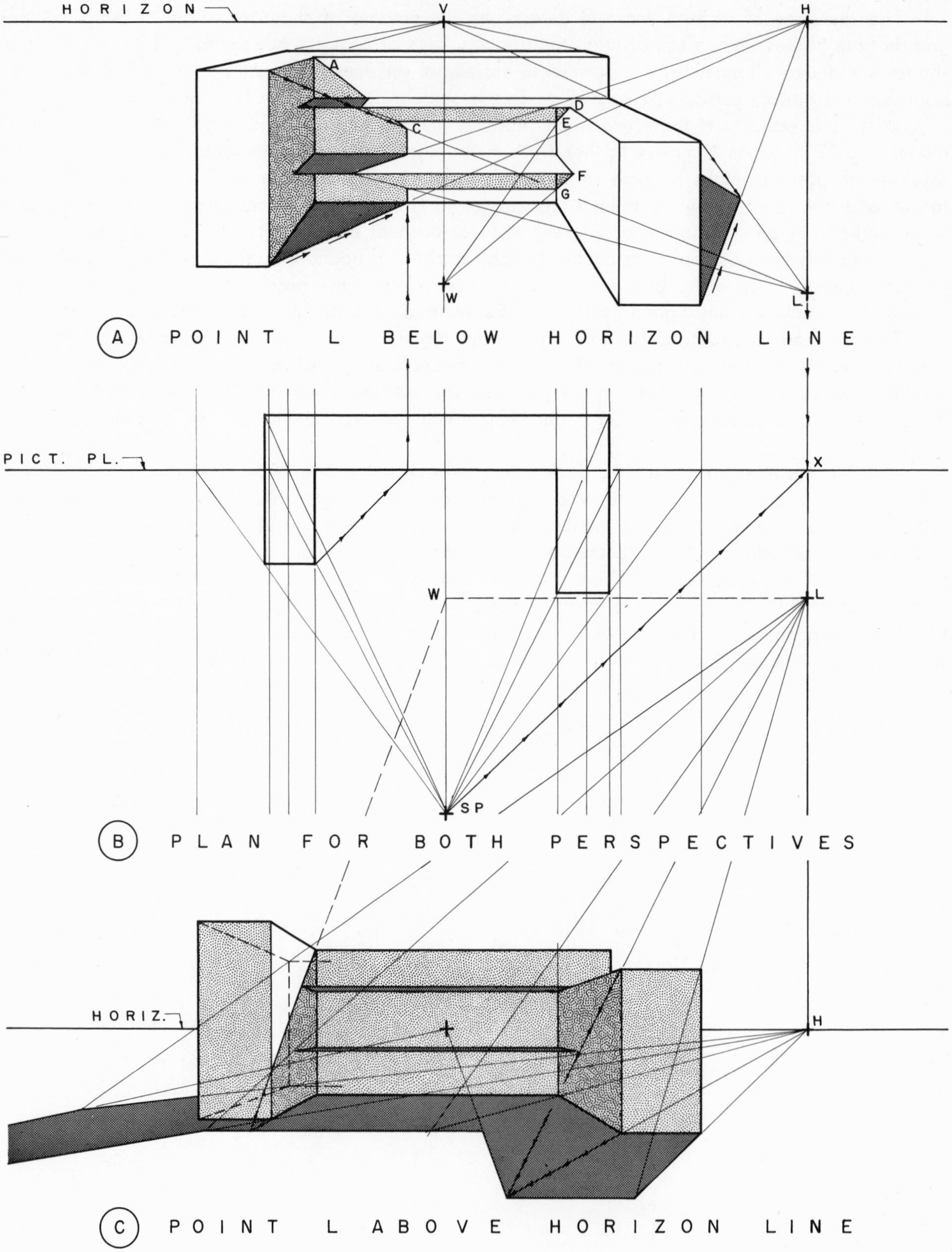

FIG. 231 SHADOWS IN ONE-POINT PERSPECTIVE

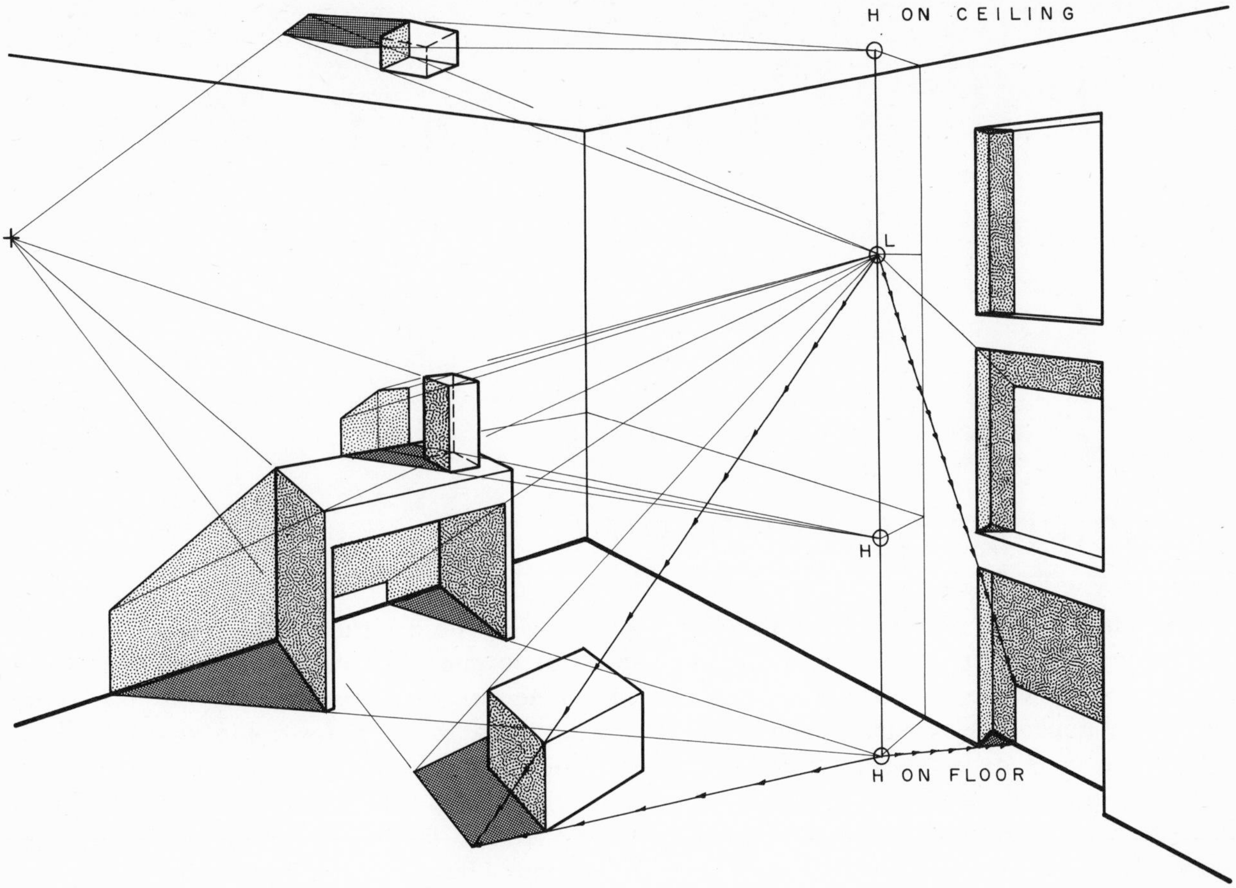

FIG. 232 SHADOWS FROM A POINT SOURCE OF LIGHT

One-point perspective shadows are constructed by the system used for two-point perspective with light oblique to the picture plane, Fig. 231. Because one set of wall planes is parallel to the picture plane it will have parallel lines for the light direction A–C on those walls, Fig. 231 A. The other set of wall planes, which is perpendicular to the picture plane, will have a vanishing point W for its light direction as shown by lines D–E and F–G. This point W will be on the vertical through V. One side of walls perpendicular to the picture plane will be in shadow. When H is to the right of V and L is below H, the right sides of walls perpendicular to the picture plane are in shadow, Fig. 231 A. When H is to the left of V and L is below H, the left surfaces are in shadow. These light and shadow conditions reverse with L above the horizon. When L is below the horizon the walls parallel to the picture plane are in light, Fig. 231 A, and when L is above the horizon they are in shadow, Fig. 231 C. A vertical line through H locates point X at its intersection with the picture plane in plan view. Line SP–X is the plan angle of light for this position of H. Lines parallel to SP–X can be used to trace light rays on plan. This procedure is used for greater accuracy when the perspective representations of horizontal areas are too small for good construction. An alternative is to provide a larger perspective substitute area as described on page 235.

Shadows from a point source of light are shown in Fig. 232. The projection of the point light source onto the floor plane is labeled H on floor. Lines radiating from this point trace the shadows of verticals on the floor. Lines from L represent light rays and terminate the shadows of verticals. A new point H must be used for each horizontal plane on which a shadow is located. These H points are all on the vertical through L at its intersections with the planes on which the shadows fall.

PART SIX

Rendering Techniques

CHAPTER 33

PRINCIPLES OF RENDERING

Rendering is the process of transforming a line drawing into a picture. The rendering may give only a suggestion of picture effect or be so complete as to approach photographic realism. It may be done in monotone, in part color, or in full color. The rendering material may be dust, spray, pencil, ink, applied sheet material, paints, or other substances. The purposes are to clarify the drawing, give a more or less complete picture of the object, and provide a setting for it. Renderings may vary greatly in the materials used and the effects produced. The personality and taste of the delineator, his training and knowledge, the object depicted, and the purpose of the presentation are some of the factors that influence the result. Entire books have been written on rendering in a single medium. There are such books available on pencil, pen and ink, scratchboard, water color, and other types of rendering. This treatise on rendering must be very elementary in order to give a brief general treatment of the subject.

Although there is great variety in media, techniques, and results in rendering, many devices are useful for rendering in any medium. The discussion of a number of these will be given in the following pages of this chapter. The reader should realize that it may not be practical to use all of the devices described in a single rendering. The delineator must choose the ones best suited to his problem. A good assortment of such tools enables him to secure better and more varied results in his rendering.

Intensity of light and shadow are important elements of rendering. Shadow casting is concerned with only the quantity of areas of shadows. Rendering often represents the qualities of shadow areas also. When the conventional direction of light is used for rendering of multi-view drawings, an octagonal prism will demonstrate variations of light and shadow intensity. The drawing of Fig. 233 A shows the relation of the plan light direction to each visible surface of the prism. Light rays, as seen from above, are perpendicular to the left area, which consequently receives the greatest possible quantity of light and is called the *high light,* HL. Light rays are at 45° to the center area which receives less light than the left area. This center surface is parallel to the front view plane and is called a *light area,* L. Light rays are parallel to the right side of the prism leaving it in shadow, S. Gradation of the flat areas of the octagon from side to side may be used to make the effect brighter and more contrasting, Fig. 233 C. When gradation of areas is employed their correct relative tones should be kept. If desired, the overall effect can be kept light for the entire octagon with adequate separation of areas when this device is used, Fig. 233 D. This shading of flat areas increases contrast and adds life to the rendering of these surfaces.

The application of the high light, light, and shadow tones of the octagon to beveled surfaces is shown in Figs. 233 E and F. It is a powerful means of separating areas and expressing form.

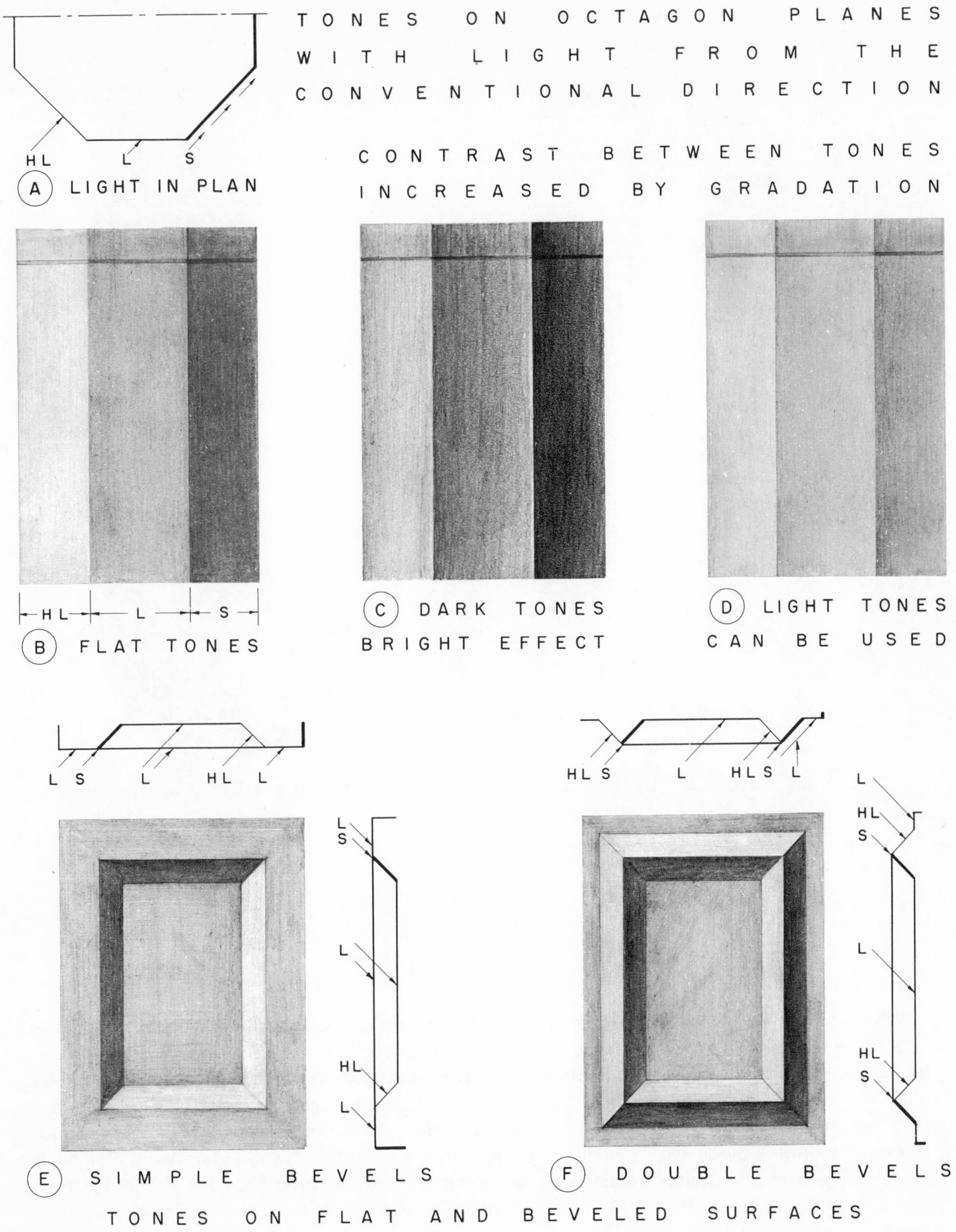

FIG. 233 HIGH LIGHT, LIGHT, AND SHADOW TONES

(B) SHADING ON CYLINDER

(C) GRADATION AT RIGHT HELPS EXPRESS FORM

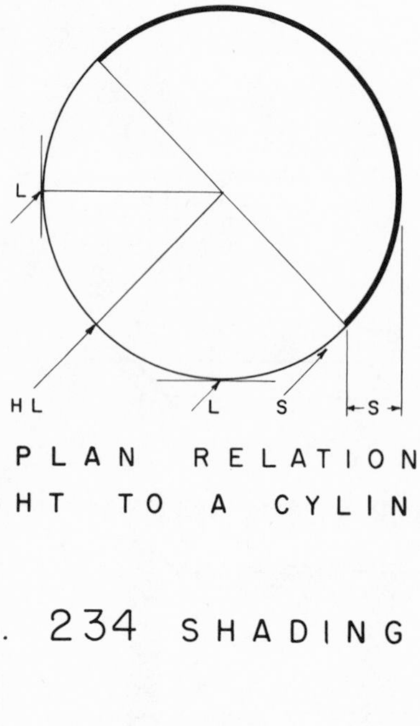

(A) PLAN RELATION OF LIGHT TO A CYLINDER

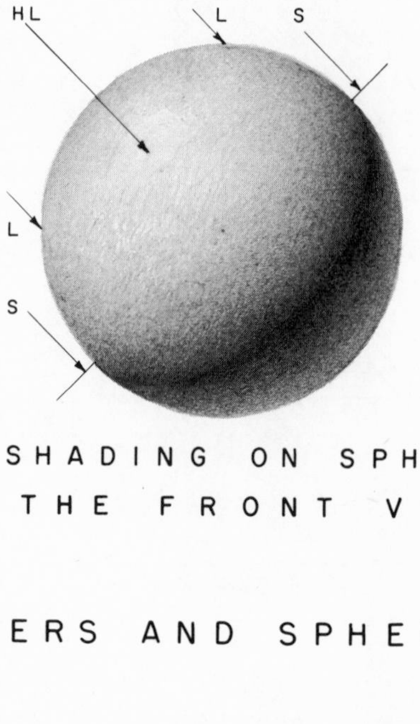

(D) SHADING ON SPHERE IN THE FRONT VIEW

FIG. 234 SHADING ON CYLINDERS AND SPHERES

When the system of high light, light, and shadow of the conventional direction of light is used on a cylinder, the high light, HL, is at the 45° point on the left, Figs. 234 A, B. There are two lights, L, one at the extreme left edge and the other at the exact center of the visible surface of the cylinder. At both these positions in plan the light rays are at 45° to the tangents to the curved surface. From the 45° tangent point of light on the right to the right edge, the surface of the cylinder is in shadow, S. When this area is made the same darkness throughout its width the cylinder seems flat on the right side, Fig. 234 B. A better treatment is to lighten the shadow area from the shade line to the right edge of the cylinder. This makes the darkest tone on the shade line and helps to model and express the cylindrical shape, Fig. 234 C. The sphere of Fig. 234 D is shaded in a similar manner. However it should be noted that the high light is located at the top left on the 45° diagonal through the center of the sphere. Light rays are perpendicular to the surface at this point.

Reflected light is used to produce variations in tone in areas that are in shadow. It is a means of expressing form, separating areas, and adding details to shadow areas. The octagonal prism of

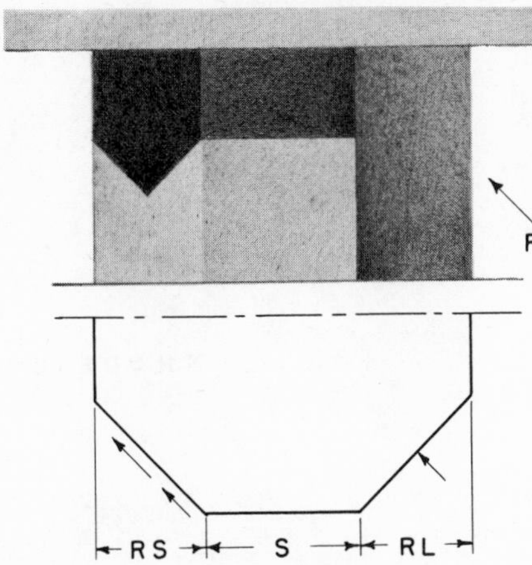

(I) OCTAGON SHADOW TONES

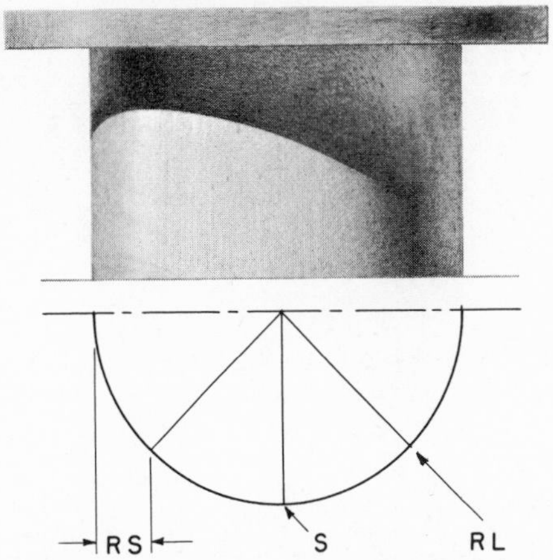

(II) SHADOW GRADATIONS

THE EFFECTS OF REFLECTED LIGHTS ON SHADOWS

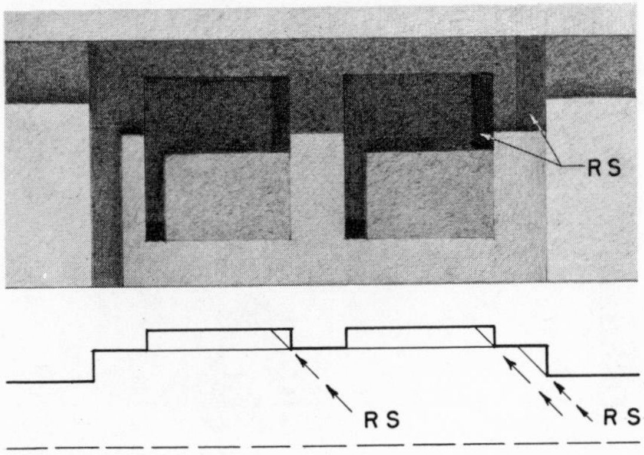

(III) REFLECTED SHADOWS FROM SMALL OFFSETS

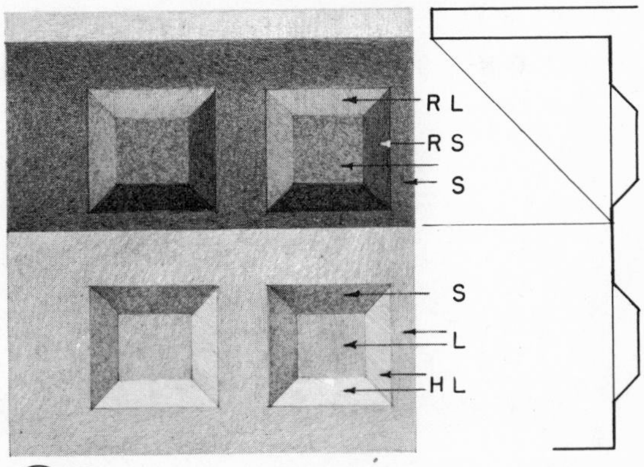

(IV) REFLECTED SHADOWS AND LIGHTS ON BEVELS

FIG. 235 REFLECTED LIGHTS AND SHADOWS

Fig. 235 I has a shadow across the top from a projecting block. *Reflected light,* RL, is assumed from the right and slanting up and back as shown by the arrows in plan and elevation. This is the commonly used direction of reflected light. Its effect is to make each visible plane in shadow a different darkness. The right plane receives the most reflected light, is lightest in shadow, and is called a reflected light, RL. The left area receives no reflected light, and is darkest. It is called a *reflected shadow,* RS. The center area receives a little less reflected light than the right area and is slightly darker. It is called shadow, S. The effect of reflected light on the shadow on a cylinder is shown in Fig. 235 II. The sequence of the shading here reverses the shading on the area of the cylinder in light. It expresses the round form of the cylinder in shadow. Reflected shadows are usually limited to small details in shadow areas, Fig. 235 III. They provide a means of showing shapes in large shadow areas that would often be blank and uninteresting without them. The small reflected shadows can be made crisp and sharp. Larger ones are sometimes suggested near the form causing the shadow reflection and then faded out from it. Their complete representation may be confusing.

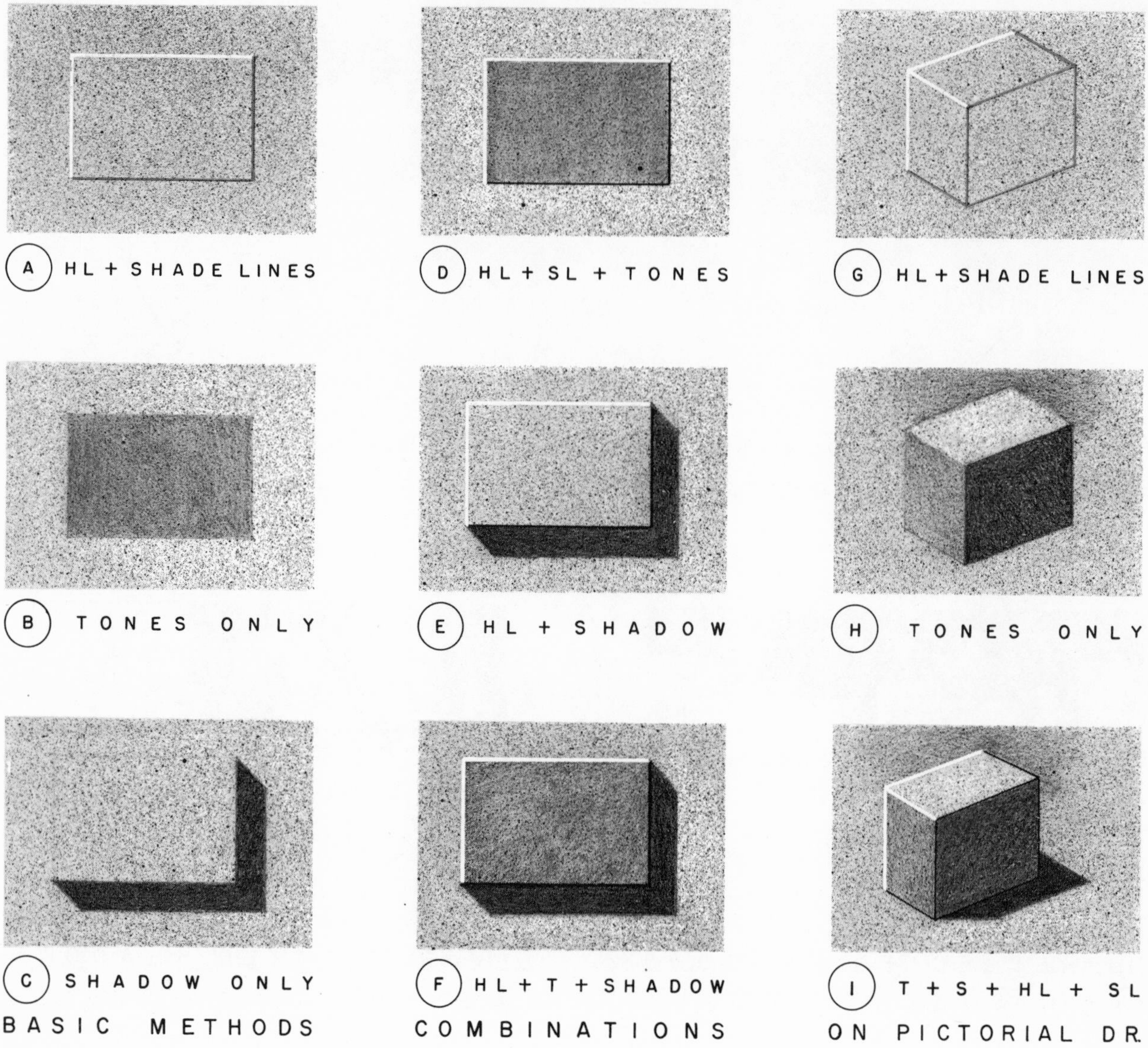

FIG. 236 SEPARATION OF PLANES IN RENDERING

Separation of planes can be done in three simple ways, Figs. 236 A, B, C. (A) By use of high lights on corners toward the source of light and shade lines on the corners away from light. This method assumes that there is no visible shadow. (B) By use of difference of tones on the adjoining areas. (C) By use of shadows when the areas are so related that the shadows are visible. Shadows form separations on one or two sides. The edges toward light can be outlined by high lights or separated by tones, or by a combination of the two methods, Figs. 236 D, E, F.

These devices for separating planes are useful in perspective and paraline renderings as well as on multi-view renderings. The high lights and reflected lights are however usually at the meeting of two visible planes on pictorial drawings and not at an edge made by a visible and concealed plane as in multi-view, Figs. 236 G, H, I.

High lights and shade lines are actual elements of the surfaces represented in rendering. Few persons observe these parts of objects. High lights are especially prominent on almost everything we

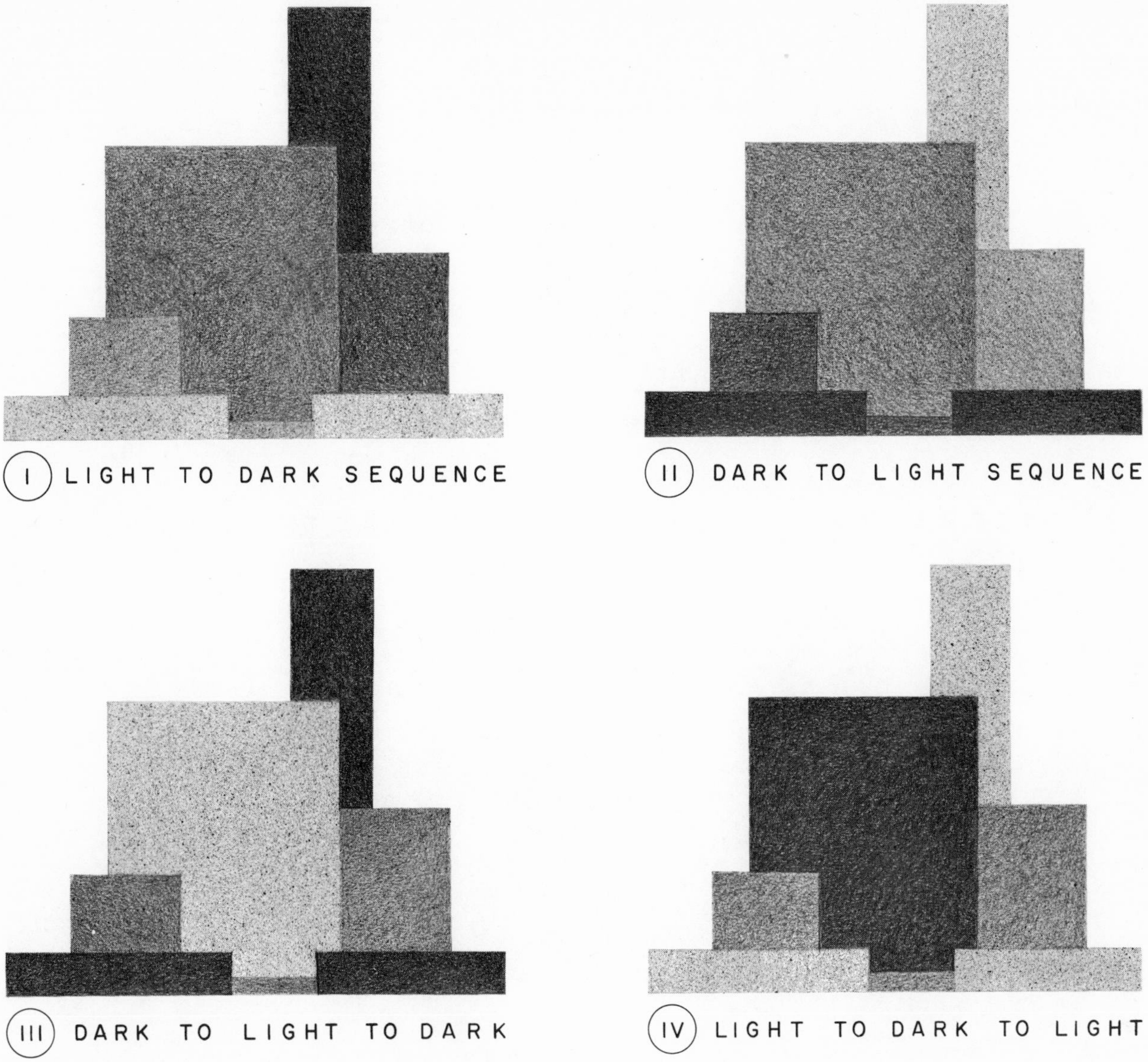

FIG. 237 EXPRESSION OF DEPTH BY SHADING

see. The use of these light and dark lines without any consideration of direction of light produces an artificial effect and should be avoided.

Expression of depth or distance away from the observer is often accomplished partially by use of tones. The tone sequence depends on the forms of the object and the effect to be achieved. Four simple tone sequences for this purpose of expressing depth are shown in Figs. 237 I, II, III, IV. They are: (I) Nearest surface lightest and each succeeding more distant surface darker. (II) Nearest plane darkest and each plane lighter as the distance away increases. (III) One of the middle planes lightest with distances from this plane expressed by increasing darkness in both directions. (IV) A middle plane darkest and distance from this plane in both directions expressed by lighter sequences of tones.

These schemes for tone sequences to express depth assume the same material throughout the design and no variations of tone caused by colors of different materials.

Shadow areas are an effective means of expressing distance perpendicular to the paper.

(A) INTEREST FOCUSED BY CONTRAST VARIATIONS

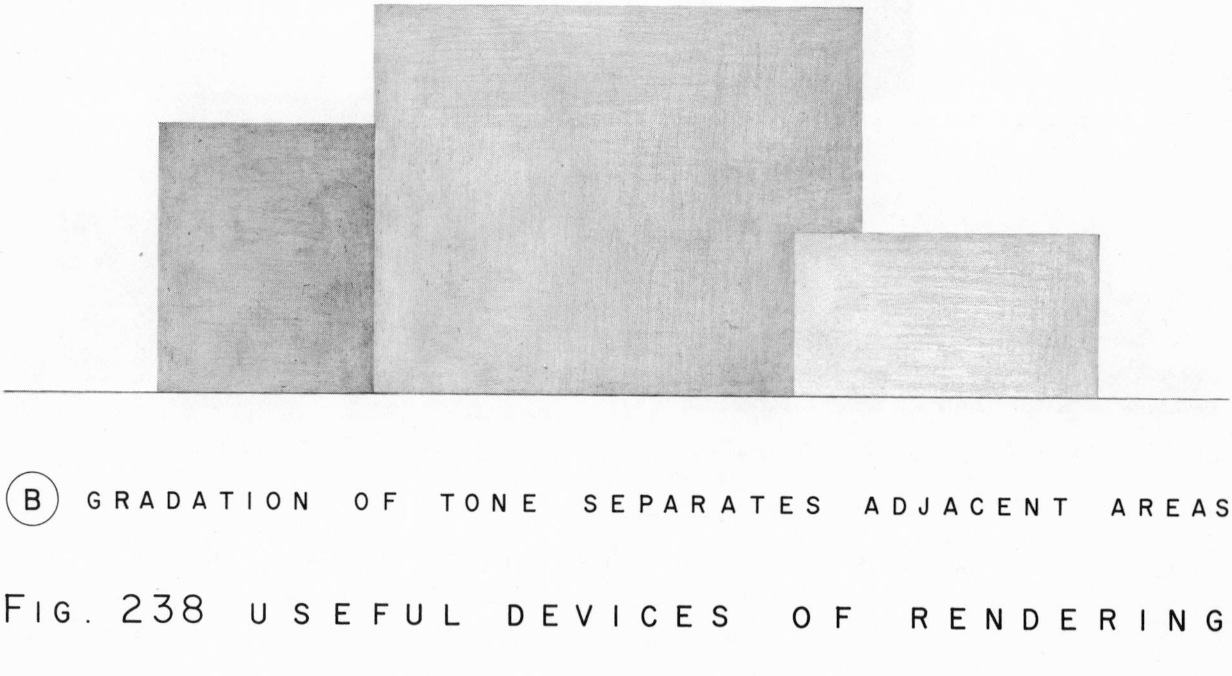

(B) GRADATION OF TONE SEPARATES ADJACENT AREAS

FIG. 238 USEFUL DEVICES OF RENDERING

The focusing of interest on one part of a rendering by extreme contrasts is a very effective device. This may be accomplished in monotone rendering by extreme contrast of shadows and light at the center of interest, Fig. 238 A. Other areas have less contrast between light and shadow. In color rendering brighter colors and greater contrasts are used in the center of interest area than in other parts of the rendering.

Gradation of tone over an area is useful for several purposes. It is effective in obtaining contrast where two planes meet without making a definite difference of tone over their general areas, Fig. 238 B. It is a means of increasing the contrast of light and dark between the areas at the top and bottom of a tall object, Figs. 239 I, II. Gradation of tones is a useful device in expressing receding surfaces of ground, roof, walls, and other areas.

(I) LIGHT BACKGROUND (II) DARK BACKGROUND

SILOUHETTE EMPHASIZED BY VERTICAL GRADATION

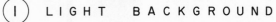

(III) GRADATIONS EXPRESS RECEDING PLANES

FIG. 239 USEFUL DEVICES OF RENDERING

Reflected light from horizontal surfaces sometimes causes the vertical surfaces of objects to be lighter at the bottom and darker toward the top. The reflected illumination is strong near the reflecting surface and quickly fades out. Few people observe closely enough to see the effect of reflected light. Experimenting with objects and good reflecting surfaces such as white cardboard in a strong light will help the reader understand the power of reflected light. When you are wearing white clothing on which the sun is shining walk up near some person or object faced away from the sun and watch the increase of light in the shadow area.

Some of the gradations of tone used in rendering can readily be explained, but others seem to be used for effect without having an obvious foundation in fact. Their use often makes the rendering clearer and more interesting.

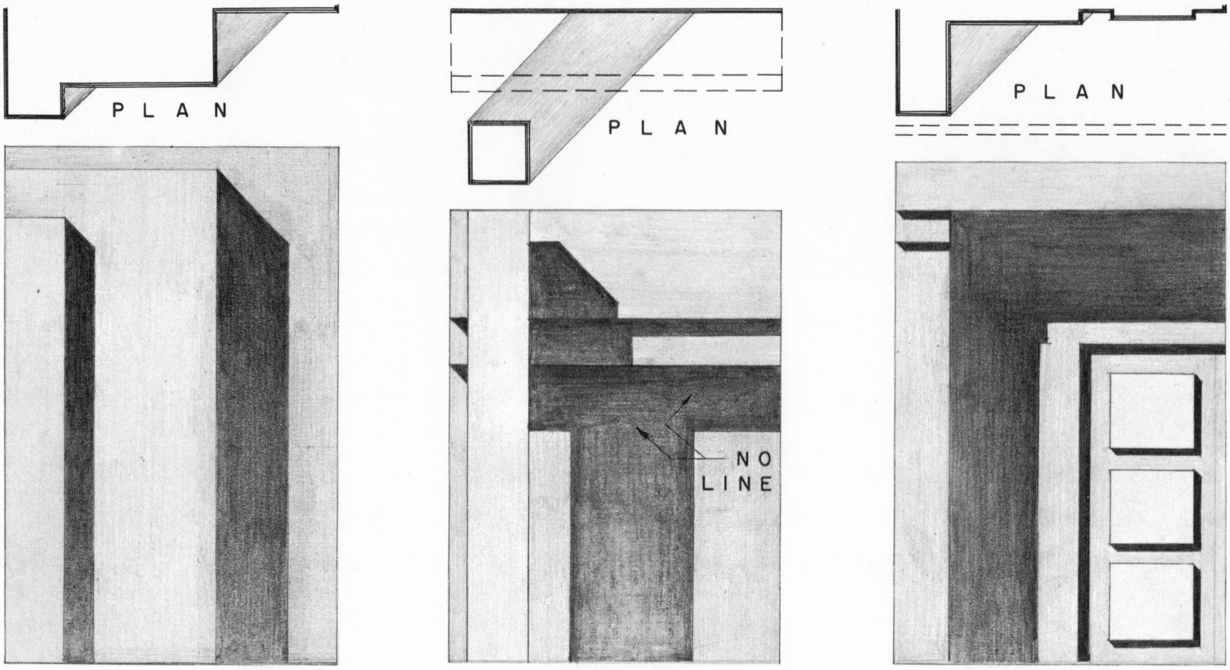

(A) LONG SHADOWS DARK AT THE TOP LIGHT AT BOTTOM

(B) TWO SHADOWS RUN TOGETHER ON SAME SURFACE

(C) THIN SHADOWS APPEAR DARKER THAN WIDE ONES

FIG. 240 GRADING AND TONE RELATIONS OF SHADOWS

Shadows take on life and sparkle when the edges away from the shape making the shadow are darkened. This gives the effect of a dark shadow without making an opaque dark blot of the entire shadow area. Long vertical shadows are often faded out lighter at the bottom because of reflection from horizontal surfaces on which the object rests. In some paintings and illustrations the edges of light areas adjoining shadows are made lighter as well as the edges of the shadows darker. Overemphasis of these devices can dominate the entire picture. More restrained use of them is normal for some rendering techniques to add life and brilliance to the effect.

Small bands of shadow appear darker than large areas on an object. Perhaps this is due to extreme contrast on the two edges in a very limited space. There is not sufficient dark area for the eye to adjust to see details within it, and thus make it appear to be less intense. It is usually necessary to make these small bands darker than the large shadow areas of a rendering in order to get them to show up correctly. A rendering should be viewed from a distance at intervals as the work progresses. The tone relations can then be seen more clearly than from the close position from which the work is done.

Connecting and overlapping shadow areas all run together. There should not be line or tone differences separating parts of a shadow area on the same plane caused by different objects.

Surroundings of the main object in a rendering are used for several purposes. They may be used in foreground and background to give the effect of distance. Their primary purpose may be to suggest a setting of time and place for the object. In all cases they should be considered as design elements. As such they can add interest in shapes and positions and are sometimes useful in focusing the attention at the correct place. Their locations, forms, and effects on the composition should be studied as carefully as the design of the object depicted is studied, Fig. 241.

AIR BRUSH RENDERING BY MEL O'BRIEN
MANN AND HARROVER—ARCHITECTS

TEMPERA RENDERING BY ROBERT E. SCHWARTZ
KEMPA AND SCHWARTZ-ARCHITECTS—J. H. LIVINGSTONE ASSOC.

FIG. 241 SURROUNDINGS ARE A PART OF RENDERING

CHAPTER 34

PENCIL RENDERING

Pencil rendering requires very little in the way of materials. The materials owned and used in some ways by every draftsman are the same ones employed by expert delineators to obtain widely varied and highly artistic results in rendering.

Paper, pencils, and erasers are the only essential materials for pencil rendering. A smooth-surfaced paper is best for fine details and smooth even tones. Rougher papers may be used for less polished, bolder type techniques, especially on large renderings, and may also be used to produce a textured or patterned effect. An assortment of pencils ranging from about 4H, the hardest, to 4B, the softest, will be helpful in producing bold or fine lines and tones ranging from dark to light. A set of 4H, 2H, F, 2B, and 4B should be adequate until there seems to be a need for additional grades.

The pencils can be sharpened with cone shaped, chisel, wedge shaped, or any other type of point that will give the type of line or tone that is needed. The cone shaped point can be used on end for fine lines and tangent to the paper for even tones, Fig. 242. The chisel point is used for broad strokes. The wedge shaped point is flattened from two sides to make a thin point in one direction and a broad one in the other direction. The wedge point can have the broad side reduced in width to make single stroke lines for representation of bricks or other details.

Experiment with different types of points and grades of leads to see what the pencils will do. Then try to produce tones and textures that should be useful for rendering. Figs. 243, 244, and 254 suggest tones and textures that may be found useful for practice and rendering.

Erasers that will erase clean and an erasing shield are very useful. One of the most difficult things in pencil rendering is to avoid smearing lines when working on the drawing. The pencils should be kept clean of the dust from sharpening, and the drawing should be protected by paper under the hand when working over a part of the rendering. The experienced person often plans the sequence of work to avoid having to rest the hand on any part of the finished rendering. When the rendering is completed a coat of fixative spray will help to prevent smudging.

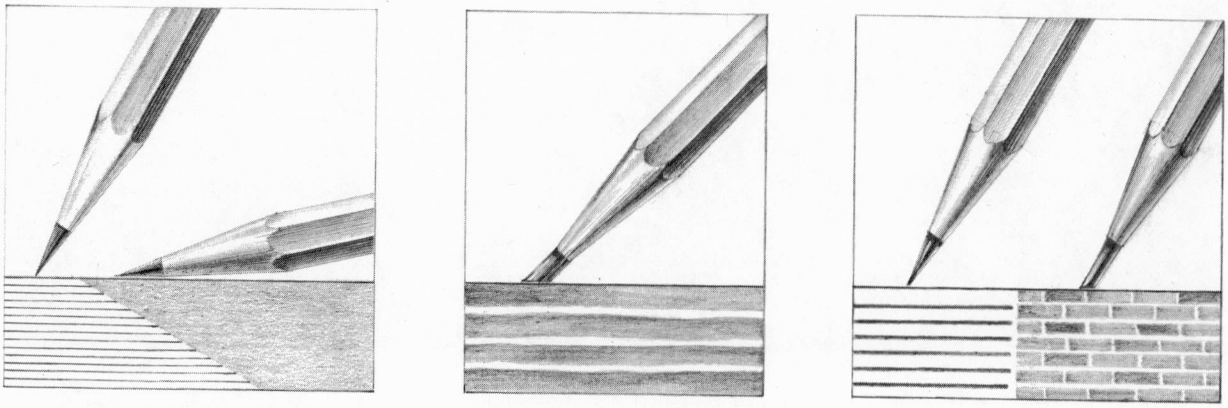

CONE POINT CHISEL POINT WEDGE POINT

FIG. 242 PENCIL POINT SHAPES AND LINES FROM THEM

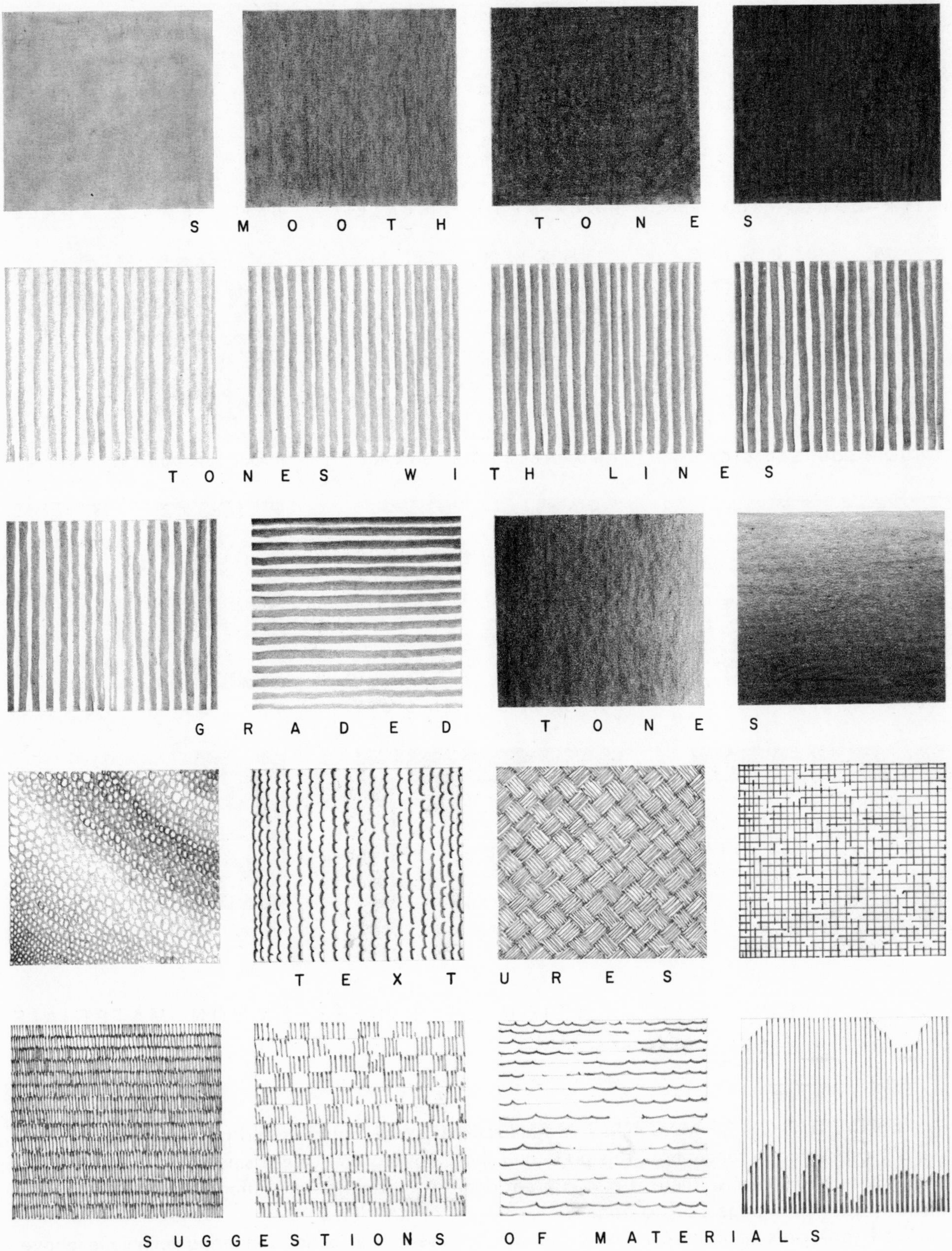

FIG. 243 PENCIL TONES, GRADATIONS, AND TEXTURES

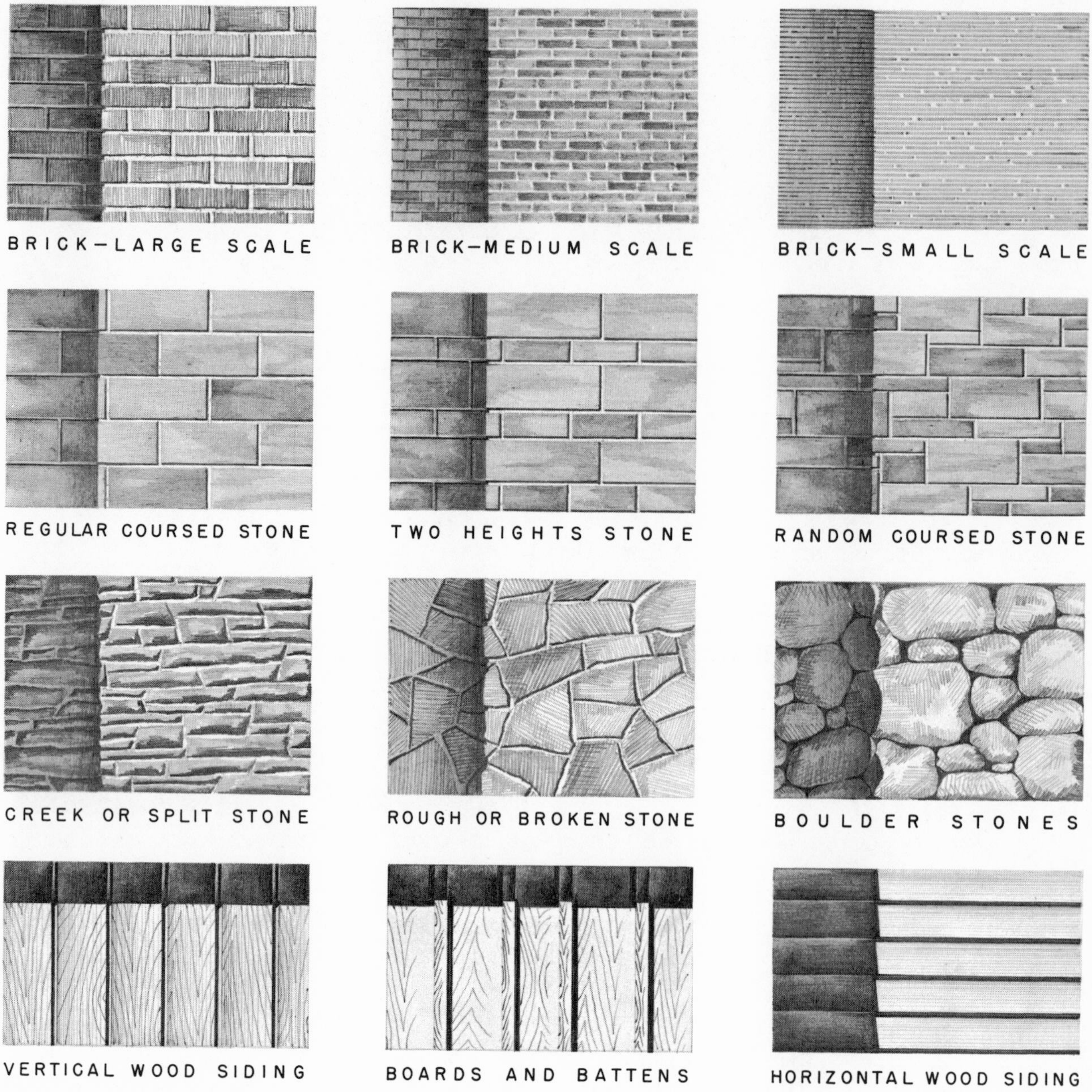

FIG. 244 PENCIL INDICATION OF THREE COMMON MATERIALS

REPRESENTATION OF MATERIALS IN RENDERING. Wall materials and plant materials are frequently represented in renderings. This page and the following one give a small amount of information on these two subjects. There is also a great deal of information on materials in the illustrations on most pages from page 257 to page 301.

Wall materials of three common types are represented in pencil rendering technique above. The examples of brick show variations of representation at different scales, examples of stone suggest some common variations of types, examples of wood show common forms.

Plant materials—hedges, shrubs, and trees—are often an accompanying part of an outdoor structure. These plants are a part of the design of cities, groups of buildings, individual buildings, walls, monuments, and other structures. Their sizes, shapes, and positions are important in design.

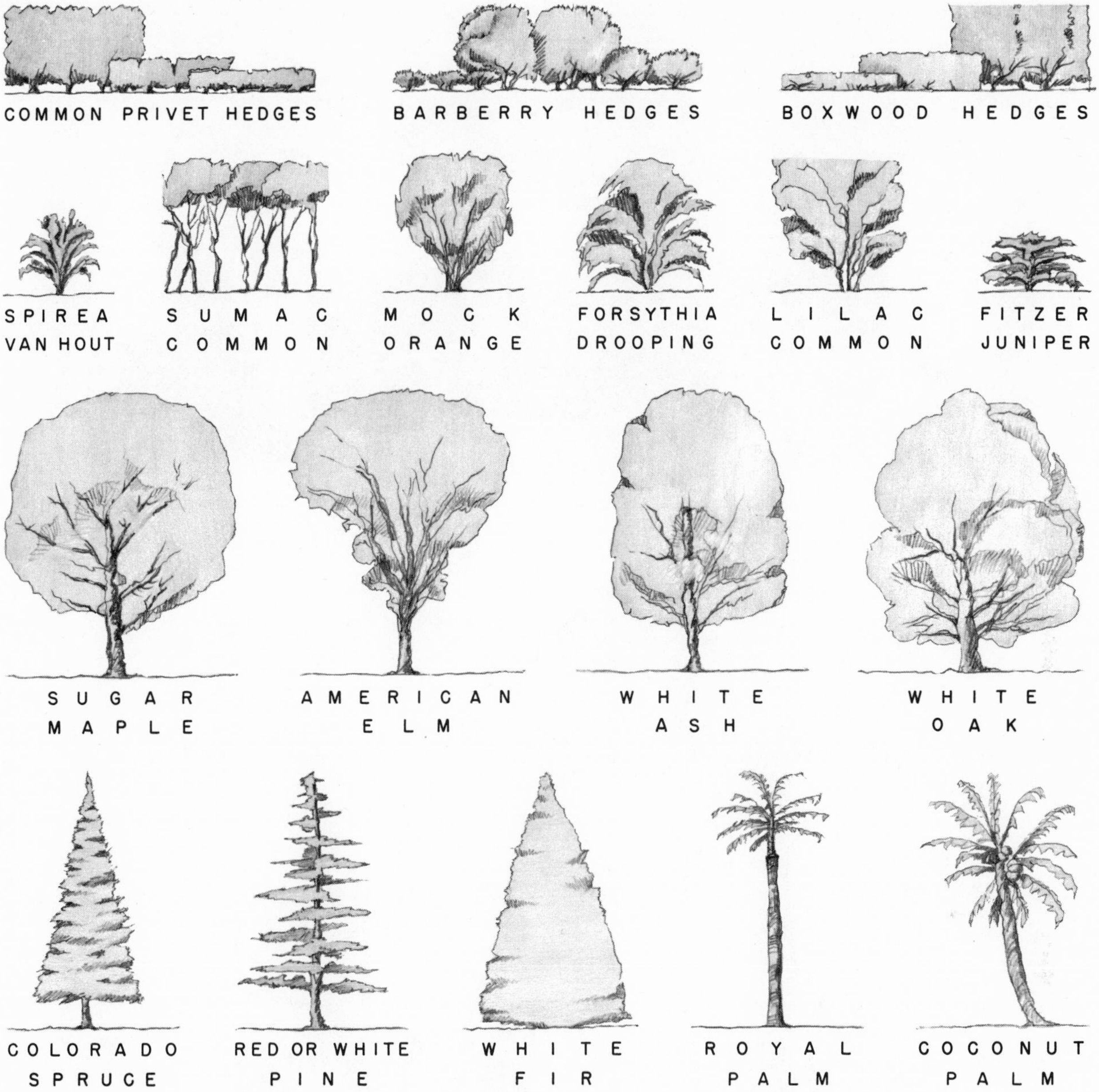

FIG. 245 GENERAL SHAPES OF COMMON TREES AND SHRUBS

An average size hedge for decorative use and pedestrian traffic control may be $2\frac{1}{2}$ to 3 feet in height. Hedges may be as small as 1 foot high and may be 15 feet or more in height.

Shrubs vary in size a great deal according to the species used and to some extent because of trimming. Many shrubs are from 3 to 10 feet in height, but others may be smaller or larger.

Shade trees of several varieties that are very widely used reach approximately the same height range of 60 to 90 feet at maturity in 50 to 300 years. The mature form of some trees is developed at a height of 30 feet or more. Newly planted and young trees are usually much more slender and have fewer large branches than mature trees. Tiny trees drawn in the shapes of mature trees may appear ridiculous. Trees of a given variety often differ in form at maturity. However some common characteristics of general proportions or pattern of branches appear in most specimens.

STUDENT RENDERING BY DAVID SMITH

PENCIL SKETCH BY EERO SAARINEN
EERO SAARINEN AND ASSOCIATES—ARCHITECTS

FIG. 246 EXAMPLES OF PENCIL RENDERING

The simplest type of pencil rendering employs tones for background, object, and shadows. The tones may be made with lines ruled mechanically parallel and close together or by going over the areas freehand with many strokes to produce smooth even values. The illustration at top of Fig. 246 is rendered in this simple technique with good relations of light and dark to define the areas. Thin light corners can be erased out clean if they are needed.

The pencil sketch at the bottom of Fig. 246 suggests textures of walls and foliage. The shadows on steps and walls are graded away from the edges. The walls are also very effectively graded from dark at the top to light at the bottom. It should be noted that the composition focuses on the area around the doorway.

Indications of materials and textures add greatly to a more complete rendering such as the ones in Figs. 247, 248, and 249 when these elements are a part of the object depicted. The grading of wall and furniture areas and shadows on the rendering of an interior add contrast and life to it. The more detailed and elaborate pencil renderings use the individual strokes of the pencil to produce patterns and indicate materials. Brick, stone, wood graining, and rough textures of rugs and upholstery materials may be suggested by their detailed rendering.

STUDENT RENDERING BY RONALD LOWRY

FIG. 247 EXAMPLE OF PENCIL RENDERING

RENDERING BY FOSTER H. HYATT
BRUCE BARNES, ARCHITECT

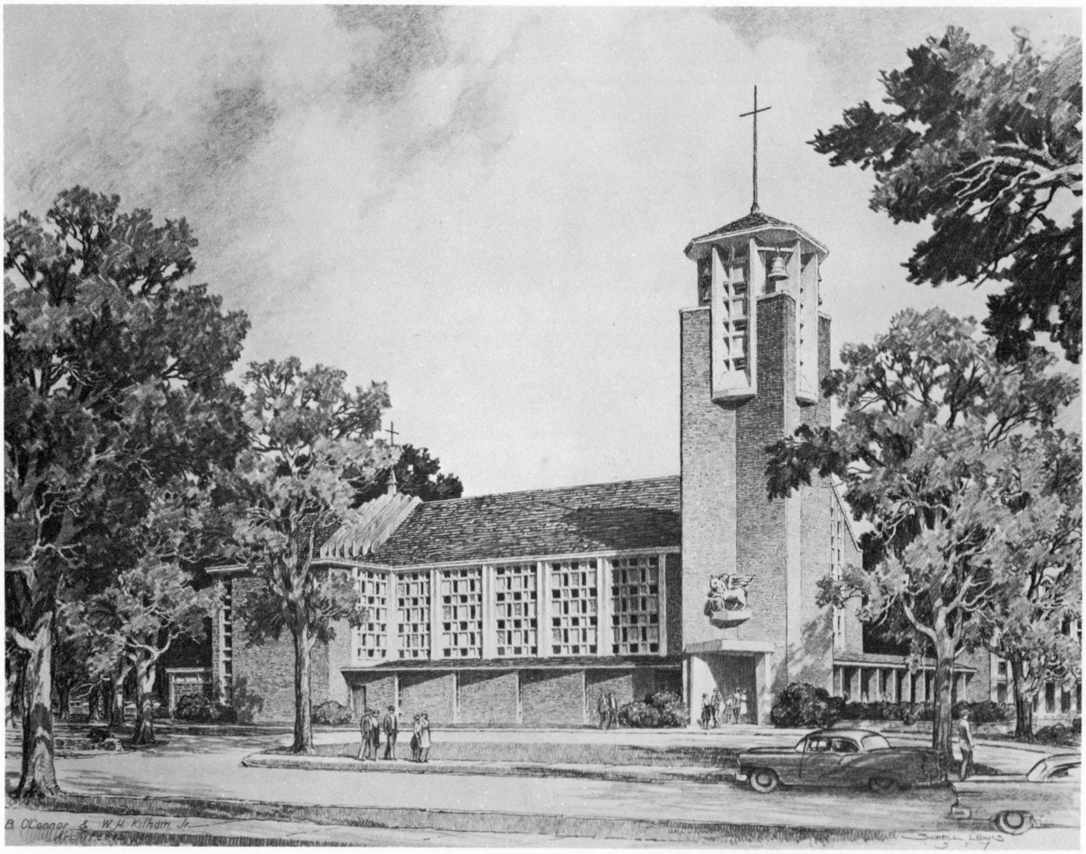

RENDERING BY SCHELL LEWIS
O' CONNOR AND KILHAM, ARCHITECTS

FIG. 248 EXAMPLES OF PENCIL RENDERING

RENDERING BY ADAM JIMENEZ
EGGERS AND HIGGENS, ARCHITECTS

RENDERING BY GILBERT K. JACOBS
MCGUIRE, SHOOK, COMPTON, AND RICHEY, INC., ARCHITECTS

FIG. 249 EXAMPLES OF PENCIL RENDERING

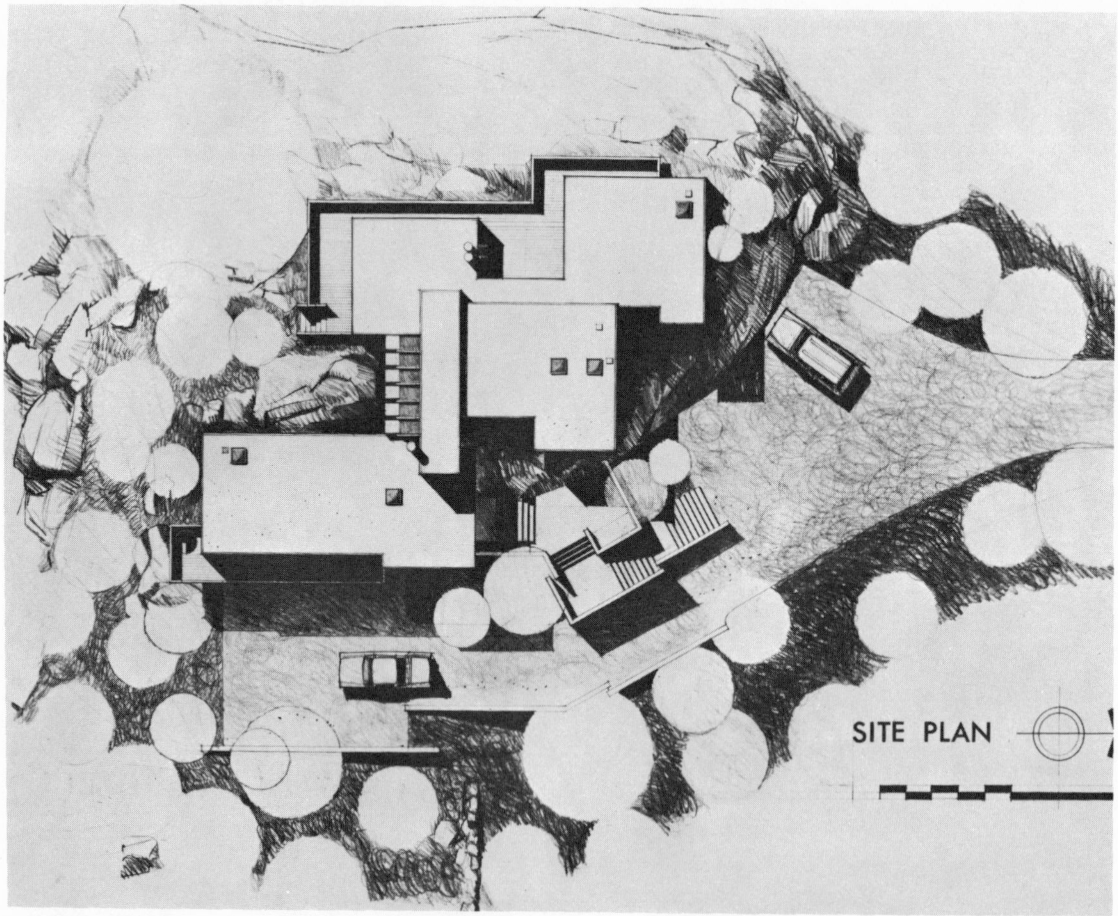

RENDERINGS BY DONALD A. REED
EARL R. FLANSBURG & ASSOCIATES, ARCHITECTS

FIG. 250 EXAMPLES OF PENCIL RENDERING

RENDERINGS BY DONALD A. REED
EARL R. FLANSBURG & ASSOCIATES, ARCHITECTS

FIG. 251 EXAMPLES OF PENCIL RENDERING

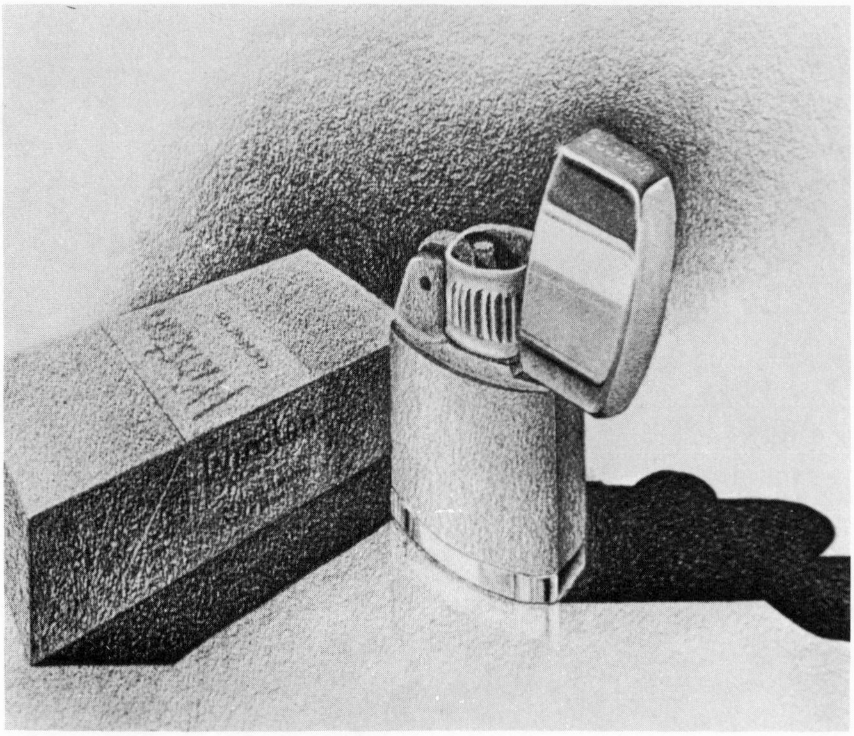

STUDENT RENDERING BY RONALD A. WENDLANDT

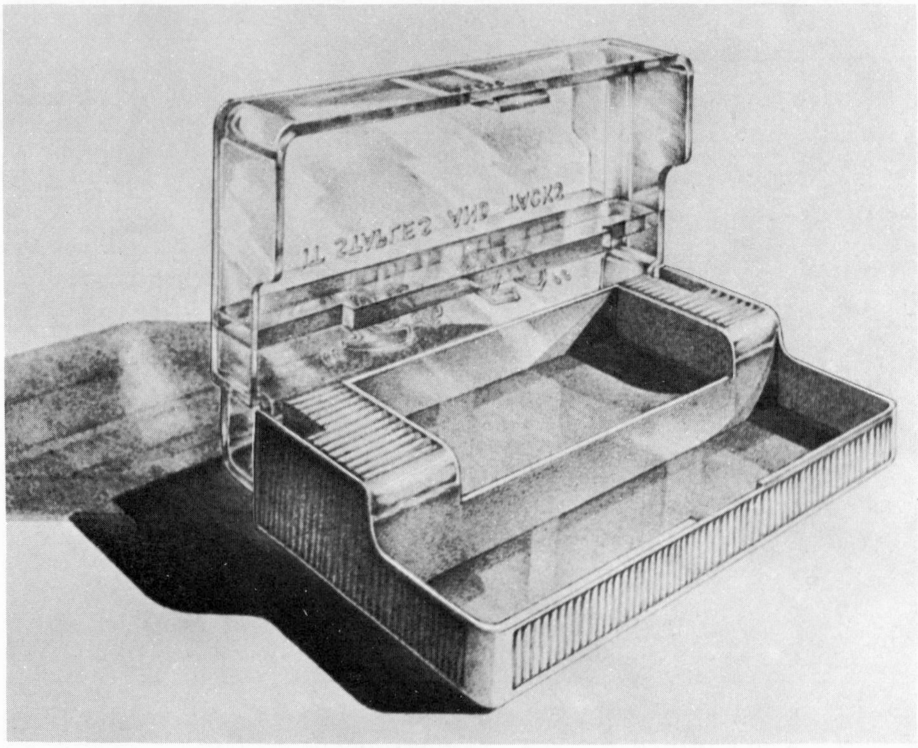

STUDENT RENDERING BY J. J. SONDERMAN

FIG. 252 EXAMPLES OF PENCIL RENDERING

STUDENT RENDERING BY M. PINTO

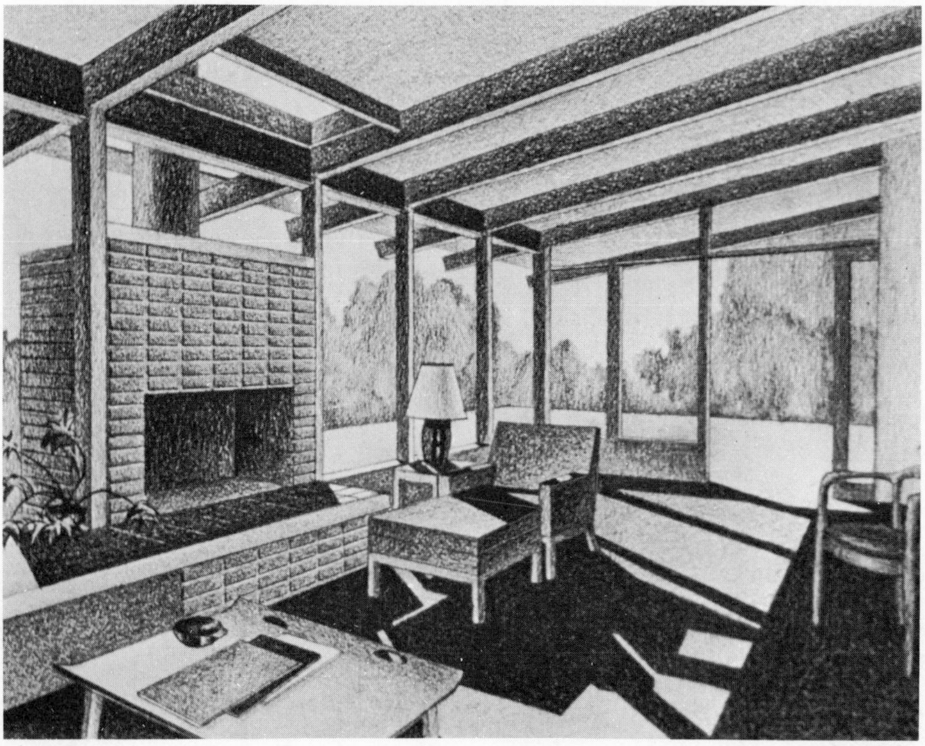

STUDENT RENDERING BY P. L. BROOKSHIRE

FIG. 253 EXAMPLES OF PENCIL RENDERING

CHAPTER **35**

PEN AND INK RENDERING

Pen and ink renderings have wide variations in technique. For more detailed renderings, tones, textures, and materials may be represented in the manner suggested by Fig. 254 and by the renderings of Fig. 255. Pens, paper, or illustration board, drawing ink, and erasers are the only materials required for freehand ink rendering. A smooth surfaced heavy paper, bristol board, or illustration board should be used. The same pen types that were described and illustrated on pages 34 and 35 for lettering are used for pen and ink rendering. Six or eight pens or more should be selected to give a wide range of line weights and variations.

Before beginning a rendering try out all of the pens to see the results obtained with each one. Then practice some of the techniques for tones and materials shown in Figs. 243, 244, and 254 and add other variations to these. Before beginning on a complete rendering select a small area of the proposed rendering for practice on scrap paper. This small practice area should contain parts of important areas of the complete rendering in both light and shadow. Practice this small area until satisfactory and interesting tones and textures are produced and then begin the complete rendering.

Ruling pens are often used either for a part of an ink rendering or for the entire rendering. Some well-known delineators use the ruling pen for their renderings and develop distinctive and effective techniques with it. A professional example of ruling pen technique for all of a rendering is shown in Fig. 256. Other professional examples in Figs. 258 and 259 and student renderings of Figs. 255 and 257 make some use of ruled lines.

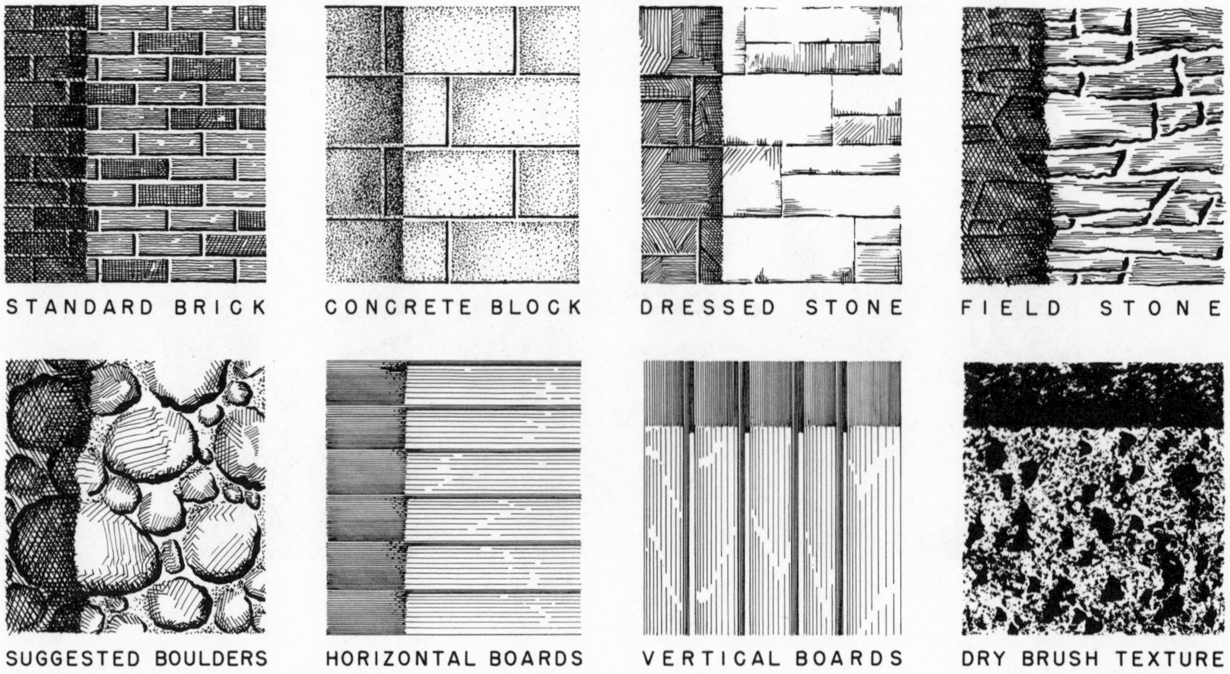

FIG. 254 REPRESENTATION OF MATERIALS WITH INK

STUDENT RENDERING BY JOHN SCHOLZ

STUDENT RENDERING BY JACK WRIGHT

FIG. 255 EXAMPLES OF PEN AND INK RENDERING

RENDERING BY FRANCIS MAH
OFFICE OF WALK C. JONES JR., ARCHITECTS

FIG. 256 EXAMPLE OF INK LINE RENDERING

Pen and ink rendering is similar to pencil rendering in some respects and is different from it in others. Fine detailed work to represent materials and produce patterns for tones or representation of texture frequently gives very much the same effect with the two media. Ink does not allow the modeling of forms as simply and easily as pencil. However forms can be modeled just as clearly and perhaps more emphatically with ink than with pencil by using dots, small pen strokes, or ruled lines to produce the gradation required. All grays are produced in pen and ink rendering by a variation in the amounts of black lines and white paper.

Pen strokes and ink areas must be given time to dry before working over them. When an ink rendering is finished it can be cleaned with a soft eraser. Do not erase so vigorously and so long that the blacks are faded and become grays.

All renderings are conventionalized and simplified representations of the object depicted to some degree. Some renderings are very much simplified and others are much more complex and realistic. The professional example of Fig. 256 is a very effective simple presentation.

STUDENT RENDERING BY RICHARD A. BAXTER

STUDENT RENDERING BY RENALDO PEREZ
INK WITH LIGHT WATER COLOR WASHES

FIG. 257 EXAMPLES OF PEN AND INK RENDERING

RENDERING BY ADAM JIMENEZ

EGGERS AND HIGGENS, ARCHITECTS

RENDERING BY RUDOLPH ASSOCIATES

ARCHITECTS: MATHERS & HALDENBY-SKIDMORE, OWINGS & MERRILL, CONSULTANTS

FIG. 258 EXAMPLES OF PEN AND INK RENDERING

ARCHITECTURAL DRAWING BY HELMUT JACOBY
AFFLECK, DESKARATS, DIMAKOPOLOUS, LEBENSOLD SISE - ARCHITECTS

FIG. 259 EXAMPLE OF PEN AND INK RENDERING

CHAPTER **36**

WASH RENDERING TECHNIQUE

The term *wash rendering* is used for illustrations made with any painting mixture in water that is applied with a brush and gives transparent tones. The medium used may be Chinese stick ink, transparent water color paints, or a semi-transparent mixture of opaque white and water colors. Even strong coffee solution can be used for wash rendering.

There are three general characteristics of wash rendering: (A) The paint materials for the washes are sufficiently transparent to allow lines and tones to show through light and medium dark washes of them. (B) The materials used are capable of gradual change in tone to allow gradation of an area and modeling to show curved shapes. (C) The paint allows repetition of washes over an area.

MATERIALS FOR WASH RENDERING. All of the materials listed here and shown in Fig. 260 can usually be obtained at an art supply store:

1. Water color board.
2. Water color brushes.
3. Paint material.
4. Small dishes or pans.
5. A large pan for water.
6. Small blotters.

1. Illustration board of some type is often used for wash renderings. It is thick cardboard with a surface coating of good paper. A slightly rough surface paper takes washes better than a smooth surface. Water color board with a surface of cold pressed water color paper is excellent for most wash renderings. Common illustration board is more likely to streak. It is less expensive and is sometimes satisfactory. The water color board should be attached firmly to the drawing board with heavy thumb tacks or drafting tape to lessen the warping from the large washes. Stretches of cold pressed water color paper are ideal for wash rendering. They are difficult to make.

2. Brushes of red sable or other materials that retain their shapes when wet are best suited for water color rendering work. Some types of brushes become soft and flabby when dipped in paint solution or water. Get three round pointed brushes of varying size if they can be obtained and are not too expensive for the use to be made of them. The large size is usually number 12 and has bristles about $1\frac{1}{4}$ inches long. The medium size should have about $\frac{7}{8}$-inch bristles and the small one $\frac{5}{8}$- or $\frac{1}{2}$-inch bristles. If only one brush is bought it should be the medium sized one. Flat red sable brushes with chisel edges are also very useful for water color rendering.

3. Paint should be limited to monotone while learning the technique of handling washes for rendering. The simplest procedure is to use a tube of ivory black or lamp black water color for this purpose. A constant mixture of one color and black is also easy to prepare and use. Any single color or mixture of two or more paints used for monotone wash rendering should be capable of producing a dark tone.

4. The small pans or dishes should be white so that it is possible to see what they have in them. It is very convenient to have about six of the small pans or dishes. Do not use a muffin pan or other connected small pans. They are a nuisance when it is necessary to empty one or pour from one to another of the small divisions.

5. A larger flat pan or small pail holding about a quart should be used for water supply. Do not attempt to use a soft drink bottle. When a person is in a hurry to wash out a brush he does not have time and patience to aim at the small opening in a bottle.

6. Small white blotters are very useful for emergencies. Keep one under the hand while running a wash. Do not use colored blotters that will fade and discolor the illustration board.

PREPARATIONS FOR WASH RENDERING. Precautions are necessary in preparing for and making a wash rendering. The drawing surface should be kept clean and free from damage. Avoid get-

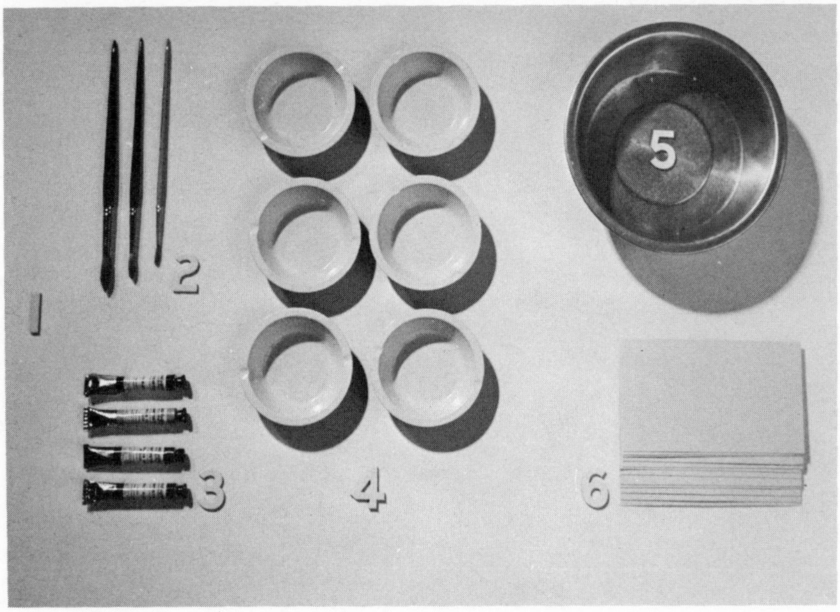

FIG. 260 MATERIALS FOR WASH RENDERING

ting grease or dirt from hands or elsewhere onto the paper. It will prevent the wash from coating the paper evenly. Erase cautiously, remembering that roughened paper absorbs wash and becomes darker whereas polished spots will be lighter when the wash is applied.

The drawing can either be made with neat pencil lines and left in pencil or it can be inked with diluted black ink. The diluted ink should give a light gray line. It will require a great deal of water and a little ink in the mixture. The paper must be kept clean when pencil lines are used. Inking the lines allows cleaning with a mild eraser after inking.

Scrap paper or illustration board of the same general type as that used for rendering is very useful for testing washes.

New pans may have an oily film on them. They should be washed with soap and water. Some brushes have been treated with a starchy material that should be washed from the bristles. Remove all lint and eraser particles from the drawing before starting a wash rendering.

To prepare the solution for the wash, squeeze about one-half inch of paint from the tube into an empty pan. Add some water and mix thoroughly with a brush. This mixture will probably be too dark to use. Pour part of it into another pan, add water and mix. Continue to dilute until it is light enough to use. The paint often settles to the bottom of the pan in a short time. It must be kept mixed when it is being used.

When beginning a rendering the paper is often very dry before the first wash is run over an area. Keep the solution for the first wash quite pale as it is more likely to streak than later washes when the paper is slightly moist. Darker washes can be used later if that seems desirable and if they can be handled successfully. There is safety from streaks in using a number of light washes instead of one dark one. However, do not go to the extreme of using such light washes that they do not produce a perceptible darkening of the area.

Incline the board at an angle of about $1\frac{1}{2}$ to 2 inches to the foot with the length of the area that is to receive the wash in the direction of the slope. See that the board is supported securely so it will not tilt when work is done on it. Place the pan of wash near the board but on the table. For a right-handed person it should be on the right side. Do not set a pan of wash on the board where it is easy to spill over the drawing. Remove other pans of wash to a distance so the brush will not be dipped into the wrong one.

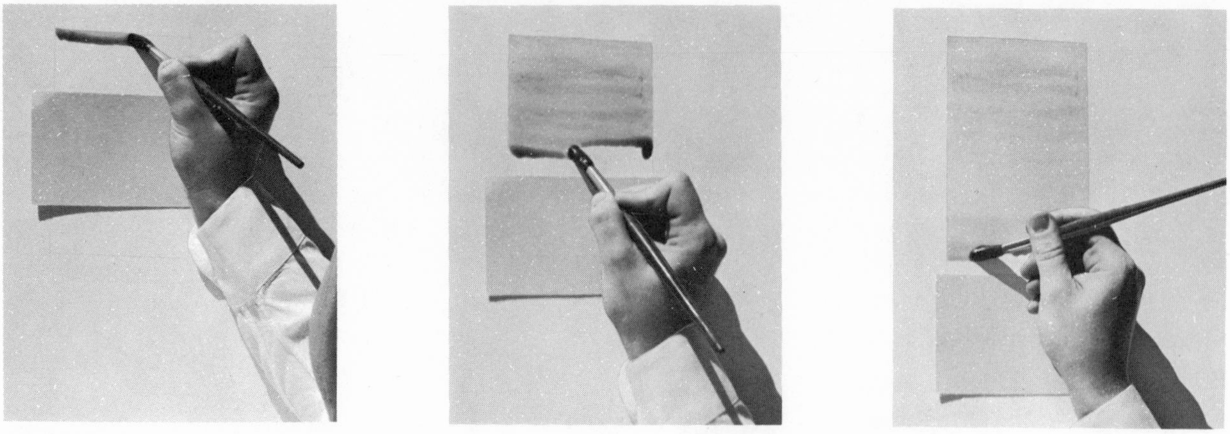

(A) BEGINNING WASH (B) MIDDLE OF WASH (C) FINISHING WASH

FIG. 261 TECHNIQUE IN RUNNING A FLAT WASH

FLAT WASHES. The flat wash is the simplest to apply. It requires a uniform darkness over an entire area. It is best to use a simple rectangular area of moderate size for a first exercise. The size may be about 3 or 4 inches wide and 5 or 6 inches long, Figs. 261 A, B, C.

The procedure in running the flat wash is to apply a small puddle of the mixture to be used across the top of the area with the brush. Fill the brush as full as possible without dripping. Hit the line exactly. Now guide the puddle down over the area about $\frac{1}{4}$ inch at a time. Add wash with the brush when necessary in order to maintain a uniform small puddle at the lower edge of the wet area.

As the wash is guided down over the area to be treated, keep the lower edge level so the puddle is uniform all along the edge of the wash. If the board is tilted too much or the puddle is large and collects at one side, the water mixture may start running in a stream over the paper and continue until it hits the floor. If this happens, blot the run immediately and firmly. Then start at the edge at once with a smaller puddle and lower the board a little if necessary. Speedy use of the blotter will often prevent streaks entirely. Do not go back into a partly dried area of the wash with the wet brush. To do so will almost always cause streaks.

Move the wash at as uniform speed as possible. If the puddle remains longer in one place it will make the wash darker. If the wash runs over the edge, move the puddle below the place, then blot to the line and press the edge of the blotter firmly. Do not attempt to blot at the edge of the puddle. An experienced person sometimes pushes the edge of the wet wash back firmly beyond the line with the finger. Because the fingers are slightly oily the wash usually stays back and is then guided over to the line with the brush. If a drop of wash gets on the dry paper, blot it instantly. The sooner it is blotted the less it will stain the paper. Turn the brush so the part of it that is running the wash to the line can be seen clearly.

As the wash approaches the bottom of the area reduce the puddle a little then guide it to the bottom line. Remember to turn the brush so it is easy to see the edge of the wash. After the wash covers the entire area, remove the fluid from the brush and touch the moist brush to the puddle at the lower end of the area. It will pick up a little of the puddle. Repeat cautiously until the puddle is removed without changing the darkness of this area. If it is permissible to do so, remove the fluid from your brush by flipping it on the floor. The brush can also be emptied by squeezing the bristles lightly at the ferrule then pulling them between the fingers. The third method is to touch the wet brush to a cloth or paper towel to remove the paint solution.

After the wash is finished, allow the board to remain tilted as it is until the moistened area has dried. As soon as the area no longer shines from being wet, the board can be moved. The area should feel dry before running another wash over it or an adjoining area.

A little thought will often prevent a great deal of trouble in running washes. Remember that the puddle runs down the slope. Turn the board so the wash can be run the easy way across the small dimension of the area. It is almost impossible to run a smooth wash over a long thin area by starting on a long edge.

Skill in handling a brush can be acquired by almost anyone with normal coordination of hand, eye, and mind. People frequently say, "I am just too nervous to do that." Most persons can control their nerves to do this type of work. It usually takes a great deal of effort and concentration for a beginner to run a wash neatly to a line. After a reasonable amount of practice this operation becomes routine and semi-automatic with many delineators. Without worry or any conscious effort the hand of the experienced person just places the brush in a correct spot and moves it along. This is difficult for a person who has not experienced it to believe. It is a case of doing something with the intuition or subconscious mind much better than it can be done by conscious effort.

The sequence of washes in making a rendering may reduce the amount of effort required and provide less opportunity for bad edges. A good procedure is to cover all possible areas with one wash. When a light, medium, and dark area adjoin each other run the light tone over all three areas. Then run the medium tone over both the medium and dark areas. Finally run the dark area only. This system avoids unnecessary repetition of washes and unnecessary repeated running of washes to lines. It assures a definite difference in the tones of the areas, Fig. 262.

In some renderings there is one important part which should be just right. In such cases this area may be rendered first and other areas rendered to suit it. There is often a tendency to put off until last the very important part of the rendering. This may result in a bad practice of the renderer waiting until he is tired and rushed for time to do the essential part of the rendering.

Borders offer their problems in avoiding streaks. If the border extends around three sides only, or is interrupted, the technique is simple. Turn the board to start the wash at one end or at the break in the border. When the corner is reached turn the border to slope diagonally so the puddle runs around the corner. After the corner is cleared so there is no danger of a run back, turn the board farther, always allowing for the puddle to run down the slope. When the border is continuous around the plate, turn the board with the slope on the diagonal and run both sides at once. Start at top and end at bottom corner.

(I) LIGHTEST WASH OVER ALL AREAS

(II) MEDIUM TONE ON MEDIUM + DARK AREAS

(III) THE DARK AREAS ARE DARKENED LAST

FIG. 262 A SUGGESTED SEQUENCE FOR WASHES

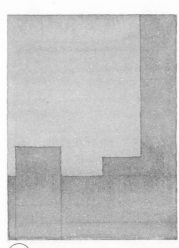

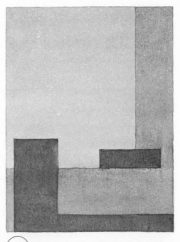

FIG. 263 EXAMPLES OF GRADED WASHES

GRADED WASHES. Graded washes change gradually and smoothly from dark to light. They are applied in the same general manner as flat washes. The important difference is that the darkness of the wash solution is gradually changed as the puddle is guided over the paper.

The simplest method for running a graded wash requires the use of a sequence of mixtures in a number of pans. It is best to have at least five or six pans so that the difference in darkness of wash in adjacent pans is slight. The pans are arranged in the order in which they are to be used. They are placed conveniently near the right edge of the board for a right-handed person. The change in darkness of the puddle is secured by using the mixture in each pan in order as the wash progresses.

A second good method of grading a wash is to start with a small quantity of the darkest mixture to be used at this time in a pan. Start the wash at the dark end with this mixture. Then dilute the mixture by adding a small amount of water to the pan with the brush at regular intervals as the wash is moved along over the area. When water is added stir the mixture thoroughly before using it. Good judgment is needed for this method of running a graded wash. If too much of the dark paint solution is used to start the wash, the addition of a small amount of water will not change it enough. The resulting wash will not vary sufficiently from dark to light. Part of the mixture in the pan can be poured out in order to get a more rapid change when the small amount of water is added.

The graded wash can be run from light to dark if that procedure is preferred. This method requires starting the wash with a small quantity of very light mixture or water in the pan. A darker mixture, which is assumed to be right for the dark end of the wash, is then added a little at a time. The solution in the pan should be practically the same as this dark mixture when the wash is ended. Some persons get better results running graded washes from dark to light, and some prefer the light to dark procedure. Often the board can be turned to run the wash either way.

In running graded washes the change in darkness of the mixture must be made a little before the corresponding change is desired on the paper. This is because of the floating down of the puddle.

A third method is used by some skillful and also by some reckless persons. The darkness of the mixture for the graded wash is changed in the brush entirely by dipping back and forth between the dark to be used and water. This procedure is not a safe one for a beginner. Try it if you wish to live dangerously, but try it first on scratch paper. It is a better method for relatively short washes than for long ones. Better results are obtained with any method by using several light washes.

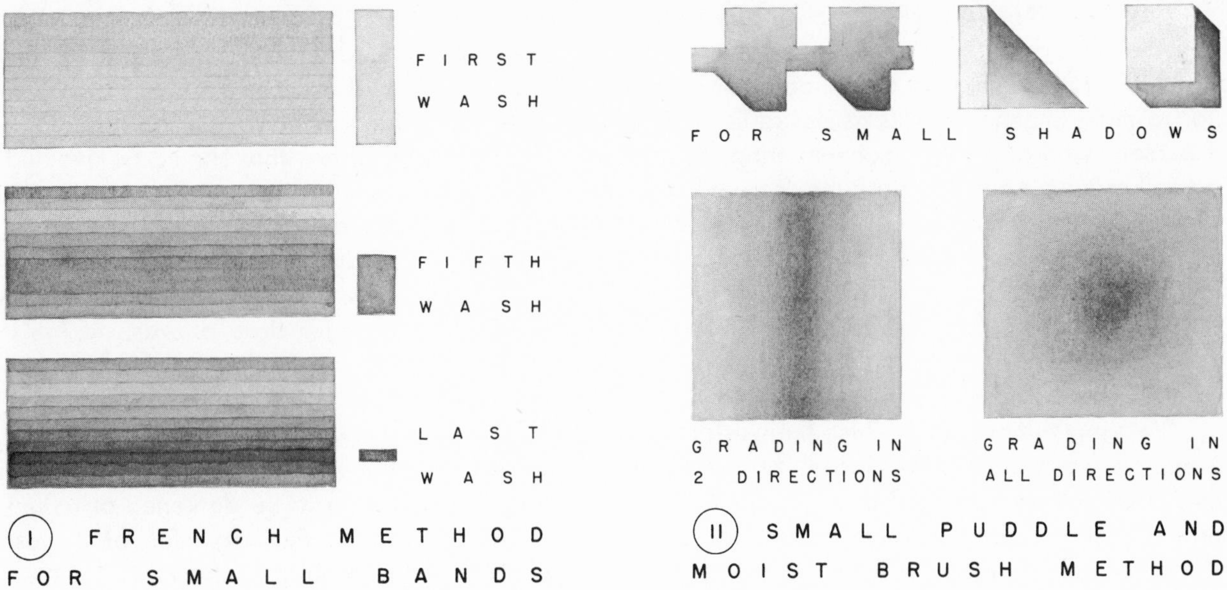

FIG. 264 GRADING WASHES IN SMALL AREAS

GRADING WASHES IN SMALL AREAS. The modeling of shading on curved surfaces requires the grading of washes in small spaces. Sometimes they must be graded in more than one direction.

The French method of grading a wash over a narrow band is useful for shading in one direction only. The procedure is to apply a sequence of flat washes over one or more of the equal small spaces into which the band is divided. These washes change so gradually and are spaced at such short intervals that the change of tone may seem to be smooth and continuous. The process is rather tedious and mechanical. It requires good judgment of the tones. Fig. 264 I.

The small puddle and moist brush method is used to fade a small wash in one or more directions. Two brushes are required. One is used to supply a small puddle of the dark wash, the other to dampen the paper at the edge of the puddle with water so the wash spreads and fades out into the moist area. This technique is illustrated in its simplest form at the top of Fig. 264 II. The second brush is dipped into water then flipped out until it will leave only a film of moisture on the paper. This film is brought to the edge of the puddle. The puddle then runs onto the moist paper and fades out. This technique requires skill and judgment to obtain good results. If the moist brush carries too much water, the water runs into the dark puddle and control of the shading is lost. This method usually works better on a level board than on an inclined one. It can be used to shade in more than one direction. In the lower left illustration of Fig. 264 II it is used to shade in two directions. In the lower right illustration of Fig. 264 II the fadeout is in all directions from a round puddle. Shading of this type is likely to be more successful when light washes are repeated several times to darken the areas.

Ruling pen washes are a means of producing neat narrow bands. It is surprising to some people that a paint mixture for rendering can be used in a ruling pen. The pen should be clean so that ink particles will not change the darkness or color of the fluid. Small shadow bands can be ruled in much more precisely than they can be put in with a brush. Shade lines at the shadow edges of projections can also be used to trim the edges.

High lights on corners toward the light source can be ruled with a mixture of water color and white. The mixture must be thick enough to cover the paint below it. It should in most cases be tinted to harmonize with the area of which it is a part.

Erasing of high lights is satisfactory when the erased band is kept narrow and trim.

STREAKS IN WASHES. Streaks seem to be an inevitable part of wash rendering. In their worst form they disfigure the plate. Some are often so pale as to be noticed only under careful scrutiny of details. Occasionally a streak occurs where it adds to the effect. It takes a very skillful delineator to make planned steaks as desirable additions to water color technique. For the great majority of persons who do water color rendering, streaks are undesirable blemishes that should be avoided. The following paragraphs describe some of the more common causes of streaks. It is hoped that a knowledge of the causes may help the reader to avoid making undesirable streaks.

The fan or runback streak is caused by having a part of the puddle run back the wrong direction into the partly dry area above the puddle edge of the wash. This may be caused by careless use of the brush in adding the wash solution to the puddle, by allowing a drop of wash to fall in the partly dry area, or by tilting the board the wrong direction before the wash has dried. It may also be caused by using the wet brush to try to correct some defect in the damp area.

Varying the speed at which the wash moves over the paper will cause streaks with most paints. When the wash edge moves slowly or the puddle is allowed to remain too long in one position, a dark band will be formed. The wash should progress down over the area to be darkened at as uniform a speed as it is possible to maintain. This requires rapid work at the beginning of a wash where lines and corners must be met as precisely as possible. It also requires patience to maintain a slower pace in the middle of an area since too-rapid progress of the puddle will cause light streaks.

Varying the amount of puddle will cause light and dark streaks. The greater the amount of puddle the darker the tone applied and the smaller the puddle the lighter the results from the wash. Dark streaks are sometimes made at each side of the wash by carrying those parts of the puddle lower and larger.

Texture produced by a wash is influenced by several things. Almost all water color paints settle out and will produce a texture effect under certain conditions. Some pigments are more noted for this characteristic than others. A rough-surfaced paper increases the rough-textured effect from the wash, whereas a smooth paper minimizes it. A large puddle run slowly helps to produce texture by settling of the pigments. A small puddle run rapidly over the paper will decrease the texture effect from the wash.

Imperfect mixing of the paint is the cause of some streaks. Most paint pigments do not dissolve in water. They are finely ground particles of earth, charcoal, metal, etc., that are held in suspension when mixed with water. They gradually settle to the bottom. After the mixture has partly settled, a light solution is obtained by dipping the brush part way down. By dipping the brush deep so it rubs over the bottom of the pan, a darker mixture is obtained. The wash in the pan must be stirred every time the brush is dipped into it in order to get a uniform darkness.

PATCHING DEFECTIVE WASHES. Patching is just as much a part of the technique of rendering as the running of washes. Skill in correcting defects and mistakes is an essential part of the training in drafting and rendering. Care and thought should be devoted to avoiding streaks in washes. It usually takes a great deal of time and effort to correct such defects. Since very few renderings are made without the necessity of some patching it is essential that skill be acquired in this necessary part of the work. Patching usually requires more skill than other phases of rendering.

Edges of washes required precise skill with the brush if they are to be neat and trim. There are very few persons who do not have some slight irregularities in the edges of the washes which they run. Even with repairs by blotting when the area is still wet there are sometimes small places where the wash extends over the line. These areas can be lightened so they are less conspicuous and often removed entirely by using a scrubbing and blotting technique. For this procedure use a small or medium sized brush. The brush should not be soft. If an old one with a somewhat blunted point is available, use it. Dip the brush in clear water, then remove most of the water, leaving enough to wet the paper but not enough to make a puddle. Scrub the dark area, which is to be removed, with the moist brush for two or three seconds, then blot. Repeat until the edge is straightened. Observe carefully to see that the scrubbing is not removing the surface of the paper. When this begins to occur the paper should be allowed to dry before proceeding with the process.

Dark spots in a wash area can be treated by the scrub and blot method described for edges of washes. When there are two or more spots, work on the worst one first so that progress can be noted by comparison with the other spots that have not been treated. Each spot usually requires several careful scrubbings with the moist brush and blottings to make a decided improvement. Care must be used to scrub only where the wash is too dark. A skillful person can often completely remove a dark spot or streak so that all trace of it has vanished.

Light spots can be darkened by different techniques. One method is to put a puddle of wash over the small light area then blot. The blotting softens the edges. This is a method for small spots. The number of applications is determined by the darkness of the mixture used. It is better to try a light mixture first so that the spot is not made too dark.

A second method for light spots is to put the wash puddle over the lightest area then fade the edge with a moist brush. This is the technique of grading a small wash. Remember to use just enough water in the brush to moisten the paper up to the edge of the puddle.

A third method is to use a light mixture and stipple (make small dots) over the area. Allow these dots to dry then repeat. Try to stipple on the very lightest places each time. When a light wash is used for stippling and a number of applications are made, the result should be a gradual darkening of the light spot to match the surrounding area. Sometimes it is preferable to use parallel strokes with an almost dry brush. These fine strokes are allowed to dry before repeating the process.

Camouflage is defined as an expedient to deceive or hide. Sometimes it is much easier to hide or at least lessen the effect of a streak than to remove it. Streaks are made prominent by contrast between near areas. A dark streak in the middle of a wash can be made much less conspicuous. This is accomplished by darkening the light areas near the streak and fading away from it.

A wash over a large area of a rendering often seems quite streaked. The delineator should keep in mind that when such a wash is broken up by later and darker washes over parts of the area, the streaks will be less prominent. There are three reasons for this subordination of the streaks. (1) Part of them have been covered by the darker washes and made less conspicuous. (2) The continuous length of some of the streaks has been shortened or interrupted. (3) The contrast caused by the addition of darker areas attracts attention away from them.

Streaks that at first seem bad in areas that are later broken up into units of stone, tile, or other material may actually be beneficial. They may prevent a hard mechanical feeling.

SCRUBBING. Work and a great deal of it is required to do satisfactory patching of washes. If there are many streaks, patching just isn't a reasonable answer. As a final resort, scrubbing of the entire plate can be tried. The most efficient procedure is to take the board to the sink and slope it so water will run from it into the sink. Then get the large pan full of clear water. Start at the top of the rendering and go over it gently and quickly with a dripping sponge. Then go back and scrub lightly with the sponge where needed. Do not scrub hard enough to remove the surface of the paper. Remove water from the paper with the sponge. Then stand board on end until paper dries.

Do not attempt to scrub a partly dry rendering. Some of the moist areas may wash down to white paper. The dry areas may be faded only a little. Wait until the entire rendering is dry.

If the scrubbing is successful the rendering will now be very pale. The streaks will be less prominent and the drawing will still be in good condition. After the paper is dry start in again building up the washes of the rendering. If the scrubbing does not give satisfactory results the only answer is to get new illustration board or paper and start over.

Scrubbing is not the answer to all the ills of rendering. It is an emergency operation that is used as a last resort to save the life of the patient. It should be avoided if possible.

Scrubbing over a limited area of the rendering is sometimes a satisfactory procedure. Cover the surrounding area with white note paper to the exact edge of the area to be scrubbed. Use a minimum amount of water in a sponge. Make all strokes start on the paper covering the surrounding area and move into the wash area. This helps prevent water from running under the masking paper. Turn the sponge to a new part of its surface for each stroke. Clean the sponge in clear water when necessary. The masking paper must be held firmly as the sponge is moved over it.

CHAPTER 37

WATER COLOR RENDERING

Water color has great flexibility in the grading of washes, in modeling to express form, and in gradual change of color. A good water color rendering has great freedom of expression and vitality. The medium requires technical skill in running and controlling washes. The preceding chapter on wash rendering should be read as a part of the preparation for water color rendering.

PAINTS FOR WASH RENDERING. The following are three common classifications of pigments for wash renderings. These classifications sometimes overlap.

1. **Monotone** water color rendering is done with any paint or other substance that can be used for this technique. Either a single pigment or material or a combination of two or more colors or pigments in a constant proportion can be used. Constant mixtures can be made of paint alone or of ground and filtered Chinese stick ink tinted with a paint. When a mixture of two or more materials is used, precautions should be taken to see that the color contents of the washes remain the same throughout the rendering. A sure way to obtain this result is to mix at one time enough dark solution for the entire rendering. This mixture should be at least as dark as any wash required. It will be the source of supply for all washes. In most cases a small amount of it will be diluted with water for use. If the dark mixture must be kept for several days a small quantity of ammonium hydroxide should be added to keep it from spoiling. A less reliable method is to make as accurate an estimate as possible of the proportion of each material used for duplicating the mixture.

2. **Transparent water colors** are obtained in tubes at any art supply store. They are made by several manufacturers. Some brands are made in two or more qualities. One is called scholastic water colors and is intended for school use. The other, labeled artist's water color, is intended for professional use. It is of higher quality and is a more expensive product. Some colors are like dyes and others are more opaque. These characteristics are derived from the materials used in the paints.

The selection of colors of paints to use is an individual problem. The answer varies with the objects and colors to be represented in the renderings to be done. With mixtures of yellow, red, and blue it is possible to get more or less perfect versions of other colors including orange, green, purple, brown, grays, and black. With the use of only three paints a person must become expert in mixing colors. This is very useful training. One of the following three-color palettes can be used with good results.

A. Cadmium yellow light.
Alizarin crimson.
Ultramarine blue.

B. Cadmium yellow light.
Cadmium red medium.
Phthalocyanine blue.

C. Hansa yellow.
Acra red.
Phthalocyanine blue.

3. **A semi-transparent effect** is secured by mixing opaque poster white with transparent water color paints. The general effect is better if some white is mixed with all washes. This mixture gives a more solid and less transparent rendering. It still partly retains the characteristics of water color rendering but requires more cautious handling.

Wet paper technique is useful in rendering some larger areas in a free style. The stretched paper or heavy water color board is wet over the required area with a soft sponge or brush and water at the beginning of such a plate. Water color paint is applied to the wet paper with a brush and allowed to spread out. This is a very effective technique for skies, masses of trees, foliage, and other large areas. As the paper begins to dry, smaller areas are rendered. Finally, when practical to do so, small details and accents are put in with a brush or ruling pen. See sky of Fig. 269.

STUDENT RENDERING BY JAMES C. SHERBONDY

STUDENT RENDERING BY ROBERT MARTIN

FIG. 265 EXAMPLES OF WATER COLOR RENDERING

STUDENT RENDERING BY WILLIAM T. MONTGOMERY
FROM A DESIGN BY WILLIAM MORGAN, ARCHITECT

STUDENT RENDERING BY VOLKER KLOTZ

FIG. 266 EXAMPLES OF WATER COLOR RENDERING

STUDENT RENDERING BY FRANK DOST
AN INTERIOR DESIGN PROBLEM

STUDENT RENDERING BY ROBERT MARTIN
PROBLEM IN ARCHITECTURAL DESIGN

FIG. 267 EXAMPLES OF WATER COLOR RENDERING

C I T Y   L I B R A R Y ,   P A L O   A L T O ,   C A L I F O R N I A
E D W A R D   D U R E L L   S T O N E ,   A R C H I T E C T

R E N D E R I N G   B Y   R .   C O R B E L L E T T I
E D W A R D   D U R E L L   S T O N E ,   A R C H I T E C T

FIG. 268 EXAMPLES OF WATER COLOR RENDERING

INTERIOR DESIGN BY JAY SETLOW
SUGAR LOAF LODGE, SUGAR LOAF, FLORIDA

RENDERING BY GEORGE C. RUDOLPH
KETCHUM AND SHARP, ARCHITECTS

FIG. 269 EXAMPLES OF WATER COLOR RENDERING

CHAPTER 38

TEMPERA RENDERING

Opaque water colors are sold under various names which include tempera, poster colors, showcard colors, and opaque water colors. They can be obtained in either jars or tubes in a wide variety of pigments and colors. They are also available in several tones of gray. Dried washes with these paints are usually sufficiently water resistant so that lines can be ruled over them and washes can be run over parts of a dried wash without having edges run.

Each application of opaque water colors over an area is usually complete in itself. There is little or no building up of one wash over another, although one wash can be used to hide another. Each wash covers and conceals anything on the area where it is run. The same mixture is normally used throughout an area. There is little danger of bad streaks. However there is also little opportunity for grading washes and modeling shapes. Instead of using a gradual change in the mixture as in transparent water color rendering, opaque washes are graded by using a sequence of bands with slight differences in color or darkness. These bands can be applied by the French method described for water color. In tempera rendering each band is applied separately and allowed to dry before another is applied touching it. In water color rendering the French method is usually employed for small bands only while large areas are also rendered in this way with tempera to give a graded effect. It is also possible with opaque colors to apply each band while the preceding painted area that it touches is still wet.

Opaque water color rendering loses some of the refinements of expression of wash rendering. It also requires a different type of technical facility and craftsmanship. Its principal advantages are simplicity of handling and the solid effects obtained. Wash renderings sometimes have a thin and paper-like tinted quality. Opaque renderings seem much more vivid and real in their presentations of colors and materials.

Short smooth glass rods or wood sticks are useful in transferring paint from jars to the pan or plate where it is to be mixed for use. Do not leave jars open for long periods of time. Even when closed tightly the paints sometimes dry hard in the jars and are then worthless.

Opaque paints are mixed and applied with brushes in much the same manner as the simple washes of transparent water color. It is advisable to use less expensive brushes than those used for water color rendering, because the opaque paints ruin brushes quickly. Flat bristle brushes such as those used for oil painting are useful for mixing opaque paints and are sometimes suitable for applying paint also. All brushes should be washed before the paints have a chance to dry in them. Enough paint mixture should be used to cover the areas of a wash uniformly. There is no necessity for putting a large puddle on the paper. One wash is usually sufficient over an area, although two coats may sometimes be used. Test samples should be allowed to dry before deciding whether the color is right, because the wet and dry paint may be different colors. Opaque paint mixtures can be used in a ruling pen. It is sometimes better to rule a line of the wash mixture around an area before filling it in with a brush. This gives more precise edges.

Opaque paints may be used for either monotone or color renderings. Opaque monotone renderings are usually more effective when the number of tones is limited. White, black, and about three grays provide a reasonable number of tones for some renderings. The use of a small number of tones gives a feeling of order and simplicity to a rendering. The use of unlimited variety of tones may create confusion and cause the rendering to seem fussy and overdone.

The example at the top of Fig. 270 is a simple monotone rendering with only a small number of tones. The example at the bottom of Fig. 270 is rendered with black, grays, and a little color.

STUDENT RENDERING BY V. H. A. ALVAREZ

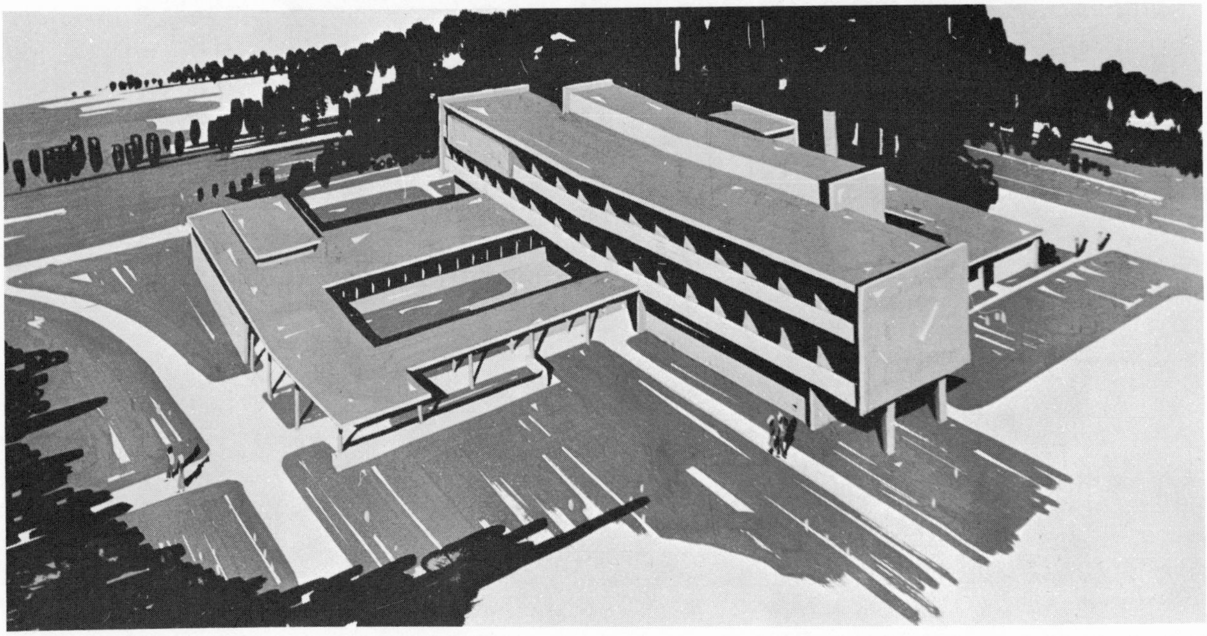

STUDENT RENDERING BY JAMES H. PRESTON

FIG. 270 EXAMPLES OF OPAQUE MONOTONE RENDERING

RENDERING BY RICHARD SCHIFF, RUDOLPH ASSOCIATES
J. SANFORD SHANLEY, ARCHITECT

RENDERING BY GEORGE C. RUDOLPH, RUDOLPH ASSOCIATES
JOSEPH WLADECK ARCHITECT

FIG. 271 EXAMPLES OF TEMPERA RENDERING

R E N D E R I N G B Y R O B E R T E. S C H W A R T Z
KEMPA AND SCHWARTZ–ARCHITECTS–J. H. LIVINGSTONE–ASSOCIATE

R E N D E R I N G B Y R O B E R T E. S C H W A R T Z
KEMPA AND SCHWARTZ–ARCHITECTS–J. H. LIVINGSTONE–ASSOCIATE

FIG. 272 EXAMPLES OF TEMPERA RENDERING

TEMPERA RENDERING BY J. WOOD
GEORGE L. DAHL, ARCHITECTS AND ENGINEERS

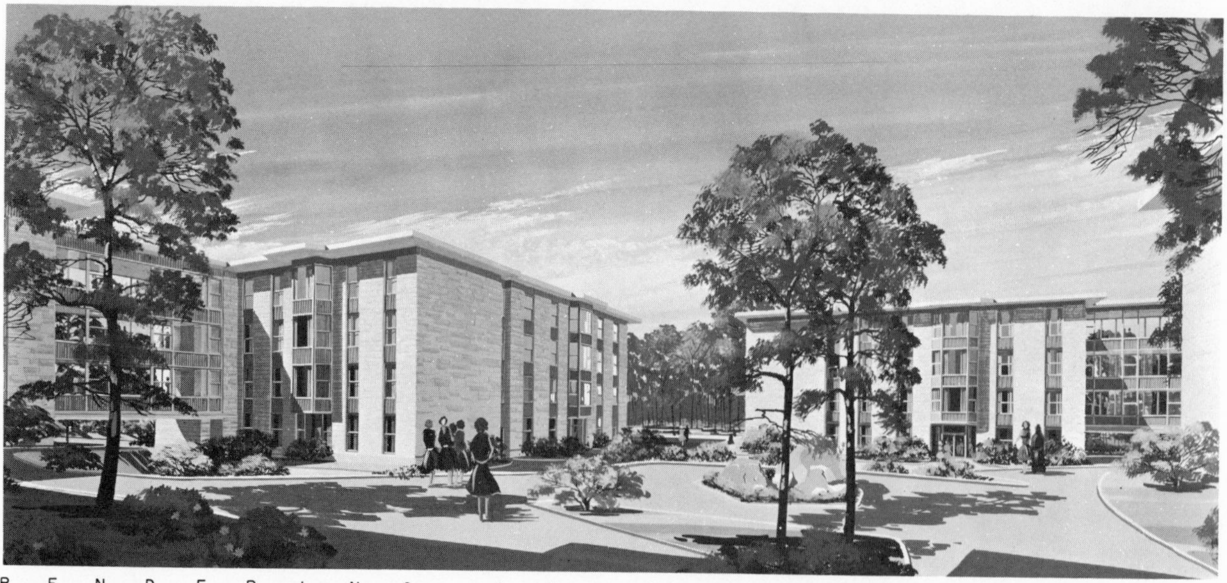

RENDERING BY ADAM JIMENEZ
EGGERS AND HIGGINS, ARCHITECTS

FIG. 273 EXAMPLES OF TEMPERA RENDERING

RENDERING BY ROBERT E. SCHWARTZ
KEMPA AND SCHWARTZ, ARCHITECTS

RENDERING BY SCHEFFER STUDIO
ARCHITECTS, KIVETT & MYERS—ENGINEERS, BURNS & McDONNELL

FIG. 274 EXAMPLES OF TEMPERA RENDERING

CHAPTER 39

SOME OTHER METHODS OF RENDERING

Spray rendering materials are very good for smooth application of tones. Spray technique can be used for either flat or graded effects. The spray solution may be of any kind of water color paint or of ink. It should be mixed to appear lighter and brighter than the tone and color desired if it is tested with a brush. The drops are darker and duller than the effect secured by brush technique using the same mixture of paints. Illustration board or stretches of either hot or cold pressed water color paper are satisfactory for spray rendering.

Spray renderings require masking around the area to which a tone or color is to be applied. If the shapes of the drawing are at all complex, masking requires more time than applying the paint. Masking over large surfaces may be done with masking tape and sheets of scrap paper. Small areas can be covered with tape only.

Spray of water color paints can be most easily and most perfectly applied with an air brush. The spray method of applying water color paints is usually called air brush technique. An air brush and compressor are expensive equipment. If they are not available other means can be used to obtain similar results. An atomizer or fixative blower can be used for this purpose, or a piece of

RENDERING BY ROY P. HARROVER
MANN AND HARROVER—ARCHITECTS

FIG. 275 EXAMPLE OF SPRAY RENDERING

RENDERING BY HELMUT JACOBY
KETCHUM AND SHARP—ARCHITECTS

FIG. 276 EXAMPLE OF AIR BRUSH RENDERING

window screen and a toothbrush can be used to produce a fine spatter. The tones of the rendering of Fig. 275 were made by applying water color with a fixative blower.

With an atomizer or air brush, do not get too close to the drawing. Tilt the board so the fine spray hits approximately perpendicular to the surface of the paper. When too much spray is applied at one time the tiny drops run together. Apply a reasonable amount, then wait for that to dry before applying more. With spray it is very difficult to tell how dark an application is. Lift a little of the mask in order to see under it and compare tones at intervals as the work progresses. Masks for clouds, trees, and other forms can sometimes be used for repetion of the same details. It is often sufficient to move these masks to new positions and hold them by hand when an air brush is used. Weights of coins or other objects can be used to hold the masks when the board is horizontal. Small areas and accents can be put in with a small brush. These freehand additions often relieve the stiffness inherent in this technique. They may also add very effective darks and bright colors in small areas with a minimum of effort.

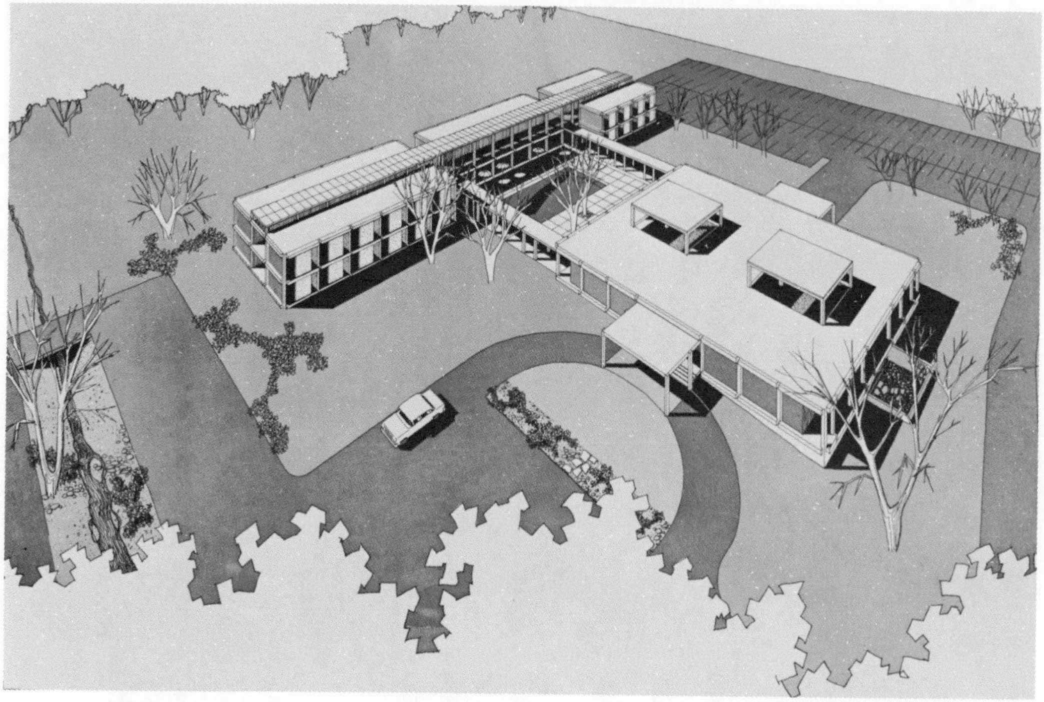

RENDERING BY JACK ST. MARTIN
MANN AND HARROVER, ARCHITECTS

FIG. 277 INK AND ZIP-A-TONE RENDERING

Printed patterns provide a limited tone variety for rendering to which black can be added. They provide a simple way to obtain mechanically uniform patterns and fairly uniform tones. The appliqué process employs printed patterns on transparent sheets of thin plastic material. The patterns are made of dots or lines in most cases, and the most commonly used ones are printed black. However some are printed white to be applied over dark surfaces. There are also solid colors and grays available. There are a great many variations of printed patterns. It is sometimes difficult to get distinctly separate tones because many of the available patterns offer little variety in darkness. However this material offers interesting possibilities for renderings.

Two layers of the same pattern can be used to make a darker tone or to produce a different pattern. When a parallel line pattern is used one layer can be at right angles to the other to darken and vary the pattern in a simple way. When this parallel line or a regular dot pattern is used in two layers it will be found that rotating the top layer slowly will produce a surprising number of pattern variations.

The bottom surface of the plastic material on which the patterns are printed is coated with an adhesive. This adhesive will keep the material from slipping around over the drawing when it is pressed against the paper by rubbing lightly. The bowl of a spoon, a polished piece of bone, thumbnail, or some other object must be rubbed vigorously over the material to make it adhere tightly to the paper.

After a pattern has been selected to be used on an area of the drawing, the material is laid over the area and rubbed lightly to keep it from slipping. The material is then scored very lightly and evenly with a sharp pointed needle or other instrument all around the edge of the area where it is to be applied. The T-square or triangle can be used to guide the cutting tool just as a line would be ruled. The material over the area is held in place and the edges lifted around it to remove the unwanted material. If the material has been scored correctly with a very sharp tool it will sepa-

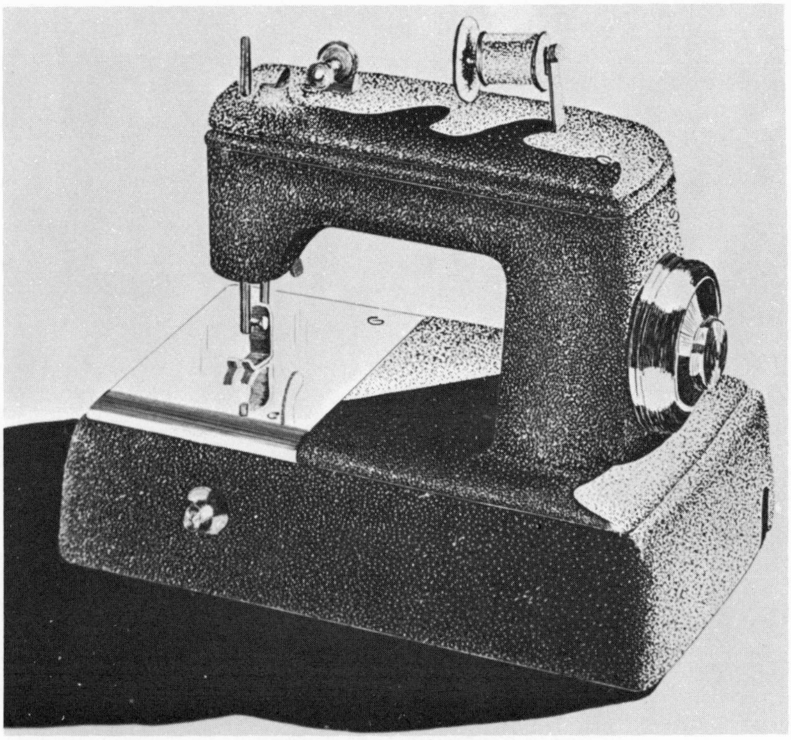

STUDENT RENDERING BY C. VAN WINKLE

FIG. 278 SCRATCHBOARD RENDERING

rate readily. Lift the material you are removing by beginning at one end of a line so it follows the cut edge along the line from one end to the other. It is not necessary to scratch completely through the material to separate it. Therefore the needle point should not damage the drawing under the material. When the material has been fitted exactly to the area it must be rubbed vigorously over every part of its surface so it will adhere firmly and permanently to the paper of the drawing.

Because the appliqué material is transparent it can be applied over the drawing lines. The pattern has some effect on the lines but usually can be turned so that it does not seriously interfere with them. The material can be applied over washes or other tones as well as over white paper. It may be used for shadows only or for other rendering purposes.

Scratchboard provides a variation of pen and ink technique for rendering. The materials required are the board itself, pens and ink, a brush for applying ink on areas, and a number of sharp pointed or edged tools for scratching the ink off. Some of these tools can be made to produce various combinations of multiple lines with one stroke. The drawing is usually made for scratchboard rendering by tracing and transferring with a pencil that will make the lines visible on both the ink and the white paper areas.

The board for this type of rendering has been coated with a thin layer of white chalky material by the manufacturer. When there are small areas of black or small black lines and comparatively large areas of white the ink is applied with a pen or brush where it is to remain. When there are large areas of black and small amounts of white the entire area is coated with ink and the whites are scratched out.

The effects produced with scratchboard offer wide variation. Some drawings are fine in detail and resemble the delicacy of engravings. Others are bold and coarse in effect. There are entire books published on the scratchboard method of rendering. These books range from ones with simple examples and text to those with very expert, detailed, and artistic professional work.

STUDENT RENDERING BY LARRY BLACKMAN

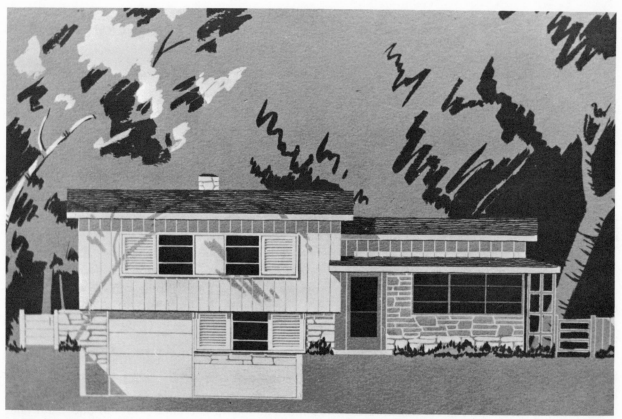

STUDENT RENDERING BY G. LIMKE

FIG. 279 RENDERINGS ON GRAY PAPER

White, black, and gray or colored paper can be used to give very effective conventionalized renderings of some subjects. The colored or gray paper or illustration board is usually better when it is medium dark or between light and medium in darkness. In most cases it is more satisfactory to avoid gaudy and brilliantly colored papers. Try to obtain a pleasing but somewhat subdued color. Poster or tempera white is satisfactory for the opaque white paint. Black waterproof drawing ink is satisfactory in most cases for the black.

Basically this technique is limited to three tones: (1) white, (2) the tone of the paper, and (3) black. However intermediate tones can be supplied with either white or black dots or lines on the paper. They can also be provided by leaving thin lines of the paper color with either white or black bands or other shapes between, Fig. 279.

This technique is most effective when there are elements of materials to be shown. Wood boards, brick, stone, tile, and other units of materials and their joints add lines, tones, and interest to a rendering. A commonly used system is to make the areas of the units white and the joints the paper color in light. In shadow the treatment is reversed with joints white and the material units the color of the paper. Because the joints are normally relatively small this makes the shadow areas dark. The joints can sometimes be made black in shadow and the units the paper color. Units of materials are sometimes shown in either light or shadow areas only but not in both. A great deal of ingenuity and good judgment are required to get the best results from this simple technique.

White tempera and black pencil on gray paper gives a good opportunity for interesting grays and fine details with the pencil. The following example of a rendering in this medium by Mr. Furno has brilliant contrast with excellent details and a strong focus of interest. This is a very effective medium. The subtle variations of gray and their effects are worth careful study, Fig. 280.

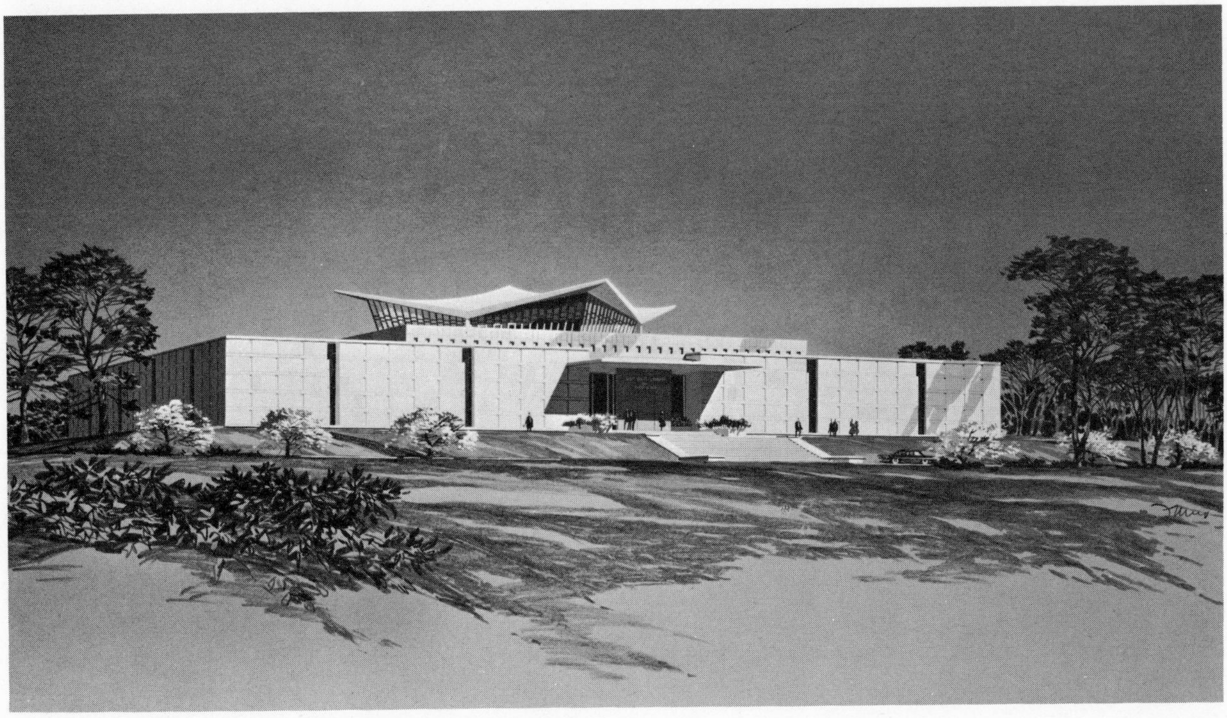

RENDERING BY VINCENT FURNO
O'CONNOR AND KILHAM, ARCHITECTS

FIG. 280 PENCIL AND WHITE TEMPERA ON GRAY PAPER

INDEX